Penitential Act

A **I confess to almighty God**
and to you, my brothers and sisters
that I have greatly sinned,
in my thoughts and in my words,
in what I have done
and in what I have failed to do,
(Strike breast)
through my fault, through my fault,
through my most grievous fault;
therefore I ask blessed Mary ever-Virgin,
all the Angels and Saints,
and you, my brothers and sisters,
to pray for me to the Lord our God.

B Have mercy on us, O Lord.
For we have sinned against you.
Show us, O Lord, your mercy.
And grant us your salvation.

Gloria

Glory to God in the highest,
and on earth peace to people of good will.

We praise you,
we bless you,
we adore you,
we glorify you,
we give you thanks for your great glory,
Lord God, heavenly King,
O God, almighty Father.

Lord Jesus Christ, Only Begotten Son,
Lord God, Lamb of God, Son of the Father,
you take away the sins of the world,
have mercy on us;
you take away the sins of the world,
receive our prayer;
you are seated at the right hand of
the Father,
have mercy on us.

For you alone are the Holy One,
you alone are the Lord,
you alone are the Most High,
Jesus Christ,
with the Holy Spirit,
in the glory of God the Father.
Amen.

MW01056469

the Only Begotten Son of God,
born of the Father before all ages.
God from God, Light from Light,
true God from true God,
begotten, not made, consubstantial
with the Father;
through him all things were made.
For us men and for our salvation
he came down from heaven,

At the words that follow, up to and including "and became man," all bow.

and by the Holy Spirit was incarnate of
the Virgin Mary,
and became man.

For our sake he was crucified under
Pontius Pilate,
he suffered death and was buried,
and rose again on the third day
in accordance with the Scriptures.
He ascended into heaven
and is seated at the right hand of
the Father.
He will come again in glory
to judge the living and the dead
and his kingdom will have no end.

I believe in the Holy Spirit, the Lord,
the giver of life,
who proceeds from the Father and the Son,
who with the Father and the Son is
adored and glorified,
who has spoken through the prophets.

I believe in one, holy, catholic and
apostolic Church.
I confess one Baptism for the forgiveness
of sins
and I look forward to the resurrection
of the dead
and the life of the world to come. Amen.

Invitation to Communion

Behold...to the supper of the Lamb.
Lord, I am not worthy
that you should enter under my roof,
but only say the word
and my soul shall be healed.

GLORY & PRAISE

THIRD EDITION

Concordat cum originali: † Alexander K. Sample, Archbishop of Portland in Oregon

Published with the approval of the Committee on Divine Worship,
United States Catholic Conference of Bishops (USCCB).

Publisher: John J. Limb
Executive Director of Products: Vic Cozzoli
Director of Music Development and Outreach: Eric Schumock
Director of Product Development: John Vogler
Manager of Music Development: Rick Modlin
Manager of Music Editorial: Angela Westhoff-Johnson
Senior Editorial Projects Manager: Amanda Weller
Editors: Jessica Crawford, C. Angelyn Jáuregui, Craig Kingsbury, Joseph Muir,
Daniel Partridge, Travis Powers
Engraving Manager: Tia Regan
Senior Typesetter/Music Layout: Melissa Schmidt
Engravers: Ward Baxter, David Brallier, Laura C. Kantor, Christy Kuiken,
Eric Nordin, William Straub
Art Director and Graphic Designer: Judy Urben
Cover Design: Stephanie Bozanich
Graphic Icons: Le Vu, Stephanie Bozanich

5536 NE Hassalo, Portland, OR 97213
Phone: (503) 281-1191
liturgy@ocp.org
ocp.org

Second Printing: December 2015

Assembly	*ISBN: 978-1-57992-218-4*	*edition 30131331*
Assembly with Readings	*ISBN: 978-1-57992-219-1*	*edition 30131335*
Choir/Cantor	*ISBN: 978-1-57992-220-7*	*edition 30131336*
Keyboard Accompaniment	*ISBN: 978-1-57992-221-4*	*edition 30131332*
Guitar Accompaniment	*ISBN: 978-1-57992-222-1*	*edition 30131333*
Solo Instrument	*ISBN: 978-1-57992-223-8*	*edition 30132854*
CD Recording Library		*edition 30131334*

ISBN 978-1-57992-218-4
EBM 12/15

Edition 30131331
Printed in U.S.A.

Preface

Glory & Praise is a name that resonates in the fifty-year history of contemporary Catholic liturgical music. Originally published in 1977 by North American Liturgy Resources (NALR), the first volume was a collection of songs by the remarkable group of pastoral musicians who made up the second wave of "folk" composers of the post-Conciliar era, most notably Carey Landry and the composers who came to be known as the St. Louis Jesuits—Bob Dufford, John Foley, Tim Manion, Roc O'Connor, and Dan Schutte, whose song "Glory and Praise to Our God" inspired the publication's title.

In an era when periodical missals were still trying to define a common repertoire, *Glory & Praise* helped to establish the guitar-based "folk" style as mainstream, and it played an important role in reducing the need for parishes to create their own home-printed songbooks, the prevailing custom at the time.

As *Glory & Praise* grew in popularity, new music publishing prompted NALR to release Volumes 2, 3 and 4, which included songs by Grayson Warren Brown, Rory Cooney, the Dameans, Michael Joncas, Tom Kendzia, and many more. These were eventually followed by a comprehensive hardbound edition that included an Order of Mass and a modest selection of well-known traditional hymns.

OCP acquired the NALR copyrights in 1994 and published its own version three years later: the bestselling *Glory & Praise, Second Edition*. That version reflected the growth in Catholic liturgical repertoire with the inclusion of Spanish and bilingual songs, new complete Mass settings, a comprehensive Psalter, and a number of songs by newer composers such as Jaime Cortez, Bernadette Farrell, Bob Hurd, Paul Inwood, Scott Soper, Christopher Walker, and others.

Now, almost twenty years later, OCP is proud to release *Glory & Praise, Third Edition*, which reflects the continuing growth and development of liturgical music in North America. The Mass settings utilize the official texts of the *Roman Missal, Third Typical Edition*, and the Order of Mass features the ICEL chants as required by the Bishops' Committee on Divine Worship. In addition, the assembly edition with lectionary readings features verbatim settings of the Responsorial Psalms and Gospel Acclamations from OCP's very popular *Respond & Acclaim* series.

Spanish and bilingual songs have been carefully selected to serve those occasions such as Christmas and the Easter Triduum when the diverse communities of a parish come together for liturgy. Many songs popular with youth from the *Spirit & Song* repertoire are likewise included, especially those that have crossed over into mainstream usage. And, in this third edition, OCP is pleased to include songs by such composers as David Haas and Marty Haugen that were not included in the second edition, as well as a significant number of traditional hymns, some with contemporary guitar arrangements.

In short, *Glory & Praise, Third Edition* presents a common repertoire for the cross-generational, English-speaking communities of the Church today.

We want to acknowledge the dedicated work of our liturgical composers, both past and present, without whom the various editions of this hymnal would not be possible. We also express our gratitude to the internal staff and external consultants who worked so diligently on this project. Without the talents and hard work of these dedicated individuals, this new edition would not have seen the light of day.

May the Lord "who gives light to our days" unite our diverse communities into one! May our song ever be, "Glory and praise to our God!"

John J. Limb, Publisher
Exaltation of the Holy Cross
September 14, 2015

CONTENTS

MASS

THE ORDER OF MASS

1 The Introductory Rites
8 The Liturgy of the Word
9 Profession of Faith (Creed)
11 The Liturgy of the Eucharist
21 The Concluding Rites

MASS SETTINGS

27 Mass of the Sacred Heart (T.R. Smith)
37 Mass of Glory (Canedo/Hurd)
47 Mass of Christ the Savior (Schutte)
58 Mass of a Joyful Heart (Angrisano/Tomaszek)
68 Heritage Mass (Alstott)
76 Misa Santa Fe (Reza)
82 Celtic Mass (C. Walker)
92 Mass of Renewal (Stephan)

LITURGY OF THE HOURS

102 Morning Prayer (Lauds)
109 Evening Prayer (Vespers)
116 Psalms
202 Canticles

HYMNS & SONGS

SEASONS AND SOLEMNITIES OF THE LORD

212 Advent
232 Advent & Christmas
234 Christmas
253 Epiphany
260 Ash Wednesday
262 Lent
281 Palm Sunday
286 Holy Thursday
294 Good Friday
303 Easter Vigil
309 Easter
337 Ascension
341 Pentecost
354 Holy Trinity
360 Christ the King

SOLEMNITIES AND FEASTS

369 Blessed Virgin Mary
381 Transfiguration
383 Holy Cross
385 Saints & Martyrs

RITUAL MUSIC

391 Christian Initiation
410 Penance & Reconciliation
419 Pastoral Care of the Sick
426 Eucharistic Exposition & Benediction
428 Funeral
446 Marriage

General Music for Worship

455 Gathering
475 Eucharistic Hymns
479 Communion
517 Social Concern & Justice
528 Ministry & Mission
544 Unity
552 Discipleship
568 Church
572 Christian Life
587 Faith
599 Trust
621 Petition & Prayer
637 Blessing
640 Comfort
655 Love
671 Peace
682 Light
689 Word
693 Creation
700 Thanksgiving
710 Praise
745 Nation & Patriotic
750 Second Coming
756 God's Kingdom
764 Providence
773 Eternal Life & Heaven
778 Morning
780 Evening

Indexes

783 Acknowledgments
*784 Index of Text & Music Sources
*785 Language Index
*786 Musical Style Index
787 Alphabetical Index of Hymn Tunes
788 Metrical Index of Hymn Tunes
789 Scriptural Index
790 Topical Index
*791 Index of Psalm and Canticle Refrains
792 Index of Suggested Psalms for the Liturgical Year
793 Liturgical Index
*794 Index of Instruments
795 Index of Titles

*These indexes are available in the accompaniment editions.

THE ORDER OF MASS

*At the Eucharist, the Church comes together to hear the Word of the Lord, to pray for the world's needs, to offer the sacrifice of the Cross in praise and thanks to God, to receive Christ Jesus in Communion, and then to be sent forth in the Spirit as disciples of the Gospel. Through the experience of these sacred mysteries in the liturgy, the "summit toward which the activity of the Church is directed," the people of God are renewed and given new strength to live out the Christian faith daily (*Sacrosanctum Concilium, *No. 10).*

1 THE INTRODUCTORY RITES

As the Church gathers, "the faithful, who come together as one, establish communion and dispose themselves properly to listen to the Word of God and to celebrate the Eucharist worthily" (GIRM, No. 46).

ENTRANCE CHANT *STAND*

A processional chant or hymn may be sung.

GREETING

After the Entrance Chant, all make the Sign of the Cross.

In the name of the Father, and of the Son, and of the Holy Spirit.

A - men.

Any of the three forms of Greeting may be used.

The grace of our Lord Jesus Christ,...be with you all.

Or Grace to you and peace from God our Father and the Lord Jesus Christ.

Or The Lord be with you.

Or *(A Bishop says, "Peace be with you.")*

And with your spir - it.

Rite for the Blessing and Sprinkling of Water

From time to time on Sundays, especially in Easter Time, there may be a blessing and sprinkling of holy water to recall Baptism. This replaces the Penitential Act below. For music during the sprinkling, see No. 47, No. 406, or No. 407. Continue with the "Gloria," No. 7, except on Sundays of Advent, Ash Wednesday and Sundays of Lent.

Penitential Act *(Omit on Ash Wednesday)*

The celebration of God's mercy takes one of the following forms:

2

I confess to almighty God
and to you, my brothers and sisters,
that I have greatly sinned,
in my thoughts and in my words,
in what I have done and in what I have failed to do,
(Strike breast) **through my fault, through my fault,**
through my most grievous fault;
therefore I ask blessed Mary ever-Virgin,
all the Angels and Saints,
and you, my brothers and sisters,
to pray for me to the Lord our God.

May almighty God have mercy on us,
forgive us our sins,
and bring us to everlasting life.

A - men.

Continue with the "Lord, Have Mercy/Kyrie, Eleison," No. 5 or No. 6.

3

Or Have mercy on us, O Lord.

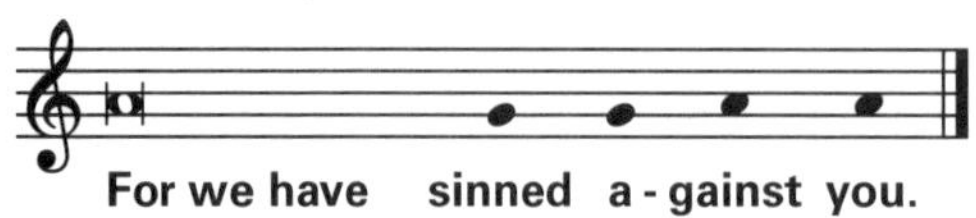
For we have sinned a - gainst you.

Show us, O Lord, your mercy.

And grant us your sal - va - tion.

May almighty God have mercy on us,
forgive us our sins,
and bring us to everlasting life.

A - men.

Continue with the "Lord, Have Mercy/Kyrie, Eleison," No. 5 or No. 6.

4

Or *Invocation...*

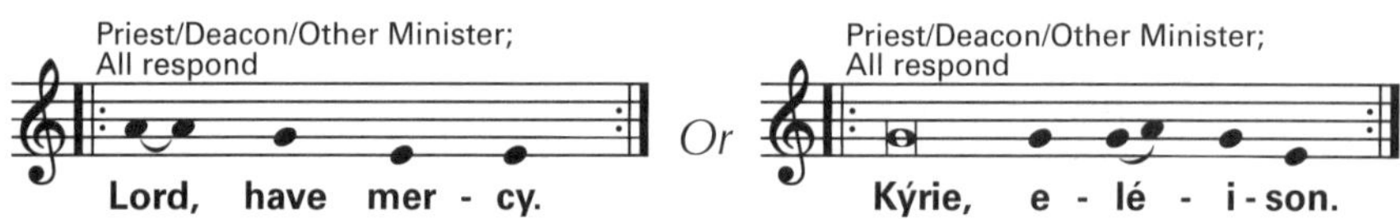
Priest/Deacon/Other Minister; All respond
Lord, have mer - cy.
Or
Priest/Deacon/Other Minister; All respond
Kýrie, e - lé - i - son.

Invocation...

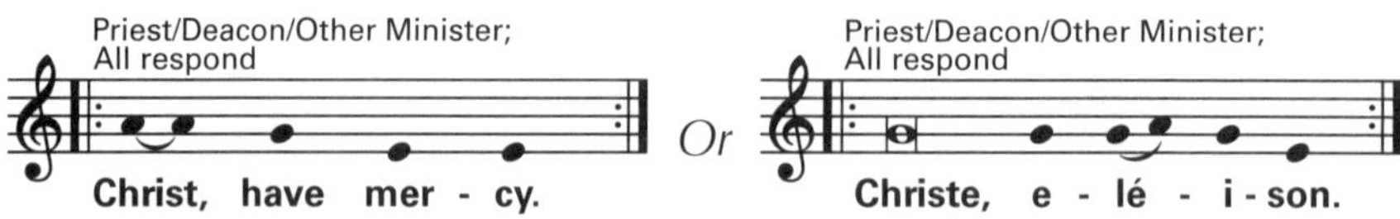
Priest/Deacon/Other Minister; All respond
Christ, have mer - cy.
Or
Priest/Deacon/Other Minister; All respond
Christe, e - lé - i - son.

Invocation...

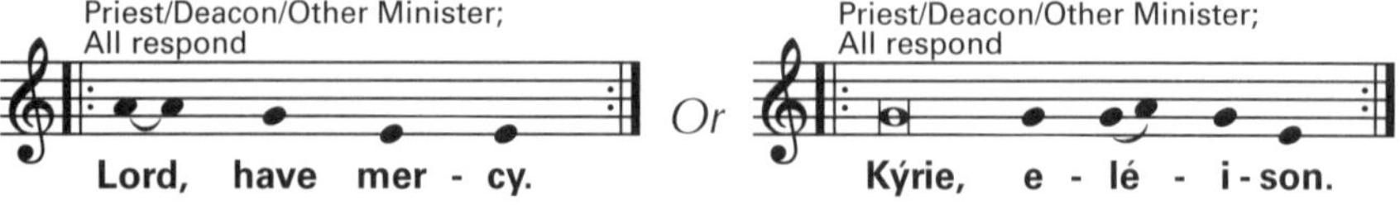
Priest/Deacon/Other Minister; All respond
Lord, have mer - cy.
Or
Priest/Deacon/Other Minister; All respond
Kýrie, e - lé - i - son.

May almighty God have mercy on us,
forgive us our sins,
and bring us to everlasting life.

A - men.

Continue with the "Gloria," No. 7, except on Sundays of Advent, Ash Wednesday and Sundays of Lent.

LORD, HAVE MERCY/KYRIE, ELEISON 5

Priest/Deacon/Other Minister
Lord, have mer - cy.
All respond
Lord, have mer - cy.
Priest/Deacon/Other Minister
Christ, have mer - cy.
All respond
Christ, have mer - cy.
Priest/Deacon/Other Minister
Lord, have mer - cy.
All respond
Lord, have mer - cy.

Or 6

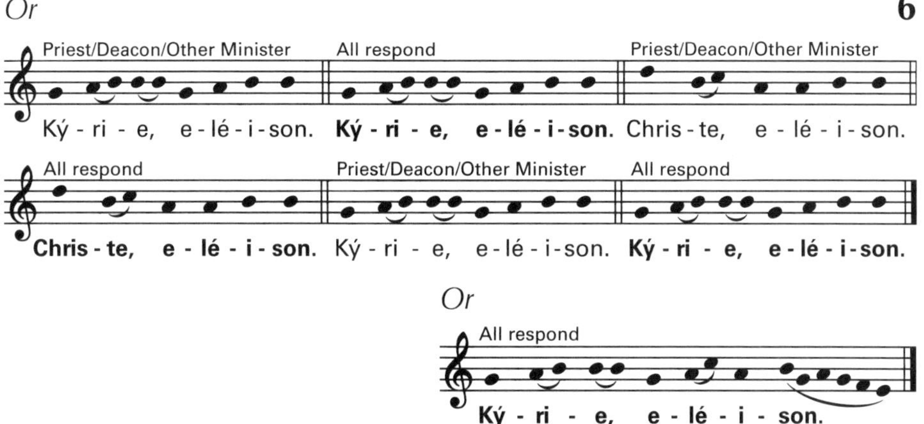
Priest/Deacon/Other Minister
Ký - ri - e, e - lé - i - son.
All respond
Ký - ri - e, e - lé - i - son.
Priest/Deacon/Other Minister
Chris - te, e - lé - i - son.
All respond
Chris - te, e - lé - i - son.
Priest/Deacon/Other Minister
Ký - ri - e, e - lé - i - son.
All respond
Ký - ri - e, e - lé - i - son.
Or
All respond
Ký - ri - e, e - lé - i - son.

Gloria

Except on Sundays of Advent, Ash Wednesday and Sundays of Lent, all sing or say:

7

Priest/Cantor/Choir
All
Glo-ry to God in the high-est, and on earth peace to peo-ple of good will.
We praise you, we bless you, we a-dore you, we glo-ri-fy you,
we give you thanks for your great glo-ry, Lord God, heav-en-ly King,
O God, al-might-y Fa-ther. Lord Je-sus Christ, On-ly Be-got-ten Son,
Lord God, Lamb of God, Son of the Fa-ther, you take a-way the sins of the world,
have mer-cy on us; you take a-way the sins of the world,
re-ceive our prayer; you are seat-ed at the right hand of the Fa-ther,
have mer-cy on us. For you a-lone are the Ho-ly One, you a-lone are the Lord,
you a-lone are the Most High, Je-sus Christ, with the Ho-ly Spir-it,
in the glo-ry of God the Fa - ther. A - men.

Or **Glory to God in the highest,
and on earth peace to people of good will.**

**We praise you,
we bless you,
we adore you,
we glorify you,
we give you thanks for your great glory,
Lord God, heavenly King,
O God, almighty Father.**

**Lord Jesus Christ, Only Begotten Son,
Lord God, Lamb of God, Son of the Father,
you take away the sins of the world,
have mercy on us;
you take away the sins of the world,
receive our prayer;
you are seated at the right hand of the Father,
have mercy on us.**

**For you alone are the Holy One,
you alone are the Lord,
you alone are the Most High,
Jesus Christ,
with the Holy Spirit,
in the glory of God the Father.
Amen.**

COLLECT

After a period of silence, the Priest says the Collect, and all respond:

Amen.

THE LITURGY OF THE WORD 8

The Lectionary *(book of readings) and the* Book of Gospels *open the rich treasure of God's word from the Jewish and Christian Scriptures. Sunday readings follow a three-year cycle: Year A emphasizes the Gospel of Matthew, Year B the Gospel of Mark, Year C the Gospel of Luke. The Church proclaims the Gospel of John especially during the seasons of Lent and Easter.*

FIRST READING *SIT*

After the reading, the reader says, "The word of the Lord," and all respond:

Thanks be to God.

RESPONSORIAL PSALM

For music for the responsorial psalm see No. 116–211.

SECOND READING

After the reading, the reader says, "The word of the Lord," and all respond:

Thanks be to God.

GOSPEL ACCLAMATION *STAND*

The assembly welcomes the proclamation of the Gospel by singing an acclamation. If it cannot be sung, it is to be omitted. For music, see Mass Settings. During Lent, see Mass Settings.

GOSPEL

Before the Gospel, the Deacon/Priest says, "The Lord be with you," and all respond:

And with your spirit.

The Deacon/Priest says, "A reading from the holy Gospel according to N.," and all respond:

Glory to you, O Lord.

After the Gospel reading, the Deacon/Priest says, "The Gospel of the Lord," and all respond:

Praise to you, Lord Jesus Christ.

HOMILY *SIT*

The Priest or Deacon preaches the good news of Christ's saving mystery.

DISMISSAL OF THE CATECHUMENS AND THE ELECT

In Masses at which catechumens or elect are present for the Liturgy of the Word, the priest may use these or similar words:

My dear friends, this community now sends you forth to reflect more deeply upon the word of God which you have shared with us today. Be assured of our loving support and prayers for you. We look forward to the day when you will share fully in the Lord's Table.

A song may be sung while the catechumens/elect are dismissed (see No. 409).

STAND

PROFESSION OF FAITH *(Credo I)* 9

On Sundays and solemnities, all sing or say the Nicene Creed:

Priest/Cantor/Choir
All
I be-lieve in one God, the Fa-ther al-might-y, mak-er of heav-en
and earth, of all things vis - i - ble and in - vis - i - ble.
I be - lieve in one Lord Je - sus Christ, the Only Be - got - ten
Son of God, born of the Father be-fore all a - ges. God from God,
Light from Light, true God from true God, be - got-ten, not made,
con-sub-stan-tial with the Fa - ther; through him all things were made.
For us men and for our sal - va - tion he came down from heav-en,
At the words that follow, up to and including "and became man," all bow.
and by the Ho - ly Spir - it was in - car-nate of the Vir - gin Mar - y,
and be-came man. For our sake he was cru - ci - fied un - der
Pon-tius Pi - late, he suffered death and was bur - ied, and rose a -
gain on the third day in accordance with the Scrip - tures.

He as - cend - ed in - to heav - en and is seated at the right hand
of the Fa - ther. He will come a - gain in glo - ry to
judge the living and the dead and his kingdom will have no end.
I be-lieve in the Ho - ly Spir - it, the Lord, the giv - er of life,
who pro - ceeds from the Father and the Son, who with the
Fa - ther and the Son is adored and glo - ri - fied, who has
spoken through the proph-ets. I be - lieve in one, ho - ly, ca - tho - lic
and a - pos - tol - ic Church. I con-fess one Bap-tism for the for -
give-ness of sins and I look for - ward to the res - ur - rec - tion
of the dead and the life of the world to come.
A - men.

Or **I believe in one God,**
the Father almighty,
maker of heaven and earth,
of all things visible and invisible.

I believe in one Lord Jesus Christ,
the Only Begotten Son of God,
born of the Father before all ages.
God from God, Light from Light,
true God from true God,
begotten, not made, consubstantial with the Father;
through him all things were made.
For us men and for our salvation
he came down from heaven,

At the words that follow, up to and including "and became man," all bow.

and by the Holy Spirit was incarnate of the Virgin Mary,
and became man.

For our sake he was crucified under Pontius Pilate,
he suffered death and was buried,
and rose again on the third day
in accordance with the Scriptures.
He ascended into heaven
and is seated at the right hand of the Father.
He will come again in glory
to judge the living and the dead
and his Kingdom will have no end.

I believe in the Holy Spirit, the Lord, the giver of life,
who proceeds from the Father and the Son,
who with the Father and the Son is adored and glorified,
who has spoken through the prophets.

I believe in one, holy, catholic and apostolic Church.
I confess one Baptism for the forgiveness of sins
and I look forward to the resurrection of the dead
and the life of the world to come. Amen.

Instead of the Nicene (Niceno-Constantinopolitan) Creed, especially during Lent and Easter Time, the baptismal Symbol of the Roman Church, known as the Apostles' Creed, may be used.

STAND

I believe in God,
the Father almighty,
Creator of heaven and earth,
and in Jesus Christ, his only Son, our Lord,

At the words that follow, up to and including "the Virgin Mary," all bow.

who was conceived by the Holy Spirit,
born of the Virgin Mary,
suffered under Pontius Pilate,
was crucified, died and was buried;
he descended into hell;
on the third day he rose again from the dead;
he ascended into heaven,
and is seated at the right hand of God the Father almighty;
from there he will come to judge the living and the dead.

I believe in the Holy Spirit,
the holy catholic Church,
the communion of saints,
the forgiveness of sins,
the resurrection of the body,
and life everlasting. Amen.

UNIVERSAL PRAYER *(Prayer of the Faithful)*

As a priestly people, we unite with one another to pray for today's needs in the Church and the world. The Deacon, cantor or other minister offers the petitions and then says or sings:

Let us pray to the Lord.
Lord, hear our prayer.

10

Deacon/Cantor/Other Minister
All
(Intercessions) Let us pray to the Lord. Lord, hear our prayer.

Music: Byzantine chant.

Christians are baptized into the paschal mystery of Christ's death and resurrection for the forgiveness of sin and fullness of salvation. This mystery is celebrated at every Mass, remembering Christ's loving deed and giving thanks and praise to God. By this action the "Sacrifice of the Cross is continuously made present in the Church" (GIRM, No. 72).

PRESENTATION AND PREPARATION OF THE GIFTS

SIT

The gifts are brought forward. If no chant is sung, the Priest may pray aloud, and all may respond:

Blessed be God for ever.

The Priest prays "...that my sacrifice and yours may be acceptable to God, the almighty Father," and all respond:

STAND

12

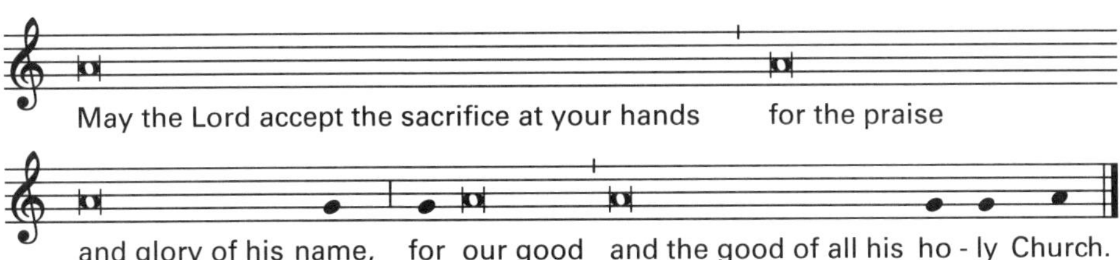
May the Lord accept the sacrifice at your hands for the praise
and glory of his name, for our good and the good of all his ho - ly Church.

Or **May the Lord accept the sacrifice at your hands**
for the praise and glory of his name,
for our good
and the good of all his holy Church.

PRAYER OVER THE OFFERINGS

The Priest says the Prayer over the Offerings; following this, the people respond:

Amen.

THE EUCHARISTIC PRAYER

PREFACE

The Eucharistic Prayer begins with a dialogue between the Priest and the assembly.

13

Priest
The Lord be with you.
All
And with your spir - it.
Priest
Lift up your hearts.
All
We lift them up to the Lord.
Priest
Let us give thanks to the Lord our God.
All
It is right and just.

At the conclusion of the Preface, the following acclamation is sung or said by all:

HOLY

14

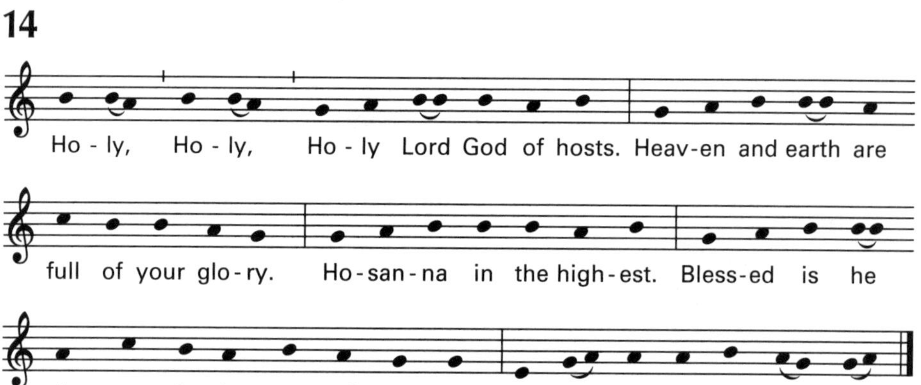
Ho - ly, Ho - ly, Ho - ly Lord God of hosts. Heav-en and earth are
full of your glo-ry. Ho-san-na in the high-est. Bless-ed is he
who comes in the name of the Lord. Ho - san - na in the high - est.

KNEEL

After the words of institution of the Eucharist, the Priest sings or says:

The mystery of faith.

All respond:

15

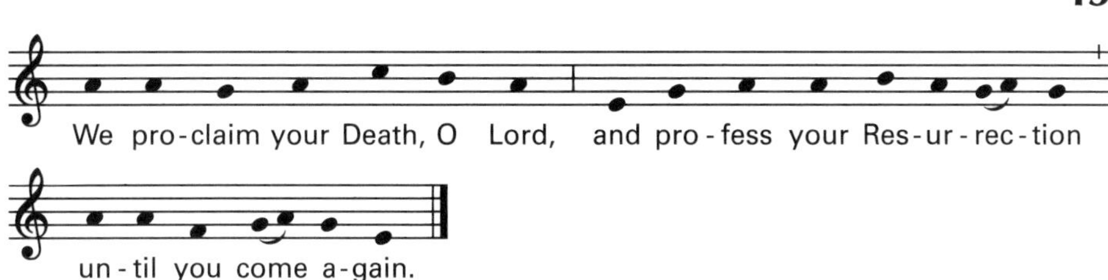
We pro-claim your Death, O Lord, and pro-fess your Res-ur-rec-tion
un-til you come a-gain.

Or **16**

When we eat this Bread and drink this Cup, we pro-claim your
Death, O Lord, un-til you come a-gain.

Or **17**

Save us, Sav-ior of the world, for by your Cross and Res-ur-rec-tion
you have set us free.

The Eucharistic Prayer culminates and concludes when the Priest sings or says:

Through him, and with him, and in him,
O God, almighty Father,
in the unity of the Holy Spirit,
all glory and honor is yours,
for ever and ever.

A - men.

THE COMMUNION RITE

The Lord's Prayer

STAND

The Priest invites all to join in the Lord's Prayer:

18

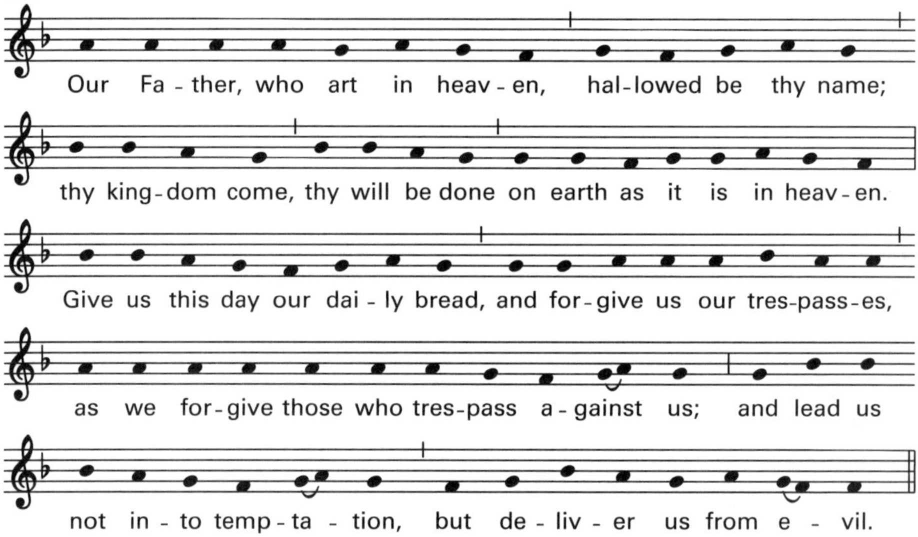

Our Fa - ther, who art in heav - en, hal-lowed be thy name;

thy king-dom come, thy will be done on earth as it is in heav - en.

Give us this day our dai - ly bread, and for-give us our tres-pass-es,

as we for-give those who tres-pass a - gainst us; and lead us

not in - to temp - ta - tion, but de - liv - er us from e - vil.

Deliver us, Lord, we pray, from every evil,
graciously grant peace in our days,
that, by the help of your mercy,
we may be always free from sin
and safe from all distress,
as we await the blessed hope
and the coming of our Savior, Jesus Christ.

For the king-dom, the power and the glo-ry are yours now and for ev - er.

Music: Chant; adapt. by Robert J. Snow, 1926–1998.

Sign of Peace

Lord Jesus Christ,
who said to your Apostles:
Peace I leave you, my peace I give you,
look not on our sins,
but on the faith of your Church,
and graciously grant her peace and unity
in accordance with your will.
Who live and reign for ever and ever.

A - men.

The peace of the Lord be with you always.

And with your spir - it.

Let us offer each other the sign of peace.

The people exchange a sign of peace, according to local custom.

Lamb of God

During the breaking of the bread and the commingling, the following litany is sung and may be repeated several times until the fraction rite is completed, ending only the final time with "grant us peace."

19

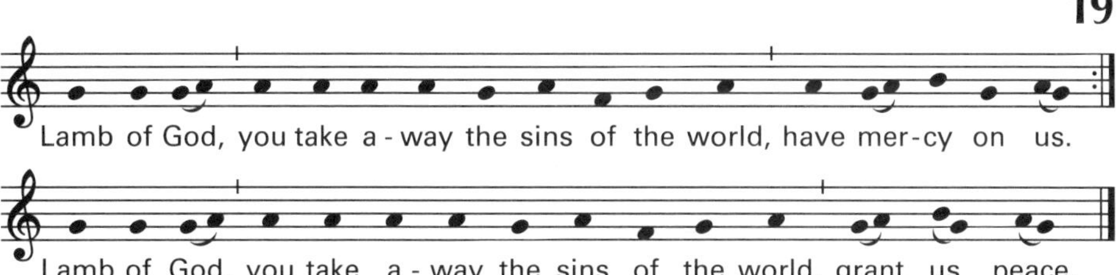
Lamb of God, you take a - way the sins of the world, have mer-cy on us.
Lamb of God, you take a - way the sins of the world, grant us peace.

The faithful kneel after the "Agnus Dei" ("Lamb of God") unless the Diocesan Bishop determines otherwise.

Communion

KNEEL

Behold the Lamb of God,
behold him who takes away the sins of the world.
Blessed are those called to the supper of the Lamb.

All respond:

20

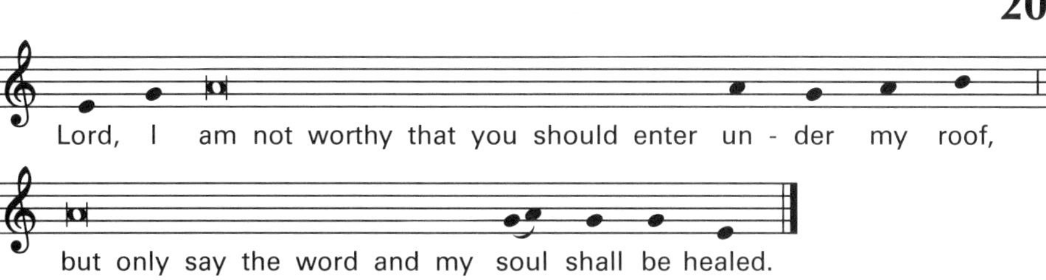
Lord, I am not worthy that you should enter un - der my roof,
but only say the word and my soul shall be healed.

Or **Lord, I am not worthy**
that you should enter under my roof,
but only say the word
and my soul shall be healed.

Communion Chant

While the Priest is receiving the Sacrament, the Communion Chant or song is begun.

The minister of Communion says, *STAND*

"The Body of Christ" or "The Blood of Christ"

and the communicant answers:

Amen.

Period of Silence or Song of Praise *SIT (OR KNEEL)*

A period of silence may now be observed, or a psalm or song of praise may be sung.

Prayer after Communion *STAND*

The Communion Rite concludes with a prayer to which all respond:

Amen.

On Thursday of the Lord's Supper, the Evening Mass concludes at this point with the Transfer of the Most Blessed Sacrament.

21 The Concluding Rites

Greeting

The Lord be with you.

And with your spir-it.

Final Blessing

May almighty God bless you,
the Father, and the Son, † and the Holy Spirit.

A - men.

A Solemn Blessing or Prayer over the People may be chosen by the Priest, in place of the above blessing.

Dismissal

The Deacon/Priest invites all to go in the peace of Christ:

22

Deacon/Priest
All
Go forth, the Mass is end - ed. Thanks be to God.

Or **23**

Deacon/Priest
All
Go and an-nounce the Gos - pel of the Lord. Thanks be to God.

Or **24**

Deacon/Priest
All
Go in peace, glorifying the Lord by your life. Thanks be to God.

Or **25**

Deacon/Priest
All
Go in peace. Thanks be to God.

At the Easter Vigil in the Holy Night, Easter Sunday during the Day, the Octave of Easter, and the Vigil Mass and Mass during the Day on Pentecost Sunday:

26

Deacon/Priest
Go forth, the Mass is end-ed, al - le - lu - ia, al - le - lu - ia.
Or
Deacon/Priest
Go in peace, al - le - lu - ia, al - le - lu - ia.
All
Thanks be to God, al - le - lu - ia, al - le - lu - ia.

A final psalm or hymn may be sung.

Mass Settings

HOLY
HOLY
HOLY

The music with which the Church celebrates the Eucharist has developed over the centuries, clothing ancient ritual elements in idioms expressive of the assembly's faith. A broad range of settings—contemporary, gospel, and traditional—invigorates the assembly's celebration and expands its vocabulary of praise. Each of these offers a unified musical approach to the Order of Mass.

Mass of the Sacred Heart

27 Lord, Have Mercy

Cantor/Choir
Lord, have mer-cy.
All
Lord, have mer-cy.
Cantor/Choir
Christ, have mer-cy.
All
Christ, have mer-cy.
Cantor/Choir
Lord, have mer-cy.
All
Lord, have mer-cy.

Music: *Mass of the Sacred Heart;* Timothy R. Smith, b. 1960,

28 Glory to God

Refrain: 1st time: Cantor/Choir, All repeat; thereafter: All
Glo - ry to God in the high - est, and on
earth peace to peo - ple of good will.
to Verses
Verse 1
1. We praise you, we bless you, we a - dore you, we glo-ri-fy

1. you, we give you thanks for your great glo - ry, Lord God,
1. heav-en - ly King, O God, al-might - y Fa-ther.
to Refrain
Verse 2
2. Lord Je - sus Christ, On-ly Be-got-ten Son, Lord God,
2. Lamb of God, Son of the Fa - ther, you take a-way the
2. sins of the world, have mer - cy on us; you take a - way the
2. sins of the world, re-ceive our prayer; you are seat - ed at the right
2. hand of the Fa - ther, have mer - cy on us.
to Refrain
Verse 3
3. For you a-lone are the Ho - ly One, you a-lone are the Lord,
3. you a - lone are the Most High, Je - sus Christ, with the
3. Ho - ly Spir - it, in the glo - ry of God the
3. Fa - ther. A - men. A - men.
to Refrain

29 ALLELUIA

Refrain
Al - le - lu - ia, al - le - lu - ia,
al - le - lu - ia.

Note: Verses available in accompaniment books.

30 LENTEN GOSPEL ACCLAMATION

Refrain
Glo - ry and praise to you, Lord Je - sus Christ!

Note: Verses available in accompaniment books.

31 HOLY

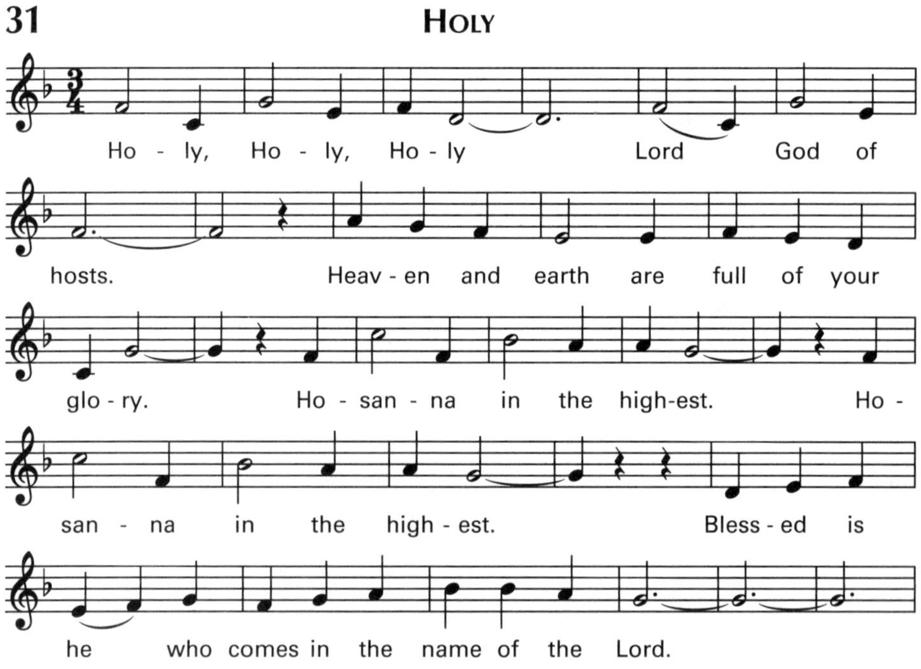
Ho - ly, Ho - ly, Ho - ly Lord God of
hosts. Heav - en and earth are full of your
glo - ry. Ho - san - na in the high-est. Ho -
san - na in the high - est. Bless - ed is
he who comes in the name of the Lord.

Ho - san - na in the high - est. Ho -
san - na in the high - est.

We Proclaim Your Death 32

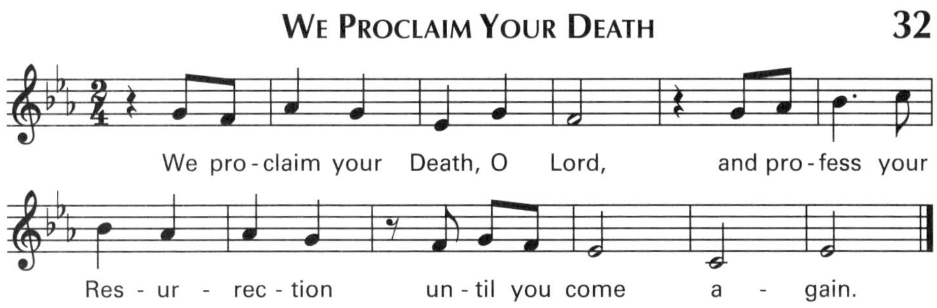
We pro - claim your Death, O Lord, and pro - fess your
Res - ur - rec - tion un - til you come a - gain.

When We Eat This Bread 33

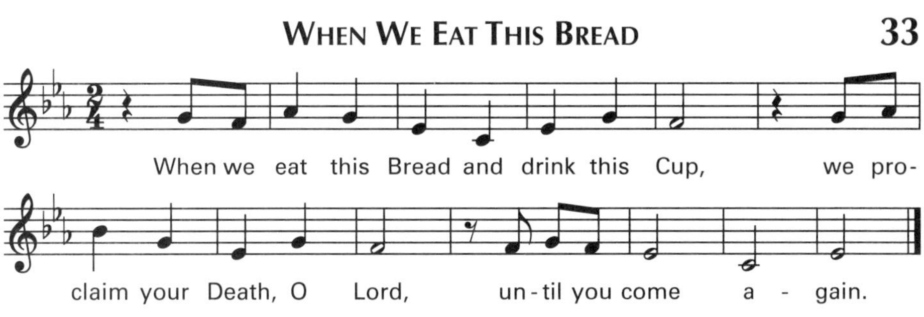
When we eat this Bread and drink this Cup, we pro-
claim your Death, O Lord, un - til you come a - gain.

Save Us, Savior 34

Save us, Sav - ior of the world, for by your Cross and
Res - ur - rec - tion you have set us free.

35 AMEN

Optional repeat
Final
A - men. A - men. A - men. men.

Music: *Mass of the Sacred Heart;* Timothy R. Smith, b. 1960, © 2014, Timothy R. Smith.

36 LAMB OF GOD

Lamb of God, you take a - way the
1, 2
sins of the world, have mer - cy on us.
Final
world, grant us peace.

Music: *Mass of the Sacred Heart;* Timothy R. Smith, b. 1960, © 2007, 2010, Timothy R. Smith.

MASS OF GLORY

37 PENITENTIAL ACT WITH INVOCATIONS

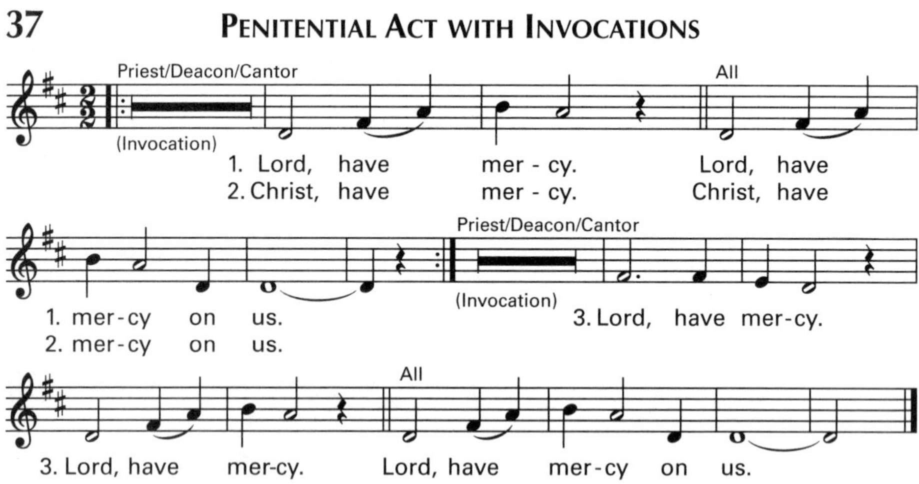
Priest/Deacon/Cantor
(Invocation)
1. Lord, have mer - cy.
2. Christ, have mer - cy.
All
Lord, have
Christ, have
1. mer-cy on us.
2. mer-cy on us.
Priest/Deacon/Cantor
(Invocation)
3. Lord, have mer-cy.
3. Lord, have mer-cy.
All
Lord, have mer-cy on us.

Note: Invocations from *The Roman Missal, 3rd Edition* are in the accompaniment books.

Music: *Mass of Glory;* Bob Hurd, b. 1950, © 1991, 2009, Bob Hurd.

Glory to God

38

Refrain: 1st time: Cantor, All repeat; thereafter: All
Glo-ry to God, glo-ry to God, glo-ry to God in the high - est,
and on earth peace to peo-ple of good will.
2 to Vss.
Last time
Glo - ry to God, glo - ry to God, glo - ry to God in the
high - est, and on earth peace to peo-ple of good will.
A - men, a - men, a - men.

Verses

1. We praise you, we bless you,
   we adore you, we glorify you,
   we give you thanks for your great glory,
   Lord God, heavenly King,
   O God, almighty Father.

2. Lord Jesus Christ, Only Begotten Son,
   Lord God, Lamb of God,
   Son of the Father,
   you take away the sins of the world,
   have mercy on us;
   you take away the sins of the world,
   receive our prayer;
   you are seated at the right hand
   of the Father,
   have mercy on us.

3. For you alone are the Holy One,
   you alone are the Lord,
   you alone are the Most High, Jesus Christ,
   with the Holy Spirit,
   in the glory of God the Father.

39 ALLELUIA! GIVE THE GLORY

Al - le - lu - ia! Al - le - lu - ia!
Al - le - lu - ia!
Give the glo - ry
1
and the hon - or to the Lord!
2
and the hon - or to the Lord!

Note: Gathering, Gospel Acclamation and Easter Vigil Psalm 118 verses are available in the accompaniment books.

Text: Ken Canedo, b. 1953, and Bob Hurd, b. 1950.
Music: *Mass of Glory*; Ken Canedo.

40 LENTEN GOSPEL ACCLAMATION

Praise and hon-or to you, O Lord Je - sus Christ.

Note: Verses available in accompaniment books.

Music: *Mass of Glory*; Ken Canedo, b. 1953, and Bob Hurd, b. 1950, © 1998, Ken Canedo and Bob Hurd. Published by OCP. All rights reserved.

41 HOLY

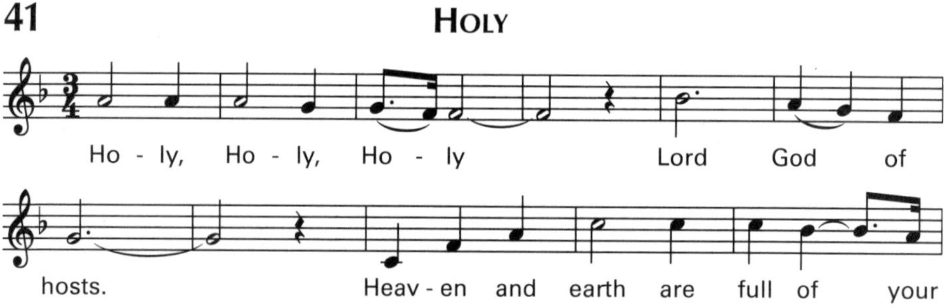
Ho - ly, Ho - ly, Ho - ly Lord God of
hosts. Heav - en and earth are full of your

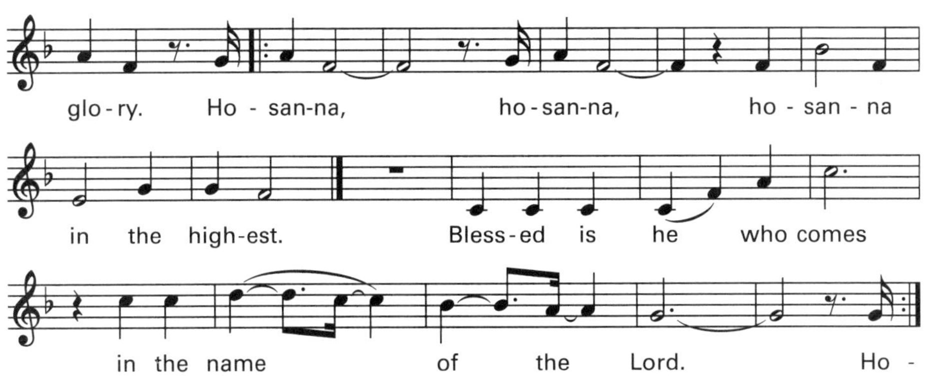
glo - ry. Ho - san-na, ho - san-na, ho - san - na
in the high-est. Bless-ed is he who comes
in the name of the Lord. Ho -

We Proclaim Your Death 42

We pro - claim your Death, O Lord, and pro - fess your
Res - ur - rec - tion un - til you come a - gain.

When We Eat This Bread 43

When we eat this Bread and drink this Cup,
we pro - claim your Death, O Lord, un - til you
come a - gain, un - til you come a - gain.

44 Save Us, Savior

Save us, Sav - ior of the world, for by your Cross and
Res - ur - rec - tion you have set us free.

Text © 2010, ICEL. All rights reserved. Used with permission.
Music: *Mass of Glory*; Ken Canedo, b. 1953, and Bob Hurd, b. 1950, © 2009, Ken Canedo and Bob Hurd.
Published by OCP. All rights reserved.

45 Amen

1
2
A - men. A - men. Al - le - lu - ia, a - men. men.
During Lent: Praise and glo-ry,

Music: *Mass of Glory*; Ken Canedo, b. 1953, and Bob Hurd, b. 1950, © 1991, Ken Canedo and Bob Hurd.
Published by OCP. All rights reserved.

46 Lamb of God

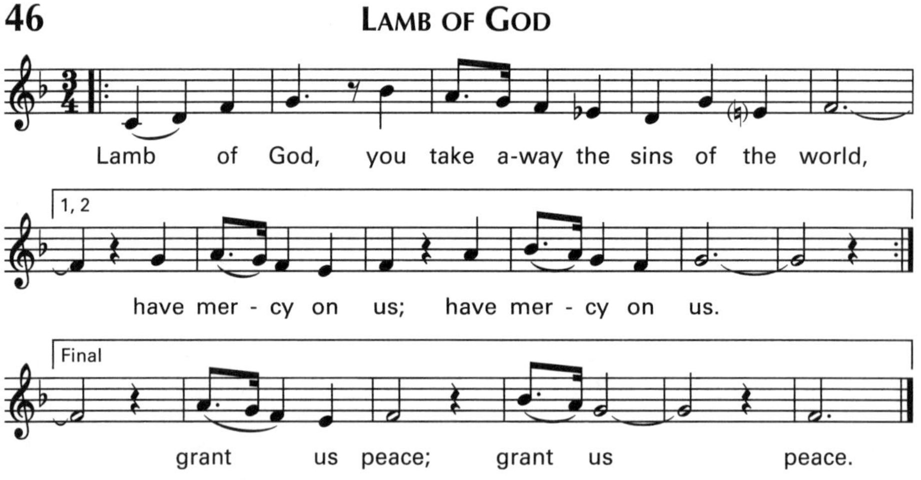
Lamb of God, you take a-way the sins of the world,
1, 2
have mer - cy on us; have mer - cy on us.
Final
grant us peace; grant us peace.

Music: *Mass of Glory*; Bob Hurd, b. 1950, © 1991, Bob Hurd. Published by OCP. All rights reserved.

Mass of Christ the Savior

Living Streams 47

(Sprinkling Rite)

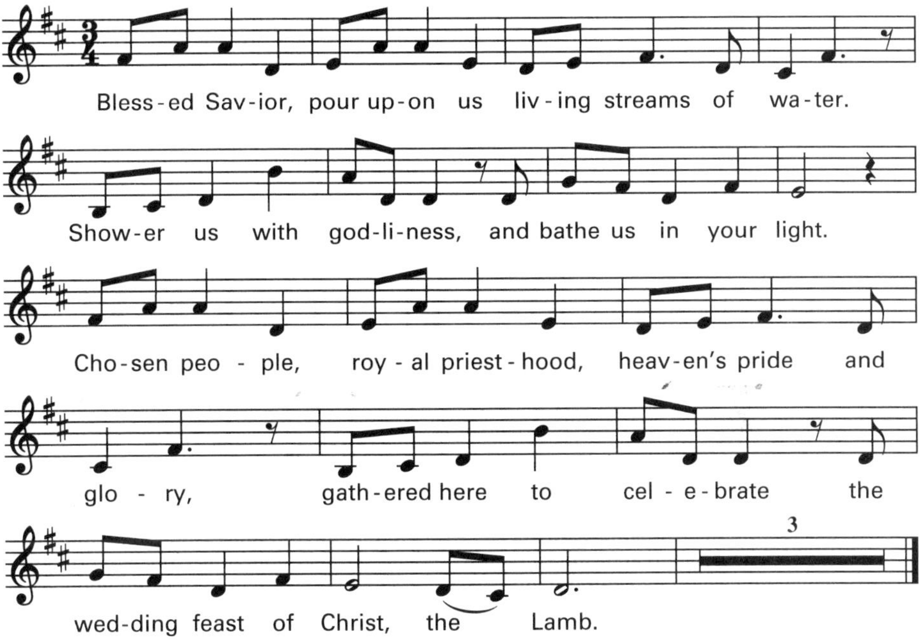

Bless-ed Sav-ior, pour up-on us liv-ing streams of wa-ter.
Show-er us with god-li-ness, and bathe us in your light.
Cho-sen peo - ple, roy - al priest - hood, heav-en's pride and
glo - ry, gath-ered here to cel - e - brate the
wed-ding feast of Christ, the Lamb.

Text and music: *Mass of Christ the Savior*; Dan Schutte, b. 1947, © 2013, Daniel L. Schutte.

Lord, Have Mercy/Kyrie, Eleison 48

Cantor/Choir; All repeat
Lord, have mer-cy.
Ký - ri - e, e - léi-son.
Cantor/Choir; All repeat
Christ, have mer-cy.
Chri - ste, e - léi-son.
Cantor/Choir; All repeat
Lord, have mer-cy, have mer-cy on us.
Ký - ri - e, e - léi-son, e - lé - i - son.

Music: *Mass of Christ the Savior*; Dan Schutte, b. 1947, © 2007, 2009, Daniel L. Schutte.

49 GLORY TO GOD

Refrain
Glo-ry to God. Glo-ry to God. Glo-ry to God in the high - est, and on earth peace, on earth peace to peo-ple of good
1-4 (1st time: to Refrain) to Verses
will.
Final
will.
Coda
A - men. A - men.
Verse 1
1. We praise you, we bless you, we a - dore you, we
1. glo-ri-fy you, we give you thanks for your great glo-ry,
to Verse 2 or Refrain
1. Lord God, heav'n-ly King, O God, al-might-y Fa - ther.
Verse 2
2. Lord Je-sus Christ, On - ly Be-got - ten Son, Lord God,
2. Lamb of God, Son of the Fa-ther, you take a-way the sins of the world,
2. have mer-cy on us; you take a-way the sins of the world,
2. re-ceive our prayer; you are seat - ed at the right hand,
to Verse 3 or Refrain
2. the right hand of the Fa-ther, have mer-cy on us.

Verse 3
3. For you a-lone are the Ho-ly One, you a-lone are the Lord,
3. you a-lone are the Most High, Je-sus Christ, with the Ho-ly
to Coda ⊕ or Refrain
3
3. Spir-it, in the glo-ry of God the Fa-ther.

ALLELUIA 50

Al-le-lu-ia. Al-le-lu-ia. Al-le-lu-ia.

Note: Verses available in accompaniment books.

LENTEN GOSPEL ACCLAMATION 51

Glo-ry to you, Word of God, Lord Je-sus Christ!

Note: Verses available in accompaniment books.

52 Holy

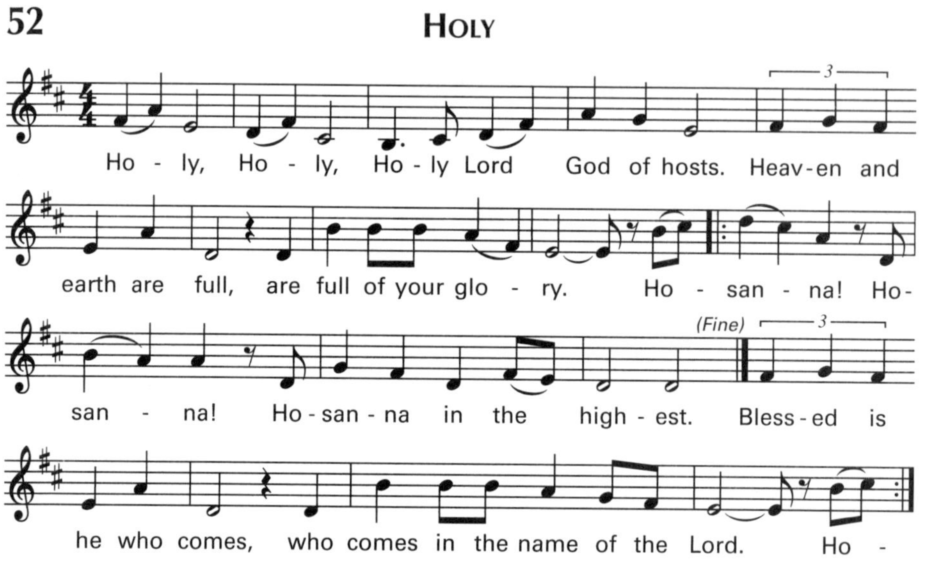
3
Ho - ly, Ho - ly, Ho - ly Lord God of hosts. Heav-en and
earth are full, are full of your glo - ry. Ho - san - na! Ho-
(Fine)
3
san - na! Ho - san - na in the high - est. Bless - ed is
he who comes, who comes in the name of the Lord. Ho -

53 We Proclaim Your Death

We pro - claim your Death, O Lord, and pro - fess your
Res - ur - rec - tion un - til you come a - gain.

54 When We Eat This Bread

When we eat this Bread and drink this Cup, we pro-
claim your Death, O Lord, un - til you come a - gain.

Save Us, Savior 55

Save us, save us, Sav-ior of the world, for by your
Cross and Res - ur - rec-tion you have set us free.

Amen 56

A - men. A - men. A - men.

Lamb of God 57

Lamb of God, you take a - way the sins of the
1, 2
world, have mer-cy on us.
Final
world, grant us peace.

Mass of a Joyful Heart

58 Lord, Have Mercy/Kyrie, Eleison

Priest/Deacon/Cantor; All repeat
Lord, have mer - cy.
Ký - ri - e, e - lé - i - son.
Priest/Deacon/Cantor; All repeat
Christ, have mer - cy.
Chri - ste, e - lé - i - son.
Priest/Deacon/Cantor

Lord, have mer - cy.
Ký - ri - e, e - lé - i-son.

All
Lord, have mer - cy.
Ký - ri - e, e - lé - i-son.

Music: *Mass of a Joyful Heart;* Steve Angrisano, b. 1965, and Tom Tomaszek, b. 1950,

59 Glory to God

Refrain

Glo-ry to God in the high - est, and on earth peace to

peo-ple of good will.

1-3 to Verses (1. We)

Final A - men. *Fine*

Verse 1

1. We praise you, we bless you, we a-dore you, we glo-ri-fy you,

1. we give you thanks for your great glo - ry, Lord God,

1. heav-en - ly King, O God, al-might - y Fa - ther.

to Refrain or Verse 2

Verse 2

2. Lord Je-sus Christ, On-ly Be-got-ten Son, Lord God, Lamb of

2. God, Son of the Fa - ther, you take a - way the
2. sins of the world, have mer - cy on us; you take a - way the
2. sins of the world, re - ceive our prayer; you are seat - ed at the right
2. hand of the Fa - ther, have mer-cy on us.

to Refrain or Verse 3

Verse 3

3. For you a - lone are the Ho - ly One, you a - lone are the Lord,
3. you a - lone are the Most High, Je - sus Christ, with the
3. Ho - ly Spir - it, in the glo - ry of God the Fa - ther.

to Refrain

Alleluia **60**

1
Al - le - lu - ia. Al - le - lu - ia, al - le -
2
lu - ia. lu - ia!

Note: Verses available in accompaniment books.

61 Lenten Gospel Acclamation

1
2
Glo - ry to you, O Word of God.
Glo - ry to you, Lord Je - sus Christ.

Note: Verses available in accompaniment books.

62 Holy

Ho-ly, Ho - ly, Ho - ly Lord God of hosts.
Heav-en and earth are full of your glo - ry. Ho - san - na in
the high - est. Bless - ed is he who comes
in the name of the Lord, in the name of the Lord. Ho -
san - na in the high - est, ho - san - na in the high - est.

63 We Proclaim Your Death

We pro-claim your Death, O Lord, and pro - fess your

Res - ur - rec - tion un - til you come a - gain.

When We Eat This Bread 64

When we eat this Bread and drink this Cup, we pro -
claim your Death, O Lord, un - til you come a - gain.

Save Us, Savior 65

Save us, Sav - ior of the world, for by your
Cross and Res - ur - rec - tion you have set us free.

Amen 66

A - men. A - men.
A - men. A - men. A - men.

67 Lamb of God

1, 2
3
Lamb of God, you take a-way the sins of the world, have
mer-cy on us.
Final
3
sins of the world, grant us peace.

Music: *Mass of a Joyful Heart*; Steve Angrisano, b. 1965,

Heritage Mass

68 Lord, Have Mercy

Lord, have mer - cy. Christ, have
mer - cy. Lord, have mer - cy.

Music: *Heritage Mass*; Owen Alstott, b. 1947,

69 Glory to God

Glo - ry to God in the high - est, and on earth peace to
peo-ple of good will. We praise you, we bless you, we a - dore you,
we glo - ri-fy you, we give you thanks for your great glo - ry,
Lord God, heav'n-ly King, O God, al-might-y Fa - ther.

Lord Je-sus Christ, On-ly Be-got-ten Son, Lord God,
Lamb of God, Son of the Fa-ther, you take a-way the
sins of the world, have mer-cy on us; you take a-way the
sins of the world, re-ceive our prayer; you are seat-ed at the
right hand of the Fa-ther, have mer-cy on us.
For you a-lone are the Ho-ly One, you a-lone are the Lord,
you a-lone are the Most High, Je-sus Christ, with the Ho-ly
Spir-it, in the glo-ry of God the Fa-ther. A-men.

Holy 70

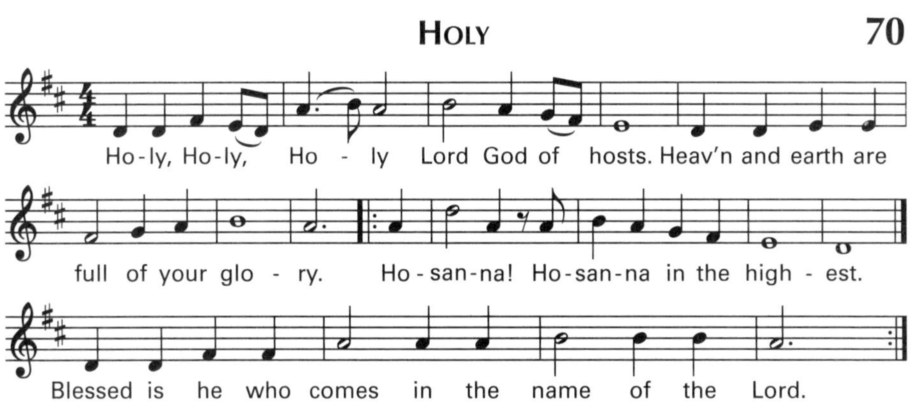
Ho-ly, Ho-ly, Ho-ly Lord God of hosts. Heav'n and earth are
full of your glo-ry. Ho-san-na! Ho-san-na in the high-est.
Blessed is he who comes in the name of the Lord.

71 We Proclaim Your Death

We pro - claim your Death, O Lord, and pro - fess your
Res - ur - rec - tion un - til you come, un - til you come a - gain.

72 When We Eat This Bread

When we eat this Bread and drink this Cup, we pro - claim your
Death, O Lord, un - til you come a - gain.

73 Save Us, Savior

Save us, Sav - ior of the world, for by your
Cross and Res - ur - rec - tion you have set us free.

74 Amen

A - men, a - men, a - men.

Lamb of God 75

Lamb of God, you take a-way the sins of the
1, 2
world, have mer-cy on us.
3
world, grant us peace.

Misa Santa Fe

Acto Penitencial, Formulario 3/ Penitential Act with Invocations 76

Sacerdote/Diácono/Cantor
Priest/Deacon/Cantor
(Invocación/
Invocation)
Cantor/All
Se-ñor, ten pie-dad. Se-ñor, ten pie-dad.
Lord, have mer-cy. Lord, have mer-cy.
Sacerdote/Diácono/Cantor
Priest/Deacon/Cantor
(Invocación/
Invocation)
Cantor/All
Cris-to, ten pie-dad. Cris-to, ten pie-dad.
Christ, have mer-cy. Christ, have mer-cy.
Sacerdote/Diácono/Cantor
Priest/Deacon/Cantor
(Invocación/
Invocation)
Cantor/All
Se-ñor, ten pie-dad. Se-ñor, ten pie-dad.
Lord, have mer-cy. Lord, have mer-cy.

Note: Invocations from *The Roman Missal, 3rd Edition* are in the accompaniment books.

77 GLORIA/GLORY TO GOD

*Estribillo/Refrain
Glo - ria a Dios en el cie - lo, y en la tie - rra
Glo - ry to God in the high - est, and on earth
paz a los hom - bres que a - ma el Se - ñor.
peace to peo - ple, to peo - ple of good will.

*Verses available in accompaniment books.

Text: Spanish © 1975, 1991, Comisión Episcopal de Pastoral Litúrgica de la Conferencia del Episcopado Mexicano. All rights reserved. Sole US agent: US Conference of Catholic Bishops. Used with permission. English © 2010, ICEL. All rights reserved. Used with permission.
Music: *Misa Santa Fe*; Mary Frances Reza, © 2009, 2011, Mary Frances Reza. Published by OCP. All rights reserved.

78 SANTO/HOLY

Español San - to, San - to, San - to es el Se - ñor, Dios del U - ni - ver - so.
English *Ho - ly, Ho - ly, Ho - ly Lord God of hosts.*
Biling. San - to, San - to, San - to es el Se - ñor, Dios del U - ni - ver - so.

Lle - nos es - tán el cie - lo y la tie - rra de tu glo - ria. Ho -
Heav - en and earth are full of your glo - ry. Ho -
Heav - en and earth are full of your glo - ry. Ho -

san - na en el cie - lo. Ho - san - na en el cie - lo. Ben -
san - na in the high - est. Ho - san - na in the high - est.
san - na en el cie - lo. Ho - san - na en el cie - lo.

di - to el que vie - ne en nom - bre del Se - ñor. Ho -
Bless - ed is he who comes in the name of the Lord. Ho -
Bless - ed is he who comes in the name of the Lord. Ho -

san - na en el cie - lo. Ho - san - na en el cie - lo.
san - na in the high - est. Ho - san - na in the high - est.
san - na en el cie - lo. Ho - san - na en el cie - lo.

Text: Spanish © 1975, 1991, Comisión Episcopal de Pastoral Litúrgica de la Conferencia del Episcopado Mexicano. All rights reserved. Sole US agent: US Conference of Catholic Bishops. Used with permission. English © 2010, ICEL. All rights reserved. Used with permission.
Music: *Misa Santa Fe*; Mary Frances Reza, © 2009, 2011, Mary Frances Reza. Published by OCP. All rights reserved.

Anunciamos Tu Muerte/We Proclaim Your Death 79

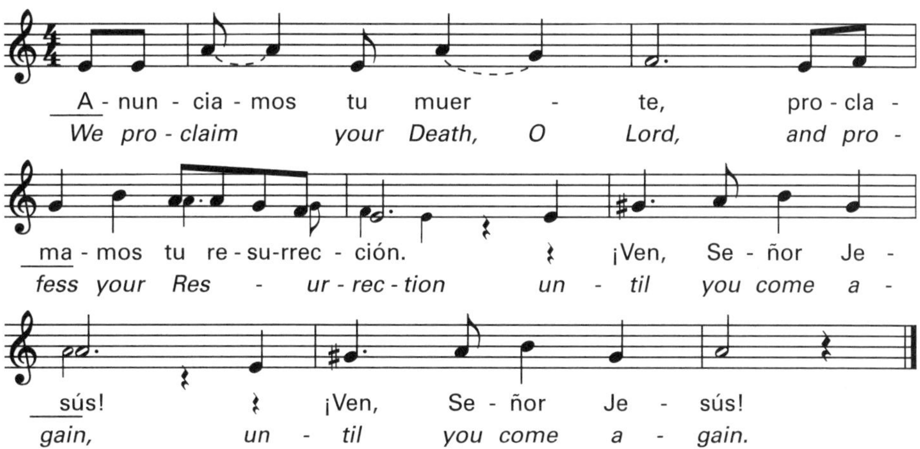
A - nun - cia - mos tu muer - te, pro - cla - ma - mos tu re - su-rrec - ción. ¡Ven, Se - ñor Je - sús! ¡Ven, Se - ñor Je - sús!
We pro - claim your Death, O Lord, and pro - fess your Res - ur - rec - tion un - til you come a - gain, un - til you come a - gain.

Text: Spanish © 1975, 1991, Comisión Episcopal de Pastoral Litúrgica de la Conferencia del Episcopado Mexicano. All rights reserved. Sole US agent: US Conference of Catholic Bishops. Used with permission.
English © 2010, ICEL. All rights reserved. Used with permission.
Music: *Misa Santa Fe*; Mary Frances Reza, © 2009, 2011, Mary Frances Reza. Published by OCP. All rights reserved.

Amén/Amen 80

A - mén, a-mén, a - mén. A - mén, a-mén, a - mén.
A - men, a-men, a - men. A - men, a-men, a - men.

Music: *Misa Santa Fe*; Mary Frances Reza, © 2009, 2011, Mary Frances Reza. Published by OCP. All rights reserved.

Cordero de Dios/Lamb of God 81

1-3. Cor - de - ro de Dios, que qui-tas el pe - ca - do del mun-do,
1-3. Lamb of God, you take a-way the sins of the world,
1, 2. ten pie-dad de no - so-tros, ten pie-dad de no - so-tros.
3. da - nos la paz, da - nos la paz.
1, 2. have mer - cy on us, have mer - cy on us.
3. grant us peace, grant us peace.

Text: Spanish © 1975, 1991, Comisión Episcopal de Pastoral Litúrgica de la Conferencia del Episcopado Mexicano. All rights reserved. Sole US agent: US Conference of Catholic Bishops. Used with permission.
Music: *Misa Santa Fe*; Mary Frances Reza, © 2009, 2011, Mary Frances Reza. Published by OCP. All rights reserved.

Celtic Mass

82 Penitential Act with Invocations

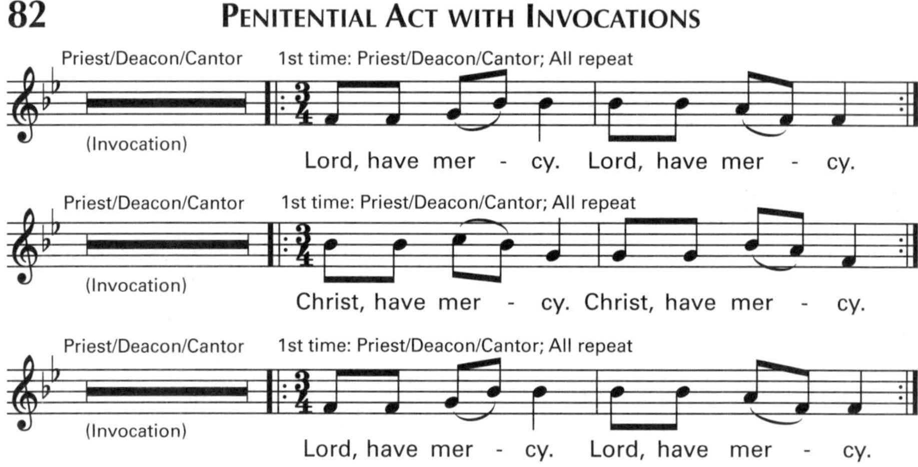
Priest/Deacon/Cantor
1st time: Priest/Deacon/Cantor; All repeat
(Invocation)
Lord, have mer - cy. Lord, have mer - cy.
Priest/Deacon/Cantor
1st time: Priest/Deacon/Cantor; All repeat
(Invocation)
Christ, have mer - cy. Christ, have mer - cy.
Priest/Deacon/Cantor
1st time: Priest/Deacon/Cantor; All repeat
(Invocation)
Lord, have mer - cy. Lord, have mer - cy.

Note: Invocations from *The Roman Missal, 3rd Edition* are in the accompaniment books.

Music: *Celtic Mass*; Christopher Walker, b. 1947,

83 Glory to God

Glo-ry to God in the high - est, and on earth peace to peo-ple of good

will. We praise you, we bless you, we a - dore you, we

glo-ri-fy you, we give you thanks for your great glo - ry, Lord God,

heav-en - ly King, O God, al-might-y Fa-ther. Lord Je-sus Christ,

On-ly Be-got - ten Son, Lord God, Lamb of God, Son of the Fa - ther,

you take a - way the sins of the world,
have mer - cy, have mer-cy on us;

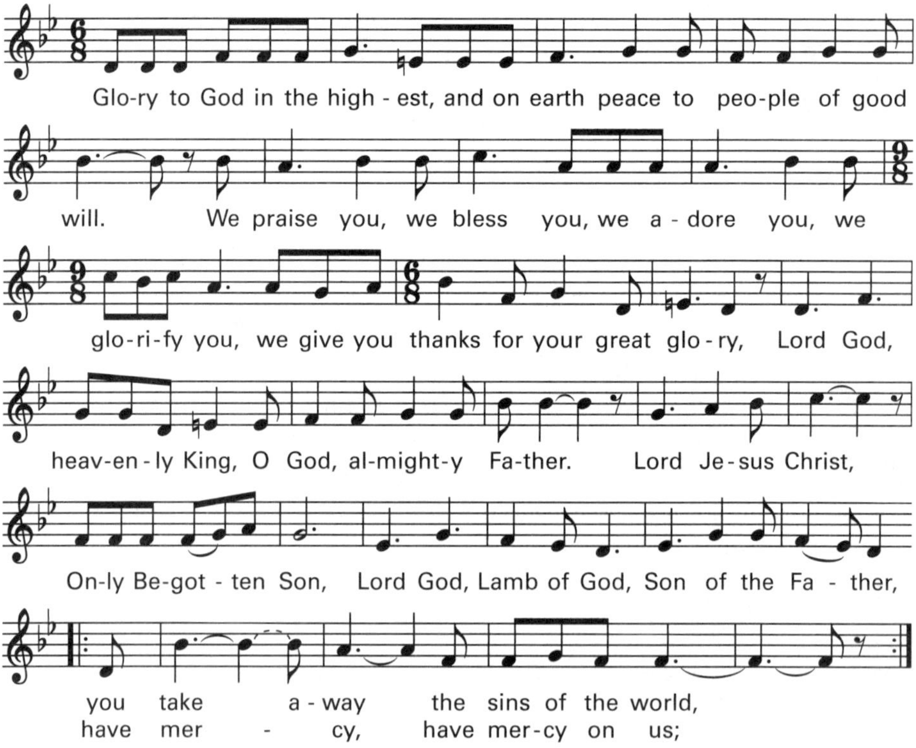

you take a - way the sins of the world, re -

ceive our prayer, re-ceive our prayer; you are seat-ed at the

right hand of the Fa-ther, have mer - cy, have mer-cy on us.

For you a-lone are the Ho-ly One, you a-lone are the

Lord, you a-lone are the Most High, Je-sus Christ, with the

Ho - ly Spir-it, in the glo-ry of God, the glo-ry of God the

Fa-ther. A - men, a - men, a - men.

Celtic Alleluia 84

Al - le - lu - ia, al - le - lu - ia.
Al - le - lu - ia, al - le - lu - ia.

Note: Verses available in accompaniment books.

85 Lenten Gospel Acclamation

Praise and hon-or, hon-or and glo-ry, glo-ry to you, Lord Je-sus Christ.

Note: Verses available in accompaniment books.

86 Holy

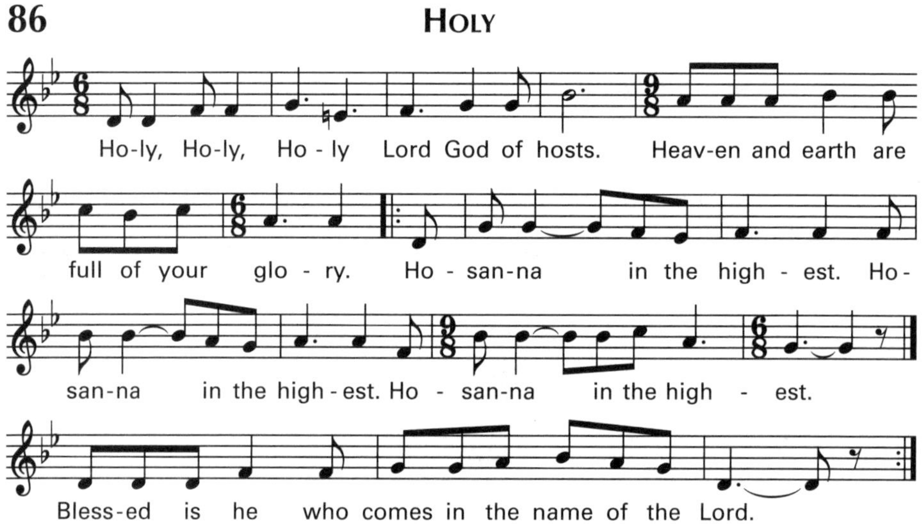
Ho-ly, Ho-ly, Ho - ly Lord God of hosts. Heav-en and earth are
full of your glo - ry. Ho - san-na in the high - est. Ho-
san-na in the high - est. Ho - san-na in the high - est.
Bless-ed is he who comes in the name of the Lord.

87 We Proclaim Your Death

We pro-claim your Death, O Lord, and pro-fess your Res-ur-rec-tion
un - til you come a - gain, un - til you come a - gain.

When We Eat This Bread 88

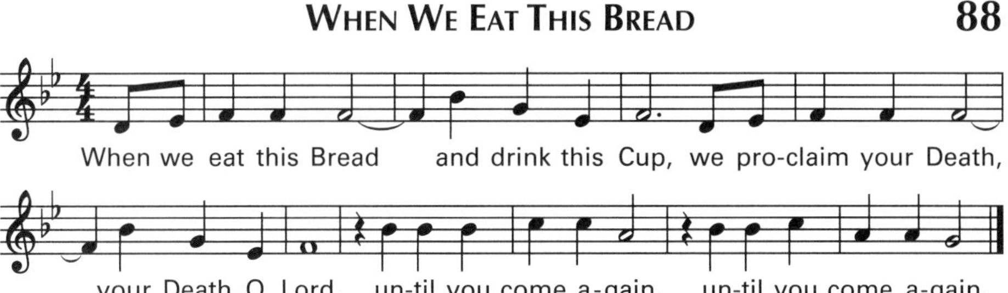
When we eat this Bread and drink this Cup, we pro-claim your Death,
your Death, O Lord, un-til you come a-gain, un-til you come a-gain.

Save Us, Savior 89

Save us, Sav-ior of the world, for by your Cross and Res-ur-rec-tion you have
set us free, for by your Cross and Res-ur-rec-tion you have set us free.

Amen 90

A-men, a - men, a - men, a-men, a-men, a - men.

Lamb of God 91

Choir/Cantor
All
1, 2
Lamb of God, you take a-way the sins of the world, have mer-cy on
3
Final
us, mer-cy on us. world, grant us peace, grant us peace.

MASS OF RENEWAL

92 KYRIE, ELEISON/LORD, HAVE MERCY

Cantor; All repeat
Ký - ri - e, e - lé - i - son. Chri - ste, e - lé - i - son. Ký - ri - e, e - lé - i - son.
Lord, have mer - cy. Christ, have mer - cy. Lord, have mer - cy.

93 GLORY TO GOD

Glo - ry to God in the high - est, and on earth peace to peo - ple
of good will. We praise you, we bless you, we a -
dore you, we glo - ri - fy you, we give you
thanks for your great glo - ry, Lord God, heav - en - ly
King, O God, al - might - y Fa - ther.
Lord Je - sus Christ, On - ly Be - got - ten Son, Lord God,

Lamb of God, Son of the Fa - ther, you take a -
way the sins of the world, have mer - cy on us; you take a -
way the sins of the world, re - ceive our prayer; you are seat - ed
at the right hand of the Fa - ther, have mer -
cy, have mer - cy on us. For you a - lone are the
Ho - ly One, you a - lone are the Lord, you a - lone are the
Most High, Je - sus Christ, with the Ho - ly Spir - it,
in the glo - ry of God the Fa - ther. A - men, a - men.

Alleluia 94

Al - le - lu - ia, al - le - lu - ia, al - le - lu - ia.
Al - le - lu - ia, al - le - lu - ia, al - le - lu - ia.

Note: Verses available in accompaniment books.

95 Lenten Gospel Acclamation

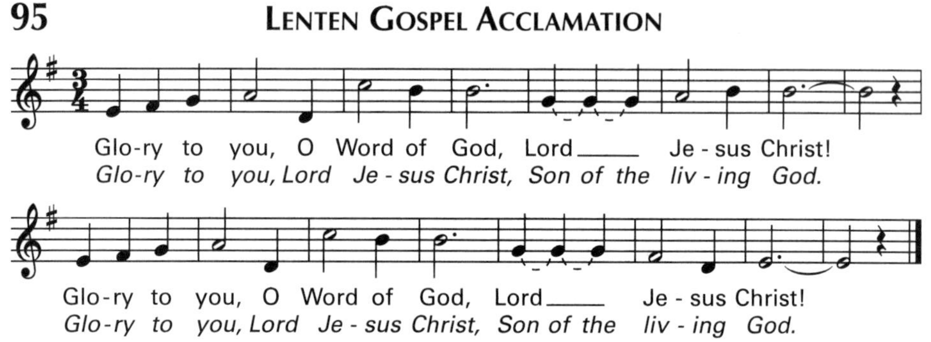
Glo-ry to you, O Word of God, Lord ___ Je - sus Christ!
Glo-ry to you, Lord Je - sus Christ, Son of the liv - ing God.
Glo-ry to you, O Word of God, Lord ___ Je - sus Christ!
Glo-ry to you, Lord Je - sus Christ, Son of the liv - ing God.

Note: Verses available in accompaniment books.

96 Holy

Ho - ly, Ho - ly, Ho - ly Lord God of hosts. Heav-en and
earth are full of your glo - ry. Ho-san-na in the high - est.
Bless-ed is he who comes in the name of the Lord. Ho-
san-na in the high-est. Ho-san-na in the high - est.

97 We Proclaim Your Death

We pro - claim your Death, O Lord, and pro - fess your
Res - ur - rec-tion un - til you come a - gain.

WHEN WE EAT THIS BREAD 98

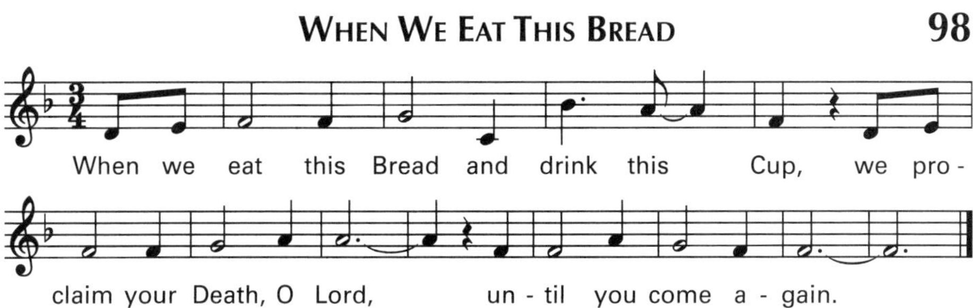
When we eat this Bread and drink this Cup, we pro-
claim your Death, O Lord, un - til you come a - gain.

SAVE US, SAVIOR 99

Save us, Sav - ior of the world, for by your Cross and Res - ur -
rec - tion you have set us free, you have set us free.

AMEN 100

A - men, a - men, a - men.

LAMB OF GOD 101

1, 2
Lamb of God, you take a-way the sins of the world, have mer - cy,
have mer - cy on us.
Final
world, grant us, grant us peace.

Morning Prayer (Lauds)

The Liturgy of the Hours is the Church's public worship of Christ, the communal celebration of praise and thanksgiving of the Church at prayer. The Hours, along with the Eucharist, take their meaning solely from the Paschal Mystery of salvation in Christ. Morning Prayer proclaims the themes of Christ as light of the world and sun of justice. It is the praise of God in creation that unites us with the prayer of Christ.

Opening Verse: Invitatory

102

All make the sign of the cross on their lips as the Cantor/Presiding Minister sings:

Cantor/Presiding Minister
All
O Lord, o-pen our lips, and we shall pro-claim your praise.

Text: Based on Psalm 51:15; Michael Joncas, b. 1951.
Music: Michael Joncas.

Invitatory Psalm: Psalm 95* *(Or an appropriate hymn)*

103

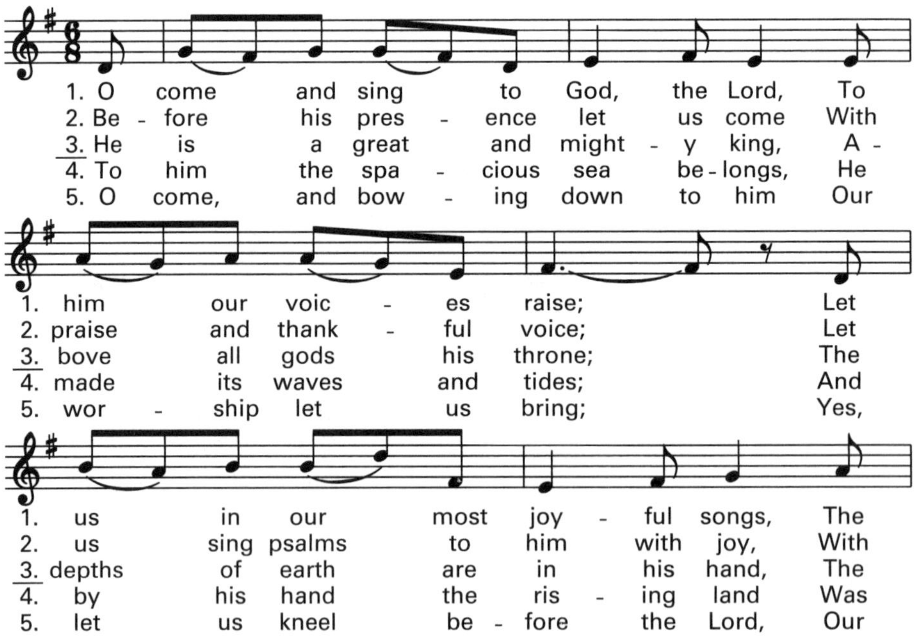

1. O come and sing to God, the Lord, To him our voic - es raise; Let us in our most joy - ful songs, The
2. Be - fore his pres - ence let us come With praise and thank - ful voice; Let us sing psalms to him with joy, With
3. He is a great and might - y king, A - bove all gods his throne; The depths of earth are in his hand, The
4. To him the spa - cious sea be - longs, He made its waves and tides; And by his hand the ris - ing land Was
5. O come, and bow - ing down to him Our wor - ship let us bring; Yes, let us kneel be - fore the Lord, Our

1. Lord, our Sav - ior, praise.
2. grate - ful hearts re - joice.
3. moun - tains are his own.
4. formed and still a - bides.
5. Mak - er and our King.

*Alternate setting of Psalm 95: No. 472.

Text: Psalm 95:1–6; *The Psalter*, 1912, alt.
Music: Michael Joncas, b. 1951,

Psalmody: Psalm 63* 104

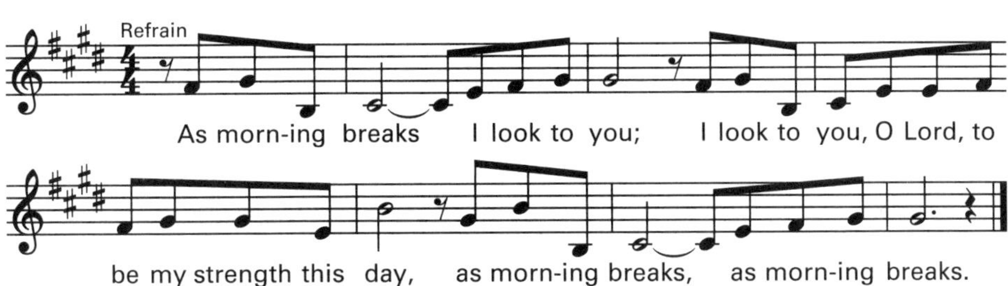
Refrain
As morn-ing breaks I look to you; I look to you, O Lord, to
be my strength this day, as morn-ing breaks, as morn-ing breaks.

1. O God, you are my God, for you I long;
   for you my soul is thirsting.
   My body pines for you,
   like a dry, weary land without water.
   So I gaze on you in your holy place
   to see your strength and your glory.
2. For your love is better than life,
   my lips will speak your praise.
   So I will bless you all my life,
   in your name I will lift up my hands.
   My soul shall be filled as with a banquet,
   my mouth shall praise you with joy.
3. On my bed I remember you.
   On you I muse through the night,
   for you have been my help;
   in the shadow of your wings I rejoice.
   My soul clings to you;
   your right hand holds me fast.

Doxology: All
4. Glo - ry to the Fa - ther, and to the Son,
4. and to the Ho - ly Spir - it, as it was in the
4. be - gin-ning, is now, and will be for - ev - er. A - men.
to Refrain

*Alternate setting of Psalm 63: No. 156. On Wednesday, Friday, and other penitential days, Psalm 51 may be used. See No. 152, No. 153, No. 154, or No. 155.

Text: Psalm 63:2–3, 4–6, 7–9; Doxology. Refrain,
Music: Michael Joncas, b. 1951,

Psalm-Prayer

Reading

Reflection on the Word of God/Homily

Gospel Canticle (Benedictus*)

All make the sign of the cross. Incense may be used during the singing of the Gospel Canticle.

105

1. Blest be the God of Is - ra - el who comes to set us free
2. With prom-ised mer - cy will God still the cov - e - nant re - call,
3. My child, as proph-et of the Lord you will pre - pare the way,

1. and rais - es up new hope for us: a Branch for Da-vid's tree.
2. the oath once sworn to A - bra - ham from foes to save us all;
3. to tell God's peo - ple they are saved from sin's e - ter - nal sway.

1. So have the proph-ets long de - clared that with a might-y arm
2. that we might wor - ship with - out fear and of - fer lives of praise,
3. Then shall God's mer - cy from on high shine forth and nev - er cease

1. God would turn back our en - e - mies and all who wish us harm.
2. in ho - li - ness and righ-teous-ness to serve God all our days.
3. to drive a - way the gloom of death and lead us in - to peace.

*For alternate settings, see No. 205 or No. 206.

Text: CMD; based on Luke 1:68–79; adapt. by Carl P. Daw, Jr., b. 1944, © 1989, Hope Publishing Co.

Music: FOREST GREEN; trad. English melody; collected and adapt. by Ralph Vaughan Williams, 1872–1958.

Intercessions

106

Brothers and sisters, let us pray to Christ, the rising sun that never sets, as we cry out with joy:

All
3
(Intercessions) Christ Je - sus, fill us with light and truth.

1. Creator of stars at night
and of dawn's new rays,
grant that we may give you thanks
and glory for the universe:

2. Good Shepherd of the sheep,
grant us protection
and guard us from evil:

3. Giver of understanding
and love to those who follow you,
enlighten our minds
and stir up our hearts.

4. Light of nations
and savior of all people,
grant us your justice and peace.

The Lord's Prayer 107

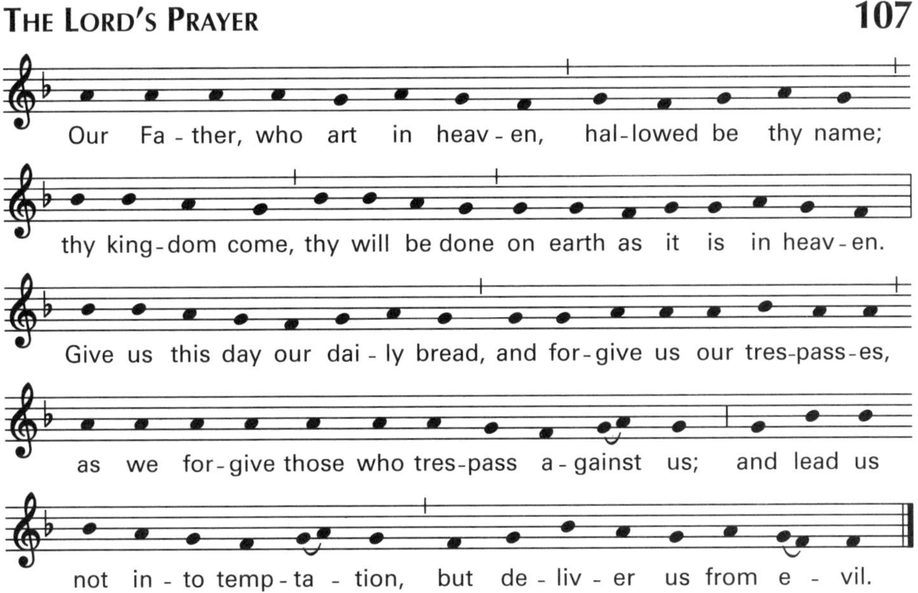
Our Fa - ther, who art in heav - en, hal-lowed be thy name;
thy king-dom come, thy will be done on earth as it is in heav - en.
Give us this day our dai - ly bread, and for-give us our tres-pass-es,
as we for-give those who tres-pass a - gainst us; and lead us
not in - to temp - ta - tion, but de - liv - er us from e - vil.

Music: Chant; adapt. by Robert J. Snow, 1926–1998.

Concluding Prayer

The presiding minister says the concluding prayer.

Blessing 108

Presiding Minister
May the Lord bless us, pro - tect us from all e - vil,
and bring us to ev - er - last - ing life.
All
A - men. A - men.

EVENING PRAYER (VESPERS)

Evening Prayer is an occasion to give thanks for the blessings of the day and for redemption in Christ. Prayer rises "like incense in the Lord's sight," and "upraised hands" become "an evening sacrifice" (Psalm 141:2). While not a part of the Church's current order of Evening Prayer, there is a long tradition, especially in religious communities, to begin the prayer with a service of Lucernarium *to accompany the lighting of the candles. A musical setting for this service is included here for optional use.*

THANKSGIVING FOR THE LIGHT

109

All make the sign of the cross as the Cantor/Presiding Minister sings:

Cantor: Light, joy and peace in our Lord Je - sus Christ.
All: Thanks be to God, Al - le - lu - ia.
(Lent: Thanks be to God, thanks be to God.)

EVENING HYMN: O RADIANT LIGHT

110

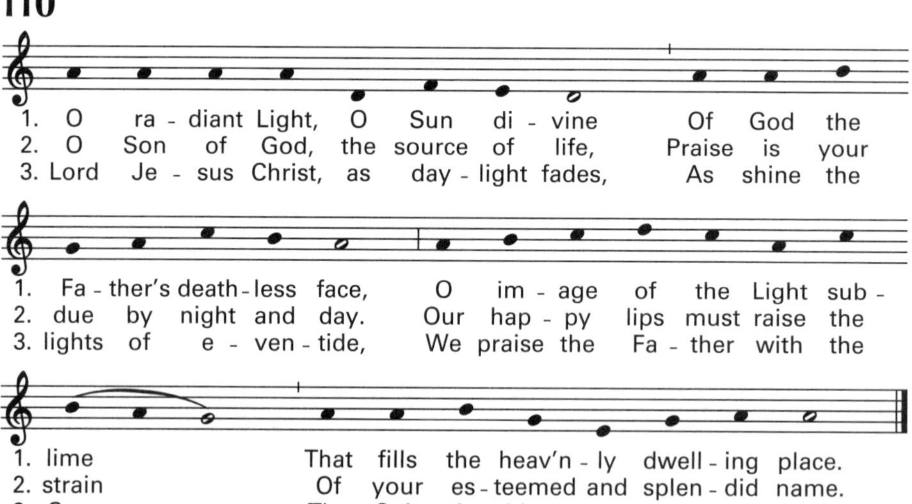

1. O ra - diant Light, O Sun di - vine Of God the Fa - ther's death - less face, O im - age of the Light sub - lime That fills the heav'n - ly dwell - ing place.
2. O Son of God, the source of life, Praise is your due by night and day. Our hap - py lips must raise the strain Of your es - teemed and splen - did name.
3. Lord Je - sus Christ, as day - light fades, As shine the lights of e - ven - tide, We praise the Fa - ther with the Son, The Spir - it blest, and with them one.

Text: LM; *Phos hilaron*, Greek, ca. 200; tr. by William G. Storey, 1923–2014, © William G. Storey.
Music: JESU DULCIS MEMORIA; Chant, Mode I.

PSALMODY: PSALM 141 — 111

Refrain

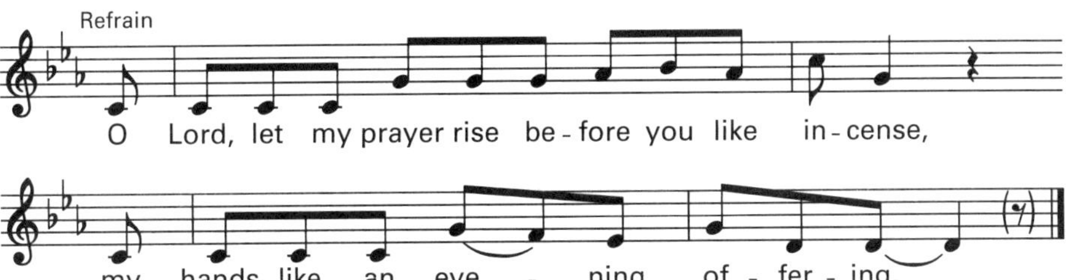
O Lord, let my prayer rise be-fore you like in-cense,
my hands like an eve - ning of - fer - ing.

Verses

1. Lord, I am calling: hasten to help me.
   Listen to me as I cry to you.
   Let my prayer rise before you like incense,
   my hands like an evening offering.
2. Lord, set a guard at my mouth,
   keep watch at the gate of my lips.
   Let my heart not turn to things that
   are wrong,
   to sharing the evil deeds done by the sinful.
   No, I will never taste their delights.
3. The good may reprove me,
   in kindness chastise me,
   but the wicked shall never anoint my head.
   Every day I counter their malice with prayer.
4. To you, Lord my God, my eyes are turned:
   in you I take refuge; do not forsake me.
   Keep me safe from
   the traps they have set for me,
   from the snares of those who do evil.

Doxology

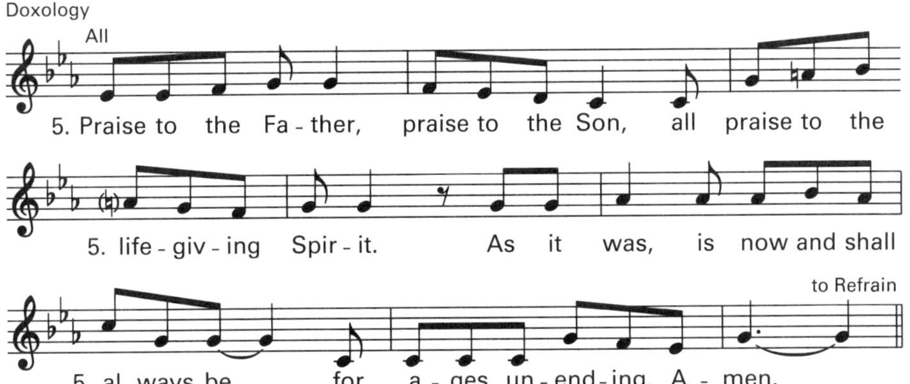
All
5. Praise to the Fa-ther, praise to the Son, all praise to the
5. life-giv-ing Spir-it. As it was, is now and shall
to Refrain
5. al-ways be for a-ges un-end-ing. A - men.

Text: Based on Psalm 141:1–5, 8–9, Doxology; Paul Inwood, b. 1947.
Music: Paul Inwood.

PSALM-PRAYER

READING

REFLECTION ON THE WORD OF GOD/HOMILY

GOSPEL CANTICLE (MAGNIFICAT*)

All make the sign of the cross. Incense may be used during the singing of the Gospel Canticle.

112

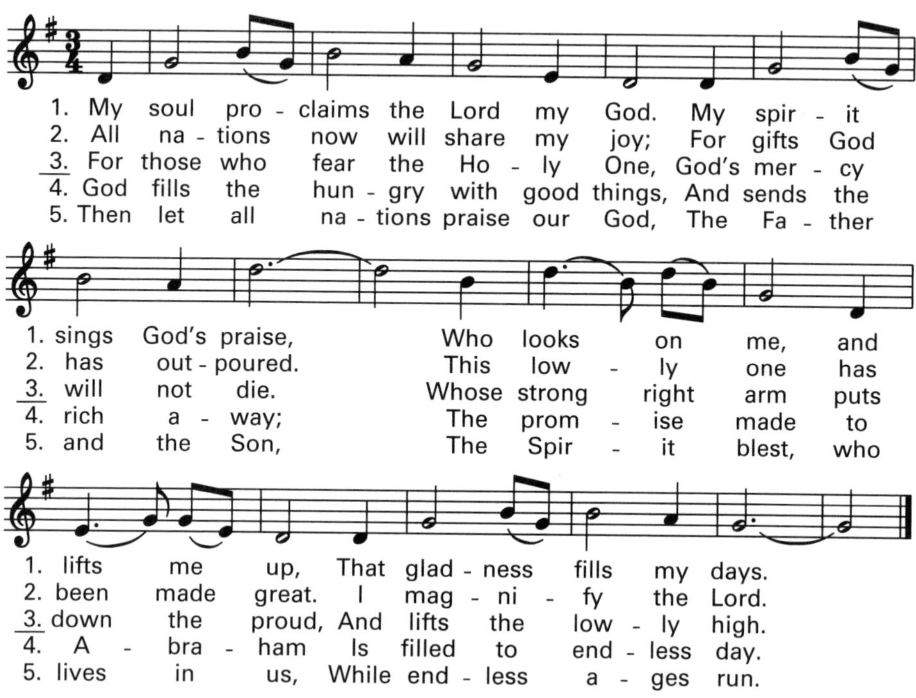
1. My soul pro - claims the Lord my God. My spir - it sings God's praise, Who looks on me, and lifts me up, That glad - ness fills my days.
2. All na - tions now will share my joy; For gifts God has out - poured. This low - ly one has been made great. I mag - ni - fy the Lord.
3. For those who fear the Ho - ly One, God's mer - cy will not die. Whose strong right arm puts down the proud, And lifts the low - ly high.
4. God fills the hun - gry with good things, And sends the rich a - way; The prom - ise made to A - bra - ham Is filled to end - less day.
5. Then let all na - tions praise our God, The Fa - ther and the Son, The Spir - it blest, who lives in us, While end - less a - ges run.

*For alternate settings, see No. 208, No. 209, No. 210 or No. 373.

Text: CM; based on Luke 1:46–55; Anne Carter, 1944–1993,
Music: NEW BRITAIN; *Columbian Harmony*, 1829.

INTERCESSIONS

113

Let us pray to the living God, source of all goodness,
to lead us in holiness of life as we say:

All
Look kind - ly on your church in Je - sus' name.

1. Strengthen all who hope in you:
rich and poor, young and old,
healthy and sick.
2. Give prosperity
to the members of our community:
lighten their burdens and grant them hope.
3. Direct our steps toward justice and peace:
and save us
from the dangers that surround us.
4. Draw all people to yourself this day:
let those who have died
find joy in your presence.

Text: James A. Wilde,
Music: Paul Inwood, b. 1947,

The Lord's Prayer

114

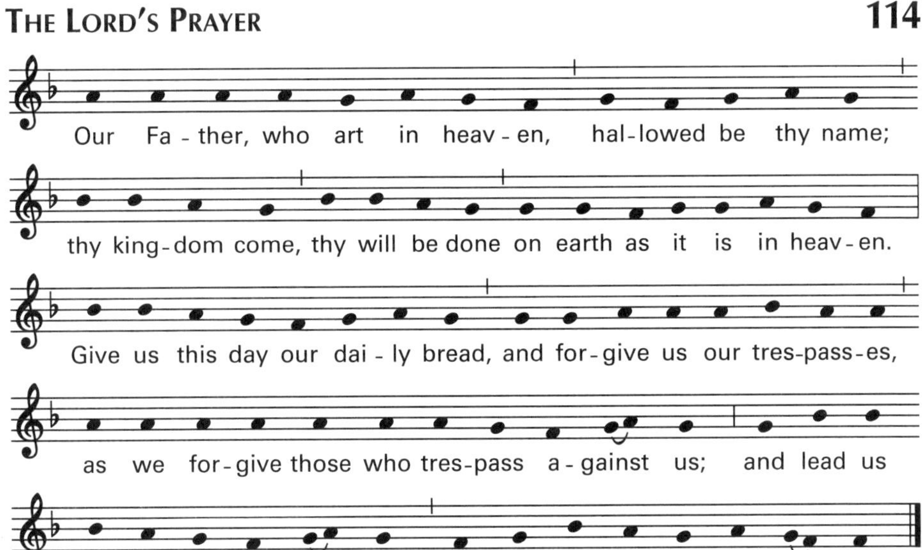
Our Fa - ther, who art in heav - en, hal-lowed be thy name;
thy king-dom come, thy will be done on earth as it is in heav-en.
Give us this day our dai - ly bread, and for-give us our tres-pass-es,
as we for-give those who tres-pass a-gainst us; and lead us
not in - to temp-ta - tion, but de - liv - er us from e - vil.

Music: Chant; adapt. by Robert J. Snow, 1926–1998.

Concluding Prayer

The presiding minister says the concluding prayer.

Blessing

115

Presiding Minister
May the Lord bless us, protect us from all evil,
and bring us to ever - last - ing life.
All respond:
A
All
A - men, A - men, A - men.
B
Alternate Amen: All
A - men.

Psalms & Canticles

Biblical psalms and canticles form the heart of the Church's song. Several kinds of religious lyrics, poems and prayers comprise the psalter. The canticles are poems, other than the psalms, found in the Jewish and Christian scriptures. Usually psalms and canticles are sung responsorially at eucharistic celebrations and antiphonally in the Liturgy of the Hours. These musical settings can help us remember key words and phrases and carry them in our hearts as we walk in the world.

Psalms

116 Psalm 16: Path of Life/Keep Me Safe

Refrain
You will show me the path of life, and
guide me to joy for - ev - er.
Alternate Refrain
Keep me safe, O God; you are my hope.

1. Keep me safe, O God; you are my hope.
   You alone will be my saving God.
2. You have taught me, God,
   with your wondrous love;
   to cherish all my days your faithful ones.
3. My portion and my cup; you hold me fast.
   With you at my side I abide in peace.
4. I will bless you, Lord; you counsel me.
   Even in the night you will guide my heart.
5. Now my heart is glad;
   my soul is filled with joy.
   Never will my God abandon me.
6. You have guided me on the path of life.
   In your presence, Lord, I am filled with joy.

Text: Based on Psalm 16. Refrain and verses, Mike Balhoff, b. 1946, Gary Daigle, b. 1957, Darryl Ducote, b. 1945,

Music: Mike Balhoff, Gary Daigle, Darryl Ducote,

PSALM 16: THE PATH OF LIFE 117

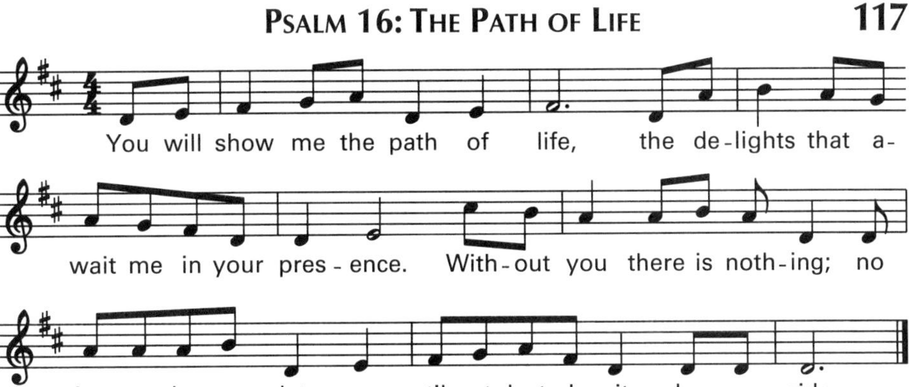
You will show me the path of life, the de-lights that a-
wait me in your pres-ence. With-out you there is noth-ing; no
joy can be com-plete un - til at last I sit by your side.

1. O God, you are my refuge,
   do not turn me away;
   I say "You are my God."
   Without you there can be no good.
2. I bless the Lord who guides me
   even in my sleep;
   my face is turned to God.
   With the Lord at my side I shall stand firm.
3. My heart exults, my spirit sings,
   even my body trusts in you;
   for you will not abandon my soul to death,
   nor let me sink into the grave.

Text: Based on Psalm 16:11, 1–2, 7–10; Scott Soper, b. 1961.
Music: Scott Soper.

PSALM 16: YOU ARE MY INHERITANCE 118

You are my in-her-i-tance, O Lord, my in-her-i-tance, O Lord.

1. O LORD, my allotted portion and my cup,
   you it is who hold fast my lot.
   I set the LORD ever before me;
   with him at my right hand
   I shall not be disturbed.
2. Keep me, O God, for in you I take refuge;
   I say to the LORD, "My Lord are you.
   O LORD, my allotted portion and my cup,
   you it is who hold fast my lot."
3. I bless the LORD who counsels me;
   even in the night my heart exhorts me.
   I set the LORD ever before me;
   with him at my right hand
   I shall not be disturbed.
4. Therefore my heart is glad
   and my soul rejoices,
   my body, too, abides in confidence;
   because you will not abandon my soul
   to the netherworld,
   nor will you suffer your faithful one
   to undergo corruption.
5. You will show me the path to life,
   fullness of joys in your presence,
   the delights at your right hand,
   at your right hand forever.

Text: Psalm 16:5, 8, 9–10, 11; 1–2, 5, 7–8, 9–10, 11.
Music: Barbara Bridge, b. 1950,

119 Psalm 18: I Love You, Lord, My Strength

I love you, Lord, I love you, Lord, my strength.

1. I love you, O Lord, my strength,
   O Lord, my rock,
   my fortress, and my Savior.
2. My God, my rock of refuge,
   my shield, my help, my stronghold!
   The Lord is worthy of all praise.
   When I call I am saved from my foes.
3. Long life to the Lord, my rock!
   Praised be the God who saves me.
   You who gave great victories to your king,
   and love shown to your anointed.

Text: Psalm 18:2–3, 3–4, 47, 51. Refrain Verse 1 based on the *New American Bible*. Verses, Jeffrey Honoré, b. 1956,
Music: Jeffrey Honoré,

120 Psalm 19: Your Words, Lord, Are Spirit and Life

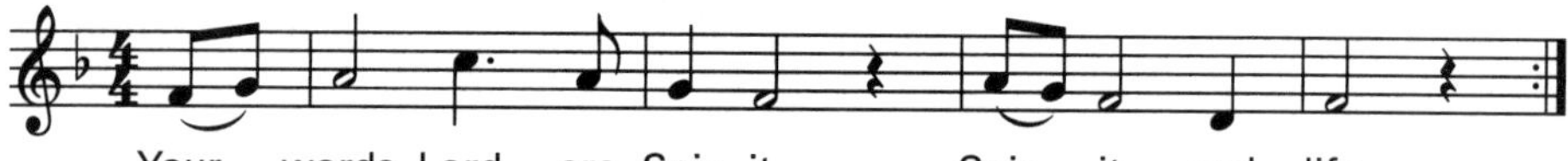
Your words, Lord, are Spir - it, Spir - it and life.

1. The law of the LORD is perfect,
   refreshing the soul.
   The decree of the LORD is trustworthy,
   giving wisdom to the simple.
2. The precepts of the LORD are right,
   rejoicing the heart;
   the command of the LORD is clear,
   enlight'ning the eye.
3. The fear of the LORD is pure,
   enduring forever;
   the statutes of the LORD are true,
   all of them just.
4. They are more precious than gold,
   than a heap of purest gold;
   sweeter also than syrup
   or honey from the comb.
5. Let the words of my mouth
   and the thought of my heart
   find favor before you, O LORD,
   my rock and my redeemer.

Text: Psalm 19:8, 9, 10, 11, 15. Refrain Verses
Music: Bob Hurd, b. 1950,

PSALM 19: LORD, YOU HAVE THE WORDS 121

Lord, you have the words of ev - er - last - ing life.

1. The law of the LORD is perfect,
refreshing the soul;
the decree of the LORD is trustworthy,
giving wisdom to the simple.

2. The precepts of the LORD are right,
rejoicing the heart;
the command of the LORD is clear,
enlightening the eye.

3. The fear of the LORD is pure,
enduring forever;
the ordinances of the LORD are true,
all of them just.

4. They are more precious than gold,
than a heap of purest gold;
sweeter also than syrup
or honey from the comb.

Text: Psalm 19:8, 9, 10, 11.
Music: Michael Joncas, b. 1951,

PSALM 22: MY GOD, MY GOD 122

My God, my God, why have you a - ban - doned me?

1. All who see me laugh at me.
They shake their heads,
they shake their heads.
You trusted in God;
let God deliver you,
deliver you, if God loves you.

2. Closely, now they press me 'round,
and pierce me through,
they pierce me through.
You trusted in God;
let God deliver you,
deliver you, if God loves you.

3. All is taken, all is lost.
Be near, my help.
Come near, my help.
I trusted in God,
may God deliver me.
O deliver me as you love me. **(to Verse 4)**

4. I long to stand in the midst of your people,
and sing your name.
Give God your laud.
Cry out your praises,
and hold fast,
hold fast to your Lord.

Text: Based on Psalm 22:2, 8–9, 17–20, 23–24.
Verses, Tim Manion, b. 1951,
Music: Tim Manion,

123 Psalm 22: My God, My God

3
My God, my God, why have you a - ban-doned me?

1. All who see me scoff;
   they mock me with parted lips,
   they wag their heads:
   "He relied on the LORD; let him deliver him,
   let him rescue him, if he loves him."
2. Indeed, many dogs surround me,
   a pack of evildoers closes in upon me;
   they have pierced my hands and feet;
   I can number all my bones.
3. They divide my garments among them,
   for my vesture they cast lots.
   But you, O LORD, be not far from me;
   O my help, hasten to my aid.
4. I will proclaim your name to my brethren;
   amidst the assembly I will praise you:
   "You who fear the LORD, praise him;
   all you descendants of Jacob,
   give glory to him."

Text: Based on Psalm 22:8–9, 17–18, 19–20, 23–24. Refrain
Verses, Timothy R. Smith, b. 1960,
Music: Timothy R. Smith,

124 Psalm 22: My God, My God/Dios Mío, Dios Mío

Dios mí - o, Dios mí - o, ¿por
My God, my God, why
qué me has a - ban - do - na - do, Dios mí - o?
have you a - ban-doned me, my God?

1. Al verme se burlan de mí,
   hacen visajes, menean la cabeza:
   "Acudió al Señor,
   que lo ponga a salvo;
   que lo libre si tanto lo quiere".
2. Me acorrala una jauría de mastines,
   me cerca una banda de malhechores:
   me taladran las manos y los pies,
   puedo contar mis huesos.
3. Se reparten mi ropa,
   echan a suerte mi túnica.
   Pero tú, Señor, no te quedes lejos;
   fuerza mía, ven corriendo a ayudarme.
4. Contaré tu fama a mis hermanos,
   en medio de la asamblea te alabaré.
   Fieles del Señor, alábenlo,
   linaje de Jacob, glorifíquenlo,
   témanle, linaje de Israel.

1. *All who see me scoff at me;*
   they mock me with parted lips,
   they wag their heads:
   "He relied on the LORD;
   let him deliver him,
   let him rescue him, if he loves him."
2. *Indeed, many dogs surround me,*
   a pack of evildoers closes in upon me;
   they have pierced my hands
   and my feet;
   I can count all my bones.
3. *They divide my garments among them,*
   and for my vesture they cast lots.
   But you, O LORD, be not far from me;
   O my help, hasten to help me.
4. *I will proclaim your name*
   to my brethren;
   in the midst of the assembly
   I will praise you:
   "You who fear the LORD, praise him;
   all you descendants of Jacob,
   give glory to him."

Text: Psalm 22 (21):8–9, 17–18a, 19–20, 23–24. Spanish English response English verses
Music: John Schiavone, b. 1947,

125 Psalm 23: The Lord Is My Shepherd/ I Shall Live in the House/The Lord Prepares a Banquet

Refrain
The Lord is my shep-herd, noth-ing shall I
want. He leads me by safe paths, I shall not fear.

Alternate Refrain 1
I shall live in the house of the
Lord all the days of my life.

Alternate Refrain 2
The Lord pre - pares a ban - quet for
me. Noth - ing shall I want.

1. The Lord is my shepherd,
I have all I need.
He lets me rest in rich green meadows.
He leads me to cool quiet pools
of fresh water.
There he revives my soul.

2. You prepare a banquet for me,
a table full,
where all my foes can see me.
You anoint my head with rich oil,
you have welcomed me,
and filled my cup to the brim.

3. He guides me in the way of virtue,
just as he said.
Though I should walk in deepest darkness,
I will not be afraid, Lord,
because you are there;
your rod and staff keep me safe.

4. Ah, Lord, your love
and your goodness follow still,
all the days of my life.
Your house, O Lord,
shall be my home,
for as long as I live.

126 Psalm 23: The Lord Is My Shepherd/ El Señor Es Mi Pastor

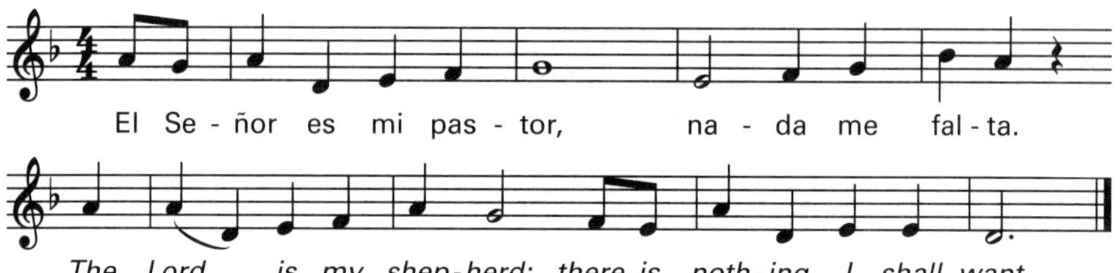
El Se - ñor es mi pas - tor, na - da me fal - ta.
The Lord is my shep-herd; there is noth-ing I shall want.

1. El Señor es mi pastor, nada me falta:
   en verdes praderas me hace recostar;
   me conduce hacia fuentes tranquilas
   y repara mis fuerzas.

2. Me guía por el sendero justo,
   por el honor de su nombre.
   Aunque camine por cañadas oscuras,
   nada temo, porque tú vas conmigo:
   tu vara y tu cayado me sosiegan.

3. Preparas una mesa ante mí,
   enfrente de mis enemigos;
   me unges la cabeza con perfume,
   y mi copa rebosa.

4. Tu bondad y tu misericordia me acompañan
   todos los días de mi vida,
   y habitaré en la casa del Señor
   por años sin término.

1. *The Lord is my shepherd;*
   I shall not want.
   In verdant pastures he gives me repose;
   beside restful waters he leads me;
   he refreshes my soul.

2. *He guides me in right paths*
   for his name's sake.
   Even though I walk in the dark valley
   I fear no evil;
   for you are at my side with your rod
   and your staff that give me courage.

3. *You spread the table before me*
   in the sight of my foes;
   you anoint my head with oil;
   my cup overflows.

4. *Only goodness and kindness follow me*
   all the days of my life;
   and I shall dwell in the house of the Lord
   for years to come.

127 Psalm 23: The Lord Is My Shepherd/ I Shall Live in the House of the Lord

Refrain
The Lord is my shep-herd; there is noth-ing I shall want.

Alternate Refrain
I shall live in the house of the Lord all the days of my life.

1. The LORD is my shepherd; I shall not want.
In verdant pastures he gives me repose;
beside restful waters he leads me;
he refreshes my soul.

2. He guides me in right paths
for his name's sake.
Even though I walk in the dark valley
I fear no evil; for you are at my side
with your rod and your staff
that give me courage.

3. You spread the table before me
in the sight of my foes;
you anoint my head with oil;
my cup overflows.

4. Only goodness and kindness
follow me all the days of my life;
and I shall dwell in the house of the LORD
for years to come.

128 Psalm 23: My Shepherd Is the Lord

My shep-herd is the Lord, noth-ing in-deed shall I want.

1. The Lord is my shepherd;
there is nothing I shall want.
Fresh and green are the pastures
where he gives me repose.
Near restful waters he leads me,
to revive my drooping spirit.

2. He guides me along the right path;
he is true to his name.
If I should walk
in the valley of darkness
no evil would I fear.
You are there with your crook
and your staff;
with these you give me comfort.

3. You have prepared a banquet for me
in the sight of my foes.
My head you have anointed with oil,
my cup is overflowing.

4. Surely goodness and kindness
shall follow me
all the days of my life.
In the Lord's own house shall I dwell
for ever and ever.

5. To the Father and Son give glory,
give glory to the Spirit.
To God who is,
who was, and who will be
for ever and ever.

129 Psalm 24: Lord, This Is the People/ Let the Lord Enter

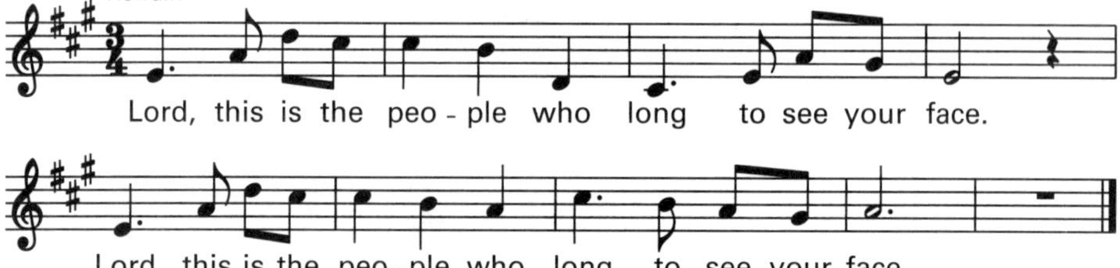
Refrain
Lord, this is the peo - ple who long to see your face.
Lord, this is the peo - ple who long to see your face.

Alternate Refrain
Let the Lord en - ter, let the Lord

en - ter, the King of glo - ry.

1. All creation is the work of God.
   The earth and all creatures
   belong to the Lord.
   From mountains to valleys,
   from ocean to land,
   the Lord God made them all.

2. Who will climb the sacred mountain,
   the holy place of God?
   Those who have not done evil,
   whose hearts are pure,
   whose eyes are not blind.

3. God will send a blessing
   to honor his faithful ones.
   Lord, this is the people
   who seek the face of Jacob's God.

Text: Based on Psalm 24:1–2, 3–4, 5–6. Refrains
Verses, Timothy R. Smith, b. 1960,
Music: Timothy R. Smith,

130 Psalm 25: I Lift Up My Soul

To you, Lord, I lift up my soul, O my God.

1. O Lord, show your ways to me.
   Teach me your paths
   and keep me in the ways of your truth,
   for you are the God that saves me.

2. The Lord is so good, so holy;
   sinners find the way,
   and in all that is right he guides the humble.
   The poor he leads in his pathways.

3. All day long I hope in your goodness.
   Remember your love,
   the love that you promised long ago,
   and the kindness that you gave
   from of old.

Text: Based on Psalm 25:1, 4–5, 8–9, 6–7; Tim Manion, b. 1951.
Music: Tim Manion.

PSALM 25: TO YOU, O LORD 131

To you, O Lord, to you, O Lord, I
lift up, I lift up my soul.

1. Your ways, O Lord,
make known to me;
teach me your paths.
Guide me in your truth and teach me,
for you are God my savior.

2. Good and upright is the Lord;
thus he shows sinners the way.
The humble he guides to justice;
he teaches the humble his way.

3. Kindness and constancy
the paths of the Lord
for those who keep covenant with him.
The friendship of the Lord
with those who revere him,
his covenant for their instruction.

Text: Psalm 25:1, 4–5, 8–10, 14. Refrain
Verses 1–2 based on the *New American Bible*
Verse 3, Michael Joncas, b. 1951,
Music: Michael Joncas,

PSALM 25: TO YOU, O LORD 132

To you, O Lord, I lift up, I lift up my soul, my God.

1. Your ways, O Lord, make known to me;
teach me your paths.
Guide me in your truth, for you are my God,
and for you I will wait.

2. Good and upright is the Lord;
he shows us the way.
He guides the meek to justice,
he teaches the humble to follow his ways.

3. Your way, O Lord,
is kindness to those who are true.
Your friendship is
with those who love you;
you reveal to them your Word.

Text: Based on Psalm 25:1, 4–5, 8–10, 14; Scott Soper, b. 1961.
Music: Scott Soper.

133 PSALM 27: THE GOODNESS OF THE LORD

I be - lieve, I be - lieve I shall see the good - ness of the
Lord in the land, in the land of the liv - ing.

1. The Lord is my light,
   the Lord is my rock, my salvation.
   The Lord is my refuge, guarding my life;
   of whom should I be afraid?
2. Only one thing I ask:
   may I live in the house of my Lord.
   I shall gaze on God's goodness all of my days;
   I shall live in the shelter of God.
3. I believe I shall see
   the goodness of God
   in the land of the living.
   Be strong, wait for the Lord.

Text: Based on Psalm 27:1, 4, 13–14.
Verses, Scott Soper, b. 1961,
Music: Scott Soper,

134 PSALM 27: THE LORD IS MY LIGHT

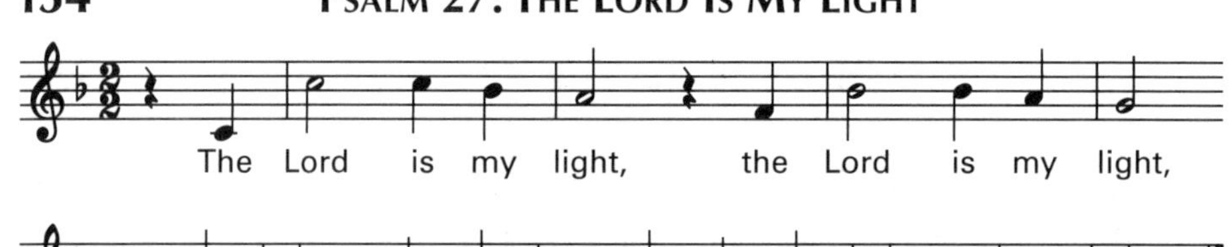
The Lord is my light, the Lord is my light,
the Lord is my light and my sal - va - tion.

1. The Lord is my light and my salvation;
   if God is my help, whom should I fear?
   The Lord is my refuge,
   my stronghold and my strength;
   why should I be afraid?
2. There is but one thing that I want:
   to live in the dwelling place of God;
   to look all my days on the beauty of the Lord,
   and contemplate God's holy temple.
3. I shall see for myself the grace of God,
   the dawn of that day among the living.
   Wait for the Lord,
   find strength in your hearts;
   have courage and wait for God.

Text: Based on Psalm 27:1, 4, 13–14.
Verses, Randall DeBruyn, b. 1947,
Music: Randall DeBruyn,

Psalm 29: The Lord Will Bless His People with Peace

135

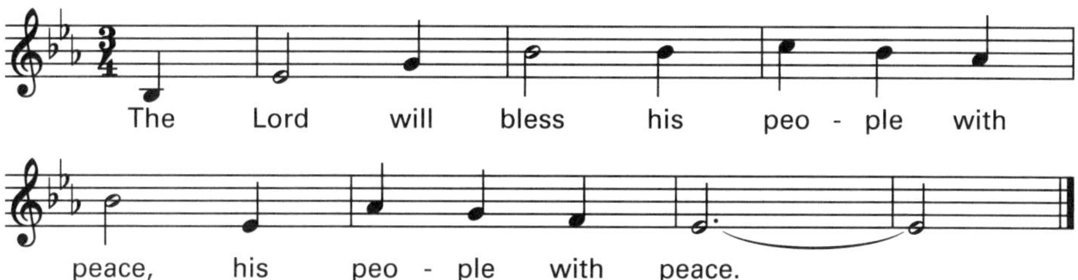
The Lord will bless his peo - ple with
peace, his peo - ple with peace.

1. Give to the LORD, you sons of God,
   give to the LORD glory and praise,
   give to the LORD the glory due his name;
   adore the LORD in holy attire.
2. The voice of the LORD is over the waters,
   the LORD, over vast waters.
   The voice of the LORD is mighty;
   the voice of the LORD is majestic.
3. The God of glory thunders,
   and in his temple all say, "Glory!"
   The LORD is enthroned above the flood;
   the LORD is enthroned as king forever.

Text: Psalm 29:1–2, 3–4, 3, 9–10. Refrain
Verses
Music: Louis Canter, b. 1955,

Psalm 30: I Will Praise You, Lord

136

I will praise you, Lord, you have res-cued me, I will praise you,
Lord, for your mer - cy. I will praise you, Lord,
you have res-cued me: I will praise you, Lord.

1. I will praise you, Lord,
   you have rescued me
   and have not let
   my enemies rejoice over me.
   O Lord, you have raised my soul
   from the dead,
   restored me to life
   from those who sink into the grave.
2. Sing psalms to the Lord,
   you who love him,
   give thanks to his holy name.
   His anger lasts but a moment;
   his favor through life.
   At night there are tears,
   but joy comes with dawn.
3. The Lord listened and had pity.
   The Lord came to my help.
   For me you have changed
   my mourning into dancing;
   O Lord my God,
   I will thank you for ever.

Text: Psalm 30:2, 4–6, 11–13. Refrain, Paul Inwood, b. 1947,
Verses
Music: Paul Inwood,

137 Psalm 31: Father, I Put My Life in Your Hands

Fa-ther, I put my life in your hands.

1. In you, O Lord, I take refuge;
   let me never be put to shame.
   Into your hands I commend my spirit;
   you will redeem me, faithful God.

2. For all my foes reproach me,
   neighbors laugh and friends stand off.
   I am forgotten like dead unremembered;
   I am like a dish cast down.

3. But my trust is in you, O Lord;
   I say, "You are my God."
   Into your hands I place my future;
   from the clutch of foes you rescue me.

4. Let your face shine on your servant;
   O save me in your love.
   Be stouthearted, and come, take courage,
   all you who now hope in the Lord.

Text: Based on Psalm 31:2, 6, 12–13, 15–16, 17, 25.
Verses, John Michael Talbot, b. 1954,
Music: John Michael Talbot,

138 Psalm 31: Father, into Your Hands I Commend My Spirit

Fa-ther, Fa-ther, in-to your hands I com-mend my spir-it.

1. You, O God, are my refuge;
   in you I shall not be put to shame.
   Rescue me, because you are just.
   Into your hands I commend my soul.
   Save me, save me, my God.

2. By my foes I am hated,
   and all those who see me laugh at me.
   Everyone runs away from my face.
   I am neglected
   like the dead in their grave;
   broken, forgotten my life.

3. All my life I will trust you,
   for you are the God of my heart.
   Rescue me from the hands of my foes.
   Guard me from those who seek
   to harm my life.
   You, Lord, hold me in your hands.

4. Grant that I may behold you;
   redeem your faithful one to life.
   Save me in your compassion and love.
   You are my strength forever, O God.
   Hold fast, all those who love the Lord.

Text: Based on Psalm 31:2, 6, 12–13, 15–16, 17, 25.
Verses, Randall DeBruyn, b. 1947,
Music: Randall DeBruyn,

Psalm 31: Father, into Your Hands/ Padre, en Tus Manos 139

(English) Fa - ther, in - to your hands I com - mend my spir - it. Fa - ther, in - to your hands I com - mend my spir - it.
(Bilingual) Pa - dre, en tus ma - nos en - co - mien - do mi es - pí - ri - tu. Fa - ther, in - to your hands I com - mend my spir - it.
(Español) Pa - dre, en tus ma - nos en - co - mien - do mi es - pí - ri - tu. Pa - dre, en tus ma - nos en - co - mien - do mi es - pí - ri - tu.

1. In you, O Lord, I take refuge;
   let me not be put to shame.
   In your justice save me.
   Into your hands I commend my spirit;
   you will redeem me, faithful God.
2. I am scorned by all my enemies,
   dreaded by friends and neighbors;
   when they see me they turn away.
   I am like one dead and forgotten,
   like a vessel broken and discarded.
3. But Lord, I trust in you;
   I say: "You are my God."
   My life is in your hands;
   save me from my enemies,
   from the hands of those who pursue me.
4. Let your face shine upon your servant;
   in your steadfast kindness save me.
   Take courage, be strong of heart,
   all you who wait for the Lord,
   all you who hope in the Lord.

1. *A ti, Señor, me acojo:*
   no quede yo nunca defraudado;
   tú que eres justo, ponme a salvo.
   En tus manos encomiendo mi espíritu:
   tú, el Dios leal, me librarás.
2. *Soy la burla de todos mis enemigos,*
   la irrisión de mis vecinos,
   el espanto de mis conocidos;
   me ven por la calle y escapan de mí.
   Me han olvidado como a un muerto,
   me han desechado
   como a un cacharro inútil.
3. *Pero yo confío en ti, Señor,*
   te digo: "Tú eres mi Dios".
   En tu mano están mis azares;
   líbrame de los enemigos,
   los enemigos que me persiguen.
4. *Haz brillar tu rostro sobre tu siervo,*
   sálvame por tu misericordia.
   Sean fuertes y valientes de corazón,
   los que esperan en el Señor.

140 Psalm 33: Lord, Let Your Mercy

Lord, let your mer-cy be on us as we place our trust in you.

1. Exult, you just, in the Lord.
It is good to sound your praises,
giving thanks to God
with your strings and voice,
making music before the Lord.

2. The word of God ever true,
all the works of God enduring.
Every mountain peak, every ocean floor,
loving labor, loving Lord.

3. Behold, the eyes of the Lord
look with love on those who hunger,
bringing health and hope
to our days of want,
bringing mercy in every need.

Text: Based on Psalm 33:1–2, 4, 6–7, 18–19. Refrain
Verses, Bob Dufford, SJ, b. 1943,
Music: Bob Dufford, SJ,

141 Psalm 33: Happy the People You Have Chosen

Hap - py the peo - ple you have cho - sen,
cho - sen to be for you a - lone.

1. Rejoice, you saints, in God.
for praise from you is right.
Music makers, sing by day,
and play with all your might!
Sing God a new song,
play well upon your strings,
for God loves truth and righteousness,
God's word does wondrous things.

2. God's kindness fills the world,
whose word the heavens forms,
whose singing mouth, to north and south,
has spoken stars and storms,
whose might forbids the waves
to trespass on the land,
and gathers all the oceans up,
to cup them in a hand.

3. God speaks and it is done,
whose word existence gives,
so let the world its God revere,
and hear the One who lives!
Your wondrous plan, O God,
is known to you alone,
and happy is this people
you have chosen for your own.

4. From heaven God looks down
upon all humankind.
God knows the dwellers of our globe,
and probes the heart and mind.
No, none escapes the glance of God,
who reigns on high.
No secret can creation keep
on earth or sea or sky.

5. No king is safe from death,
though armies guard him well.
No warrior, armed and mounted strong,
can long escape from hell.
But see! The eyes of God
gaze earthward, west and east,
to snatch the poor from famine's thrall,
and call them to the feast.

6. So wait upon the One
who is our help and shield.
Rejoice, you saints, to sing the name,
proclaim God's might revealed.
Grant, O God,
your loving kindness all our days;
we hope in you, we trust in you,
to you be endless praise.

Text: Based on Psalm 33; Rory Cooney, b. 1952.
Music: Rory Cooney.

Psalm 33: The Lord Fills the Earth with His Love

The Lord fills the earth with his love, his love, the
Lord fills the earth with his love.

1. The word of the Lord is faithful
   and all his works to be trusted.
   The Lord loves justice and right,
   and he fills the earth with his love.
2. By his word the heavens were made,
   by the breath of his mouth all the stars.
   The Lord collects the waves of the ocean,
   he stores up the depths of the sea.
3. They are happy whose God is the Lord,
   the people he has chosen as his own.
   From the heavens the Lord looks forth,
   and he sees all the children of the earth.
4. Our soul is waiting for the Lord.
   The Lord is our help and our shield.
   May your love be upon us, O Lord,
   as we place all our hope in you.

Psalm 34: Taste and See

143

Taste and see, taste and see that the Lord is good, the Lord is good.

1. I will bless the Lord at all times,
   his praise always on my lips.
   The Lord shall be the glory of my soul;
   the humble shall hear and be glad.
2. Glorify the Lord with me,
   together let us praise his name.
   I sought the Lord: he answered me;
   he set me free from all my fear.
3. Look upon the Lord and be radiant;
   hide not your face from the Lord.
   He heard the cry of the poor;
   he rescued them from all their woes.
4. The angel of the Lord is with his people
   to rescue those who trust in him.
   Taste and see the goodness of the Lord;
   seek refuge in him and be glad.
5. Saints of the Lord, revere him;
   those who fear him lack nothing.
   Lions suffer want and go hungry,
   but those who seek him lack no blessing.
6. Children of the Lord come and hear,
   and learn the fear of the Lord.
   Who is he who longs for life,
   whose only love is for his wealth?
7. Keep evil words from your tongue,
   your lips from speaking deceit.
   Turn aside from evil and do good;
   seek and strive after peace.

144 PSALM 34: TASTE AND SEE

Taste and see the good-ness of the Lord, let us taste the good-ness of the Lord.

1. I will bless the Lord,
his praise be ever in my mouth.
Let my soul glory in the Lord;
the lowly will hear and be glad.

2. Glorify the Lord with me;
together we'll praise his name.
I sought the Lord, and he answered me,
delivered me from all my fears.

3. Look to him and be radiant with joy,
and your face will not blush with shame.
Afflicted ones call out to him;
from all their distress they are saved.

Text: Based on Psalm 34:2–9; John Michael Talbot, b. 1954.
Music: John Michael Talbot.

145 PSALM 34: TASTE AND SEE/GUSTEN Y VEAN

Español Gus - ten y ve - an qué bue - no es el Se - ñor.
Biling. Gus - ten y ve - an qué bue - no es el Se - ñor.
English Taste and see the good- ness of the Lord.
Gus - ten y ve - an qué bue - no es el Se - ñor.
Taste and see the good- ness of the Lord.
Taste and see the good- ness of the Lord.

1. Bendigo al Señor en todo momento,
su alabanza está siempre en mi boca;
mi alma se gloría en el Señor:
que los humildes lo escuchen
y se alegren.

2. Proclamen conmigo
la grandeza del Señor,
ensalcemos juntos su nombre.
Yo consulté al Señor y me respondió,
me libró de todas mis ansias.

3. Miren al Señor y quedarán radiantes,
no asomará en sus caras la vergüenza.
Si el afligido invoca al Señor,
lo escuchará y lo salva
de sus angustias.

4. El ángel del Señor protege y salva
a los que honran y temen al Señor.
Gusten y vean qué bueno es el Señor,
dichoso aquel que se acoge a Dios.

1. *I will bless the LORD at all times,*
his praise shall be ever in my mouth.
Let my soul glory in the LORD;
the lowly will hear me and be glad.

2. *Glorify the LORD with me,*
let us together extol his name.
I sought the LORD, [who] answered me
and delivered me from my fears.

3. *Look to the Lord; be radiant with joy.*
And let your faces
not blush with shame.
The poor called out,
and the Lord heard and rescued them
from all their distress.

4. *The angel of the Lord*
encamps around those who fear God
and delivers them.
O taste and see that the Lord is good;
happy are those who take refuge in God.

Text: Psalm 34 (33):2–3, 4–5, 6–7, 8–9. Spanish refrain and verses 1 and 2 English and Spanish verses 3 and 4, Mary Frances Reza,
Music: Mary Frances Reza,

Psalm 34: I Will Always Thank the Lord 146

1
2
I will al-ways thank the Lord; I will al-ways praise God's name. name.

1. I will thank the Lord at all times,
   I will always praise God's name.
   My soul will boast of the Lord;
   the poor will hear and be glad.
2. Join with me in the praise of the Lord;
   together we shall sing God's praise.
   I called, and God answered my plea;
   from my fears the Lord set me free.
3. Look to God and shine with joy;
   you will never be ashamed.
   I begged God to listen to me;
   God took my burdens away.

Text: Based on Psalm 34:2–3, 4–5, 6–7; Scott Soper, b. 1961.
Music: Scott Soper.

Psalm 40: Here I Am/ God, My God, Come to My Aid 147

Refrain
Here I am, Lord, here I am. I come to do your will.

Alternate Refrain
God, my God, come to my aid, come to my aid, come to my aid; come.

1. Long was I waiting for God,
   and then he heard my cry.
   It was he who taught this song to me,
   a song of praise to God.
2. You asked me not for sacrifice,
   for slaughtered goats or lambs.
   No, my heart,
   you gave me ears to hear you,
   then I said, "Here I am."
3. You wrote it in the scrolls of law
   what you would have me do.
   Doing that is what has made me happy,
   your law is in my heart.
4. I spoke before your holy people,
   the good news that you save.
   Now you know that I will not be silent,
   I'll always sing your praise.

Text: Based on Psalm 40:8, 14, 2, 4, 7–10. Refrains © 1969, 1981, ICEL. All rights reserved. Used with permission.
Verses, Rory Cooney, b. 1952, © 1971, 1991, OCP. All rights reserved.
Music: Rory Cooney, © 1971, 1991, OCP. All rights reserved.

148 Psalm 42: O God, for You I Long

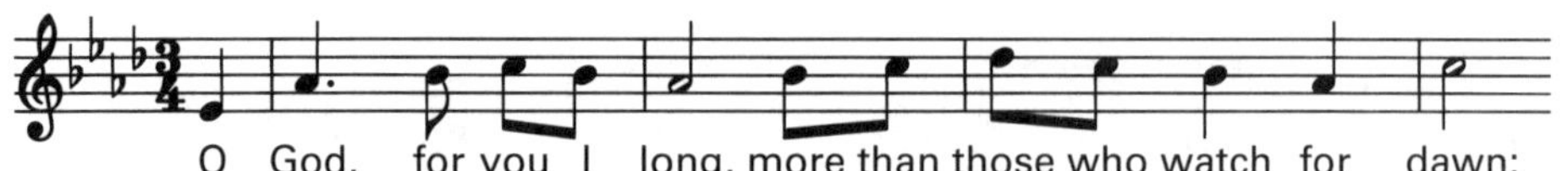
O God, for you I long, more than those who watch for dawn:

like the deer that yearns for wa - ter, so I thirst for you, my God.

1. Like the deer
that yearns for running streams,
so I long for you, my God,
as my spirit longs to behold
the God of my life.

2. I drink tears as if they were my bread
by night and by day,
as I hear it said all day long:
"Where is your God?"

3. All these things will I remember
as I pour out my soul,
how I would lead the rejoicing crowd
to the house of our God.

4. Why so sad within me, O my soul,
why cast down and grieving now?
Hope in God:
I will praise you still,
my Savior, my God.

5. Still my spirit dies within me
as I think of you today.
As an exile from my homeland,
I cry to you, Lord.

6. By day you bring me comfort
in the shelter of your love.
By night I will sing and praise
the God of my life.

Text: Based on Psalm 42:2–7, 9; Bernadette Farrell, b. 1957.
Music: Bernadette Farrell.

149 Psalm 42/43: As the Deer Longs

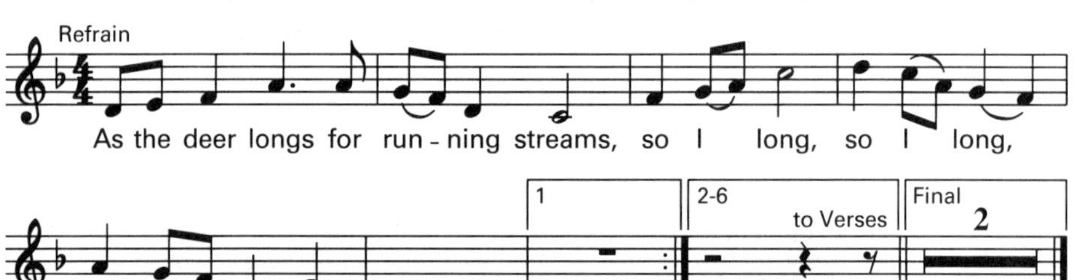
Refrain
As the deer longs for run - ning streams, so I long, so I long,
so I long for you.
1
2-6
to Verses
Final
2

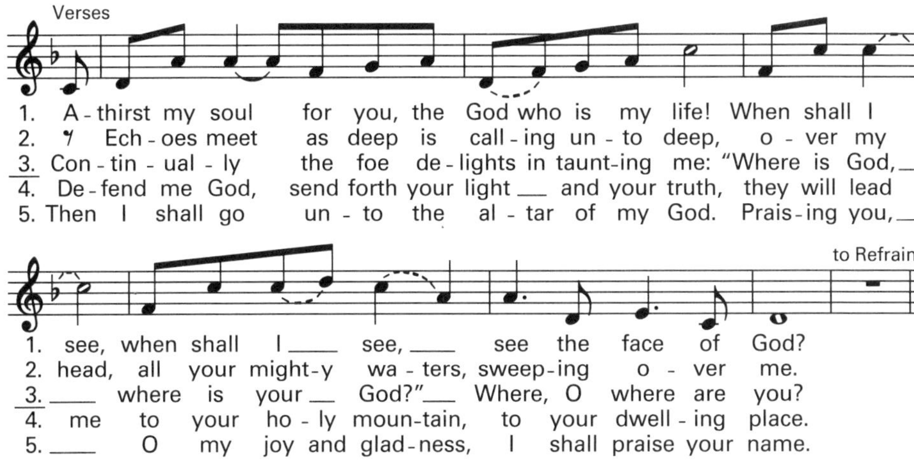
Verses
1. A - thirst my soul for you, the God who is my life! When shall I
2. Ech - oes meet as deep is call - ing un - to deep, o - ver my
3. Con - tin - ual - ly the foe de - lights in taunt-ing me: "Where is God,
4. De - fend me God, send forth your light and your truth, they will lead
5. Then I shall go un - to the al - tar of my God. Prais - ing you,
to Refrain
1. see, when shall I see, see the face of God?
2. head, all your might - y wa - ters, sweep - ing o - ver me.
3. where is your God?" Where, O where are you?
4. me to your ho - ly moun - tain, to your dwell - ing place.
5. O my joy and glad - ness, I shall praise your name.

Text: Based on Psalm 42:2, 3, 8, 4; Psalm 43:3, 4; Bob Hurd, b. 1950.
Music: Bob Hurd.

Psalm 45: The Queen Stands 150

The queen stands at your right hand, ar - rayed in gold.

1. The queen takes her place
   at your right hand in gold of Ophir.
2. Hear, O daughter and see; turn your ear,
   forget your people and your father's house.
3. So shall the king desire your beauty;
   for he is your lord.
4. They are borne in with gladness,
   borne in with joy;
   they enter the palace of the king.

Text: Psalm 45:10, 11, 12, 16.
Music: Kevin Keil (ASCAP), b. 1956,

Psalm 47: God Mounts His Throne 151

God mounts his throne to shouts of joy: Al - le - lu - ia, al - le - lu - ia!

1. All peoples, clap your hands,
   cry to God with shouts of joy!
   For the Lord Most High we must fear,
   great King over all the earth.
2. God goes up with shouts of joy;
   the Lord goes up with trumpet blast.
   Sing praise for God, sing praise for God,
   sing praise to our King.
3. God is King of all the earth.
   Sing praise with all your skill.
   God is King over the nations;
   he reigns on his holy throne.

Text: Psalm 47:6, 2–3, 6–9. Refrain, Paul Inwood, b. 1947,
Music: Paul Inwood,

152 PSALM 51: CREATE IN ME

Refrain
Fine
Cre - ate in me a clean heart.
Verses
1. Have mer - cy on me, God, in your com - pas - sion.
2. O pu - ri - fy my heart and teach me wis - dom;
3. O give me back the joy of your sal - va - tion;
to Refrain
1. Re - move my sin. Wash me from my guilt.
2. then I shall be clean - er than the snow.
3. a will - ing spir - it sus - tain in me.

Text: Based on Psalm 51:12, 3–4, 8–9, 14; Bob Hurd, b. 1950.
Music: Bob Hurd.

153 PSALM 51: BE MERCIFUL, O LORD

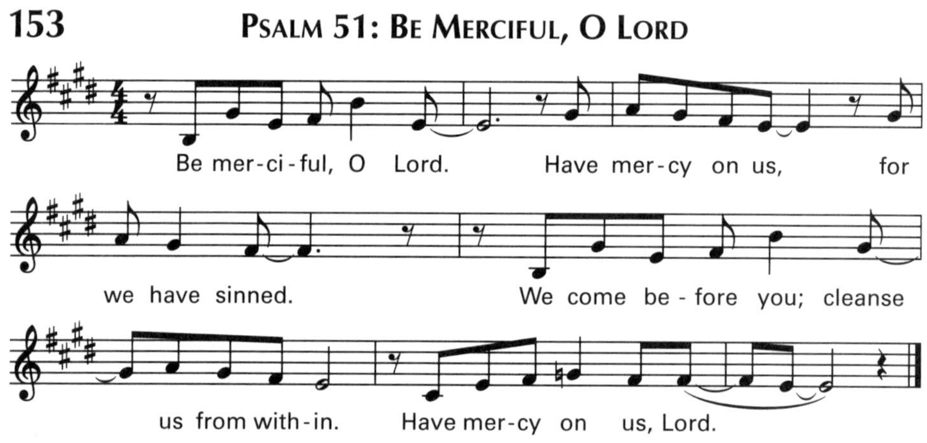
Be mer - ci - ful, O Lord. Have mer - cy on us, for
we have sinned. We come be - fore you; cleanse
us from with - in. Have mer - cy on us, Lord.

1. Have mercy on me in your goodness, Lord.
In your great compassion
wipe out my offense.
Wash me from guilt, Lord,
cleanse me from my sin.
Have mercy on me, Lord.

2. Create a clean heart for me, O God.
And a steadfast spirit, renew within me.
Cast me not out from your presence, O Lord.
Take not your Spirit from me.

3. Give me the joy of your salvation, Lord,
and a willing spirit sustain within me.
Open my lips,
let my mouth proclaim your praise.
Have mercy on me, Lord.

Text: Based on Psalm 51:3–4, 12–13, 17.
Verses, Steve Angrisano, b. 1965,
Music: Steve Angrisano,

PSALM 51: CREATE IN ME

Cre - ate in me a clean heart, O God, a
clean heart, O God, cre - ate in me.

1. O God, in your goodness have mercy
   on me.
   In your compassion wipe out my offense.
   Thoroughly wash me from my guilt,
   and cleanse me from my sins.

2. For I acknowledge my offense
   and my sin is always before me;
   against only you have I sinned,
   and done what is evil in your eyes.

3. A clean heart create for me, O God,
   a steadfast spirit renew in me.
   Cast me not out from your presence,
   O God.
   Take not your Holy Spirit from me.

4. Give us back the joy of our salvation,
   and renew in us a willing spirit.
   O Lord, open my lips, Lord, open my lips.
   And we will sing your praise.

PSALM 51: CREATE IN ME/ OH DIOS, CREA EN MÍ

155

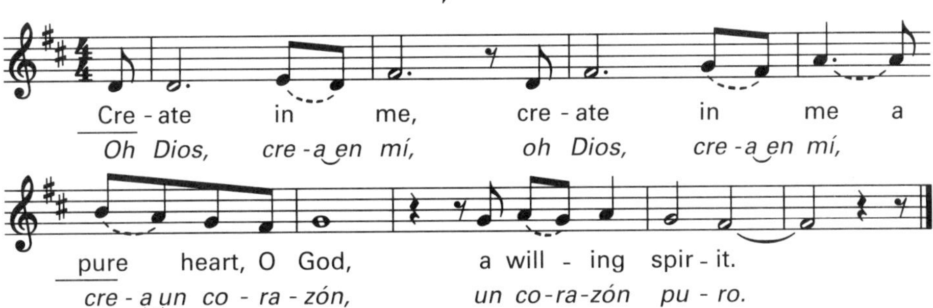
Cre - ate in me, cre - ate in me a
Oh Dios, cre - a en mí, oh Dios, cre - a en mí,
pure heart, O God, a will - ing spir - it.
cre - a un co - ra - zón, un co - ra - zón pu - ro.

1. Have mercy on me, O God,
   in your kindness
   blot out my offenses;
   wash me, wash away my guilt,
   cleanse me completely of my sin.

2. Create in me, God,
   a pure heart
   and give me a steadfast spirit;
   do not cast me out
   from your presence,
   nor remove your holy spirit.

3. Give me back the joy
   of your salvation,
   sustain in me a willing spirit.
   Open my lips, O Lord,
   and I shall proclaim your praise.

1. *Piedad de mí, Señor,*
   por tu bondad,
   por tu inmensa compasión
   borra mi culpa;
   lava del todo mi delito,
   purifícame, tú, de mi pecado.

2. *Oh Dios, crea en mí*
   un corazón puro,
   pon en mí un espíritu firme;
   no me arrojes lejos de tu rostro,
   no me quites tu santo espíritu.

3. *Dame la alegría de tu salvación,*
   mantén en mí un alma generosa.
   Enseñaré a los malvados
   tus caminos,
   se volverán a ti los pecadores.

156 Psalm 63: My Soul Is Thirsting/ As Morning Breaks

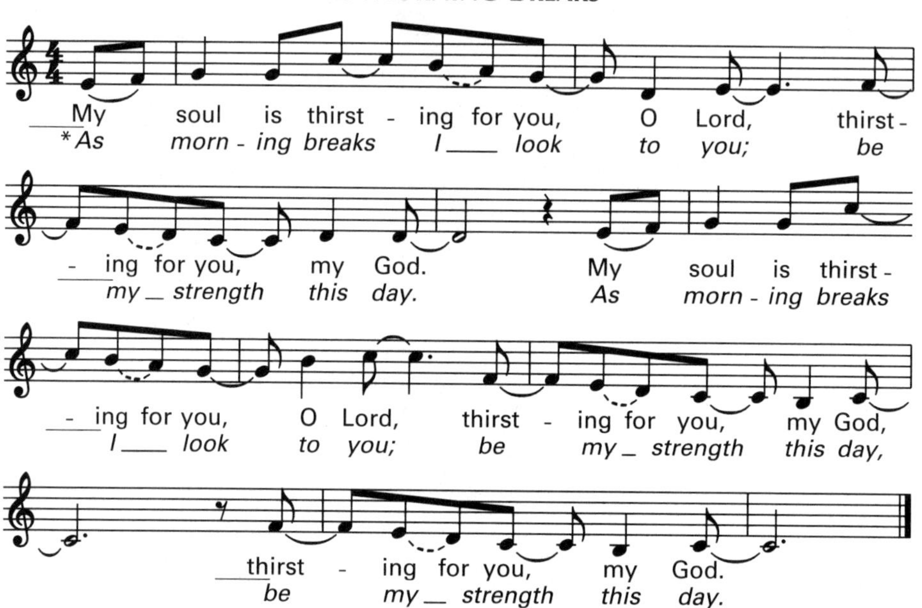
My soul is thirst - ing for you, O Lord, thirst -
*As morn - ing breaks I look to you; be
- ing for you, my God. My soul is thirst -
my strength this day. As morn - ing breaks
- ing for you, O Lord, thirst - ing for you, my God,
I look to you; be my strength this day,
thirst - ing for you, my God.
be my strength this day.

1. O God, you are my God,
   and I will always praise you.
   In the shadow of your wings
   I cling to you and you hold me high.
2. Through the day you walk with me;
   all the night your love surrounds me.
   To the glory of your name I lift my hands,
   I sing your praise.
3. I will never be afraid,
   for I will not be abandoned.
   Even when the road grows long and
   weary your love will rescue me.

*Alternate refrain text.

Text: Based on Psalm 63:2, 5–9. Refrain © 1969, 1981, ICEL. Alternate refrain fr. *The Liturgy of the Hours* © 1974, ICEL. Verses, Steve Angrisano, b. 1965, © 1997, 1998, Steve Angrisano. Published by OCP.
Music: Steve Angrisano, © 1997, 1998, Steve Angrisano. Published by OCP.

Psalm 63: My Soul Thirsts 157

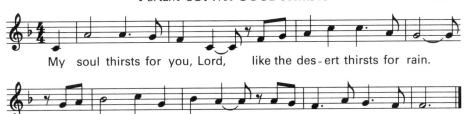

My soul thirsts for you, Lord, like the des-ert thirsts for rain.
It is your face I long for; you a-lone are life to me.

1. I have walked in your temple,
   and seen your mighty deeds.
   Your love, O Lord, means more to me,
   than all my days of life.

2. I can count on your mercy
   to feed my hungry heart,
   for when I lift my hands in need,
   a banquet you provide.

3. I will make my dwelling
   in the shelter of your wings.
   Your hand, O Lord, will keep me safe
   through darkest night and day.

Text: Based on Psalm 63:2–9; Dan Schutte, b. 1947.
Music: Dan Schutte.

Psalm 66: Let All the Earth Cry Out 158

Let all the earth cry out to God with joy, with joy.

1. Cry out with joy to God, all the earth!
   O sing to the glory of his name!
   O render him glorious praise,
   say to God:
   "How tremendous your deeds."

2. Before you all the earth shall bow,
   shall sing to you, sing to your name!
   Come and see the works of God!
   Tremendous his deeds among men!

3. He turned the sea into dry land;
   they passed through the river dry-shod.
   Let our joy then be in him—
   he rules evermore by his might!

4. Come and hear,
   all who fear God,
   I will tell what he did for my soul:
   to him I cried aloud,
   with high praise ready on my tongue!

159 Psalm 66: Let All the Earth

Let all the earth cry out, let all the earth cry out
to God with joy, al - le - lu - ia, al - le -
1-5
1: to Ref.
2-5: to Vss.
Final
lu - ia. ia. Al - le - lu - ia, al - le -
lu - ia. Al - le - lu - ia, al - le - lu - ia.

1. Cry out with joy to God, all the earth;
   O sing to the glory of his name.
   O render him glorious praise.
   Say to God, "How awesome your deeds!"

2. "Before you all the earth shall bow down,
   shall sing to you, sing to your name!"
   Come and see the works of God:
   awesome his deeds
   among the children of men.

3. He turned the sea into dry land;
   they passed through the river on foot.
   Let our joy, then, be in him;
   he rules forever by his might.

4. Come and hear, all who fear God;
   I will tell what he did for my soul.
   Blest be God,
   who did not reject my prayer,
   nor withhold from me his merciful love.

Psalm 67: O God, Let All the Nations 160

O God, let all the na - tions praise your name,
let all the na - tions praise your name.

1. Lord, look with favor on us;
   show us your face.
   Reveal to the faithful your way, Lord,
   salvation for all the world.
2. May the nations sing and be glad,
   for your word governs all the world.
   Your justice will guide all nations,
   all people on the earth.
3. Lord, may we sing your praise;
   may we sing to you all of our days.
   O God, we ask you to bless us,
   as we honor your name.

Text: Based on Psalm 67:2–3, 5, 6, 8. Refrain
Verses, Timothy R. Smith, b. 1960,
Music: Timothy R. Smith,

Psalm 72: Justice Shall Flourish/ Lord, Every Nation 161

Refrain — to Verses 1-2, 4-5

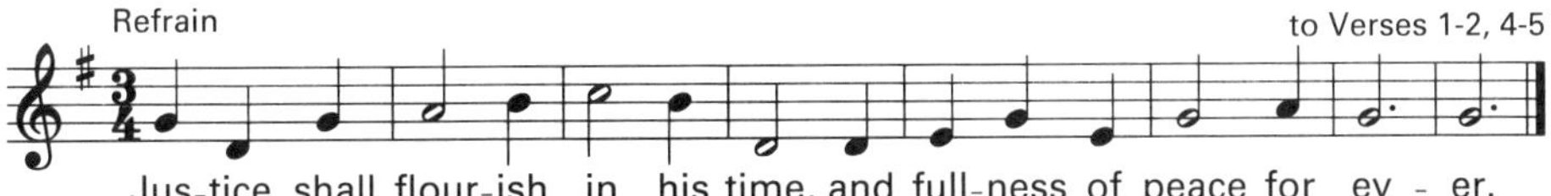
Jus-tice shall flour-ish in his time, and full-ness of peace for ev - er.

Alternate Refrain — to Verses 1-4

Lord, ev-'ry na-tion on earth will a - dore you.

1. O God, with your judgment
   endow the king,
   and with your justice, the king's son;
   he shall govern your people
   with justice
   and your afflicted ones with judgment.
2. Justice shall flower in his days,
   and profound peace,
   'til the moon be no more.
   May he rule from sea to sea,
   and from the River to the ends of the earth.
3. From the islands and Tarshish
   shall kings come with gifts;
   from Arabia and Sheba they come.
   All the kings of the earth pay him homage;
   all the nations shall serve him.
4. For he shall rescue the poor
   when he cries out,
   and the afflicted
   when he has no one to help him.
   He shall have pity for the lowly and poor;
   the lives of the poor he shall save.
5. May his name be blessed forever,
   and while the sun lasts
   his name shall remain.
   In him shall all the tribes
   of the earth be blessed;
   all the nations
   shall proclaim his happiness.

Text: Psalm 72:1–2, 7–8, 12–13, 17; 1–2, 7–8, 10–11, 12–13. Refrains Verses based on the *New American Bible*
Music: Rory Cooney, b. 1952,

162 PSALM 80: THE VINEYARD OF THE LORD/ LORD, MAKE US TURN TO YOU

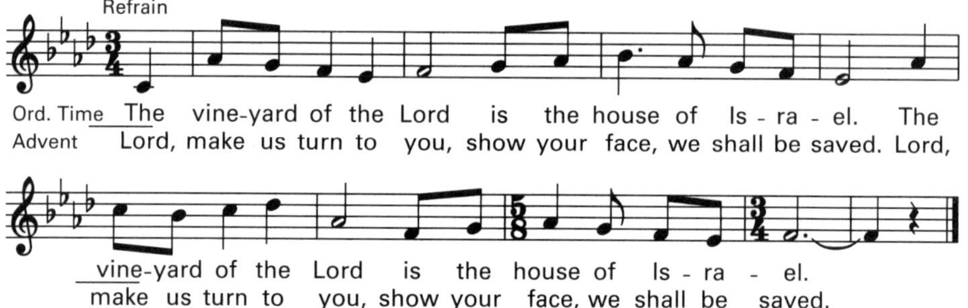
Refrain
Ord. Time The vine-yard of the Lord is the house of Is - ra - el. The
Advent Lord, make us turn to you, show your face, we shall be saved. Lord,
vine-yard of the Lord is the house of Is - ra - el.
make us turn to you, show your face, we shall be saved.

Ordinary Time Verses

1. A vine from Egypt you transplanted;
   you drove away the nations and planted it.
   It put forth its foliage to the Sea,
   its shoots as far as the River.

2. Why have you broken down its walls,
   so that every passer-by plucks its fruit,
   the boar from the forest lays it waste,
   and the beasts of the field feed upon it?

3. Once again, O LORD of hosts,
   look down from heaven, and see;
   take care of this vine,
   and protect what your right hand
   has planted,
   the son of man whom you yourself
   made strong.

4. Then we will no more withdraw from you;
   give us new life,
   and we will call upon your name.
   O LORD, God of hosts, restore us;
   if your face shine upon us,
   then we shall be saved.

Advent Verses

1. O shepherd of Israel, hearken,
   from your throne upon the cherubim,
   shine forth.
   Rouse your power,
   and come to save us.

2. Once again, O LORD of hosts,
   look down from heaven, and see;
   take care of this vine,
   and protect what your right hand
   has planted,
   the son of man whom you yourself
   made strong.

3. May your help be with the man
   of your right hand,
   with the son of man whom you yourself
   made strong.
   Then we will no more withdraw from you;
   give us new life,
   and we will call upon your name.

163 PSALM 84: HOW LOVELY IS YOUR DWELLING PLACE

How love - ly is your dwell-ing place, O Lord God of Hosts!

1. My soul yearns and pines
for the courts of the Lord,
my heart and my flesh cry out;
Even the sparrow may find a home,
the swallow a nest for her young;
Your altars, my king and my God!

2. How happy are they
who may dwell in your courts,
how happy when you are their strength;
Though they might go through
the valley of death,
they make it a place of springs.
Your first rain will bring it to life.

3. O Lord of Hosts, hear my cry,
and hearken, O God of Jacob;
One day in your house
is worth much more to me
than ten thousand anywhere else;
The Lord is my sun and my shield!

Text: Based on Psalm 84:2–7, 9, 11–12; Michael Joncas, b. 1951.
Music: Michael Joncas.

Psalm 85: Come, O Lord/ Lord, Let Us See Your Kindness 164

Refrain
Come, O Lord, and set us free. Come, and set us free.

Alternate Refrain
Lord, let us see your kind - ness; Lord, grant us your sal-va - tion.

1. Now I will hear what God proclaims,
the Lord who speaks of peace.
Near to us now, God's saving love
for those who believe.

2. Mercy and faithfulness shall meet,
in justice and peace, embrace.
Truth shall blossom from the earth
as the heavens rejoice.

3. Our God shall grant abundant gifts,
the earth shall yield its fruit.
Justice shall march before our God
and guide us to peace.

Text: Isaiah 35:4, Psalm 85:8–14. Refrains © 1969, 1981, ICEL. All rights reserved. Used with permission.
Verses, Mike Balhoff, b. 1946, Gary Daigle, b. 1957, Darryl Ducote, b. 1945, © 1978, 1993, Damean Music.
All rights reserved. Used with permission.
Music: Mike Balhoff, Gary Daigle, Darryl Ducote, © 1978, 1993, Damean Music.
All rights reserved. Used with permission.

Psalm 85: Let Us See Your Kindness 165

Let us see your kind-ness, O Lord, grant us your sal-va - tion, O God.

1. God, how I long
for the peace you proclaim,
your salvation and glory
near to all who revere your name.

2. Kindness and truth shall meet,
justice and peace shall kiss;
truth shall spring forth from the earth
and justice look down from heaven.

3. You, yourself, will give these gifts;
our land shall yield its fruit.
Justice shall walk before you,
and salvation along your way.

Text: Based on Psalm 85:8, 9–10, 11–12, 13–14; Dominic MacAller, b. 1959.
Music: Dominic MacAller.

166 Psalm 85: Lord, Let Us See Your Kindness

Lord, let us see your kind-ness; Lord, let us see your kind-ness.
Your kind - ness and sal - va - tion grant us, O Lord.

1. I will hear what the Lord proclaims:
   peace and salvation close at hand,
   always near to those who fear him;
   glory dwelling in our land.
2. Kindness and truth shall meet at last;
   justice and peace embrace in love.
   Truth shall spring up from the earth,
   and justice shall look down from heaven above.
3. God will grant abundant grace;
   earth will spring up with boundless life.
   Blessings flow ever before him
   to prepare his way.

Text: Based on Psalm 85:9–10, 11–12, 13–14; Scott Soper, b. 1961.
Music: Scott Soper.

167 Psalm 89: For Ever I Will Sing

For ev-er I will sing the good-ness of the Lord.

1. How I feel like singing,
   announcing to the world
   your constant faithful love, O Lord.
   You have shown the greatness of your love;
   by covenant you chose us as your own
   until the end of time.
2. O how blest are they
   who can know the joyous grace
   that comes from praising you, my Lord.
   At your very name how they rejoice,
   and in your justice you will raise them up.
   Their hearts reflect your love.
3. For you are our splendor,
   the reason for our strength;
   the cause of all our hopes and dreams.
   Only by your love do we exist.
   Only by your choice glorified;
   for you, O Lord, are God.
4. I have found my servant David,
   and with my holy oil anointed him
   that he be strong.
   He shall know my faithful hand is there.
   He shall say of me: "You are my Father,
   my savior, God, my rock."

Text: Based on Psalm 89:2–5, 16–18, 21–22, 27. Refrain © 1969, 1981, ICEL. All rights reserved. Used with permission.
Verses, Tim Schoenbachler, b. 1952, © 1979, 1991, OCP.
Music: Tim Schoenbachler, © 1979, 1991, OCP. All rights reserved.

168 Psalm 90: In Every Age

In ev - 'ry age, O Lord, you have been our
ref - uge, you have been our ref - uge.

1. You return us to dust,
saying, "Return, O children, to earth."
For to you a thousand years
are like yesterday passed,
or as a watch of the night.

2. You sweep us away in a dream.
At dawn we are like morning grass
that rises to the morning sun,
then withers and fades.

3. Teach us to treasure our days.
Give wisdom to our hearts.
Return, O Lord, how long must we wait?
Pity your servants.

4. Fill our day-break with your love
that we may rejoice in song.
May your gracious eye watch over us
and the work of our hands.

Psalm 91: Be with Me, Lord — 169

Be with me, Lord, when I am in trou - ble.
When I am in trou - ble, be with me, Lord.

1. If you seek a shelter,
then come to the Lord, our God.
Say to the Lord,
"My refuge, I place my trust in you."

2. No evil shall snare you,
no harm come upon your home.
God sends to you his angels
to guard you on your way.

3. Your feet shall not stumble;
the angels will lift you high.
You shall defy the viper
and those who cause you harm.

4. Because of your love,
because of your faithfulness,
God will indeed be with you
to save you from all fear.

Psalm 91: Be with Me, Lord — 170

Be with me, Lord; be with me, Lord, when I am in trou-ble and need.

1. You who dwell in the shelter
of God, Most High,
who abide in Almighty's shade,
say to the Lord: "My refuge, my
stronghold, my God in whom I trust."

2. Evil shall never befall you,
nor affliction come near to your tent.
Unto his angels he's given command
to guard you in all your ways.

3. On their hands the angels will bear you up,
lest you dash your foot 'gainst a stone.
Lion or viper might strike at your life,
but you will not come to harm.

4. Cling to the Lord and
he'll surely deliver you;
he raises up all who call on his name.
He will bring joy to your hearts and
bless you with peace in all your days.

171 Psalm 95: If Today You Hear God's Voice

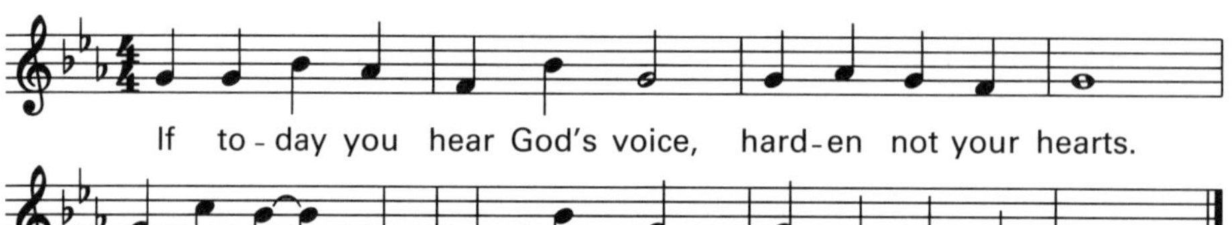
If to-day you hear God's voice, hard-en not your hearts.
If to-day you hear God's voice, hard-en not your hearts.

1. Come, let us sing joyfully to the LORD;
   let us acclaim the Rock of our salvation.
   Let us come into his presence with thanksgiving;
   let us joyfully sing psalms to him.
2. Come, let us bow down and worship;
   let us kneel before the LORD who made us.
   For he is our God,
   and we are the people he shepherds,
   the flock he guides.
3. O, that today you would hear his voice:
   "Harden not your hearts as at Meribah,
   as in the day of Massah in the desert."
   Where your fathers tempted me;
   they tested me though they had seen my works.

172 Psalm 95: If Today You Hear His Voice

If to-day you hear his voice, hard-en not your
hearts, hard-en not your hearts.

1. Come, let us sing with joy,
   sing praise to the Rock who saves us.
   Come now with open hearts,
   singing songs of thanks,
   singing songs of praise.
2. Come, let us kneel to God,
   bow down to the Lord who made us.
   We are the flock of God;
   God who shepherds us,
   God who guides us home.
3. If you should hear God's voice,
   do not let your hearts be hardened
   as in that desert land;
   there they saw my works,
   still they tested me.

PSALM 96: PROCLAIM HIS MARVELOUS DEEDS 173

Pro-claim his mar-vel-ous deeds to all the na-tions.

1. Sing to the LORD, sing a new song;
sing to the LORD, all you lands.
Sing to the LORD; bless his name.

2. Announce his salvation, day after day.
Tell his glory among all the lands;
among all peoples, his wondrous deeds.

3. Give to the LORD, you families of nations,
give the LORD glory and praise;
give to the LORD the glory due his name!

4. Worship the LORD in holy attire.
Tremble before him, all the earth;
say among the nations: The LORD is king.
He governs his people with equity.

Text: Psalm 96:1–2, 2–3, 7–8, 9–10. Refrain © 1969, 1981, ICEL. All rights reserved. Used with permission.
Verses based on the *New American Bible* © 1970, CCD. All rights reserved. Used with permission.
Music: Timothy R. Smith, b. 1960, © 1996, Timothy R. Smith. Published by OCP. All rights reserved.

PSALM 96: TODAY A SAVIOR IS BORN 174

To - day, to - day a Sav - ior has been born; a
Sav-ior has been born to us. He is Christ the Lord,
Christ the Lord, Je - sus Christ the Lord.

1. Sing a new song to the Lord.
Sing to the Lord, all the earth.
Sing to the Lord, sing to the Lord.
Sing to the Lord, bless his name!

2. Proclaim his help day by day.
Tell among the nations his glory.
Tell of his works, tell of his works,
and his wonders among all the peoples.

3. Let the heavens rejoice and earth be glad,
let the sea and all within it thunder praise.
All of the land, all that it bears:
rejoice at the presence of the Lord.

Text: Psalm 96:1–2, 2–3, 11–12. Refrain, Bernadette Farrell, b. 1957, © 1993, Bernadette Farrell. Published by OCP.
All rights reserved. Verses © 1963, The Grail (England). All rights reserved. Used with permission of A.P. Watt, Ltd.
Music: Bernadette Farrell, © 1993, Bernadette Farrell. Published by OCP. All rights reserved.

175 PSALM 96: TODAY OUR SAVIOR IS BORN

To-day our Sav-ior is born! To-day our Sav-ior is born!
This is the day, this is the day, Christ, our Sav-ior is born!

1. Sing to our God a joyful song!
   Everyone bless God's name.
   Tell of God's wondrous deeds;
   sing to all the world.
2. Heaven be glad and earth rejoice,
   let every ocean roar!
   Every forest, every tree
   joins the song of joy!
3. Cry out with joy for God has come,
   come to rule the earth.
   God will rule the world with love,
   righteousness and truth.

Text: Based on Luke 2:11; Psalm 96:1–3, 11–12, 13; Jaime Cortez, b. 1963.
Music: Jaime Cortez.

176 PSALM 97: THE LORD IS KING

The Lord is King! The Lord is King,
the Most High o - ver all the earth.

1. Let earth rejoice, the Lord God reigns.
   Exult, you shores; be glad, you plains.
   Justice serves as God's high throne, alleluia!
2. The skies proclaim that God is just:
   God's glory plain to all of us.
   Unseen spirits, join our song, alleluia!
3. You alone bring hope to birth:
   greater you than all the earth.
   Far beyond all other gods, alleluia!

Text: Based on Psalm 97:1–2, 6–7, 9.

Psalm 98: All the Ends of the Earth 177

Refrain
All the ends of the earth have seen sal - va - tion.
All the ends of the earth have seen the sav - ing pow - er of
God, the sav - ing pow - er of God.
Verses
1. Let us sing a new song for the won - drous deeds of our
2. All the ends of the earth have ___ seen the pow - er of
3. Sing the prais - es of God; with the harp and song ___ give
1. God, whose ho - ly arm has ___ pre -
2. God. Ring out your joy. Break in - to
3. praise. O trum - pets sound! Joy - ful - ly
to Refrain
1. vailed, bring - ing sal - va - tion and vic - t'ry.
2. song; all ___ you lands ___ sing praise.
3. sing; sing to the rul - er of all!

Text: Based on Psalm 98:1, 3–6; Bob Hurd, b. 1950.
Music: Bob Hurd.

178 Psalm 98: All the Ends of the Earth

All the ends of the earth have
seen the sav-ing pow-er of God.

1. O sing to the Lord a new song,
for he has done wondrous deeds.
Yes, his right hand and holy arm
have won the victory.

2. The Lord has revealed salvation;
his justice prevails on earth.
And to the house of Israel
the Lord bestows his love.

3. Give praise with a soaring melody;
O sing with the strings and harp.
With trumpets and the sound of horn,
acclaim the King, the Lord.

Text: Based on Psalm 98:1, 2–3, 5–6.
Verses, Ken Canedo, b. 1953,
Music: Ken Canedo,

179 Psalm 98: The Lord Has Revealed

The Lord has re-vealed to the na-tions,
sav - ing pow'r, sav - ing pow'r, sav - ing pow'r.

1. Sing a new song, all you lands,
of the marvelous deeds of the Lord.
Salvation is born of God's right hand
and holy arm.

2. The saving power of God
has been revealed to all the lands.
His kindness and truth
forever faithful to the house of Israel.

3. All of the ends of the earth
have seen the salvation of God.
Shout to the Lord, dance for joy,
sing your praise.

4. Play out your song on the harp,
create a melodious song.
With trumpets and horn
acclaim our King and our God.

Text: Based on Psalm 98:1, 2–3, 3–4, 5–6.
Verses, Timothy R. Smith, b. 1960,
Music: Timothy R. Smith,

PSALM 100: WE ARE GOD'S PEOPLE 180

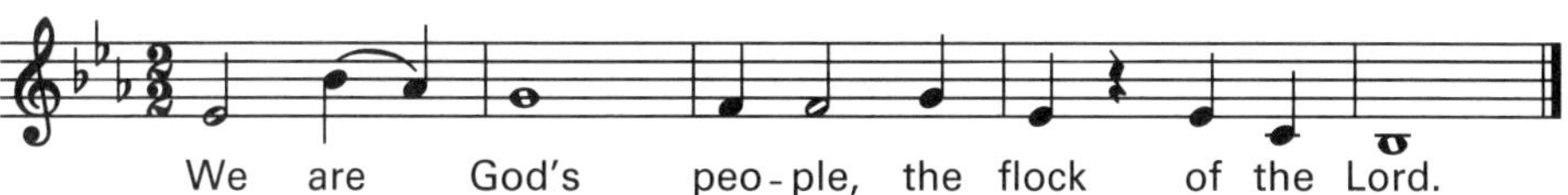
We are God's peo-ple, the flock of the Lord.

1. Let all the earth shout for joy.
   Serve the Lord with gladness.
   Sing to the Lord with joyful song.
2. Know that the Lord is God.
   He made us, to him we belong,
   and we are the sheep of his flock.
3. Enter his gates with thanks,
   the courts of the Lord with praise.
   Give thanks and bless his name.
4. Forever God is good.
   His love is everlasting,
   faithful for all generations.

Text: Based on Psalm 100:3b, 1–2, 4, 5; Timothy R. Smith, b. 1960,
Music: Timothy R. Smith,

PSALM 103: THE LORD IS KIND AND MERCIFUL 181

The Lord is kind and mer-ci-ful, and par-dons all our sins.

1. Bless the Lord, O my soul.
   Let all that is in me bless his name.
2. Slow to anger and quick to heal,
   and mighty in justice to those in need.
3. Keep in mind the works of God,
   who redeems you from evil
   and brings you home.
4. As high as the sky is above the earth,
   so far God lifts us above our sins.

Text: Based on Psalm 103:1a, 8, 2a–3, 11a, 12b. Refrain
Verses, Bob Dufford, SJ, b. 1943,
Music: Bob Dufford, SJ,

PSALM 103: THE LORD IS KIND AND MERCIFUL 182

The Lord is kind and mer-ci-ful; mer-ci-ful is the Lord.

1. Bless the LORD, O my soul;
   and all my being, bless his holy name.
   Bless the LORD, O my soul,
   forget not all his benefits.
2. He pardons all your iniquities,
   he heals all your ills.
   He redeems your life from destruction,
   and crowns you with kindness
   and compassion.
3. The LORD secures justice
   and the rights of all the oppressed.
   He has made known his ways to Moses,
   and his deeds to the children of Israel.
4. Merciful and gracious is the LORD,
   slow to anger and abounding in kindness.
   For as the heavens are high above the earth,
   so surpassing is his kindness
   toward those who fear him.

Text: Psalm 103:1–2, 3–4, 6–7, 8, 11. Refrain
Verses
Music: Ricky Manalo, CSP, b. 1965,

183 PSALM 104: SEND FORTH YOUR SPIRIT, O LORD

Send forth your Spir - it, O Lord, and re - new the face of the earth.

1. Bless the Lord, O my soul,
   O Lord, how great you are!
   How many are your works, O Lord,
   the earth is full of your riches!
2. You take back your Spirit, they die,
   back to the dust from which they came;
   you send forth your Spirit,
   they are created, the whole earth is renewed!
3. Your glory will last forever,
   may you rejoice in all your works.
   May my thoughts be pleasing to you,
   I find my joy in you, Lord.

Alternate Verses for the Easter Vigil

1. Bless the Lord, O my soul,
   O Lord, how great you are!
   With glory and with majesty clothed;
   you are covered with light!
2. Foundation of earth you made sure,
   standing firm from age to age.
   You placed the ocean like a robe,
   the waters covered the hills.
3. The valleys are flowing with springs;
   rivers run between the hills;
   the birds of heaven dwell on their banks,
   they make their nests as they sing.
4. You send down your rain on the hills.
   All your blessings fill the earth.
   You give the cattle grass for their food,
   and plants for crops to be grown.
5. In wisdom you made all these things.
   Lord, they are numberless.
   Your riches fill the whole of the earth.
   Bless the Lord, O my soul!

Text: Based on Psalm 104:1, 24, 29–30, 31, 34; 1–2, 5–6, 10, 12, 13–14, 24, 35; Christopher Walker, b. 1947.
Music: Christopher Walker.

184 PSALM 104: LORD, SEND OUT YOUR SPIRIT

Lord, send out your Spir-it, and re - new the face of the earth.

1. Bless the LORD, O my soul!
   O LORD, my God, you are great indeed!
   How manifold are your works, O LORD!
   The earth is full of your creatures.
2. If you take away their breath,
   they perish and return to their dust.
   When you send forth your spirit,
   they are created,
   and you renew the face of the earth.
3. May the glory of the LORD endure forever;
   may the LORD be glad in his works!
   Pleasing to him be my theme;
   I will be glad in the LORD.

Text: Psalm 104:1, 24, 29–30, 31, 34.
Music: Ken Canedo, b. 1953,

PSALM 104: LORD, SEND OUT YOUR SPIRIT 185

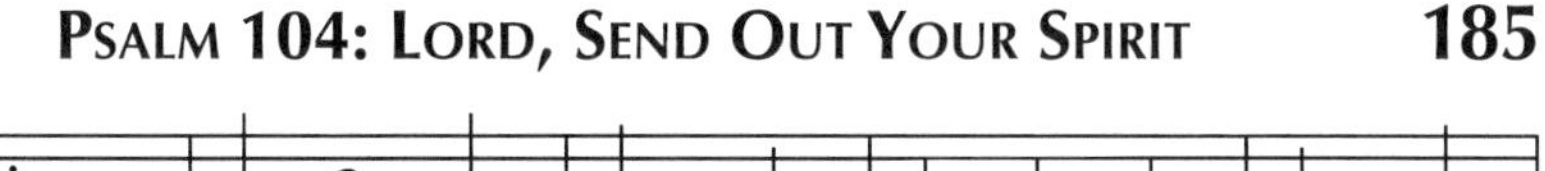

Lord, send out your Spir - it, and re - new the
face of the earth.
1
2
earth.

1. Bless the Lord, O my soul.
   O Lord, my God, you are great indeed!
   How manifold are your works, O Lord!
   The earth is full of your creatures.
2. If you take away their breath, O Lord,
   they die and return to their dust.
   When you send forth your spirit they live.
   You renew the face of the earth.
3. May the glory of the Lord endure forever,
   and may the Lord be glad in his works!
   Pleasing to him be my theme;
   for I rejoice in the Lord.

Text: Psalm 104:1, 24, 29–30, 31, 34. Refrain
Verses, Joe Zsigray, b. 1953,
Music: Joe Zsigray,

PSALM 116: OUR BLESSING-CUP/ I WILL WALK WITH THE LORD/THE CUP OF SALVATION 186

Refrain I
Our bless-ing-cup is a com-mu-nion with the Blood, the Blood of Christ.

Refrain II
I will walk with the Lord in the land, the land of the liv-ing.

Refrain III
The cup of sal-va-tion I will take, and call the name of the Lord.

1. How shall I make a return
   for the goodness God has done for me?
   The cup of salvation I will take
   and call God's name.
2. Precious in the eyes of the Lord
   is the dying of his faithful one.
   I am the servant of the Lord
   who set me free.
3. Sacrifice and thanks I will give
   in the presence of God's chosen ones.
   My vow to the Lord I shall fulfill
   and call God's name.

Text: Refrain I
Refrains II and III and verses based on Psalm 116:9, 12–13, 15–16bc, 17–18; Scott Soper, b. 1961,

Music: Scott Soper,

187 PSALM 116: OUR BLESSING-CUP/ EL CÁLIZ QUE BENDECIMOS

*Refrain
Our bless-ing-cup is a com-mu-nion with the Blood of Christ.

*Estribillo
El cá - liz que ben - de - ci - mos es la co-mu -
nión de la san - gre de Cris - to.

1. What shall I return to the LORD
   for all his bounty to me?
   I will lift the cup of salvation
   and call on the name of the LORD.
2. I believed, even when I said,
   "I am greatly afflicted."
   Precious in the eyes of the LORD
   the dying of his faithful ones.
3. O LORD, I am your servant,
   your servant, the son of your handmaid;
   you have brought me freedom.
   To you will I offer sacrifice of thanksgiving
   and call upon your name, O LORD.
4. My vows to the LORD I will pay
   in the presence of all his people,
   in the courts of the house of the LORD,
   in the midst of you, Jerusalem.

1. *¿Cómo pagaré al Señor*
   todo el bien que me ha hecho?
   Alzaré la copa de la salvación,
   invocando tu nombre, Señor.
2. *Tenía fe, aún cuando dije:*
   "Cómo soy de desgraciado".
   Mucho le cuesta al Señor
   la muerte de sus fieles.
3. *Señor, yo soy tu siervo,*
   el hijo de tu esclava;
   tú rompiste mis cadenas.
   A ti ofrezco un sacrificio de alabanza,
   invocando tu nombre, Señor.
4. *Mis votos al Señor cumpliré*
   en presencia de todo su pueblo;
   en el atrio de la casa del Señor,
   en medio de ti, Jerusalén.

*The response may be sung in only one language or bilingually. It is repeated in either case.

Psalm 116: Our Blessing-Cup 188

Our bless-ing-cup is a com-mu-nion in the Blood of Christ.

1. How shall I make a return to the Lord
   for all the good he has done for me?
   The cup of salvation I will take up,
   and I will call upon the name of the Lord.

2. Taste and see, taste and see
   the sweetness of the Lord,
   the goodness of the Lord.

3. Every time you eat of this bread,
   every time you drink of this cup
   you proclaim the death of the Lord
   until he comes.

Text: Psalm 116:12–13; 34:9; 1 Corinthians 11:26. Refrain © 1969, 1981, ICEL. All rights reserved. Used with permission.
Verses, Michael Joncas, b. 1951, © 1979, OCP. All rights reserved.
Music: Michael Joncas, © 1979, OCP. All rights reserved.

Psalm 116: In the Presence of God 189

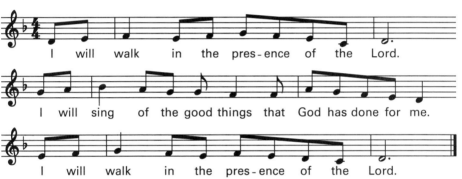

I will walk in the pres-ence of the Lord.

I will sing of the good things that God has done for me.

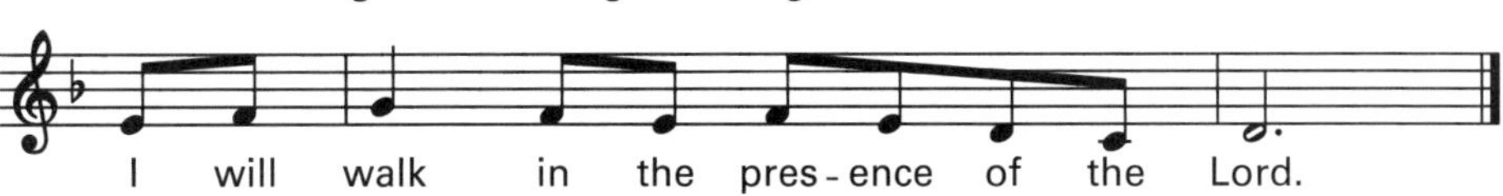
I will walk in the pres-ence of the Lord.

Verses: Ordinary Time

1. Love you, I love you;
   you have heard my voice.
   I will call your name, cry out your name,
   as long as I shall live.

2. Comfort me, you care for me,
   you have rescued me.
   You have heard my cry,
   have heard my plea.
   You save my soul from death.

3. Gracious is your hand, O God,
   merciful and just.
   God, your love protects the lowly ones;
   your kindness has no end.

4. Deliver me, deliver me.
   Deliver my soul from death,
   my eyes from tears, my feet from snares.
   In the land of the living, I shall walk.

Verses: Lent

1. In my grief, in my pain
   I believed in you.
   How precious is our death to you,
   how precious in your eyes.

2. Here I am, your servant, Lord,
   free to speak your name.
   Words of thanks and praise be on my lips,
   and ever in my heart.

3. I will pay my vows to you,
   here among your people.
   In the presence of your faithful ones,
   I give my life to you.

Text: Based on Psalm 116:1–10, 15–18; Tom Kendzia, b. 1954.
Music: Tom Kendzia.
Text and music © 1996, Tom Kendzia. Published by OCP. All rights reserved.

190 PSALM 118: GIVE THANKS TO THE LORD

Give thanks to the Lord for he is good, his
love is ev - er - last - ing.

1. Let the house of Israel say,
"His mercy endures forever."
Let the house of Aaron say,
"His mercy endures forever."
Let all those who fear the LORD say,
"His mercy endures forever."

2. I was hard pressed and falling,
but the LORD helped me.
My strength and my courage is the LORD,
and he has been my Savior.
The joyful shout of victory
in the houses of the just.

3. The stone the builders rejected
has become the cornerstone.
By the LORD has this been done;
it is wonderful, it is wonderful in our eyes.
This day the LORD has made;
let us be glad and rejoice in it.

191 PSALM 118: THIS IS THE DAY

This is the day that the Lord has made; let us re-joice
and be glad; for this is the day that the Lord has
made; al - le - lu - ia, al - le - lu - ia!
1-4
1st time: repeat to Verses
Final
ia! Al - le - lu - ia, al - le - lu - ia!

1. Give thanks to God; the Lord is good.
God's mercy endures forever.
Let the house of Israel say:
"God's mercy endures forever."

2. The Lord's right hand is lifted up;
the hand of the Lord is mighty.
I shall not die, but live to tell
the marvelous works of God.

3. The stone which the builders rejected
has become the cornerstone.
This is the work of the Lord;
how wonderful, how wonderful in our eyes!

PSALM 118: THIS IS THE DAY 192

This is the day the Lord has made; let us re-joice and be glad.

This is the day the Lord has made; let us re-joice and be glad.

1. Give thanks to the LORD, for he is good,
   his mercy endures forever.
   Let the house of Israel say,
   "His mercy endures forever."

2. The LORD's right hand has struck with pow'r;
   the LORD's right hand is exalted.
   I shall not die, but live, and
   declare the works of the LORD.

3. The stone which the builders rejected
   has become the cornerstone.
   By the LORD has this been done;
   it is wonderful in our eyes.

PSALM 122: LET US GO REJOICING 193

Let us go re - joic-ing, re - joic - ing to the house of the
Lord. Let us go re - joic - ing to the house of the Lord.

1. How I rejoiced to hear them say,
   "Let us go to the house of the Lord."
   And now within your walls
   we are standing, O Jerusalem.

2. Jerusalem, a city firmly built,
   knit together in unity and strength.
   There the tribes go up,
   the tribes of the Lord,
   making pilgrimage.

3. There the tribes give thanks
   to the name of the Lord,
   according to the law of Israel.
   There are set the thrones of judgment
   for the house of David.

4. Let us pray for the good of Jerusalem,
   and for those who love you
   prosperity and peace,
   peace within your ramparts and your towers,
   peace in your dwellings.

5. For the sake of my people and my friends,
   I say peace be to you, Jerusalem.
   For love of God's house
   I pray for you and your prosperity.

194 Psalm 126: The Lord Has Done Great Things

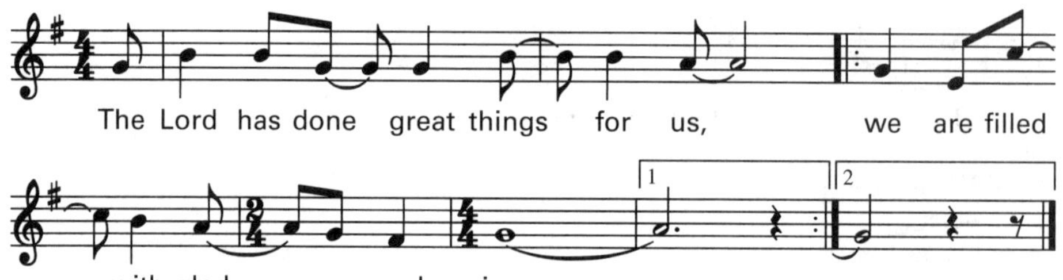
The Lord has done great things for us, we are filled
with glad - ness and joy,

1. When God set the captives of Zion free,
we were more like children in a dream.
Then you could hear
our laughter and cheers;
then you could hear our shouts of joy.

2. They said in amazement to the world,
"Indeed, God has done great things for them."
Truly our God has done great things,
and so we are glad, we shout for joy.

3. Restore all our fortunes, God of love,
like rivers that save the desert lands.
Those who have gone to sow in tears
shall go back to reap with songs of joy.

Text: Based on Psalm 126:1–2, 2–3, 4–5.
Verses, Jaime Cortez, b. 1963,
Music: Jaime Cortez,

195 Psalm 128: O Blessed Are Those

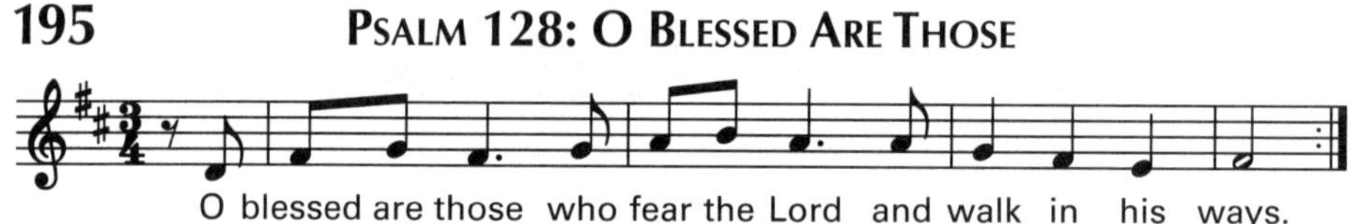
O blessed are those who fear the Lord and walk in his ways.

1. O blessed are those who fear the Lord
and walk in his ways!
By the labor of your hands you shall eat.
You will be happy and prosper.

2. Your wife like a fruitful vine
in the heart of your house;
your children like shoots of the olive
around your table.

3. Indeed thus shall be blest
all those who fear the Lord.
May the Lord bless you from Zion
all the days of your life!

Text: Psalm 128:1, 2, 3, 4–5,
Music: Paul Inwood, b. 1947,

Psalm 130: Out of the Depths 196

Out of the depths, I cry to you, O Lord.

1. From out of the depths,
   I cry to you, Lord;
   O hear the sound of my voice.
   Lord, open your ears and listen to me;
   I plead for your kindness, O God.
2. If you, O Lord, should number our sins,
   then Lord, who would survive?
   But you are forgiveness for our sins;
   for this we adore you, O God.
3. I trust in you, Lord, my soul looks to you
   as watchmen wait for the dawn.
   And more than the watchmen
   wait for the dawn,
   let Israel wait for the Lord.
4. For with you is found forgiveness of sin;
   you show your mercy to all.
   And you will deliver your chosen ones;
   deliver your people, O God.

Text: Based on Psalm 130:1–2, 3–4, 5–6, 7–8.
Verses, Scott Soper, b. 1961,
Music: Scott Soper,

Psalm 130: With Our God There Is Mercy 197

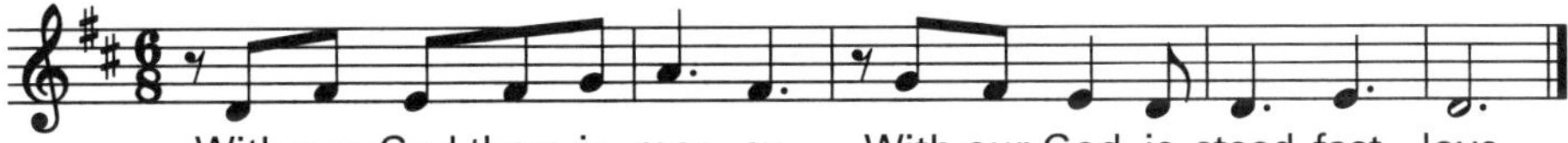
With our God there is mer - cy. With our God is stead-fast love.

1. Out of the depths
   I cry to you, O Lord.
   Hear my voice,
   the sound of my pleading.
2. Mark but our sins, O Lord,
   and who might stand?
   But you forgive,
   and thus we revere you.
3. My soul waits for the Lord,
   I count on God's word.
   my soul yearns for the Lord
   as the deepest night waits the day.
   As we count on the dawn,
   so we count on the Lord.
4. Kind is our God,
   who keeps us close in care.
   We shall be saved from all our iniquity.

Text: Based on Psalm 130:1–2, 3–4, 5–6, 7–8; Tim Manion, b. 1951.
Music: Tim Manion.

198 PSALM 138: ON THE DAY I CALLED

Lord, on the day I called for help, you an-swered me, you an-swered me.

1. I shall thank you, God of my heart,
you have heard my troubled word.
While angels watch, your name I praise;
I dance before your holy place.
2. For your love and your faithfulness,
I thank your name,
your promise surpasses your fame.
I called for your help
all night and day long:
you heard me, and made me strong.
3. From on high,
from the heavens the poor you see,
you drive the proud to their knees.
Though I live
in the midst of trouble and woe,
you save me, and foil my foe.
4. Your strong hand shall come to my aid:
you shall be all good to me.
Forever shall your love abide;
do not cast your child aside.

Text: Based on Psalm 138:1–2, 2–3, 6–7, 7–8. Refrain
Verses, Rory Cooney, b. 1952,
Music: Rory Cooney,

199 PSALM 145: I WILL PRAISE YOUR NAME/ THE HAND OF THE LORD FEEDS US

Refrain
I will praise your name for ev-er, my king and my God, my king and my God.
Alternate Refrain
The hand of the Lord feeds us; he an - swers all our needs, he an - swers all our needs.

1. I will praise you, God and king;
I will bless your name forever.
Every day I will bless you,
praise your name forever.
2. You are grace and mercy, Lord,
slow to anger, filled with kindness.
You are good to all your children,
loving all creation.
3. Let your works give thanks to you;
let your faithful ever bless you;
let them praise your strength, your glory,
and proclaim your kingdom.
4. Every word you speak in faith,
every work you do is holy.
You lift up all who stumble,
you raise up the lowly.

Text: Based on Psalm 145:1–2, 8–9, 10–11, 13–14. Refrains Verses, Scott Soper, b. 1961,
Music: Scott Soper,

Psalm 145: I Will Praise Your Name/ The Hand of the Lord 200

Refrain
to Verses 1, 3, 4
I will praise your name for ev - er, my king and my God.

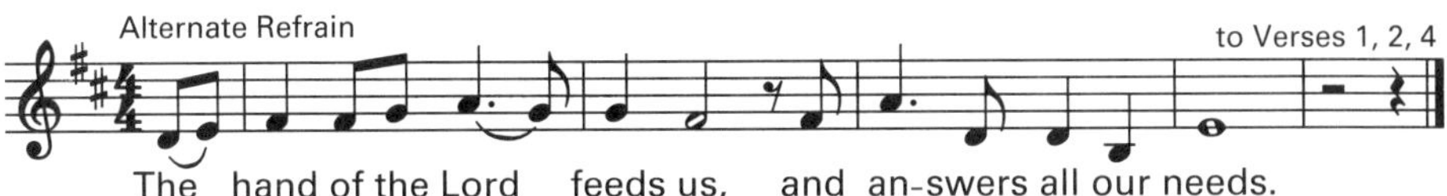
Alternate Refrain
to Verses 1, 2, 4
The hand of the Lord feeds us, and an-swers all our needs.

1. God is merciful and gracious,
   slow to anger, full of kindness.
   The Lord is faithful to all his people,
   compassionate to all creation.

2. Lord, we lift our eyes to the heavens,
   and you feed us in due season.
   The treasures, Lord, that you impart
   fulfill every desire.

3. All of your people bless your name
   in a holy song of thanksgiving,
   singing of your eternal reign,
   declaring your holy power.

4. Lord, your justice lasts forever,
   your loving deeds from age to age.
   You are near to all who call,
   never far from faithful hearts.

Psalm 146: Praise the Lord, My Soul/ Lord, Come and Save Us 201

Refrain
Praise the Lord, my soul! Praise the Lord, my soul!
Alternate Refrain
Lord, come and save us. Lord, come and save us.

1. It is the Lord who preserves fidelity forever,
   who does justice to those who are oppressed.
   It is he who gives bread to the hungry,
   the Lord who sets pris'ners free.

2. The Lord who opens the eyes of the blind,
   the Lord who raises up those
   who are bowed down.
   It is the Lord who loves the just,
   the Lord who protects the stranger.

3. The Lord upholds the orphan
   and the widow,
   but thwarts the path of the wicked.
   The Lord will reign forever,
   the God of Sion from age to age.
   Alleluia!

Note: Refrain: 23rd Sunday in OT, Year B; 32nd Sunday in OT, Year B; 26th Sunday in OT, Year C.
Alternate Refrain: 3rd Sunday of Advent, Year A.

202 EXODUS 15: TO GOD BE PRAISE AND GLORY

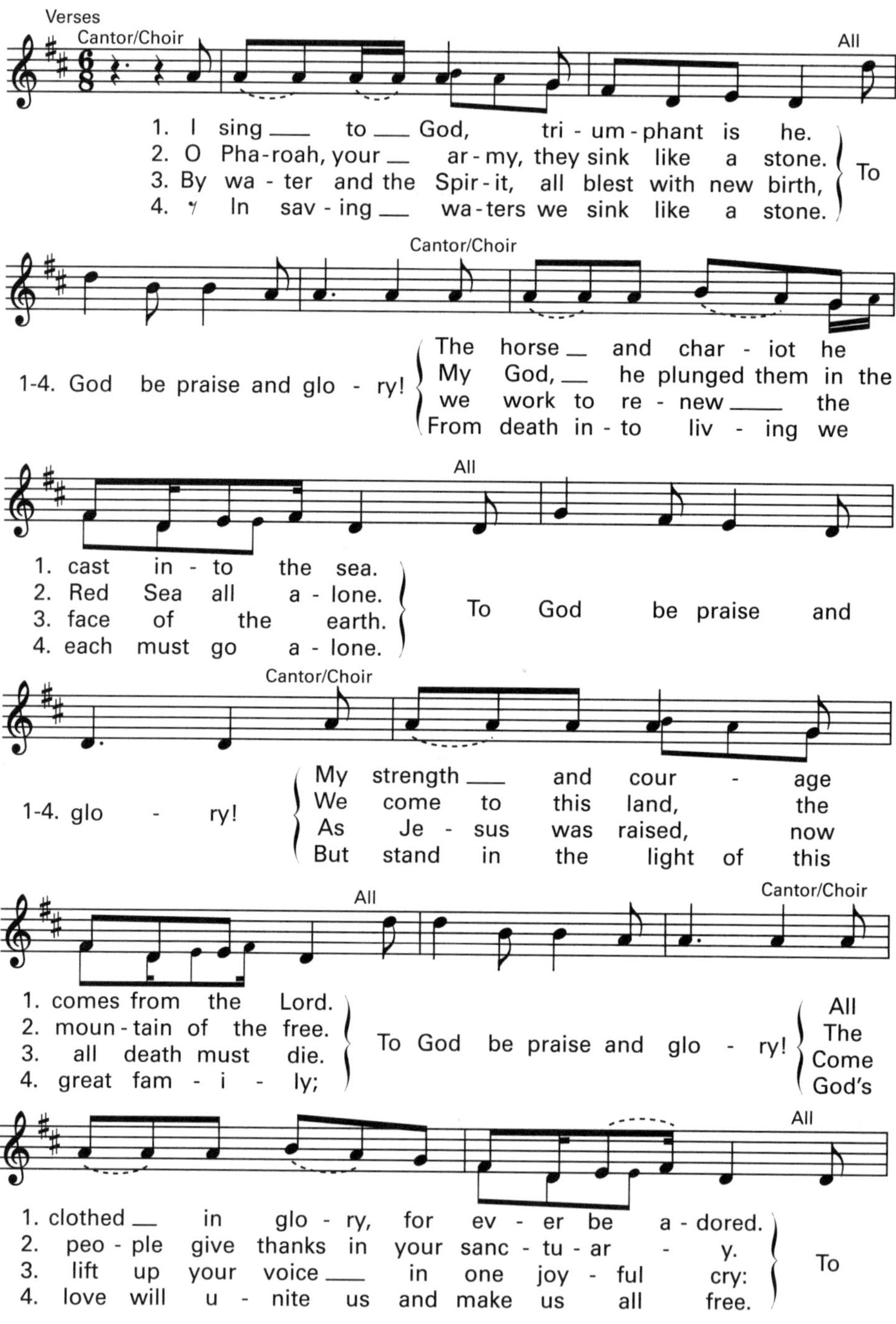
Verses
Cantor/Choir
All
1. I sing ___ to ___ God, tri - um - phant is he.
2. O Pha - roah, your ___ ar - my, they sink like a stone.
3. By wa - ter and the Spir - it, all blest with new birth,
4. In sav - ing ___ wa - ters we sink like a stone.
To
Cantor/Choir
1-4. God be praise and glo - ry!
The horse ___ and char - iot he
My God, ___ he plunged them in the
we work to re - new ___ the
From death in - to liv - ing we
All
1. cast in - to the sea.
2. Red Sea all a - lone.
3. face of the earth.
4. each must go a - lone.
To God be praise and
Cantor/Choir
1-4. glo - ry!
My strength ___ and cour - age
We come to this land, the
As Je - sus was raised, now
But stand in the light of this
All
Cantor/Choir
1. comes from the Lord.
2. moun - tain of the free.
3. all death must die.
4. great fam - i - ly;
To God be praise and glo - ry!
All
The
Come
God's
All
1. clothed ___ in glo - ry, for ev - er be a - dored.
2. peo - ple give thanks in your sanc - tu - ar - y.
3. lift up your voice ___ in one joy - ful cry:
4. love will u - nite us and make us all free.
To

1-4. God be praise and glo - ry! I am free!
Refrain
I will sing to the Lord, tri -
um - phant is he: the horse and char - i - ot he
1
2, Final
to Verses
cast in - to the sea! I will cast in - to the sea!

Text: Based on Exodus 15:19–21; Janèt Sullivan Whitaker, b. 1958.
Music: Janèt Sullivan Whitaker.

Isaiah 12: We Shall Draw Water 203

We shall draw wa - ter joy - ful-ly, sing-ing joy - ful-ly,
sing-ing joy - ful-ly; we shall draw wa - ter
joy - ful-ly from the well-springs of sal - va - tion.

1. Truly God is our salvation;
   we trust, we shall not fear.
   For the Lord is our strength,
   the Lord is our song;
   he became our Savior.
2. Give thanks, O give thanks to the Lord;
   give praise to his holy name!
   Make his mighty deeds known to
   all of the nations; proclaim his greatness.
3. Sing a psalm, sing a psalm to the Lord
   for he has done glorious deeds.
   Make known his works to all of the earth;
   people of Zion, sing for joy,
   for great in your midst, great in your midst
   is the Holy One of Israel.

Text: Based on Isaiah 12:3, 2, 4–6; Paul Inwood, b. 1947.
Music: Paul Inwood.

204 DANIEL 3: GLORY AND PRAISE FOR EVER

Refrain
Glo-ry and praise, glo - ry and praise, glo-ry and praise for ev-er!

1. Blessed are you, O Lord, the God of our fathers,
   praiseworthy and exalted above all forever;
   and blessed is your holy and glorious name, **(to Response I)**

All
to Refrain
Resp. I: praise-wor-thy and ex - alt-ed a-bove all for all a - ges.
Resp. II: praise-wor-thy and ex - alt-ed a-bove___ all for - ev - er.

2. Blessed are you in the temple of your holy glory, **(to Response II)**
3. Blessed are you on the throne of your kingdom, **(to Response II)**
4. Blessed are you who look into the depths
   from your throne upon the cherubim, **(to Response II)**

Text: Daniel 3:52, 53, 54, 55. Refrain © 1969, 1981, 1997, ICEL. All rights reserved. Used with permission.
Verses © 1970, 1997, 1998, CCD. All rights reserved. Used with permission.
Music: Timothy R. Smith, b. 1960, © 2008, Timothy R. Smith. Published by OCP. All rights reserved.

205 LUKE 1: BENEDICTUS

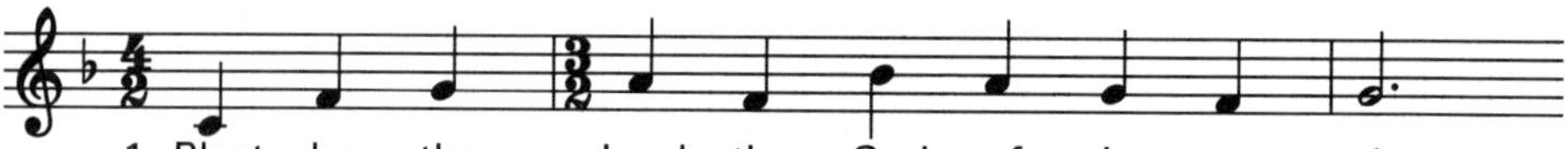

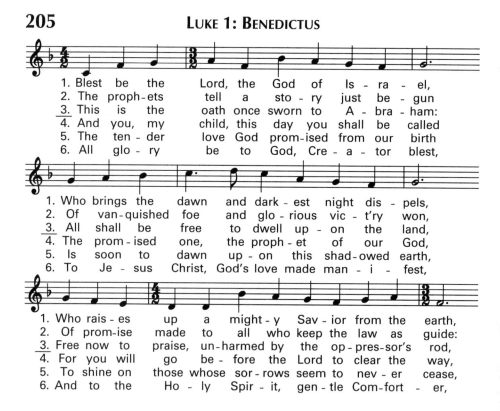

1. Blest be the Lord, the God of Is - ra - el,
2. The proph-ets tell a sto - ry just be - gun
3. This is the oath once sworn to A - bra - ham:
4. And you, my child, this day you shall be called
5. The ten - der love God prom-ised from our birth
6. All glo - ry be to God, Cre - a - tor blest,

1. Who brings the dawn and dark - est night dis - pels,
2. Of van-quished foe and glo - rious vic - t'ry won,
3. All shall be free to dwell up - on the land,
4. The prom - ised one, the proph - et of our God,
5. Is soon to dawn up - on this shad-owed earth,
6. To Je - sus Christ, God's love made man - i - fest,

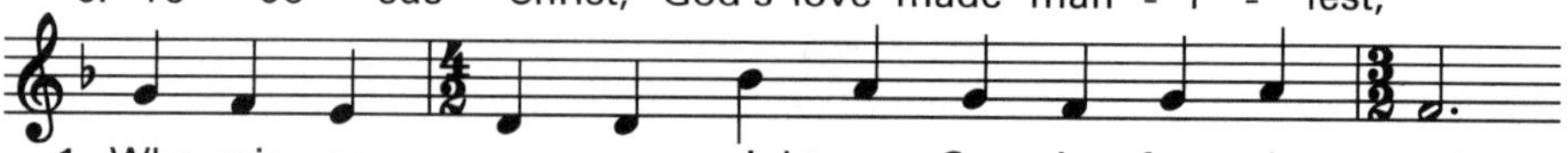

1. Who rais - es up a might - y Sav - ior from the earth,
2. Of prom-ise made to all who keep the law as guide:
3. Free now to praise, un-harmed by the op - pres-sor's rod,
4. For you will go be - fore the Lord to clear the way,
5. To shine on those whose sor - rows seem to nev - er cease,
6. And to the Ho - ly Spir - it, gen - tle Com-fort - er,

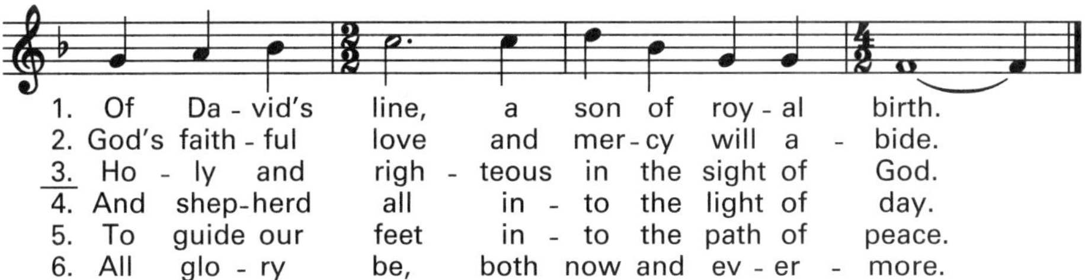
1. Of Da - vid's line, a son of roy - al birth.
2. God's faith - ful love and mer - cy will a - bide.
3. Ho - ly and righ - teous in the sight of God.
4. And shep-herd all in - to the light of day.
5. To guide our feet in - to the path of peace.
6. All glo - ry be, both now and ev - er - more.

Text: *Benedictus;* based on Luke 1:68–79; Owen Alstott, b. 1947,
Music: Bernadette Farrell, b. 1957,

LUKE 1: BENEDICTUS 206

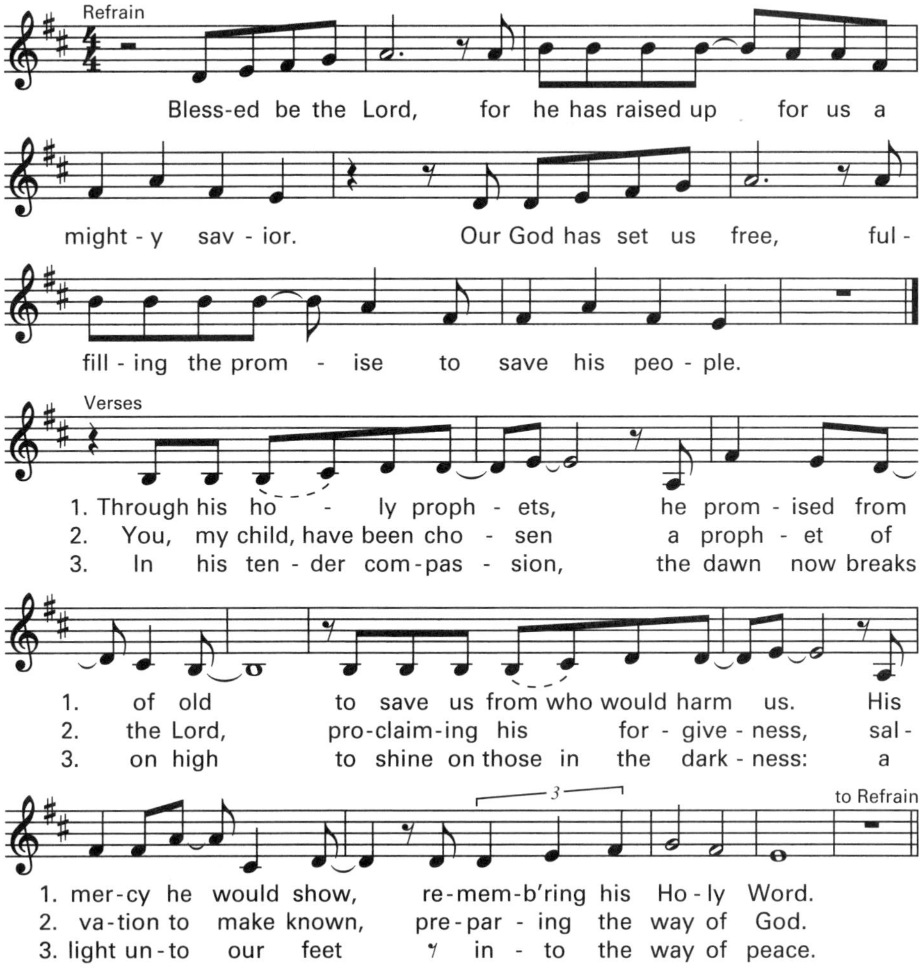

Refrain

Bless-ed be the Lord, for he has raised up for us a might - y sav - ior. Our God has set us free, ful - fill - ing the prom - ise to save his peo - ple.

Verses

1. Through his ho - ly proph - ets, he prom - ised from of old to save us from who would harm us. His mer - cy he would show, re - mem - b'ring his Ho - ly Word.
2. You, my child, have been cho - sen a proph - et of the Lord, pro - claim - ing his for - give - ness, sal - va - tion to make known, pre - par - ing the way of God.
3. In his ten - der com - pas - sion, the dawn now breaks on high to shine on those in the dark - ness: a light un - to our feet in - to the way of peace.

to Refrain

Text: *Benedictus;* based on Luke 1:68–79; Steve Angrisano, b. 1965, and Curtis Stephan, b. 1973.
Music: Steve Angrisano and Curtis Stephan.

207 LUKE 1: MARY'S SONG

Hap-py are they who be-lieve that the prom-ise of the Lord will be ful-filled.

1. I sing with all my soul
   and praise the Lord.
   My heart is glad
   because of God, my Savior;
   for he has looked
   upon his humble servant,
   and who am I to merit his attention?
2. I may henceforth regard myself as
   happy, because my God
   has done great things for me,
   and every generation gives assent:
   the Lord is mighty and his name is holy!
3. He gives his grace anew in every age
   to all who live in reverence with him.
   Grace is his strength, but he unmasks all pride
   and strips us bare of our self-conceit.
4. Dethroning those who hold authority,
   the poor and humble people
   he makes great.
   He gives in great abundance
   to the hungry,
   sends the rich away with empty hands.
5. His servant Israel he has remembered.
   He has been merciful to all his people,
   for so had been his promise
   to our parents:
   to Abraham and to his seed forever.

Text: Based on Luke 1:45–55; Huub Oosterhuis, b. 1933; tr. by David Smith, b. 1933, Exclusive agent for English-language countries: OCP.
Music: Michael Joncas, b. 1951,

208 LUKE 1: MAGNIFICAT

Respuesta/Response

Ma-gni-fi-cat a-ni-ma me-a Do-mi-num.

Estrofas

1. Todo mi ser celebra
   lo grande que es Dios.
2. Mi espíritu se alegra en mi salvador.
3. Mi Dios ha hecho
   grandes cosas en mí.
4. Y sus favores alcanzan
   a quien le es fiel.
5. Bajó al poderoso, al humilde él alzó.
6. Al hambriento colmó de bienes
   y al rico le quitó.
7. Dios salva a Israel, su fiel sirviente.
8. De su misericordia Dios se acordó.

Verses

1. *Sing out, my soul,*
   the greatness of the Lord.
2. *My spirit finds joy in God my savior.*
3. *The Almighty has done*
   great things for me.
4. *God has mercy*
   on those who fear the Lord.
5. *He has cast down the mighty*
   and lifted up the poor.
6. *The hungry he's filled with good things,*
   sent the rich empty away.
7. *God has helped his servant, Israel.*
8. *God remembered his promise*
   from of old.

Text: Based on Luke 1:46–55; Pedro Rubalcava, b. 1958.
Music: Pedro Rubalcava.

LUKE 1: MAGNIFICAT

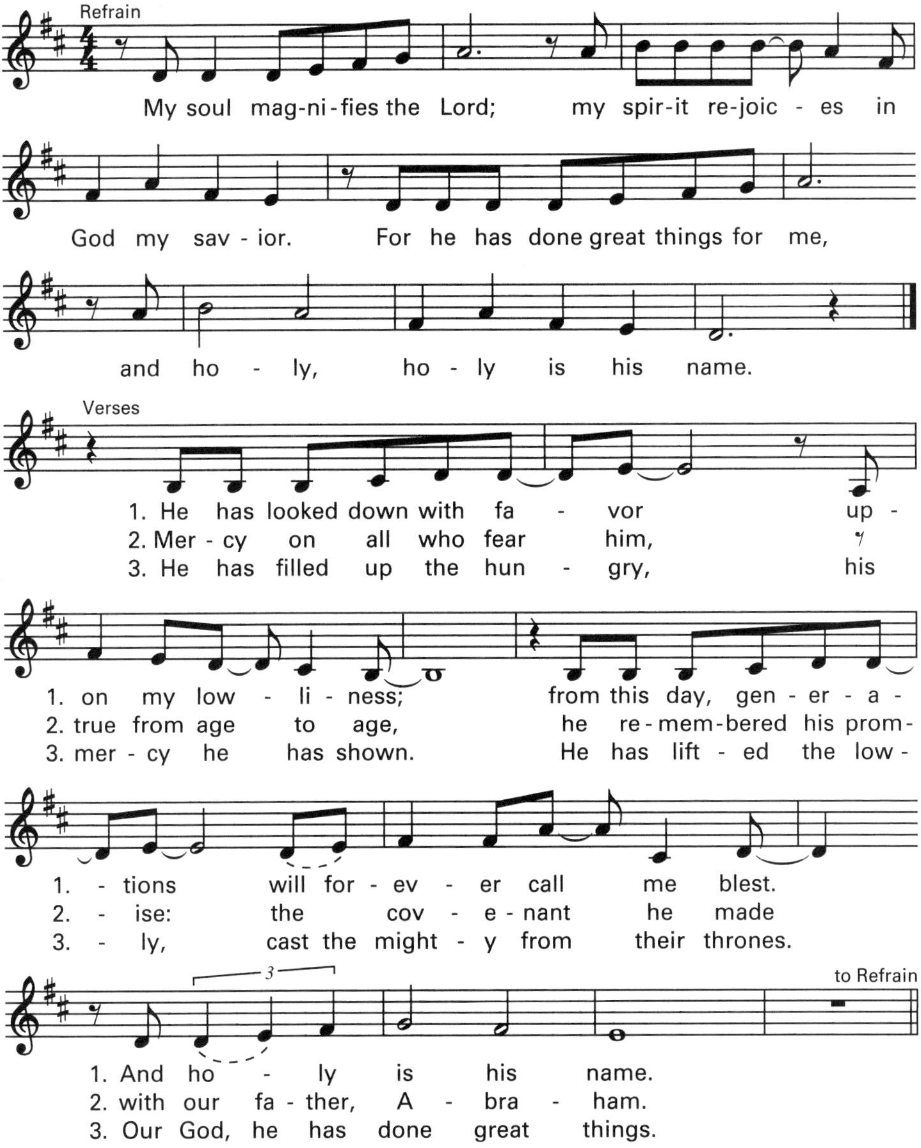

209

Refrain

My soul mag-ni-fies the Lord; my spir-it re-joic - es in
God my sav - ior. For he has done great things for me,
and ho - ly, ho - ly is his name.

Verses

1. He has looked down with fa - vor up - on my low - li - ness; from this day, gen - er - a - tions will for - ev - er call me blest. And ho - ly is his name.
2. Mer - cy on all who fear him, true from age to age, he re-mem-bered his prom - ise: the cov - e - nant he made with our fa - ther, A - bra - ham.
3. He has filled up the hun - gry, his mer - cy he has shown. He has lift - ed the low - ly, cast the might - y from their thrones. Our God, he has done great things.

to Refrain

Text: *Magnificat*; based on Luke 1:46–55; Steve Angrisano, b. 1965, and Curtis Stephan, b. 1973.
Music: Steve Angrisano and Curtis Stephan.

210 Luke 1: Magnificat

1. My soul pro - claims the great-ness of the Lord.
2. Through me great deeds will God make man - i - fest,
3. God's might - y arm, pro - tec - tor of the just,
4. Soon will the poor and hun - gry of the earth
5. All glo - ry be to God, Cre - a - tor blest,
1. My spir - it sings to God, my sav - ing God,
2. And all the earth will come to call me blest.
3. Will guard the weak and raise them from the dust.
4. Be rich - ly blest, be giv - en great - er worth.
5. To Je - sus Christ, God's love made man - i - fest,
1. Who on this day a - bove all oth - ers fa - vored me
2. Un-bound-ed love and mer - cy sure will I pro - claim
3. But might - y kings will swift - ly fall from thrones cor - rupt.
4. And Is - ra - el, as once fore-told to A - bra - ham,
5. And to the Ho - ly Spir - it, gen - tle Com - fort - er,
1. And raised me up, a light for all to see.
2. For all who know and praise God's ho - ly name.
3. The strong brought low, the low - ly lift - ed up.
4. Will live in peace through-out the prom-ised land.
5. All glo - ry be, both now and ev - er - more.

Text: Based on Luke 1:46–55; Owen Alstott, b. 1947,
Music: Bernadette Farrell, b. 1957,

LUKE 2: SONG OF SIMEON

Now, O God, let your ser - vant go.

Let me go in peace ac - cord - ing to your word.

For my eyes be - hold your sav - ing work:

1
a light for all the world, al - le - lu - ia.

Final
Al - le - lu - ia, al - le - lu - ia.

Text: Based on Luke 2:29–32; *Nunc dimittis*; Janèt Sullivan Whitaker, b. 1958.
Music: Janèt Sullivan Whitaker.

Guidelines for the Reception of Communion

For Catholics: As Catholics, we fully participate in the celebration of the Eucharist when we receive Holy Communion. We are encouraged to receive Communion devoutly and frequently. In order to be properly disposed to receive Communion, participants should not be conscious of grave sin and normally should have fasted for one hour. A person who is conscious of grave sin is not to receive the Body and Blood of the Lord without prior sacramental confession except for a grave reason where there is no opportunity for confession. In this case, the person is to be mindful of the obligation to make an act of perfect contrition, including the intention of confessing as soon as possible *(Code of Canon Law, canon 916)*. A frequent reception of the Sacrament of Penance is encouraged for all.

For our fellow Christians: We welcome our fellow Christians to this celebration of the Eucharist as our brothers and sisters. We pray that our common baptism and the action of the Holy Spirit in this Eucharist will draw us closer to one another and begin to dispel the sad divisions which separate us. We pray that these will lessen and finally disappear, in keeping with Christ's prayer for us "that they may all be one" *(Jn 17:21)*.

Because Catholics believe that the celebration of the Eucharist is a sign of the reality of the oneness of faith, life, and worship, members of those churches with whom we are not yet fully united are ordinarily not admitted to Holy Communion. Eucharistic sharing in exceptional circumstances by other Christians requires permission according to the directives of the diocesan bishop and the provisions of canon law *(canon 844 § 4)*. Members of the Orthodox Churches, the Assyrian Church of the East, and the Polish National Catholic Church are urged to respect the discipline of their own Churches. According to Roman Catholic discipline, the Code of Canon Law does not object to the reception of communion by Christians of these Churches *(canon 844 § 3)*.

For those not receiving Holy Communion: All who are not receiving Holy Communion are encouraged to express in their hearts a prayerful desire for unity with the Lord Jesus and with one another.

For non-Christians: We also welcome to this celebration those who do not share our faith in Jesus Christ. While we cannot admit them to Holy Communion, we ask them to offer their prayers for the peace and the unity of the human family.

HYMNS & SONGS

"Thankfully sing to God psalms, hymns and holy songs" (Colossians 3:16). From the earliest centuries of Christianity, hymns and songs have played a major role in the liturgies and devotions of the faithful. A hymn is a song of praise or thanksgiving to God. All hymns are songs; but in contemporary liturgy the term "song" includes a wide variety of other musical forms: verse-refrain, litany, ostinato, chant, acclamation, spiritual and call-response. Often, but not always, liturgical song is based on scripture. Songs bring to expression and realize externally the inner attitudes of adoration, joy, sadness or petition, and they draw together in unity the diverse dispositions of community members. "A liturgical celebration can have no more solemn or pleasing feature than the whole assembly's expressing its faith and devotion in song." (Musicam Sacram, No. 16) *St. Augustine said simply, "They who love, sing."*

SEASONS AND SOLEMNITIES OF THE LORD

COME, THOU LONG-EXPECTED JESUS 212

1. Come, thou long - ex - pect - ed Je - sus, Born to
2. Is - rael's strength and con - so - la - tion, Hope of
3. Born thy peo - ple to de - liv - er, Born a
4. By thine own e - ter - nal Spir - it Rule in
1. set thy peo - ple free! From our fears and
2. all the earth thou art; Dear de - sire of
3. child, and yet a king: Born to reign in
4. all our hearts a - lone; By thine all - suf -
1. sins re - lease us, Let us find our rest in thee.
2. ev - 'ry na - tion, Joy of ev - 'ry long - ing heart.
3. us for - ev - er, Now thy gra - cious king - dom bring.
4. fi - cient mer - it Raise us to thy glo - rious throne.

Text: 87 87; Charles Wesley, 1707–1788.
Music: STUTTGART; Christian F. Witt's *Psalmodia Sacra*, Gotha, 1715; adapt. by Henry J. Gauntlett, 1805–1876.

213 A Voice Cries Out

Verse 1
1. Con - sole my peo - ple, the ones dear to me; speak to the
1. heart of Je - ru - sa - lem: the time of your mourn - ing is
1. end - ed now, the Lord of life will come.
Refrain
A voice cries out in the wil - der - ness: "Pre - pare a
way for the Lord!" A voice cries out in the wil - der -
ness: "Make straight a high - way for God!"
Verses 2, 4
2. Ev - 'ry val - ley is made a plain, ev - 'ry moun - tain is
4. Zi - on, shout from the moun - tain top, lift up your voice, O Je -
2. lev - eled; the glo - ry of God shall then be re -
4. ru - sa - lem, and say to the peo - ple of God's own
to Refrain
2. vealed, and the na - tions will sing in praise.
4. land, "Be - hold, be - hold your God!"
Verse 3
3. A voice shouts: "Cry!" O what shall I cry? All flesh is like
3. grass and its flow - ers: the grass may with - er, the

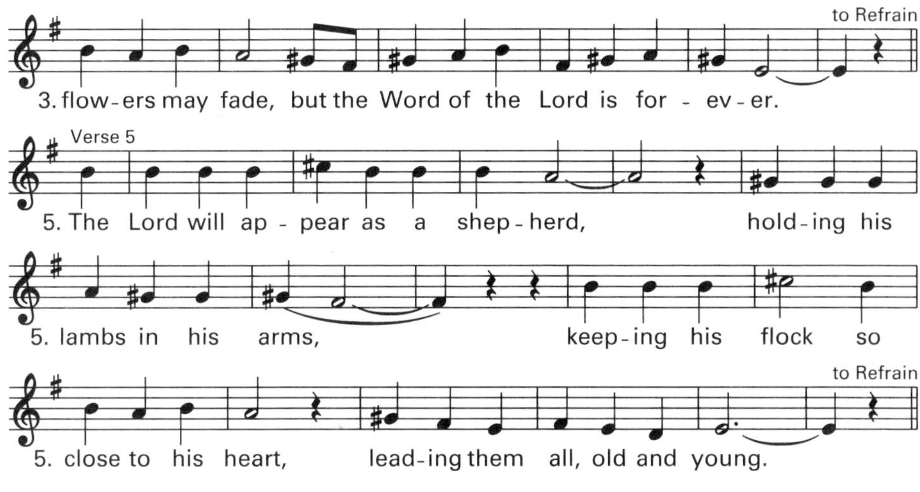
to Refrain
3. flow-ers may fade, but the Word of the Lord is for - ev - er.
Verse 5
5. The Lord will ap - pear as a shep - herd, hold - ing his
5. lambs in his arms, keep - ing his flock so
to Refrain
5. close to his heart, lead - ing them all, old and young.

Text: Based on Isaiah 40:1–11; Michael Joncas, b. 1951.
Music: Michael Joncas.

Beyond the Moon and Stars 214

Refrain

Be-yond the moon and stars, as deep as night, so great our hun-ger, Lord, to see your light. The spar-row finds her home be-neath your wing. So may we come to rest where an-gels sing.

Verses

1. Our eyes have longed to see your lov - ing face, to live with - in your courts for all our days.
2. Your roads have led us, Lord, 'cross des - ert sand. We place our hopes and dreams with - in your hand.
3. Up - on our dark - ness, Lord, a light has shone. You chose to dwell with us in flesh and bone.
4. With shin - ing star at night, and cloud by day, you brought us here to see your love's dis - play.
5. When life's great jour - ney ends, and day is done, then may our eyes be - hold your Ho - ly One.

to Refrain

215 Christ, Circle Round Us

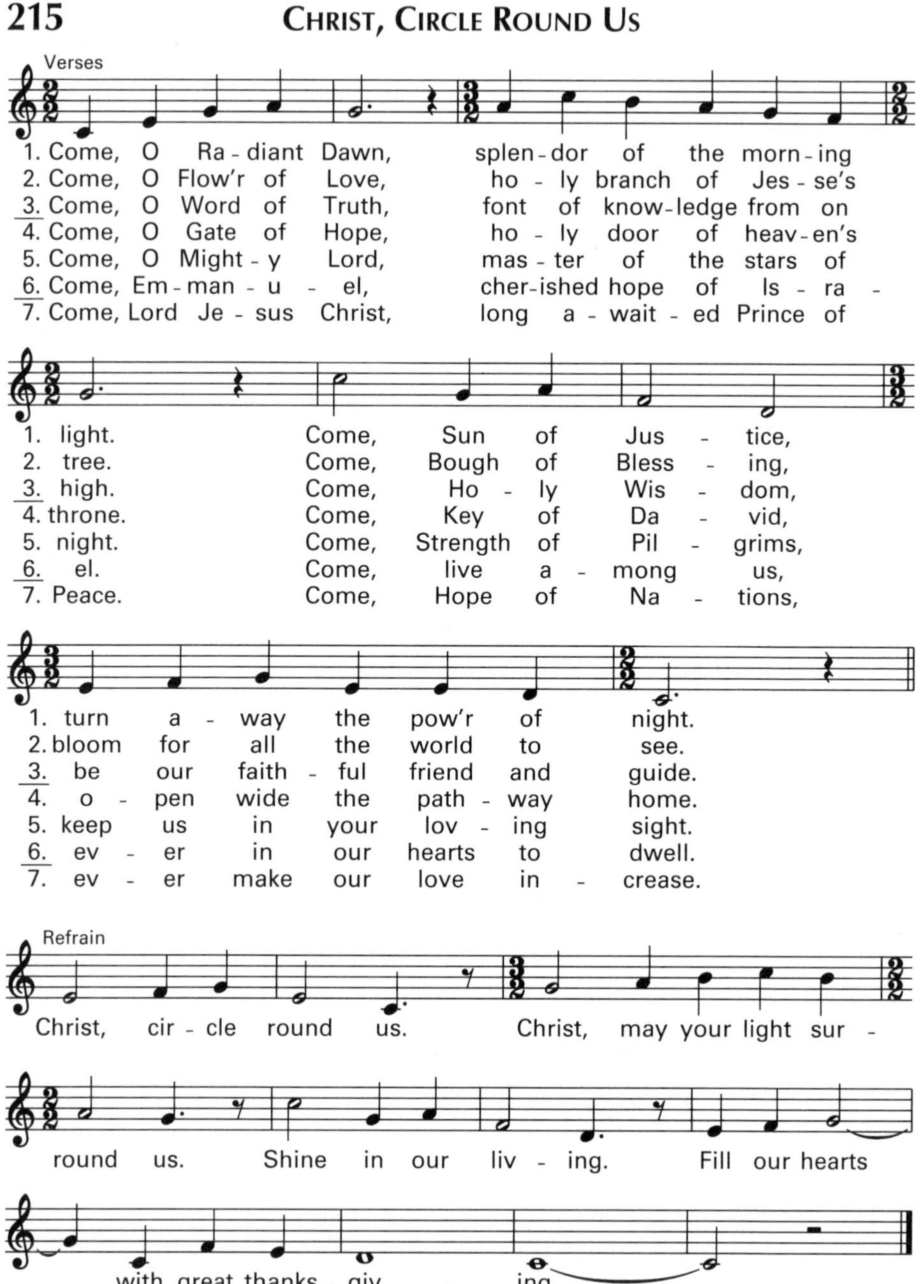
Verses
1. Come, O Ra - diant Dawn, splen - dor of the morn - ing light. Come, Sun of Jus - tice, turn a - way the pow'r of night.
2. Come, O Flow'r of Love, ho - ly branch of Jes - se's tree. Come, Bough of Bless - ing, bloom for all the world to see.
3. Come, O Word of Truth, font of know - ledge from on high. Come, Ho - ly Wis - dom, be our faith - ful friend and guide.
4. Come, O Gate of Hope, ho - ly door of heav - en's throne. Come, Key of Da - vid, o - pen wide the path - way home.
5. Come, O Might - y Lord, mas - ter of the stars of night. Come, Strength of Pil - grims, keep us in your lov - ing sight.
6. Come, Em - man - u - el, cher - ished hope of Is - ra - el. Come, live a - mong us, ev - er in our hearts to dwell.
7. Come, Lord Je - sus Christ, long a - wait - ed Prince of Peace. Come, Hope of Na - tions, ev - er make our love in - crease.
Refrain
Christ, cir - cle round us. Christ, may your light sur - round us. Shine in our liv - ing. Fill our hearts with great thanks - giv - ing.

Text: Based on Advent *'O' Antiphons*; Dan Schutte, b. 1947.
Music: Based on *Salve Regina* (Chant, Mode V); Dan Schutte.

READY THE WAY 216

Refrain
*
Read-y the way, read-y the way, read-y the way
1
2
of the Lord. of the Lord.
Verse 1
1. Make straight the road, raise the val - leys, and
1. moun-tains make low. Turn-ing from sin, let the bro-ken be whole,
to Refrain
1. and read-y the way of the Lord.
Verses 2, 3
2. As we wait for you, give us the strength to walk
3. Let us see your face; in our hearts we pre-
2. in your truth, so we may love more like you
3. -pare a place. Come bring this world your mer - cy and grace
to Refrain
2. and
3. as we
read-y the way for you, Lord.

*Last time: Repeat final phrase twice.

Text: Based on Isaiah 40:3, 4a; Curtis Stephan, b. 1973.
Music: Curtis Stephan.

217 Creator of the Stars of Night

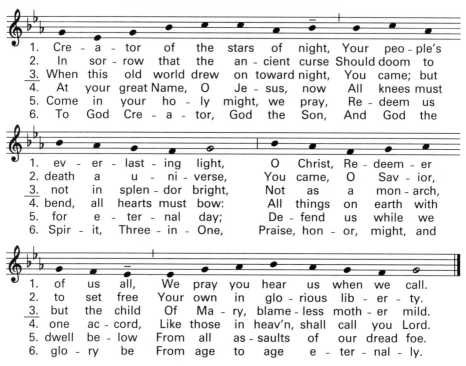

1. Cre - a - tor of the stars of night, Your peo - ple's
2. In sor - row that the an - cient curse Should doom to
3. When this old world drew on toward night, You came; but
4. At your great Name, O Je - sus, now All knees must
5. Come in your ho - ly might, we pray, Re - deem us
6. To God Cre - a - tor, God the Son, And God the

1. ev - er - last - ing light, O Christ, Re - deem - er
2. death a u - ni - verse, You came, O Sav - ior,
3. not in splen - dor bright, Not as a mon - arch,
4. bend, all hearts must bow: All things on earth with
5. for e - ter - nal day; De - fend us while we
6. Spir - it, Three - in - One, Praise, hon - or, might, and

1. of us all, We pray you hear us when we call.
2. to set free Your own in glo - rious lib - er - ty.
3. but the child Of Ma - ry, blame - less moth - er mild.
4. one ac - cord, Like those in heav'n, shall call you Lord.
5. dwell be - low From all as - saults of our dread foe.
6. glo - ry be From age to age e - ter - nal - ly.

Text: LM; Latin, 9th cent.; tr. fr. *The Hymnal 1982*, © 1985, The Church Pension Fund.

Music: CONDITOR ALME SIDERUM; Chant, Mode IV.

218 On Jordan's Bank

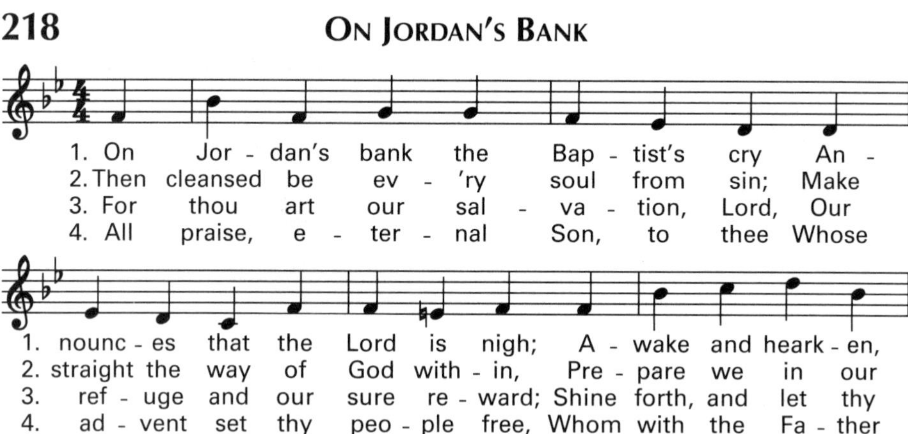
1. On Jor - dan's bank the Bap - tist's cry An -
2. Then cleansed be ev - 'ry soul from sin; Make
3. For thou art our sal - va - tion, Lord, Our
4. All praise, e - ter - nal Son, to thee Whose
1. nounc - es that the Lord is nigh; A - wake and heark - en,
2. straight the way of God with - in, Pre - pare we in our
3. ref - uge and our sure re - ward; Shine forth, and let thy
4. ad - vent set thy peo - ple free, Whom with the Fa - ther

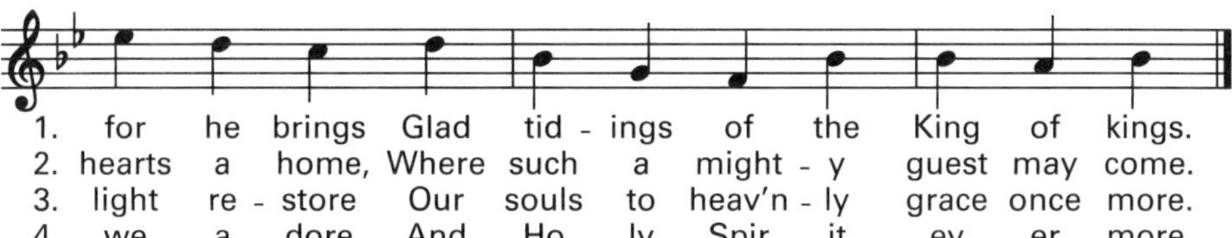
1. for he brings Glad tid - ings of the King of kings.
2. hearts a home, Where such a might - y guest may come.
3. light re - store Our souls to heav'n - ly grace once more.
4. we a - dore And Ho - ly Spir - it ev - er - more.

Text: LM; Charles Coffin, 1676–1749; tr. by John Chandler, 1806–1876, alt.
Music: WINCHESTER NEW; Georg Wittwe's *Musikalisches Hand-Buch*, Hamburg, 1690; adapt. by William H. Havergal, 1793–1870.

219 EMMANUEL

Refrain

Come, come, Em-man - u-el! Son of God, ap-pear. Heav-en and
earth, re-joice! Sal - va-tion is draw-ing near. 

Verses

1. O come, O come, Em - man - u - el,
That mourns in lone - ly ex - ile here
2. O come, O Wis - dom from on high,
To us the path of knowl-edge show,
3. O come, O Rod of Jes - se's stem;
That trust your might - y pow'r to save,
4. O come, De - sire of na - tions, bind
Make all our sad di - vi - sions cease,
5. Re - joice! Em - man - u - el
Re - joice! Em - man - u - el

(to Refrain)

1. And ran - som cap - tive Is - ra - el,
Un - til the Son of God ap - pear.
2. Who or - dered all things might - i - ly;
And teach us in her ways to go.
3. From ev - 'ry foe de - liv - er them
And give them vic - t'ry o'er the grave.
4. In one the hearts of hu - man - kind;
And be for us the King of Peace.
5. shall come to thee, O Is - ra - el.
shall come to thee, O Is - ra - el. *(Fine)*

Text: Refrain, Steve Angrisano, b. 1965, © 2004, Steve Angrisano.
 Verses based on *'O' Antiphons*.
Music: Steve Angrisano,

220 MARANATHA

Refrain

Come, O Lord, and set us free. Ma - ra - na - tha.

Verses

1. Des - ert and dry land will grow green in praise; clay will re-
2. Strength-en the hearts of the fear - ful and weak; be strong; fear
3. We have been wait-ing and long - ing for light; watch-ing for
4. Give us a star in the sky day and night; sign of your
5. Shep - herd of Is - ra - el rise and shine forth; rouse up your

1. joice with full bloom. Show - ers of flow - ers giv'n
2. not, God is near. Com - ing in pow - er and
3. signs of the Lord. "Prom - ised of a - ges," "Mes-
4. prom - ise to save. O - ver the moun-tains we
5. pow - er to save. Look down up - on us; take

to Refrain

1. birth in dead earth; in col - ors they ech - o his song.
2. loos-ing our bonds; ___ set-ting the cap - tives free.
3. si - ah to come," ___ hear us, we beg you: "Come, save!"
4. fol - low its light ___ hop-ing for sign of your life.
5. care of this vine: ___ care for the work of your hand.

Text: Based on Isaiah 35; Romans 13; James 5; Tim Schoenbachler, b. 1952.
Music: Tim Schoenbachler.

221 EVERY VALLEY

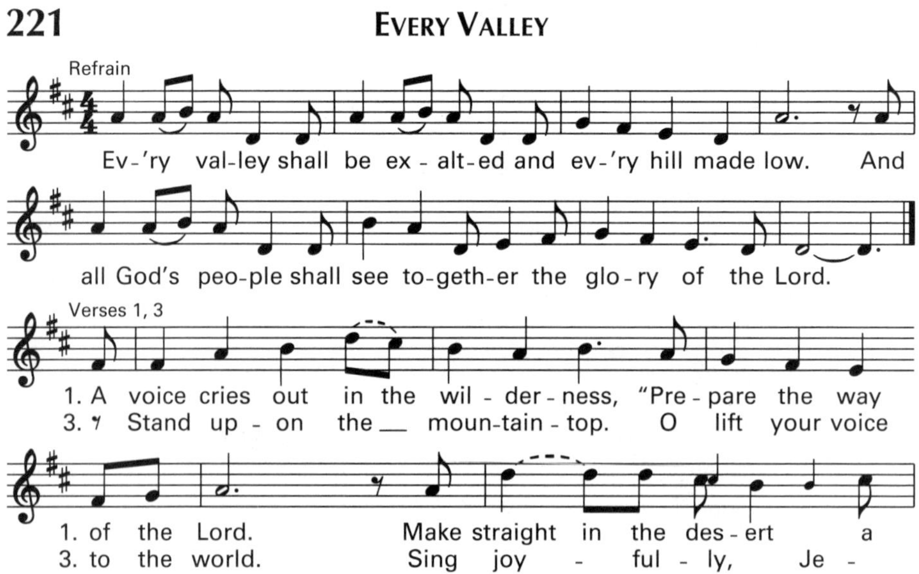
Refrain
Ev-'ry val-ley shall be ex - alt-ed and ev-'ry hill made low. And
all God's peo-ple shall see to-geth-er the glo - ry of the Lord.
Verses 1, 3
1. A voice cries out in the wil - der - ness, "Pre - pare the way
3. Stand up - on the ___ moun-tain - top. O lift your voice
1. of the Lord. Make straight in the des - ert a
3. to the world. Sing joy - ful - ly, Je -

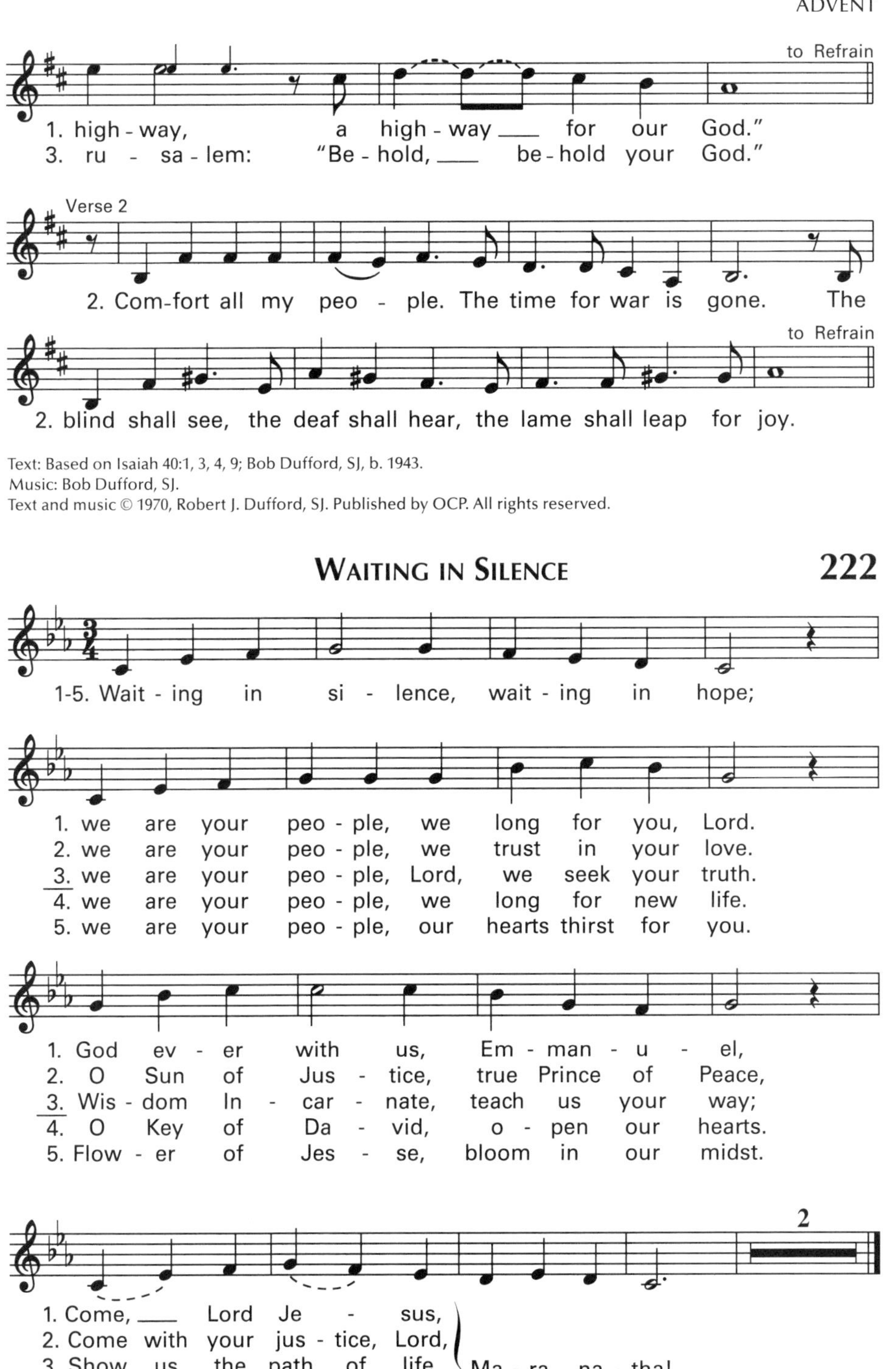
to Refrain
1. high - way, a high - way ___ for our God."
3. ru - sa - lem: "Be - hold, ___ be - hold your God."
Verse 2
2. Com-fort all my peo - ple. The time for war is gone. The
to Refrain
2. blind shall see, the deaf shall hear, the lame shall leap for joy.
1-5. Wait - ing in si - lence, wait - ing in hope;
1. we are your peo - ple, we long for you, Lord.
2. we are your peo - ple, we trust in your love.
3. we are your peo - ple, Lord, we seek your truth.
4. we are your peo - ple, we long for new life.
5. we are your peo - ple, our hearts thirst for you.
1. God ev - er with us, Em - man - u - el,
2. O Sun of Jus - tice, true Prince of Peace,
3. Wis - dom In - car - nate, teach us your way;
4. O Key of Da - vid, o - pen our hearts.
5. Flow - er of Jes - se, bloom in our midst.
2
1. Come, ___ Lord Je - sus,
2. Come with your jus - tice, Lord,
3. Show us the path of life,
4. Give us new vi - sion, Lord,
5. Make us your gar - den, Lord,
Ma - ra - na - tha!

Text: Based on Isaiah 40:1, 3, 4, 9; Bob Dufford, SJ, b. 1943.
Music: Bob Dufford, SJ.

Waiting in Silence 222

223 People, Look East

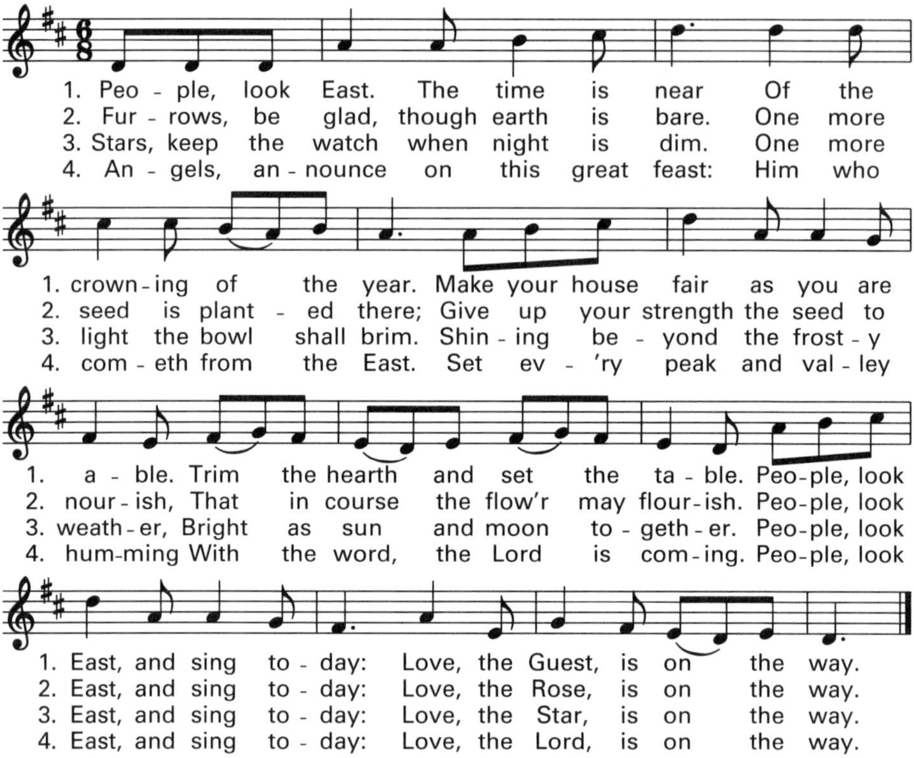

1. Peo - ple, look East. The time is near Of the
2. Fur - rows, be glad, though earth is bare. One more
3. Stars, keep the watch when night is dim. One more
4. An - gels, an - nounce on this great feast: Him who

1. crown - ing of the year. Make your house fair as you are
2. seed is plant - ed there; Give up your strength the seed to
3. light the bowl shall brim. Shin - ing be - yond the frost - y
4. com - eth from the East. Set ev - 'ry peak and val - ley

1. a - ble. Trim the hearth and set the ta - ble. Peo-ple, look
2. nour - ish, That in course the flow'r may flour - ish. Peo-ple, look
3. weath - er, Bright as sun and moon to - geth - er. Peo-ple, look
4. hum-ming With the word, the Lord is com - ing. Peo-ple, look

1. East, and sing to - day: Love, the Guest, is on the way.
2. East, and sing to - day: Love, the Rose, is on the way.
3. East, and sing to - day: Love, the Star, is on the way.
4. East, and sing to - day: Love, the Lord, is on the way.

Text: 87 98 87; *The Oxford Book of Carols,* 1928; Eleanor Farjeon, 1881–1965, © 1957, Eleanor Farjeon. All rights reserved. Reprinted by permission of Harold Ober Assoc., Inc.
Music: BESANÇON; trad. French carol.

224 Patience, People

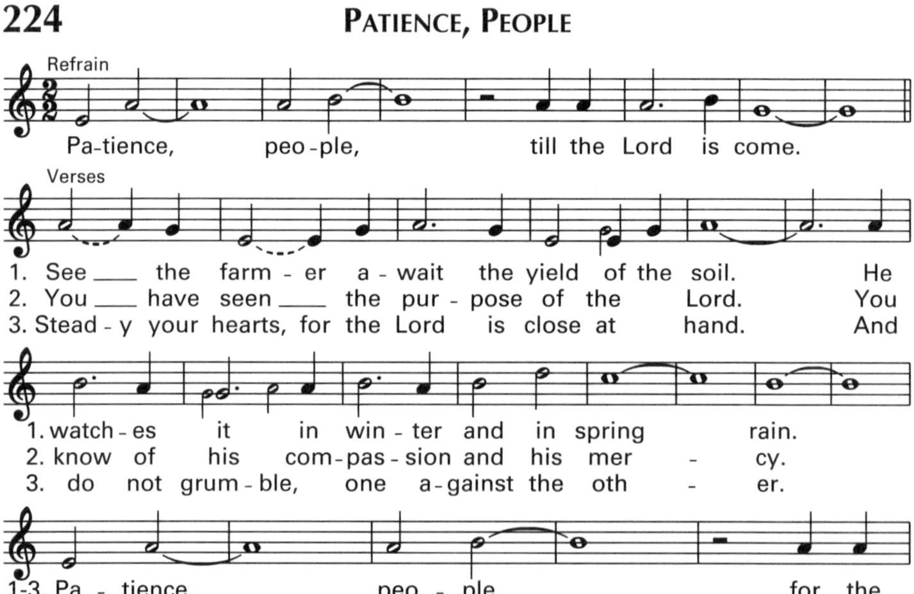
Refrain
Pa-tience, peo - ple, till the Lord is come.
Verses
1. See ___ the farm - er a - wait the yield of the soil. He
2. You ___ have seen ___ the pur - pose of the Lord. You
3. Stead - y your hearts, for the Lord is close at hand. And
1. watch - es it in win - ter and in spring rain.
2. know of his com - pas - sion and his mer - cy.
3. do not grum - ble, one a - gainst the oth - er.
1-3. Pa - tience, peo - ple, for the

2
1-3. Lord is com - ing.

Text: Based on James 5:7–9, 11; John Foley, S.J., b. 1939.
Music: John Foley, S.J.

LET THE KING OF GLORY COME 225

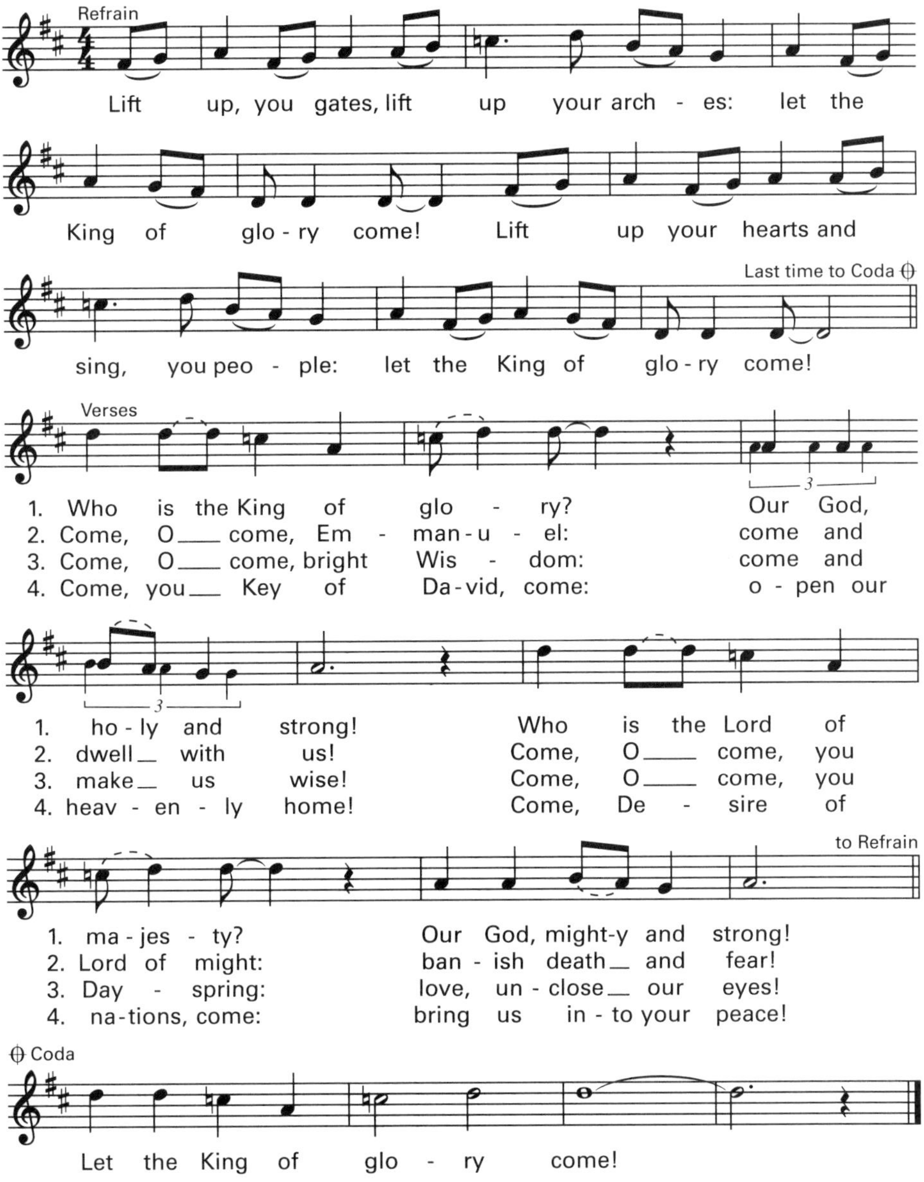

Refrain

Lift up, you gates, lift up your arch - es: let the
King of glo - ry come! Lift up your hearts and
sing, you peo - ple: let the King of glo - ry come!

Last time to Coda

Verses

1. Who is the King of glo - ry? Our God, ho - ly and strong! Who is the Lord of ma - jes - ty? Our God, might-y and strong!
2. Come, O come, Em - man - u - el: come and dwell with us! Come, O come, you Lord of might: ban - ish death and fear!
3. Come, O come, bright Wis - dom: come and make us wise! Come, O come, you Day - spring: love, un - close our eyes!
4. Come, you Key of Da-vid, come: o - pen our heav - en - ly home! Come, De - sire of na-tions, come: bring us in - to your peace!

to Refrain

Coda

Let the King of glo - ry come!

Text: Based on Psalm 24 and the *'O' Antiphons*; Michael Joncas, b. 1951,
Music: Michael Joncas,

226 THE KING SHALL COME WHEN MORNING DAWNS

1. The King shall come when morn - ing dawns And
2. Not, as of old, a lit - tle child, To
3. O bright - er than the ris - ing morn When
4. O bright - er than that glo - rious morn Shall
5. The King shall come when morn - ing dawns And
1. light tri - um - phant breaks, When beau - ty gilds the
2. bear, and fight, and die, But crowned with glo - ry
3. he, vic - to - rious, rose And left the lone-some
4. this fair morn - ing be, When Christ, our King, in
5. light and beau - ty brings. Hail, Christ, the Lord! Thy
1. east - ern hills And life to joy a - wakes.
2. like the sun That lights the morn - ing sky.
3. place of death, De - spite the rage of foes.
4. beau - ty comes, And we his face shall see!
5. peo - ple pray: Come quick - ly King of kings.

Text: CM; Greek; tr. by John Brownlie, 1859–1925, alt.
Music: MORNING SONG; *Sixteen Tune Settings*, Philadelphia, 1812; *Kentucky Harmony*, 1816.

227 LET THE VALLEYS BE RAISED

Refrain

Let the val - leys be raised and the moun - tains made low. Ev-'ry mead-
- ow and field o-ver-turn. Make the path - way straight
and the high-way run smooth for the com - ing of God in our day.

Verses

1. God, ___ you come to your peo - ple as you prom-
2. You, lit-tle ___ child, go be - fore him like the proph-
3. God, ___ you come like the morn - ing on the dark-

1. - ised of old. You have raised up a Sav-
2. - ets of old, bring-ing news of his com-
3. - ness of night, as a light to the peo-

to Refrain
1. - ior in the sight of us all.
2. - ing by the mer - cy of God.
3. - ple, like the break - ing of day.

Text: Based on Isaiah 40:3–5; Luke 1:68–79; Dan Schutte, b. 1947.
Music: Dan Schutte.

O Come, O Come, Emmanuel 228

Verses

1. O come, O come, Em - man - u - el, And
2. O come, Thou Wis - dom from on high, Who
3. O come, O come, Thou Lord of might, Who
4. O come, Thou Rod of Jes - se's stem, From
5. O come, Thou Key of Da - vid, come, And
6. O come, Thou Day - spring from on high And
7. O come, De - sire of na - tions, bind In

1. ran - som cap - tive Is - ra - el, That mourns in
2. or - d'rest all things might - i - ly; To us the
3. to thy tribes on Si - nai's height In an - cient
4. ev - 'ry foe de - liv - er them That trust thy
5. o - pen wide our heav - 'nly home; Make safe the
6. cheer us by thy draw - ing nigh; Dis - perse the
7. one the hearts of all ___ hu - man - kind; Bid thou our

1. lone - ly ex - ile here Un - til the Son of
2. path of knowl - edge show, And teach us in her
3. times didst give the law, In cloud and maj - es -
4. might - y pow'r to save, And give them vic - t'ry
5. way that leads on high, And close the path to
6. gloom - y clouds of night, And death's dark shad - ow
7. sad di - vi - sions cease, And be thy - self our

1. God ap - pear.
2. ways to go.
3. ty and awe.
4. o'er the grave.
5. mis - er - y.
6. put to flight.
7. Prince of Peace.

Refrain

Re - joice! Re - joice! Em - man - u - el Shall come to thee, O Is - ra - el!

Text: LM with refrain; Latin, 9th cent.; verses 1, 3–6, para. in *Psalteriolum Cantionum Catholicarum*, Cologne, 1710; tr. by John Mason Neale, 1818–1866; verses 2, 7 tr. fr. *The Hymnal 1940*, alt.
Music: VENI, VENI, EMMANUEL; Chant, Mode I; *Processionale*, French, 15th cent.; adapt. by Thomas Helmore, 1811–1890.

229 Save Us, O Lord

Refrain
Save us, O Lord; car-ry us back. Rouse your pow-er and come.
Res-cue your peo-ple; show us your face. Bring us back.
Verse 1
1. O Shep-herd of Is - ra - el, hear us. Re - turn and we shall be
1. saved. A - rise, O Lord; hear our cries, O Lord: bring us back!
to Refrain
Verse 2
2. How long will you hide from your peo-ple? We long to
2. see your face. Give ear to us. Draw near to us, Lord God of hosts!
to Refrain
Verse 3
3. Turn a-gain; care for your vine; pro - tect what your
3. right hand has plant-ed. Your vine-yards are tram-pled, up -
3. root-ed, and burned. Come to us, Fa - ther of might!
to Refrain

Text: Based on Psalm 80; Bob Dufford, SJ, b. 1943.
Music: Bob Dufford, SJ.

READY THE WAY

Verses

1. "Read - y the way of the Lord! Read - y the
2. "Let ev - 'ry val - ley be filled. Let ev - 'ry
3. Des - ert and waste-land will bloom. Des - ert and
4. Those who are blind will then see. Those who are
5. Strength-en the ones who are weak. Strength-en the

1. way of the Lord!" A voice ___ cries out in the wil - der-
2. val - ley be filled. Let ev - 'ry moun-tain be hum -
3. waste-land will bloom. Glo - ry and splen - dor will fill the
4. deaf will then hear. Those who are lame will then leap for
5. ones who are weak. Say to the fright-ened: "Have cour -

1. ness: "Read - y the way of the Lord!" (to Verse 2)
2. bled; let ev - 'ry val - ley be filled." (to Refrain)
3. land. Des - ert and waste-land will bloom. (to Verse 4)
4. joy. Those who are mute will then sing. (to Refrain)
5. age." Strength-en the ones who are weak. (to Refrain)

Refrain
Here is your God, com-ing with your vin - di - ca - tion.
Look and be-hold the sav - ing pow - er of God.

1, 2 to Verses 3, 5 | Final

The sav - ing pow - er of God.

Text: Based on Isaiah 35:1–6; 40:1–5, 9–11; Ezekiel 11:19–20; Bob Hurd, b. 1950.
Music: Bob Hurd.

231 Alleluia! Hurry, the Lord Is Near

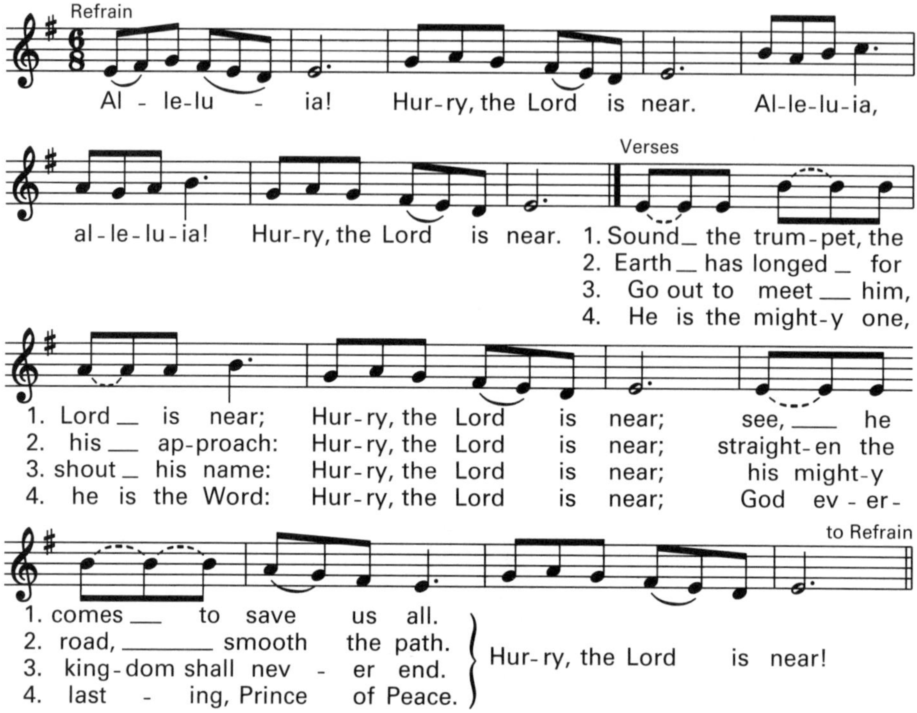

Refrain

Al - le-lu - ia! Hur-ry, the Lord is near. Al-le-lu-ia, al-le-lu-ia! Hur-ry, the Lord is near.

Verses

1. Sound_ the trum-pet, the Lord_ is near; Hur-ry, the Lord is near; see,_ he comes_ to save us all. Hur-ry, the Lord is near!
2. Earth_ has longed_ for his_ ap-proach: Hur-ry, the Lord is near; straight-en the road,_ smooth the path. Hur-ry, the Lord is near!
3. Go out to meet_ him, shout_ his name: Hur-ry, the Lord is near; his might-y king-dom shall nev - er end. Hur-ry, the Lord is near!
4. He is the might-y one, he is the Word: Hur-ry, the Lord is near; God ev - er-last - ing, Prince of Peace. Hur-ry, the Lord is near!

to Refrain

Text: Patrick Lee, b. 1930,
Music: Ernest Sands, b. 1949,

232 Advent Lamb of God

1, 2
Lamb of God, you take a-way the sins of the world, have mer - cy on
us, have mer - cy on us.
Final
world, grant us peace, grant us peace.

Music: Adapt. by Kevin Keil (ASCAP), b. 1956,

233 ADVENT/CHRISTMAS GOSPEL ACCLAMATION

Refrain: 1st time: Cantor, All repeat; thereafter: All

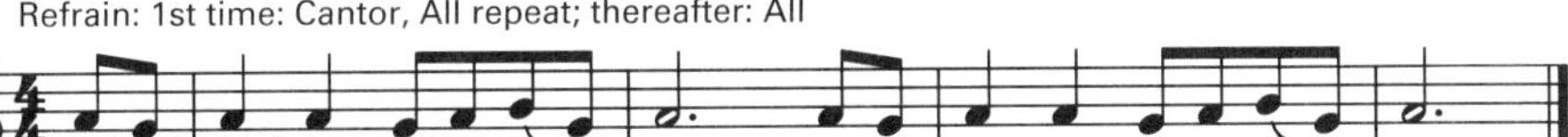
Al-le-lu-ia, al-le-lu - ia. Al-le-lu-ia, al-le-lu - ia.

*Verses 1-4

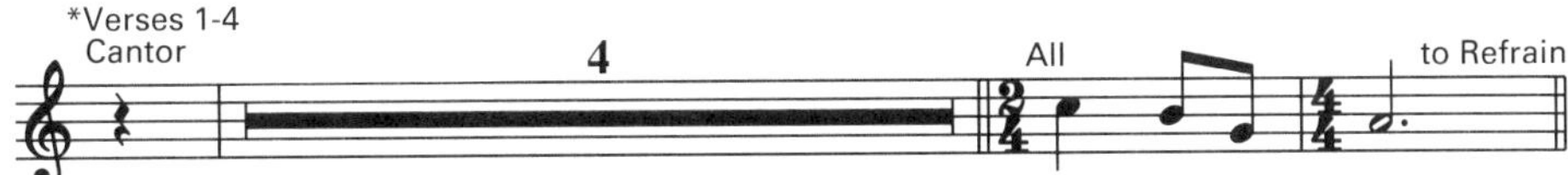
Cantor
4
All
to Refrain

1. You are the joy of ev'ry human heart, king of all the nations. Lord Je-sus, come!
2. You are Lord, our justice and our mercy. Show us how to live:
3. Eternal light, and sun of justice, shine in all our darkness:
4. Emmanuel, the joy of all nations, come to us and save us:

*Verses 5-7

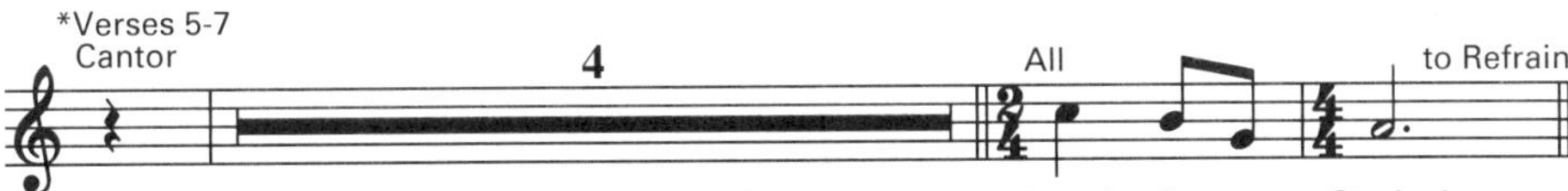
Cantor
4
All
to Refrain

5. Born today, our justice and our mercy, God in flesh among us: Lord, Je-sus Christ!
6. You are light that shines in the darkness, star to guide the nations:
7. You are born of water and the Spirit, fountain of our dreams:

*Verses 1–4, Advent; verse 5, Christmas; verse 6, Epiphany; verse 7, Baptism of the Lord.

Text and music: David Haas, b. 1957,

234 WAKE FROM YOUR SLEEP

1. Wake from your sleep, a Sav-ior is born. God's ho-ly child gives light to this morn, all our dark-ness to dis-pel. Praise to our God whose glo-ry we tell.
2. Come from your fields as shep-herds of old. Wel-come this child whom proph-ets fore-told. God has made the earth his home. Praise to our God, the Sav-ior has come.
3. Stay with us now, O Lord of the earth. Make of our hearts a place for your birth. Though our cares be great or small, Je-sus the Lord, be born in us all.
4. Now shall the earth take joy in her tears. Now shall our hearts be turned from their fears. All the earth shall sing God's praise. Je-sus the Lord, be born on this day.
4

Text and music: Dan Schutte, b. 1947,

235 O Come, All Ye Faithful/ Venid, Fieles Todos

Verses
1. O come, all ye faith - ful, joy - ful and tri - um - phant, O
2. Sing, choirs of an - gels, sing in ex - ul - ta - tion,
3. Yea, Lord, we greet thee, born this hap - py morn - ing,
4. Ad - é - ste fi - dé - les, lae - ti tri - um - phán - tes, Ve -
1. *Ve - nid, fie - les to - dos, a Be - lén va - ya - mos go -*
2. *En po - bre pe - se - bre ya - ce él re - cli - na - do, al*
3. *Can - tad ju - bi - lo - sas, ce - les - tes cria - tu - ras: re -*
4. *Je - sús, ce - le - bra - mos tu ben - di - to nom - bre con*
1. come ye, O come ye to Beth - le - hem;
2. Sing, all ye cit - i - zens of heav'n a - bove!
3. Je - sus, to thee be all glo - ry giv'n;
4. ní - te, ve - ní - te in Béth - le - hem.
1. *zo - sos, triun - fan - tes y lle - nos de a - mor, y al*
2. *mun - do o - fre - cien - do e - ter - na sal - va - ción. Al*
3. *sue - nen los cie - los con vues - tra can - ción. ¡Al*
4. *him - nos so - lem - nes de gra - to lo - or. Por*
1. Come and be - hold him, born the King of an - gels;
2. Glo - ry to God, all glo - ry in the high - est;
3. Word of the Fa - ther, now in flesh ap - pear - ing;
4. Na - tum vi - dé - te Re - gem an - ge - ló - rum.
1. *rey de los cie - los hu - mil - de ve - re - mos.*
2. *san - to Me - sí - as, el Ver - bo hu - ma - na - do,*
3. *Dios bon - da - do - so glo - ria en las al - tu - ras!*
4. *si - glos e - ter - nos la hu - ma - ni - dad te hon - re.*
Refrain
English O come, let us a - dore him, O come, let us a - dore him, O
Latin Ve - ní - te, a - do - ré - mus, ve - ní - te, a - do - ré - mus, ve -
Español *Ve - nid, a - do - re - mos, ve - nid, a - do - re - mos, ve -*
come, let us a - dore him, Christ, the Lord!
ní - te, a - do - ré - mus Dó - mi - num.
nid, a - do - re - mos a Cris - to el Se - ñor.

Text: Irregular with refrain; John F. Wade, ca. 1711–1786; English tr. by Frederick Oakeley, 1802–1880, alt.; Spanish tr. by Juan Bautista Cabrera, 1837–1916, alt.
Music: ADESTE FIDELES; John F. Wade.

ANGELS WE HAVE HEARD ON HIGH 236

Verses

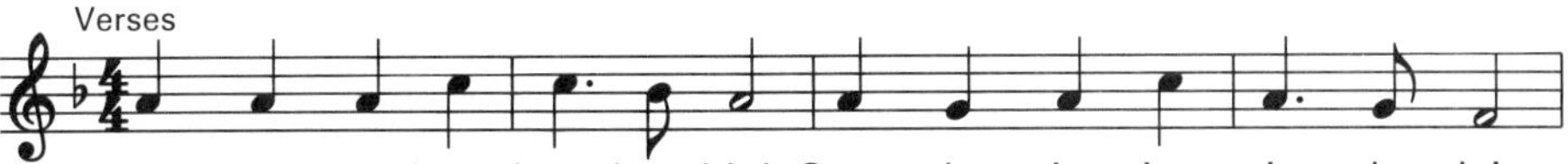

1. An - gels we have heard on high Sweet - ly sing - ing o'er the plains,
2. Shep - herds, why this ju - bi - lee? Why your joy - ous strains pro - long?
3. Come to Beth - le - hem and see Him whose birth the an - gels sing;
4. See him in a man - ger laid Whom the an - gels praise a - bove;

1. And the moun - tains in re - ply Ech - o back their joy - ous strains.
2. Say what may the tid - ings be Which in - spire your heav'n - ly song.
3. Come, a - dore on bend - ed knee Christ, the Lord, the new - born King.
4. Ma - ry, Jo - seph, lend your aid, While we raise our hearts in love.

Refrain
Glo - ri - a in ex - cel - sis De - o!
Glo - ri - a in ex - cel - sis De - o!

Text: 77 77 with refrain; trad. French carol, ca. 18th cent.; tr. fr. *Crown of Jesus Music, II*, London, 1862; tr. by James Chadwick, 1813–1882, and others, alt.
Music: GLORIA; trad. French carol.

CHILDREN, RUN JOYFULLY 237

Refrain

Chil - dren, run joy - ful - ly, Je - sus is born. Tell all the
moun - tains to sing. Pray to our Fa - ther in
heav - en this day: Thank you, for Je - sus is born.

Verse 1

Shepherds stood watching, keeping their sheep,
and suddenly angels appeared.
"Don't be afraid. We bring you great joy:
Your Savior is born this night."

Verse 2

"And this will be a sign to you:
the baby will lie in a manger
in the city of David, in Bethlehem.
Go now, visit your Lord."

Text: Verses based on Luke 2:8–12; Bob Dufford, SJ, b. 1943.
Music: Bob Dufford, SJ.

238 AWAY IN A MANGER

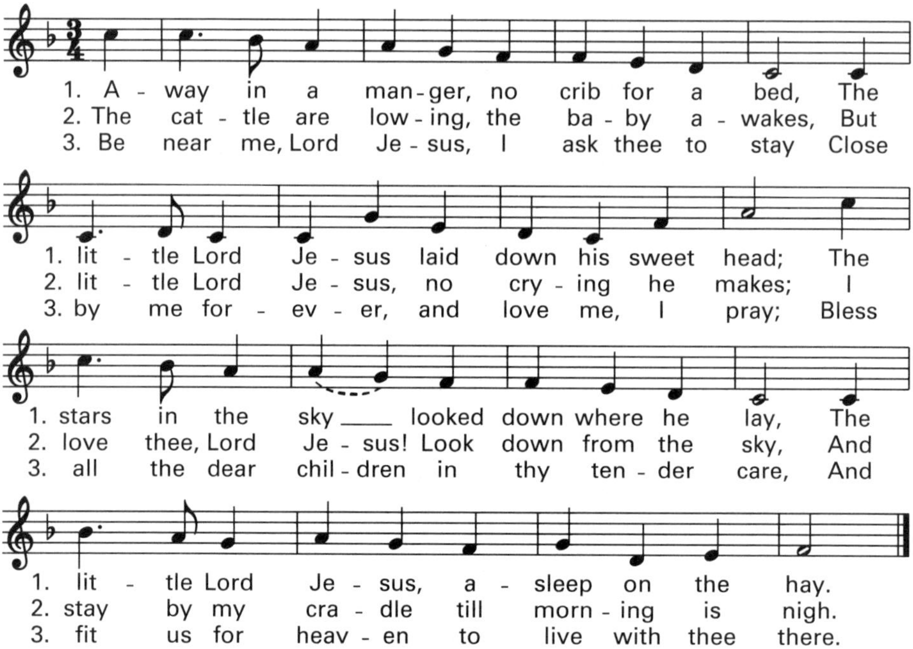

1. A - way in a man-ger, no crib for a bed, The
2. The cat - tle are low - ing, the ba - by a - wakes, But
3. Be near me, Lord Je - sus, I ask thee to stay Close

1. lit - tle Lord Je - sus laid down his sweet head; The
2. lit - tle Lord Je - sus, no cry - ing he makes; I
3. by me for - ev - er, and love me, I pray; Bless

1. stars in the sky ____ looked down where he lay, The
2. love thee, Lord Je - sus! Look down from the sky, And
3. all the dear chil - dren in thy ten - der care, And

1. lit - tle Lord Je - sus, a - sleep on the hay.
2. stay by my cra - dle till morn - ing is nigh.
3. fit us for heav - en to live with thee there.

Text: 11 11 11 11; verses 1–2, *Little Children's Book for Schools and Families*, ca. 1885; verse 3, John T. McFarland, 1851–1913; Gabriel's *Vineyard Songs*, 1892, alt.
Music: MUELLER; attr. to James R. Murray, 1841–1905.

239 GOOD CHRISTIAN FRIENDS, REJOICE

1-3. Good Chris-tian friends, re-joice, With heart and soul and voice;

1. Give ye heed to what we say: Je - sus Christ is born to - day!
2. Now ye hear of end - less bliss; Je - sus Christ was born for this!
3. Now ye need not fear the grave; Je - sus Christ was born to save!

1. Ox and ass be - fore him bow, And he is in the man-ger now.
2. He has o-pened heav-en's door, And we are blest for ev - er-more.
3. Calls you one and calls you all, To gain his ev - er - last - ing hall.

1. Christ is born to - day! Christ is born to - day!
2. Christ was born for this! Christ was born for this!
3. Christ was born to save! Christ was born to save!

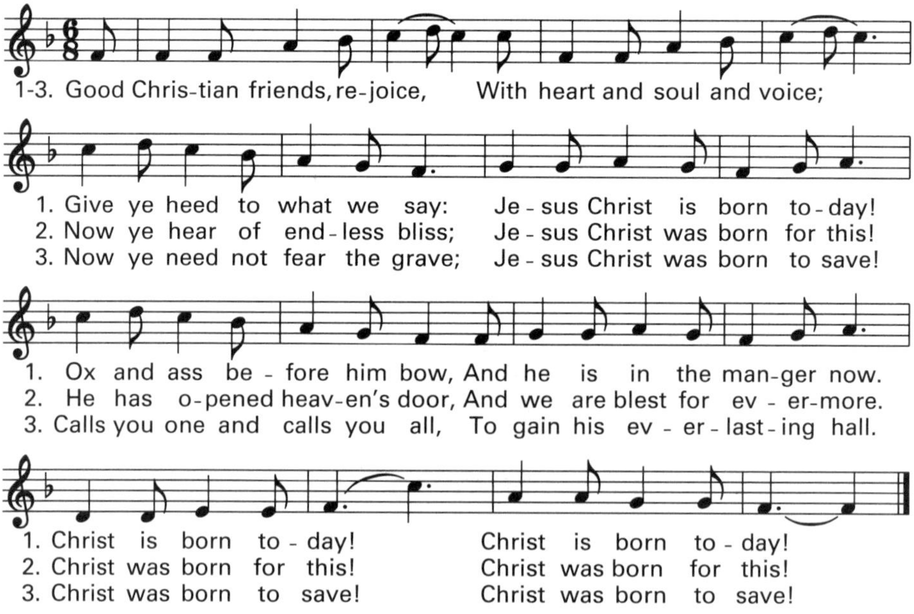

Text: 66 77 78 55; Latin and German, 14th cent.; tr. by John M. Neale, 1818–1866, alt.
Music: IN DULCI JUBILO; J. Klug's *Geistliche Lieder*, Wittenberg, 1535.

JOY TO THE WORLD 240

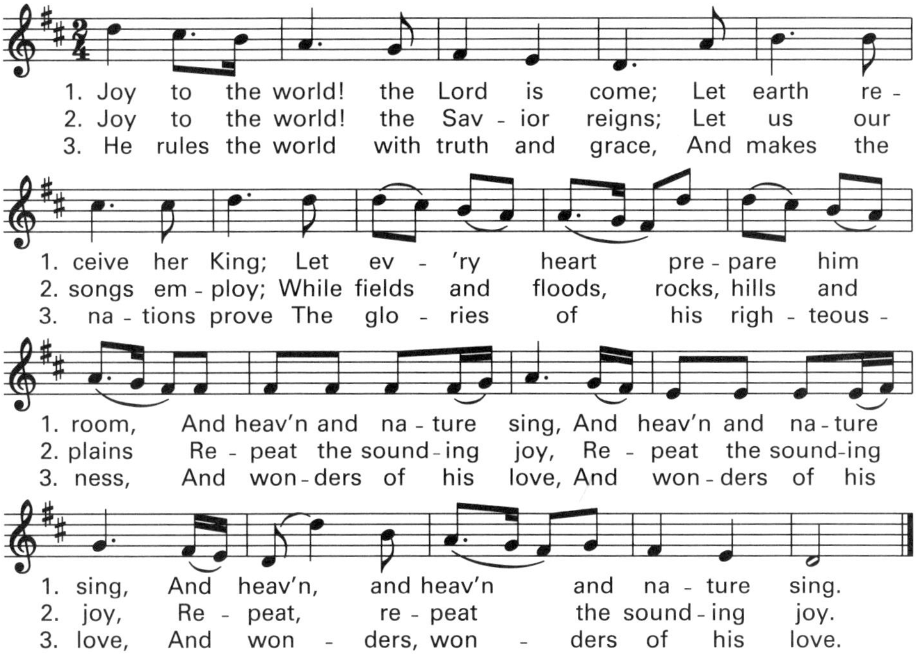

1. Joy to the world! the Lord is come; Let earth re - ceive her King; Let ev - 'ry heart pre - pare him room, And heav'n and na - ture sing, And heav'n and na - ture sing, And heav'n, and heav'n and na - ture sing.

2. Joy to the world! the Sav - ior reigns; Let us our songs em - ploy; While fields and floods, rocks, hills and plains Re - peat the sound - ing joy, Re - peat the sound - ing joy, Re - peat, re - peat the sound - ing joy.

3. He rules the world with truth and grace, And makes the na - tions prove The glo - ries of his righ - teous - ness, And won - ders of his love, And won - ders of his love, And won - ders, won - ders of his love.

Text: CM with repeats; based on Psalm 98:4–9; Isaac Watts, 1674–1748, alt.
Music: ANTIOCH; T. Hawkes' *Collection of Tunes*, 1833; George Frideric Handel, 1685–1759; adapt. by Lowell Mason, 1792–1872, alt.

WHO HAS KNOWN 241

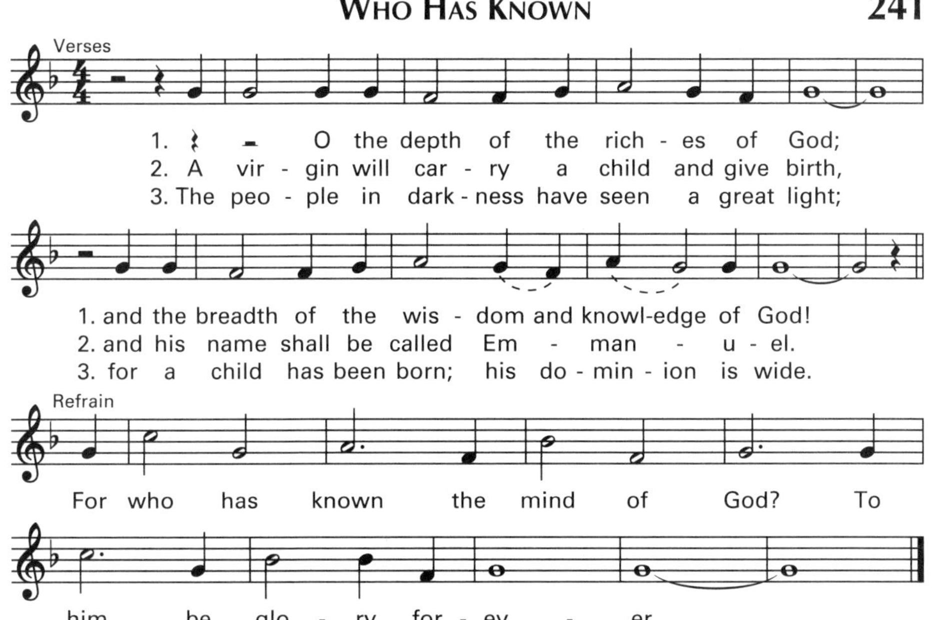
Verses
1. O the depth of the rich - es of God;
2. A vir - gin will car - ry a child and give birth,
3. The peo - ple in dark - ness have seen a great light;
1. and the breadth of the wis - dom and knowl-edge of God!
2. and his name shall be called Em - man - u - el.
3. for a child has been born; his do - min - ion is wide.
Refrain
For who has known the mind of God? To
him be glo - ry for - ev - er.

Text: Based on Isaiah 9, Matthew 1, Romans 11; John Foley, SJ, b. 1939.
Music: John Foley, SJ.

242 Go, Tell It on the Mountain

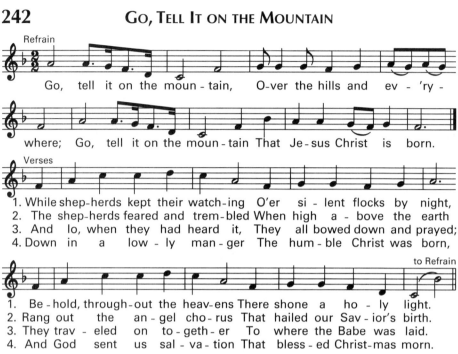

Refrain

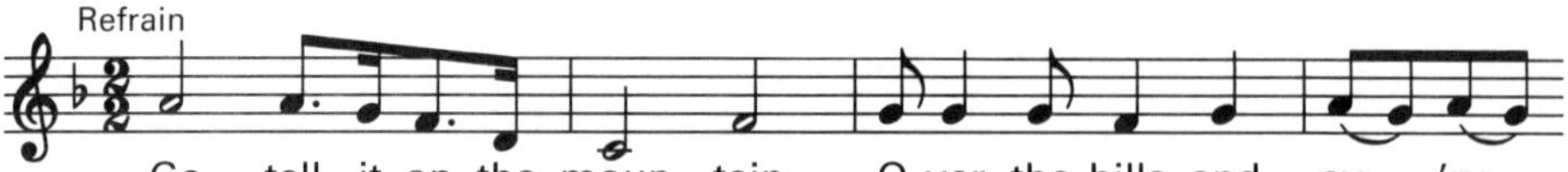

Go, tell it on the moun - tain, O-ver the hills and ev - 'ry - where; Go, tell it on the moun-tain That Je-sus Christ is born.

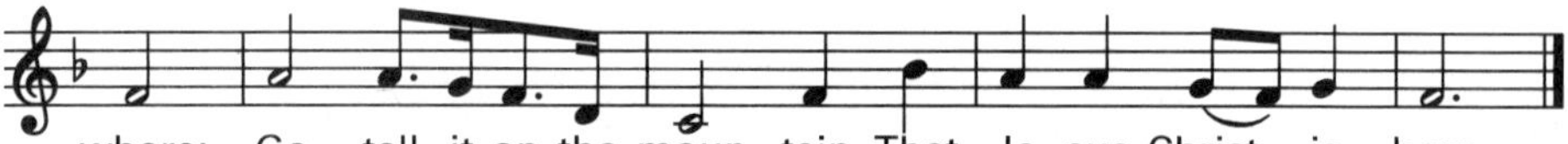

Verses

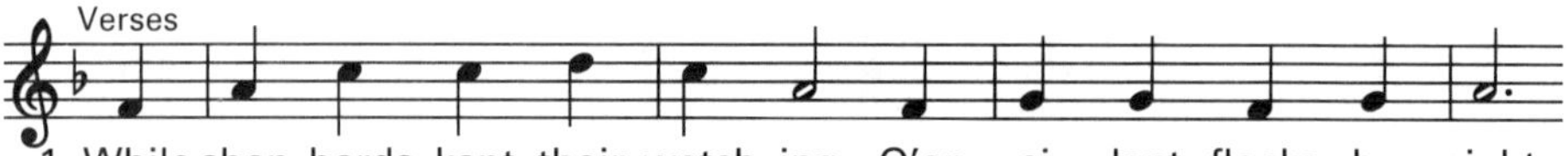

1. While shep-herds kept their watch-ing O'er si - lent flocks by night,
2. The shep-herds feared and trem-bled When high a - bove the earth
3. And lo, when they had heard it, They all bowed down and prayed;
4. Down in a low - ly man - ger The hum - ble Christ was born,

to Refrain

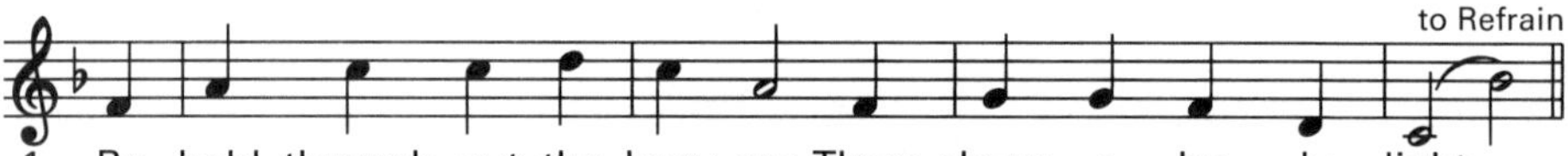

1. Be - hold, through-out the heav-ens There shone a ho - ly light.
2. Rang out the an - gel cho - rus That hailed our Sav - ior's birth.
3. They trav - eled on to - geth - er To where the Babe was laid.
4. And God sent us sal - va - tion That bless - ed Christ-mas morn.

Text: 76 76 with refrain; fr. *American Negro Songs and Spirituals,* 1940; John W. Work, Jr., 1872–1925, alt.
Music: GO TELL IT; Spiritual.

243 God Rest You Merry, Gentlemen

Verses

1. God rest you mer - ry, gen-tle-men, Let noth-ing you dis - may;
2. From God our heav'n-ly Fa - ther A bless-ed an - gel came,
3. "Fear not, then," said the an - gel, "Let noth-ing you af - fright;
4. Now to the Lord sing prais - es, All you with - in this place,

1. Re - mem-ber Christ our Sav - ior Was born on Christ-mas Day
2. And un - to cer - tain shep - herds Brought tid-ings of the same,
3. This day is born a Sav - ior Of Vir-gin pure and bright,
4. And with true love and char - i - ty Each oth - er now em - brace;

1. To save us all from Sa-tan's pow'r When we were gone a - stray.
2. How that in Beth - le - hem was born The Son of God by name.
3. To free all those who trust in him From Sa - tan's pow'r and might."
4. This ho - ly tide of Christ - mas Is filled with heav'n-ly grace.

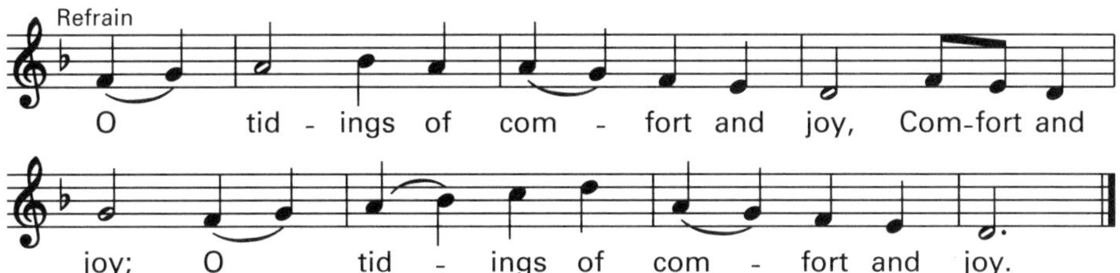
Refrain
O tid - ings of com - fort and joy, Com-fort and
joy; O tid - ings of com - fort and joy.

Text: 86 86 86 with refrain; trad. English carol, 18th cent.
Music: GOD REST YOU MERRY; trad. English carol; melody fr. *Little Book of Christmas Carols*, ca. 1846.

O Little Town of Bethlehem 244

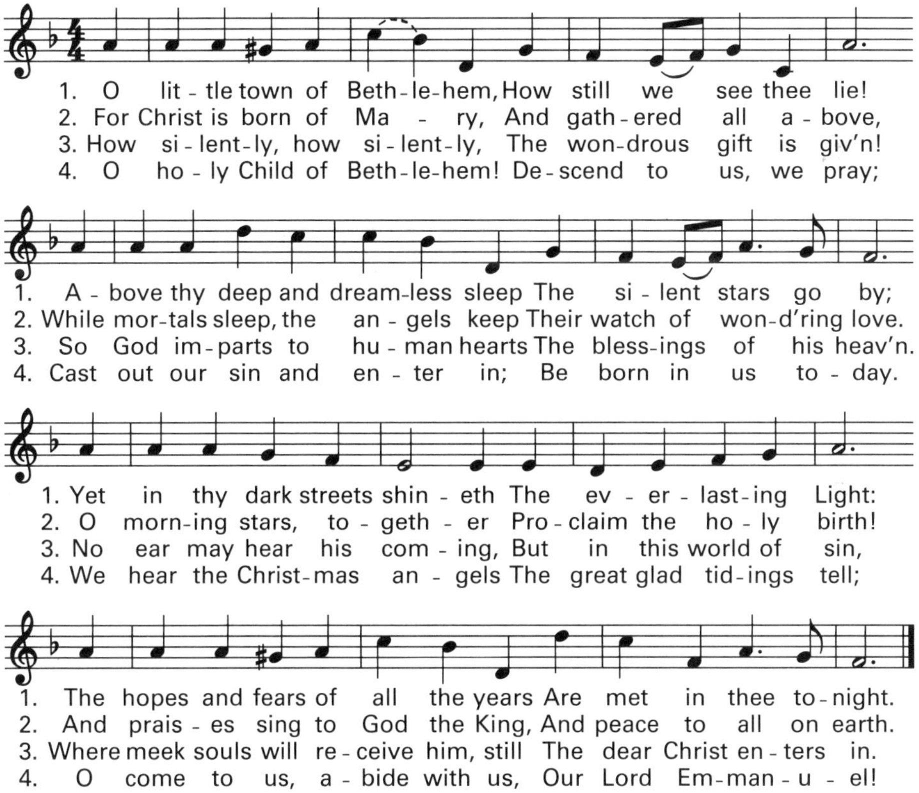

1. O lit - tle town of Beth - le - hem, How still we see thee lie!
2. For Christ is born of Ma - ry, And gath - ered all a - bove,
3. How si - lent - ly, how si - lent - ly, The won - drous gift is giv'n!
4. O ho - ly Child of Beth - le - hem! De - scend to us, we pray;

1. A - bove thy deep and dream - less sleep The si - lent stars go by;
2. While mor - tals sleep, the an - gels keep Their watch of won - d'ring love.
3. So God im - parts to hu - man hearts The bless - ings of his heav'n.
4. Cast out our sin and en - ter in; Be born in us to - day.

1. Yet in thy dark streets shin - eth The ev - er - last - ing Light:
2. O morn - ing stars, to - geth - er Pro - claim the ho - ly birth!
3. No ear may hear his com - ing, But in this world of sin,
4. We hear the Christ - mas an - gels The great glad tid - ings tell;

1. The hopes and fears of all the years Are met in thee to - night.
2. And prais - es sing to God the King, And peace to all on earth.
3. Where meek souls will re - ceive him, still The dear Christ en - ters in.
4. O come to us, a - bide with us, Our Lord Em - man - u - el!

Text: 86 86 76 86; Phillips Brooks, 1835–1893, alt.
Music: ST. LOUIS; Lewis H. Redner, 1831–1908.

245 Hark! the Herald Angels Sing

Verses

1. Hark! the her - ald an - gels sing: "Glo - ry to the
2. Christ, by high - est heav'n a - dored, Christ, the ev - er -
3. Hail the heav'n - born Prince of Peace! Hail the Sun of

1. new - born King; Peace on earth, and mer - cy mild,
2. last - ing Lord; Late in time, be - hold him come,
3. Righ - teous - ness! Light and life to all he brings,

1. God and sin - ners rec - on - ciled!" Joy - ful, all ye
2. Off - spring of a vir - gin's womb. Veiled in flesh the
3. Ris'n with heal - ing in his wings. Mild he lays his

1. na - tions, rise, Join the tri - umph of the skies; With an -
2. God - head see! Hail th'in - car - nate De - i - ty! Pleased as
3. glo - ry by, Born that we no more may die, Born to

1. gel - ic hosts pro - claim: "Christ is born in Beth - le - hem!"
2. man with us to dwell; Je - sus, our Em - man - u - el!
3. raise us from the earth, Born to give us sec - ond birth.

Refrain

Hark! the her - ald an - gels sing, "Glo - ry to the new - born King."

Text: 77 77 D with refrain; Charles Wesley, 1707–1788, alt.
Music: MENDELSSOHN; Felix Mendelssohn, 1809–1847; adapt. by William H. Cummings, 1831–1915.

246 Lo, How a Rose E'er Blooming

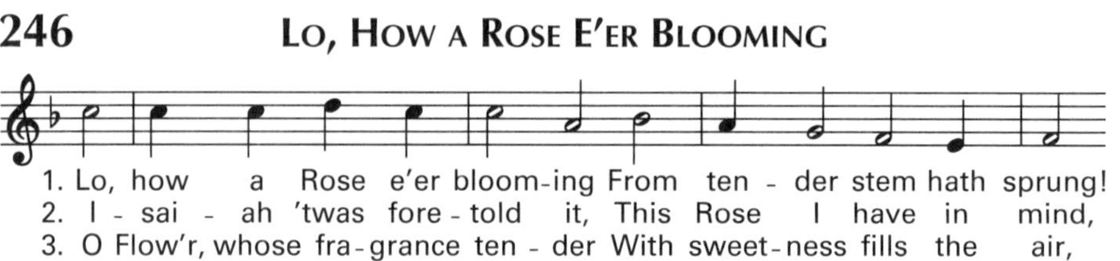
1. Lo, how a Rose e'er bloom - ing From ten - der stem hath sprung!
2. I - sai - ah 'twas fore - told it, This Rose I have in mind,
3. O Flow'r, whose fra - grance ten - der With sweet - ness fills the air,

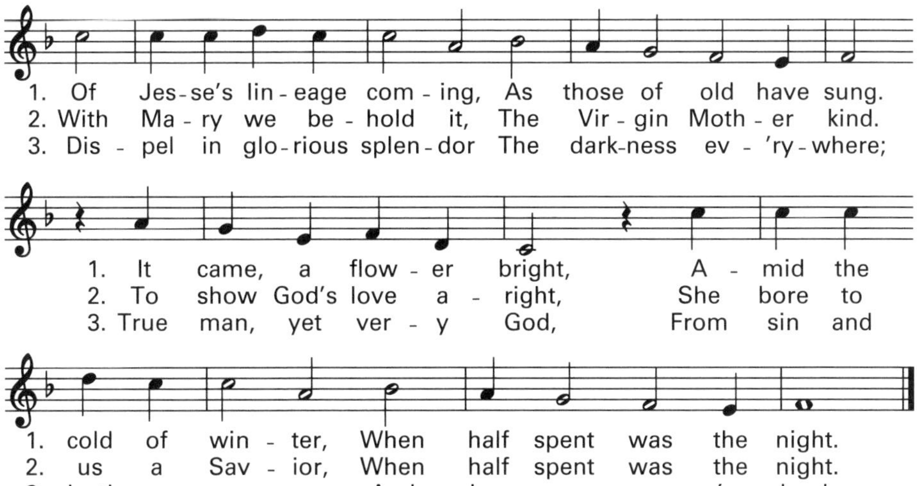
1. Of Jes-se's lin-eage com-ing, As those of old have sung.
2. With Ma-ry we be-hold it, The Vir-gin Moth-er kind.
3. Dis-pel in glo-rious splen-dor The dark-ness ev-'ry-where;
1. It came, a flow-er bright, A-mid the
2. To show God's love a-right, She bore to
3. True man, yet ver-y God, From sin and
1. cold of win-ter, When half spent was the night.
2. us a Sav-ior, When half spent was the night.
3. death now save us, And share our ev-'ry load.

Text: 76 76 6 76; based on Isaiah 11:1; trad. German carol, 15th cent.; tr. by Theodore Baker, 1851–1934, alt.
Music: ES IST EIN' ROS' ENTSPRUNGEN; *Alte Catholische Geistliche Kirchengesänge*, Cologne, 1599.

See Amid the Winter's Snow 247

1. See a-mid the win-ter's snow, born for us on earth be-low,
2. Say, you ho-ly shep-herds, say, tell your joy-ful news to-day.
1. see, the gen-tle lamb ap-pears, prom-ised from e-ter-nal years.
2. Why have you now left your sheep on the lone-ly moun-tain steep?
1. There with-in a man-ger lies he who built the star-ry skies;
2. "As we watched at dead of night, there ap-peared a won-drous light;

1
to Verse 2
1. he who, throned in heights sub-lime, sits a-mid the cher-u-bim.

Final
2. an-gels sing-ing 'Peace on earth' told us of the Sav-ior's birth."

Text: 77 77 D; Edward Caswall, 1814–1878.
Music: WINTER'S SNOW; Kevin Keil, ASCAP, b. 1956,

248 O Come, Little Children

1. O come, lit - tle chil - dren; come one and come
2. O see in the man - ger so meek and so
3. His bed, lit - tle chil - dren, a man - ger with

1. all, O come to the man - ger in Beth - le-hem's
2. mild, O see in the soft light the heav - en - ly
3. hay; His Moth - er and Jo - seph in ec - sta - sy

1. stall, And see what our Fa - ther in heav - en a -
2. Child, In swad - dling clothes fold - ed, his beau - ty more
3. pray, The shep - herds in won - der their glad wor-ship

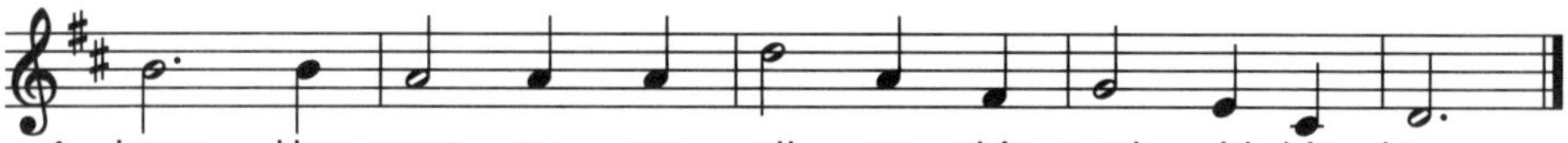

1. bove Has sent to us all on this earth with his love.
2. sweet Than an - gels, whose voic - es his low - ly birth greet.
3. bring, While cho - rus of an - gels sweet Glo - ri - as sing.

Text: 11 11 11 11; Johann C. von Schmid, 1768–1854; tr. by Melanie Schute, 1885–1922, alt.
Music: IHR KINDERLEIN, KOMMET; Johann A. Schulz, 1749–1800.

249 Rise Up, Shepherd, and Follow

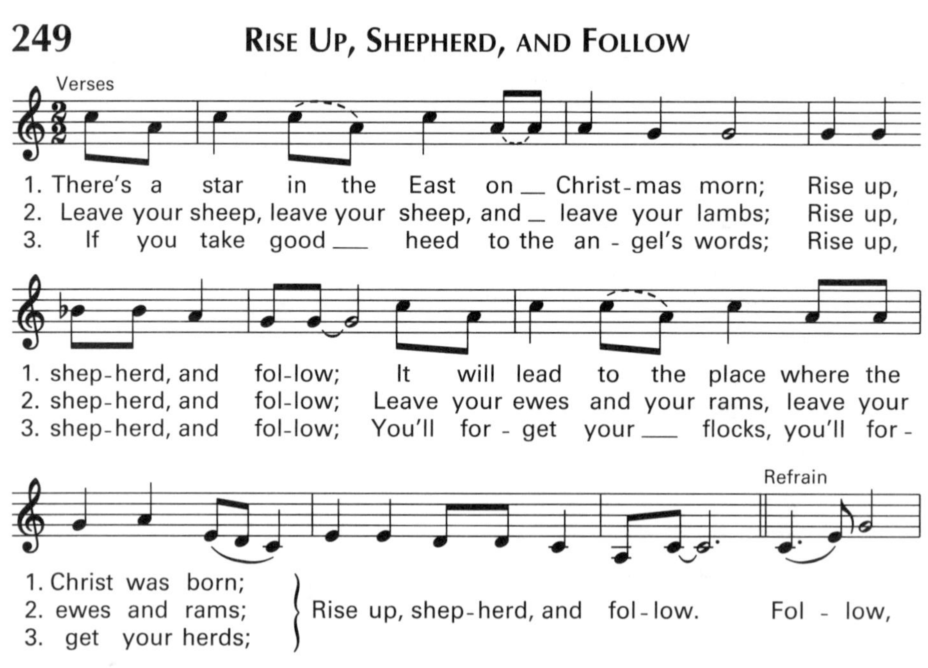
Verses
1. There's a star in the East on __ Christ-mas morn; Rise up,
2. Leave your sheep, leave your sheep, and __ leave your lambs; Rise up,
3. If you take good ___ heed to the an - gel's words; Rise up,
1. shep-herd, and fol-low; It will lead to the place where the
2. shep-herd, and fol-low; Leave your ewes and your rams, leave your
3. shep-herd, and fol-low; You'll for - get your ___ flocks, you'll for -
1. Christ was born;
2. ewes and rams;
3. get your herds;
Rise up, shep-herd, and fol - low.
Refrain
Fol - low,

fol - low; Rise up, shep - herd, and fol-low. Fol-low the Star of
Beth - le - hem; Rise up, shep-herd, and fol - low.

Text: 10 7 11 7 with refrain.
Music: RISE UP, SHEPHERD; Spiritual.

It Came upon the Midnight Clear 250

1. It came up - on the mid - night clear, That glo - rious
2. Still through the clo - ven skies they come, With peace - ful
3. And ye, be-neath life's crush - ing load, Whose forms are
4. For, lo, the days are has - tening on, By proph - et

1. song of old, From an - gels bend - ing near the
2. wings un - furled, And still their heav'n - ly mu - sic
3. bend - ing low, Who toil a - long the climb - ing
4. bards fore - told, When with the ev - er - cir - cling

1. earth To touch their harps of gold: "Peace on the earth, good
2. floats O'er all the wea - ry world: A - bove its sad and
3. way With pain - ful steps and slow, Look now! for glad and
4. years Comes 'round the age of gold; When peace shall o - ver

1. will to all From heav'n's all gra - cious King;" The
2. low - ly plains They bend on hov - 'ring wing, And
3. gold - en hours Come swift - ly on the wing: O
4. all the earth Its an - cient splen - dors fling, And

1. world in sol - emn still-ness lay, To hear the an - gels sing.
2. ev - er o'er its Ba - bel sounds The bless-ed an - gels sing.
3. rest be - side the wea - ry road And hear the an - gels sing.
4. all the world give back the song Which now the an - gels sing.

Text: CMD; Edmund H. Sears, 1810–1876, alt.
Music: CAROL; Richard S. Willis, 1819–1900, alt.

251 INFANT HOLY, INFANT LOWLY

1. In - fant ho - ly, in - fant low - ly, For his bed a
2. Flocks were sleep - ing, shep - herds keep - ing Vig - il till the
3. As we jour - ney to the sta - ble Like the wise - men
4. Wake our spir - its from their slum - ber; Send the dark - ness
1. cat - tle stall; Ox - en low - ing, lit - tle know - ing
2. morn - ing new. Saw the glo - ry, heard the sto - ry,
3. long a - go, We are hop - ing to dis - cov - er
4. on its way. Fill our hearts with joy and won - der
1. Christ the babe is Lord of all. Swift are wing - ing,
2. Tid - ings of a gos - pel true. Thus re - joic - ing,
3. What these pil - grims came to know. All are wel - come
4. On this bless - ed Christ - mas day. Songs of an - gels
1. an - gels sing - ing, No - els ring - ing, tid - ings bring - ing:
2. free from sor - row, Prais - es voic - ing greet the mor - row:
3. at this man - ger, King and shep - herd, friend and strang - er.
4. all a - round us; Grace and bless - ing now sur - round us.
1. Christ the babe is Lord of all.
2. Christ the babe was born for you.
3. Christ the babe is Lord of all.
4. Christ be with us as we go.

Text: 87 87 88 77. Verses 1 and 2, Polish carol; tr. by Edith M. Reed, 1885–1933.
Verses 3 and 4, Dan Schutte, b. 1947,
Music: W ZLOBIE LEZY; Polish carol.

SILENT NIGHT/ NOCHE DE PAZ

1. Si - lent night! Ho - ly night! All is calm,
2. Si - lent night! Ho - ly night! Shep-herds quake
3. Si - lent night! Ho - ly night! Son of God,
1. No - che de paz, No - che de a-mor; To - do duer-me en
2. No - che de paz, No - che de a-mor; Mi - ra qué gran
3. No - che de paz, No - che de a-mor; Al Di - vi - no
1. all is bright Round yon Vir - gin
2. at the sight; Glo - ries stream from
3. love's pure light Ra - diant beams from
1. de - rre - dor. En - tre los as - tros que es -
2. res - plan - dor Lu - ce en el ros - tro del
3. Sal - va - dor Que por no - so - tros na-
1. Moth - er and child! Ho - ly In - fant so
2. heav - en a - far; Heav'n - ly hosts sing
3. thy ho - ly face, With the dawn of re -
1. par - cen su luz Be - lla a - nun - cian - do al ni -
2. Ni - ño Je - sús, En el pe - se - bre del
3. ció en un por - tal. Him - nos can - te - mos de a -
1. ten - der and mild, Sleep in heav - en - ly
2. "Al - le - lu - ia! Christ the Sav - ior is
3. deem - ing grace, Je - sus, Lord, at thy
1. ñi - to Je - sús, Bri - lla la es - tre - lla de
2. mun - do la luz, Bri - lla la es - tre - lla de
3. mor ce - les - tial. ¡Glo - ria por siem - pre al Se -
1. peace, Sleep in heav - en - ly peace.
2. born, Christ the Sav - ior is born."
3. birth, Je - sus, Lord, at thy birth.
1. paz, Bri - lla la es - tre - lla de paz.
2. paz, Bri - lla la es - tre - lla de paz.
3. ñor! ¡Glo - ria por siem - pre al Se - ñor!

Text: Irregular; Joseph Mohr, 1792–1848; English tr. by John F. Young, 1820–1885;
Spanish tr. of verse 1 by Federico Fliedner, 1845–1901; Spanish tr. of verses 2 and 3, anon.
Music: STILLE NACHT; Franz X. Gruber, 1787–1863.

253 ANGELS, FROM THE REALMS OF GLORY

1. An - gels, from the realms of glo - ry, Wing your flight o'er
2. Shep-herds, in the fields a - bid - ing, Watch-ing o'er your
3. Sag - es, leave your con - tem-pla-tions, Bright - er vi - sions
4. Though an in - fant now we view him, He shall fill his
5. All cre - a - tion, join in prais-ing God, the Fa - ther,

1. all the earth; Ye who sang cre - a - tion's sto - ry,
2. flocks by night, God on earth is now re - sid - ing;
3. beam a - far; Seek the great De - sire of Na - tions,
4. Fa - ther's throne, Gath - er all the na - tions to him;
5. Spir - it, Son, Ev - er - more your voic - es rais - ing,

1. Now pro - claim Mes - si - ah's birth:
2. Yon - der shines the in - fant light:
3. Ye have seen his na - tal star: Come and wor-ship,
4. Ev - 'ry knee shall then bow down:
5. To the e - ter - nal Three - in - One:

1-5. come and wor - ship, Wor - ship Christ, the new - born King.

Text: 87 87 87; verses 1–3, James Montgomery, 1771–1854; verse 4, *Christmas Box*, 1825; verse 5, *Salisbury Hymn Book*, 1857.
Music: REGENT SQUARE; Henry T. Smart, 1813–1879.

254 SONGS OF THANKFULNESS AND PRAISE

1. Songs of thank-ful-ness and praise, Je - sus, Lord, to thee we raise,
2. Man - i - fest at Jor-dan's stream, Proph-et, Priest, and King su-preme;
3. Grant us grace to see thee, Lord, Mir-rored in thy ho - ly Word;

1. Man - i - fest-ed by the star To the sag - es from a - far;
2. And at Ca - na, wed-ding guest, In thy God-head man - i - fest;
3. May we im - i - tate thee now, And be pure, as pure art thou;

1. Branch of roy - al Da-vid's stem In thy birth at Beth-le-hem;
2. Man - i - fest in pow'r di - vine, Chang-ing wa - ter in - to wine;
3. That we like to thee may be At thy great E - pi-pha-ny;

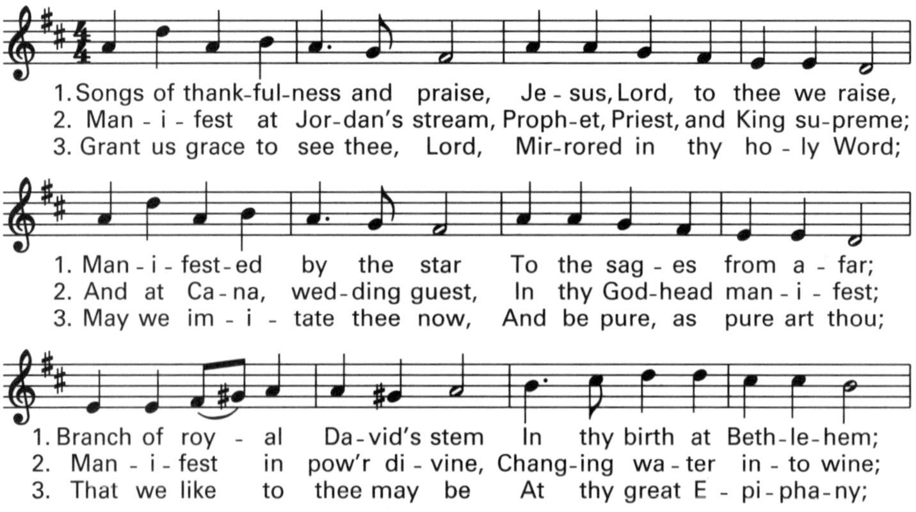

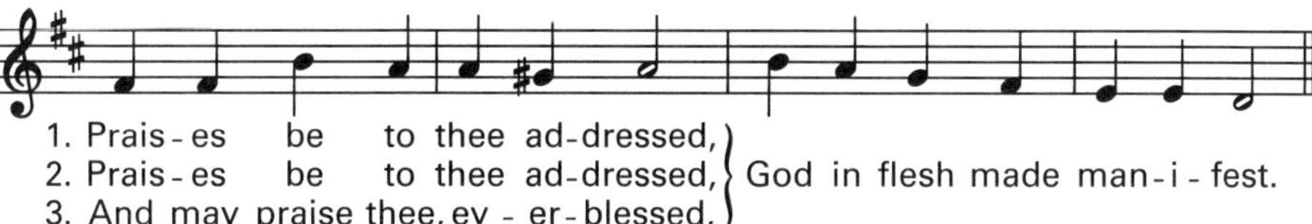
1. Prais - es be to thee ad - dressed,
2. Prais - es be to thee ad - dressed, God in flesh made man - i - fest.
3. And may praise thee, ev - er - blessed,

Text: 77 77 D; Christopher Wordsworth, 1807–1885, alt.
Music: SALZBURG; Jakob Hintze, 1622–1702; adapt. by Johann Sebastian Bach, 1685–1750.

We Three Kings 255

Verses

1. We three kings of O - ri - ent are; Bear - ing gifts we
2. Born a King on Beth - le-hem's plain, Gold I bring to
3. Frank - in - cense to of - fer have I: In - cense owns a
4. Myrrh is mine; its bit - ter per - fume Breathes a life of
5. Glo - rious now be - hold him a - rise, King and God and

1. tra - verse a - far Field and foun - tain, Moor and moun - tain,
2. crown him a - gain, King for - ev - er, Ceas - ing nev - er
3. De - i - ty nigh; Prayer and prais - ing Glad - ly rais - ing,
4. gath - er - ing gloom; Sor - rowing, sigh - ing, Bleed - ing, dy - ing,
5. Sac - ri - fice; "Al - le - lu - ia, Al - le - lu - ia!"

1. Fol - low - ing yon - der star.
2. O - ver us all to reign.
3. Wor - ship him, God on high.
4. Sealed in the stone - cold tomb.
5. Sounds through the earth and skies.

Refrain

O star of won - der, star of night, Star with roy - al beau - ty bright; West - ward lead - ing, still pro - ceed - ing, Guide us to thy per - fect light.

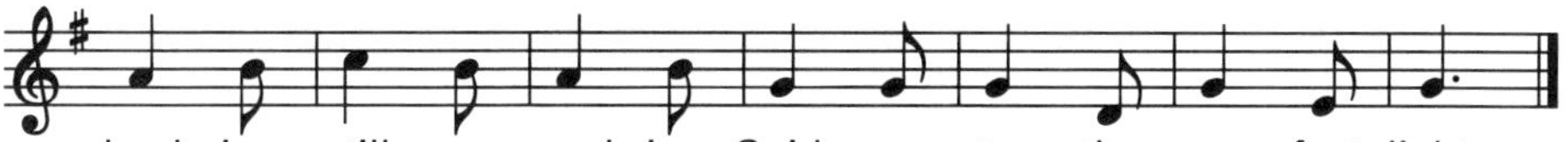

Text: 88 44 6 with refrain; based on Matthew 2:1–11; John H. Hopkins, Jr., 1820–1891, alt.
Music: KINGS OF ORIENT; *Carols, Hymns and Songs*, 1863; John H. Hopkins, Jr.

256 WHAT CHILD IS THIS

Verses

1. What child is this, who, laid to rest, On Ma - ry's lap is
2. Why lies he in such mean es - tate Where ox and ass are
3. So bring him in - cense, gold, and myrrh, Come peas - ant, king, to

1. sleep - ing? Whom an - gels greet with an - thems sweet, While
2. feed - ing? Good Chris - tian, fear: for sin - ners here The
3. own him; The King of kings sal - va - tion brings, Let

1. shep - herds watch are keep - ing?
2. si - lent Word is plead - ing.
3. lov - ing hearts en - throne him.

Refrain

This, this is Christ the King, Whom shep - herds guard and an - gels sing; Haste, haste to bring him laud, the babe, the son of Ma - ry.

Note: This song may be combined with *Child of the Poor*; use accompaniment and instructions found for *Child of the Poor*.

Text: 87 87 with refrain; Bramley and Stainer's *Christmas Carols New and Old*, 1871; William C. Dix, 1837–1898.
Music: GREENSLEEVES; trad. English melody, 16th cent.; Bramley and Stainer's *Christmas Carols New and Old*, 1871.

257 CHILD OF THE POOR

Verses
1. Help-less and hun-gry, low - ly he lies, wrapped in the
2. Who is the strang-er here in our midst, look - ing for
3. Bring all the thirst - y, all who seek peace; bring those with
1. chill of mid - win - ter; comes now a - mong us, born in - to
2. shel - ter a - mong us? Who is the out-cast? Who do we
3. noth-ing to of - fer. Strength-en the fee - ble, say to the
1. pov - er - ty's em - brace, new life for the world.
2. see a - mid the poor, the chil - dren of God?
3. fright-ened heart: "Fear not: here is your God!"

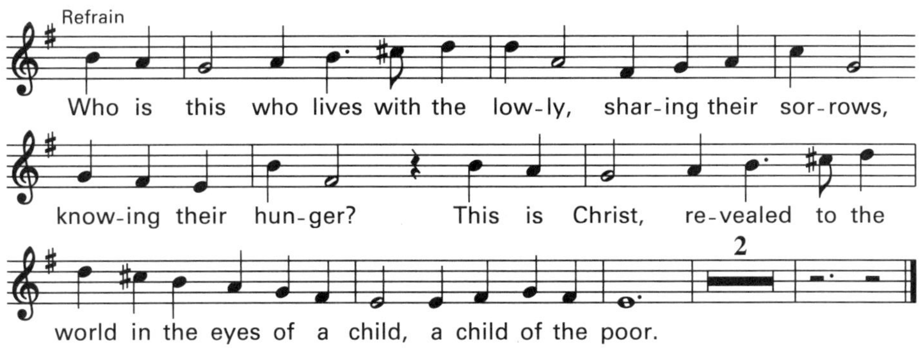
Refrain
Who is this who lives with the low-ly, shar-ing their sor-rows,
know-ing their hun-ger? This is Christ, re-vealed to the
world in the eyes of a child, a child of the poor.
2

Note: *Child of the Poor* may be sung with *What Child Is This* in the following manner: *Child of the Poor*, verse 1, followed by *What Child Is This*, verse 1; *Child of the Poor*, verse 2, followed by *What Child Is This*, verse 2; both songs sung simultaneously on verse 3.

Text and music: Scott Soper, b. 1961,

As with Gladness Men of Old 258

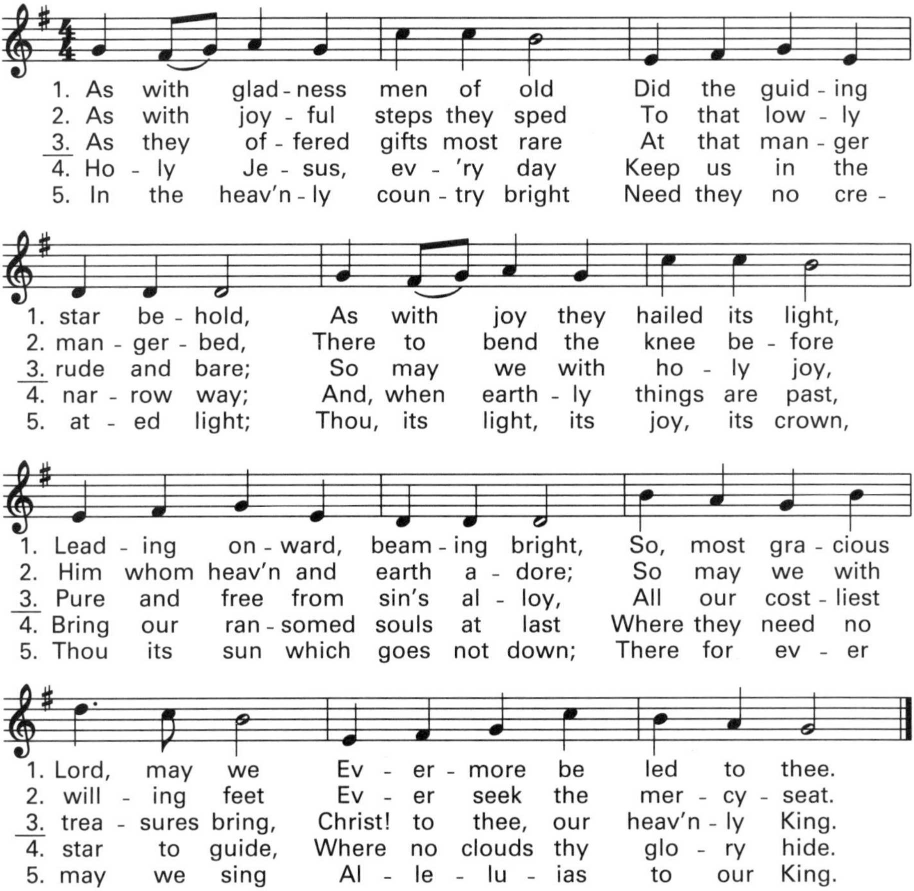

1. As with gladness men of old
Did the guiding star behold,
As with joy they hailed its light,
Leading onward, beaming bright,
So, most gracious Lord, may we
Evermore be led to thee.

2. As with joyful steps they sped
To that lowly manger-bed,
There to bend the knee before
Him whom heav'n and earth adore;
So may we with willing feet
Ever seek the mercy-seat.

3. As they offered gifts most rare
At that manger rude and bare;
So may we with holy joy,
Pure and free from sin's alloy,
All our costliest treasures bring,
Christ! to thee, our heav'nly King.

4. Holy Jesus, ev'ry day
Keep us in the narrow way;
And, when earthly things are past,
Bring our ransomed souls at last
Where they need no star to guide,
Where no clouds thy glory hide.

5. In the heav'nly country bright
Need they no created light;
Thou, its light, its joy, its crown,
Thou its sun which goes not down;
There for ever may we sing
Alleluias to our King.

Text: 77 77 77; William C. Dix, 1837–1898.
Music: DIX; Conrad Kocher, 1786–1872; adapt. by William H. Monk, 1823–1889.

259 The First Nowell

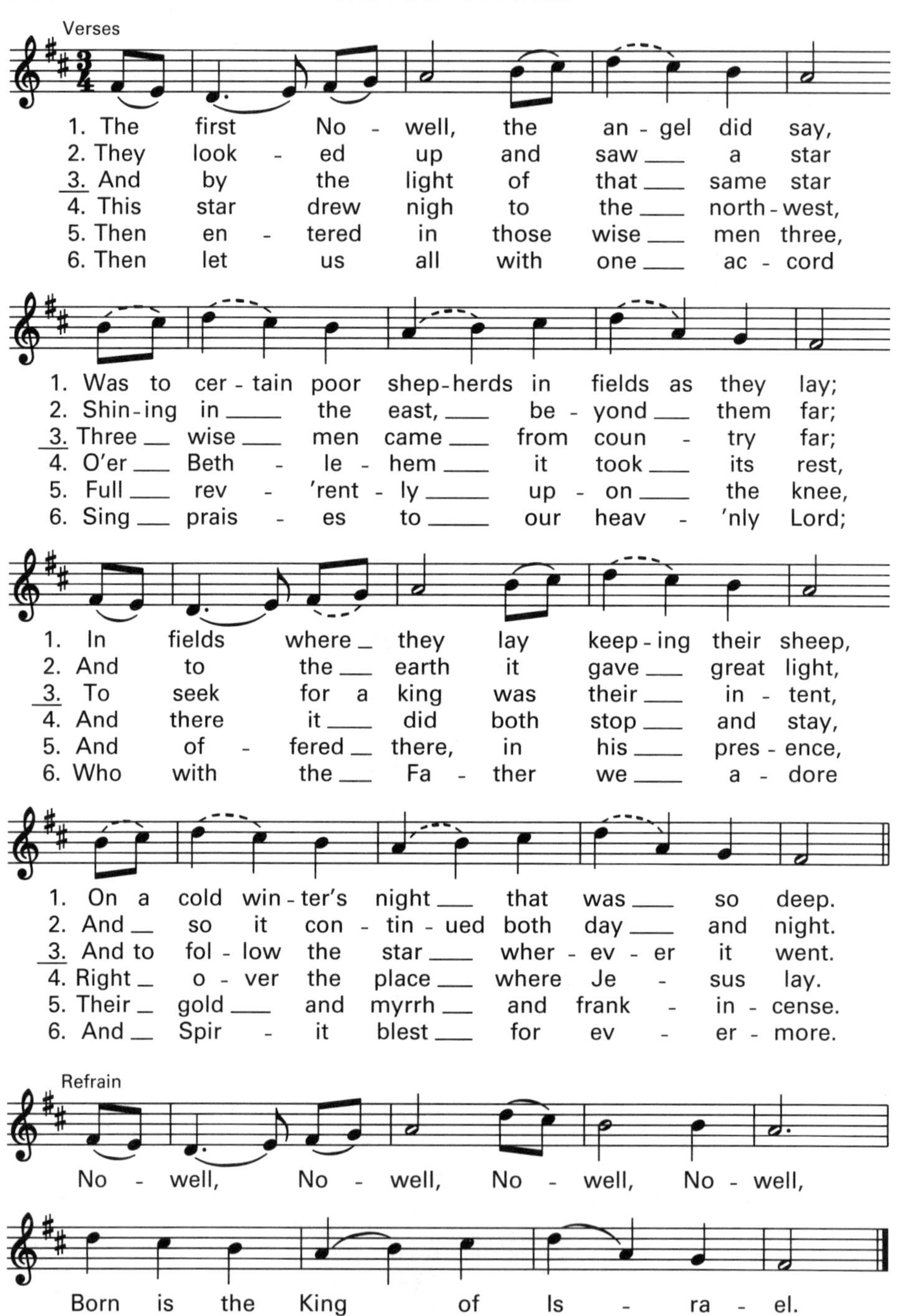
Verses
1. The first No - well, the an - gel did say,
2. They look - ed up and saw a star
3. And by the light of that same star
4. This star drew nigh to the north - west,
5. Then en - tered in those wise men three,
6. Then let us all with one ac - cord
1. Was to cer - tain poor shep-herds in fields as they lay;
2. Shin-ing in the east, be - yond them far;
3. Three wise men came from coun - try far;
4. O'er Beth - le - hem it took its rest,
5. Full rev - 'rent - ly up - on the knee,
6. Sing prais - es to our heav - 'nly Lord;
1. In fields where they lay keep - ing their sheep,
2. And to the earth it gave great light,
3. To seek for a king was their in - tent,
4. And there it did both stop and stay,
5. And of - fered there, in his pres - ence,
6. Who with the Fa - ther we a - dore
1. On a cold win - ter's night that was so deep.
2. And so it con - tin - ued both day and night.
3. And to fol - low the star wher - ev - er it went.
4. Right o - ver the place where Je - sus lay.
5. Their gold and myrrh and frank - in - cense.
6. And Spir - it blest for ev - er - more.
Refrain
No - well, No - well, No - well, No - well,
Born is the King of Is - ra - el.

Text: Irregular with refrain; trad. English carol, 17th cent.; verse 6, alt.
Music: THE FIRST NOWELL; trad. English carol, 17th cent.

Ashes to Ashes

Refrain

Ash - es to ash - es, from dust un - to dust. The
cross on our fore - head, your prom - ise, O God.
Read - y us to fol - low the way of your Son, to rise from these
ash - es, re - deemed in the fire of your love.

Verses: Ash Wednesday

1. Sound the trum - pet in Zi - on, an - nounce from the Lord
2. Rend your hearts, not your gar - ments; re - turn to the Lord,
3. We have seen in the heav - ens and held in our arms
4. Let us fast from un - kind - ness and turn from our greed,
5. Though this life that we trea - sure must fade like the grass,

to Refrain

1. that the day of God's fa - vor is ev - er close at hand.
2. who de - lights when we of - fer a tru - ly hum - ble heart.
3. what the hand of our Mak - er can fash - ion out of dust.
4. giv - ing bread to the hun - gry and lift - ing up the poor.
5. heav - en's glo - ry a - waits those who put their trust in God.

Verses: Throughout Lent

1. We a - bide in the shad - ow of God's might - y arm, for the
2. As the high - est of heav - ens sur - pass - es the earth, so the
3. Though his na - ture is ho - ly yet Christ be - came sin, so that

to Refrain

1. Lord is our ref - uge, the Rock in whom we trust.
2. might of God's mer - cy is far be - yond our shame.
3. we might in - her - it the ho - li - ness of God.

Text and music: Dan Schutte, b. 1947,

261 Ashes

1. We rise a-gain from ash-es, from the good we've failed to do. We rise a-gain from ash-es, to cre-ate our-selves a-new. If all our world is ash-es, then must our lives be true, an of-fer-ing of ash-es, an of-fer-ing to you.
2. We of-fer you our fail-ures, we of-fer you at-tempts, the gifts not ful-ly giv-en, the dreams not ful-ly dreamt. Give our stum-bl-ings di-rec-tion, give our vi-sions wid-er view, an of-fer-ing of ash-es, an of-fer-ing to you.
3. Then rise a-gain from ash-es, let heal-ing come to pain, though spring has turned to win-ter, and sun-shine turned to rain. The rain we'll use for grow-ing, and cre-ate the world a-new from an of-fer-ing of ash-es, an of-fer-ing to you.
4. Thanks be to the Fa-ther, who made us like him-self. Thanks be to his Son, who saved us by his death. Thanks be to the Spir-it who cre-ates the world a-new from an of-fer-ing of ash-es, an of-fer-ing to you.

262 At the Cross Her Station Keeping/ Stabat Mater Dolorosa

1. At the cross her sta-tion keep-ing, Stood the mourn-ful Moth-er weep-ing, Close to Je-sus to the last.
2. Through her heart, his sor-row shar-ing, All his bit-ter an-guish bear-ing, Now at length the sword has passed.
3. O how sad and sore dis-tressed, Was that Moth-er high-ly blest Of the sole be-got-ten One!
1. *Sta-bat Ma-ter do-lo-ró-sa Ju-xta cru-cem la-cri-mó-sa, Dum pen-dé-bat Fí-li-us.*
2. *Cu-jus á-ni-mam ge-mén-tem, Con-tri-stá-tam et do-lén-tem, Per-tran-sí-vit glá-di-us.*
3. *O quam tri-stis et af-flí-cta Fu-it il-la be-ne-dí-cta Ma-ter U-ni-gé-ni-ti!*

4. Christ above in torment hangs,
She beneath beholds the pangs
Of her dying, glorious Son.

5. Is there one who would not weep,
Whelmed in miseries so deep,
Christ's dear Mother to behold?

6. Can the human heart refrain
From partaking in her pain,
In that Mother's pain untold?

7. Bruised, derided, cursed, defiled,
She beheld her tender Child,
All with bloody scourges rent.

8. For the sins of his own nation
Saw him hang in desolation
Till his spirit forth he sent.

9. O thou Mother! Font of love,
Touch my spirit from above,
Make my heart with thine accord.

10. Make me feel as thou hast felt;
Make my soul to glow and melt
With the love of Christ, my Lord.

11. Holy Mother, pierce me through,
In my heart each wound renew
Of my Savior crucified.

12. Let me share with thee his pain,
Who for all my sins was slain,
Who for me in torment died.

13. Let me mingle tears with thee,
Mourning him who mourned for me,
All the days that I may live.

14. By the cross with thee to stay;
There with thee to weep and pray,
All I ask of thee to give.

15. Virgin of all Virgins best!
Listen to my fond request:
Let me share thy grief divine.

4. *Quae maerébat et dolébat,*
Pia Mater, dum vidébat
Nati poenas íncliti.

5. *Quis non posset contristári,*
Piam Matrem contemplári
Doléntem cum Fílio?

6. *Quis est homo qui non fleret,*
Matrem Christi si vidéret
In tanto supplício?

7. *Pro peccátis suae gentis*
Vidit Jesum in torméntis,
Et flagéllis súbditum.

8. *Vidit suum dulcem Natum*
Moriéntem desolátum,
Dum emísit spíritum.

9. *Eia Mater, fons amóris,*
Me sentíre vim dolóris
Fac, ut tecum lúgeam.

10. *Fac ut árdeat cor meum*
in amándo Christum Deum,
ut sibi compláceam.

11. *Sancta Mater, istud agas,*
Crucifíxi fige plagas
Cordi meo válide.

12. *Tui Nati vulneráti,*
Tam dignáti pro me pati,
Poenas mecum dívide.

13. *Fac me vere tecum flere,*
Crucifíxo condolére,
Donec ego víxero.

14. *Juxta crucem tecum stare,*
Ac me tibi sociáre
In planctu desídero.

15. *Virgo vírginum praeclára,*
Mihi jam non sis amára:
Fac me tecum plángere.

Text: 88 7; *Stabat Mater dolorosa*; Jacapone da Todi, 1230–1306; tr. by Edward Caswall, 1814–1878, alt.
Music: STABAT MATER; *Maintzisch Gesangbuch*, 1661.

Forty Days and Forty Nights **263**

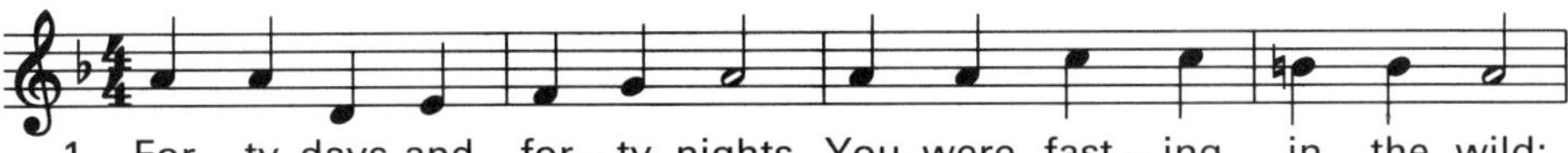

1. For - ty days and for - ty nights You were fast - ing in the wild;
2. Shall not we your sor-row share And from world - ly joys ab - stain,
3. Then if Sa - tan on us press, Flesh or spir - it to as - sail,
4. So shall we have peace di - vine: Ho - lier glad - ness ours shall be;
5. Keep, O keep us, Sav - ior dear, Ev - er con - stant by your side;

1. For - ty days and for - ty nights Tempt - ed, and yet un - de-filed.
2. Fast- ing with un - ceas-ing prayer, Strong with you to suf - fer pain?
3. Vic - tor in the wil - der-ness, Grant we may not faint nor fail!
4. Round us, too, shall an - gels shine, Such as served you faith-ful - ly.
5. That with you we may ap - pear At th'e - ter - nal Eas - ter-tide.

Text: 77 77; George H. Smyttan, 1822–1870, alt.
Music: HEINLEIN; melody attr. to Martin Herbst, 1654–1681, alt.

264 CHANGE OUR HEARTS

Refrain
Change our hearts this time, your word says it can be. Change our minds this time, your life could make us free. We are the peo - ple your call set a-part, Lord, this time change our
1-3 to Verses
hearts.
Final
hearts. This time change our hearts. This time change our minds. This time change our hearts, change our hearts.
Verse 1
1. Brought by your hand to the edge of our dreams, one foot in par-a-dise, one in the waste; drawn by your prom-is-es, still we are lured by the shad-ows and the chains we leave be-hind. But
to Refrain
Verses 2, 3
2. Now as we watch you stretch out your hands, of-f'ring a - bun - dan -
3. Show us the way that leads to your side, o - ver the moun-tains

2. ces, __ full - ness of joy. Your milk and hon - ey seem dis - tant, un -
3. ___ and sands of the soul. Be for us man - na, ___ wa - ter from
to Refrain
2. real, when we have bread and wa - ter in our hands. But
3. stone, _____ light which says we nev - er walk a - lone. And
Verses
1. Lead us, Lord, in - to the des - ert; lead us through the
2. In this time of sa - cred strug - gle, in this time of
3. Lord, we hun - ger for your pres - ence; Lord, we're thirst - ing
4. Teach us, Lord: who is our neigh - bor? Is it friend, or
1. wil - der - ness. Through this jour - ney we will fol - low,
2. sac - ri - fice, we re - joice, for we re - mem - ber
3. for your grace. When con - sum - ing all but you, Lord,
4. en - e - my? When we wel - come or con - demn them,
1, 4
1: to Verse 2
2: to Refrain
2, 3
1. for we long to see your face.
2. that you lead us in - to life.
3. all we gain is emp - ti - ness.
4. it is you, O let us see.
Refrain
Gra - cious God, mer - cy is your name. Re - deem -
Gra - cious God, we bless your ho - ly name. Re - ceiv -
1
2
2
ing Love, you give your life a - way.
ing love, we give our lives a - way.

Gracious God 265

266 Again We Keep This Solemn Fast

1. A - gain we keep this sol - emn fast, A gift of
faith from ag - es past, This Lent which binds us
lov - ing - ly To faith and hope and char - i - ty.

2. The law and proph - ets from of old In fig - ured
ways this Lent fore - told, Which Christ, all ag - es'
Lord and Guide, In these last days has sanc - ti - fied.

3. More spar - ing, there - fore, let us make The words we
speak, the food we take, Our sleep, our laugh - ter,
ev - 'ry sense; Learn peace through ho - ly pen - i - tence.

4. Let us a - void each harm - ful way That lures the
care - less mind a - stray; By watch - ful prayer our
spir - its free From schem - ing of the e - ne - my.

5. We pray, O bless - ed Three - in - One, Our God while
end - less ag - es run, That this, our Lent of
for - ty days, May bring us growth and give you praise.

Text: LM; *Ex more docti mystico*; ascr. to St. Gregory the Great, ca. 540–604; tr. by Peter J. Scagnelli, b. 1949, and John M. Neale, 1818–1866, alt., © Peter J. Scagnelli. Published by World Library Publications, wlpmusic.com. All rights reserved. Used with permission.
Music: ERHALT UNS, HERR; J. Klug's *Geistliche Lieder*, Wittenberg, 1543; adapt. by Johann Sebastian Bach, 1685–1750, alt.

267 Return to Me

Refrain
Re-turn to me; I meet you more than half-way,
long - ing to gath - er you to my - self.
Verses
1. The more that I call, the far - ther you wan-der.
2. How could I for - get, for - get my be - lov - ed?
3. And when the sheep strays, the shep-herd will fol - low,

3
to Refrain
1. Have you for - got - ten all so soon, my cho - sen one?
2. Do you not know who I am; your heal - er?
3. ven - tur - ing all to find and save the lost one.

Text: Hosea 11; Matthew 18:10–14; adapt. by Bob Hurd, b. 1950.
Music: Bob Hurd.

Beyond the Days 268

Refrain

Be - yond the days of hope and mys - t'ry we
see a light of faith re - newed, and in our long - ing
we thirst for guid - ance to walk with you day by
1-4 to Verses
day.
Final
day, to walk with you day by day.

Verses

1. For - ty days and nights, you guide the steps of our jour - ney. May your pres - ence be felt in the whis - per of your voice.
2. Not on bread a - lone are we to walk on this jour - ney. Speak the words that give life to the yearn - ings of our hearts.
3. In your hands, O God, we feel the touch of your guid - ance. Keep us safe in your care: may your gen - tle - ness be there.
4. On our Lent - en path we see the dawn of a new day. Be our vi - sion of hope; be the prom - ise of our lives.

to Refrain

269 How Long, O Lord

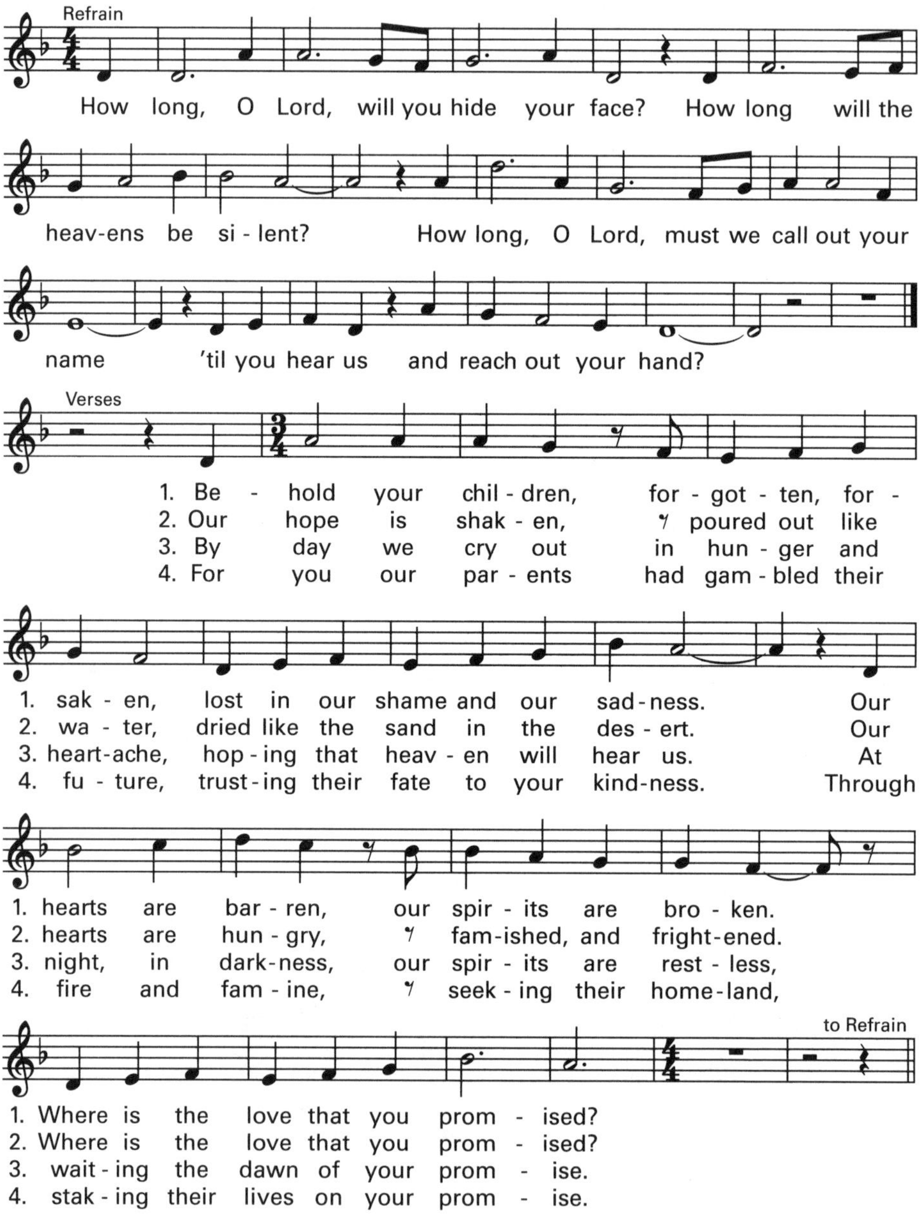

Refrain

How long, O Lord, will you hide your face? How long will the heav-ens be si - lent? How long, O Lord, must we call out your name 'til you hear us and reach out your hand?

Verses

1. Be - hold your chil - dren, for - got - ten, for - sak - en, lost in our shame and our sad - ness. Our hearts are bar - ren, our spir - its are bro - ken. Where is the love that you prom - ised?
2. Our hope is shak - en, poured out like wa - ter, dried like the sand in the des - ert. Our hearts are hun - gry, fam - ished, and fright - ened. Where is the love that you prom - ised?
3. By day we cry out in hun - ger and heart - ache, hop - ing that heav - en will hear us. At night, in dark - ness, our spir - its are rest - less, wait - ing the dawn of your prom - ise.
4. For you our par - ents had gam - bled their fu - ture, trust - ing their fate to your kind - ness. Through fire and fam - ine, seek - ing their home - land, stak - ing their lives on your prom - ise.

to Refrain

Text: Based on Psalm 13, 22; Dan Schutte, b. 1947.
Music: Dan Schutte.

In Your Love Remember Me

270

Refrain

In you I hope all the day long be-cause of your

good-ness, O Lord. Re - mem - ber the love you've

shown from of old. In your love re - mem - ber me.

1, 2 to Verses

Final

love re - mem - ber me.

Verse 1 2

1. Do not let me down, pro - tect me from my

1. foes. Turn to me for I am weak;

1. my eyes are al - ways on you.

to Refrain

Verse 2

2. What joy is life in you! What peace is

2. life in you! For you a - lone give me

2. joy and peace. You a-lone are my Lord.

to Refrain

271 In These Days of Lenten Journey

Refrain
In these days of Len-ten jour-ney we have seen and we have heard
the call to sow jus-tice in the lives of those we serve.
2
Verses
1. We reach out to those who are home-less, to
2. We o - pen our eyes to the hun - gry and
3. We o - pen our ears to the wea - ry and
4. We call on the Spir - it of Jus - tice and
1. those who live with - out warmth. In the cool-ness of
2. see the fac - es of Christ. As we nour - ish all
3. hear the cry of the poor. To the voic - es that
4. pray for righ-teous-ness' sake. We will sing for the
1. eve - ning we'll shel - ter their dreams; we will
2. peo - ple who hun - ger for food, may their
3. ech - o the song of de - spair, we will
4. free - dom of all the op - pressed; we will
2
to Refrain
1. clothe them in mer - cy and peace.
2. faith in our God be re - newed.
3. show our com - pas - sion and care.
4. loos - en the bonds of dis - tress.

Text and music: Ricky Manalo, CSP, b. 1965,

272 Led by the Spirit

1. Led by the Spir - it of our God, we go to fast and
2. Led by the Spir - it, we con - front temp - ta - tion face to
3. Led by the Spir - it, now draw near the wa - ters of re -
4. Led by the Spir - it, now sing praise to God the Trin - i -

1. pray With Christ in - to the wil - der-ness; we join his
2. face, And know full well we must re - ly on God's re -
3. birth With hearts that long to wor-ship God in spir - it
4. ty: The Source of Life, the liv - ing Word made flesh to

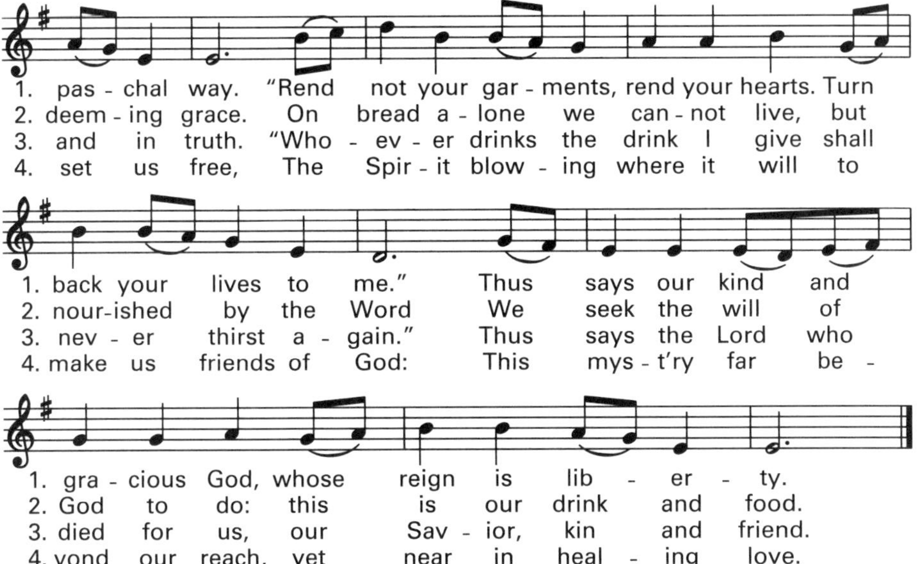
1. pas - chal way. "Rend not your gar - ments, rend your hearts. Turn
2. deem - ing grace. On bread a - lone we can - not live, but
3. and in truth. "Who - ev - er drinks the drink I give shall
4. set us free, The Spir - it blow - ing where it will to
1. back your lives to me." Thus says our kind and
2. nour-ished by the Word We seek the will of
3. nev - er thirst a - gain." Thus says the Lord who
4. make us friends of God: This mys - t'ry far be -
1. gra - cious God, whose reign is lib - er - ty.
2. God to do: this is our drink and food.
3. died for us, our Sav - ior, kin and friend.
4. yond our reach, yet near in heal - ing love.

Text: CMD; based on Joel 2:12–13; Matthew 4:1–4; Mark 1:12–15; John 4:5–42; Bob Hurd, b. 1950,

Music: KINGSFOLD; trad. English melody; *English Country Songs*, 1893; adapt. by Ralph Vaughan Williams, 1872–1958.

The Glory of These Forty Days 273

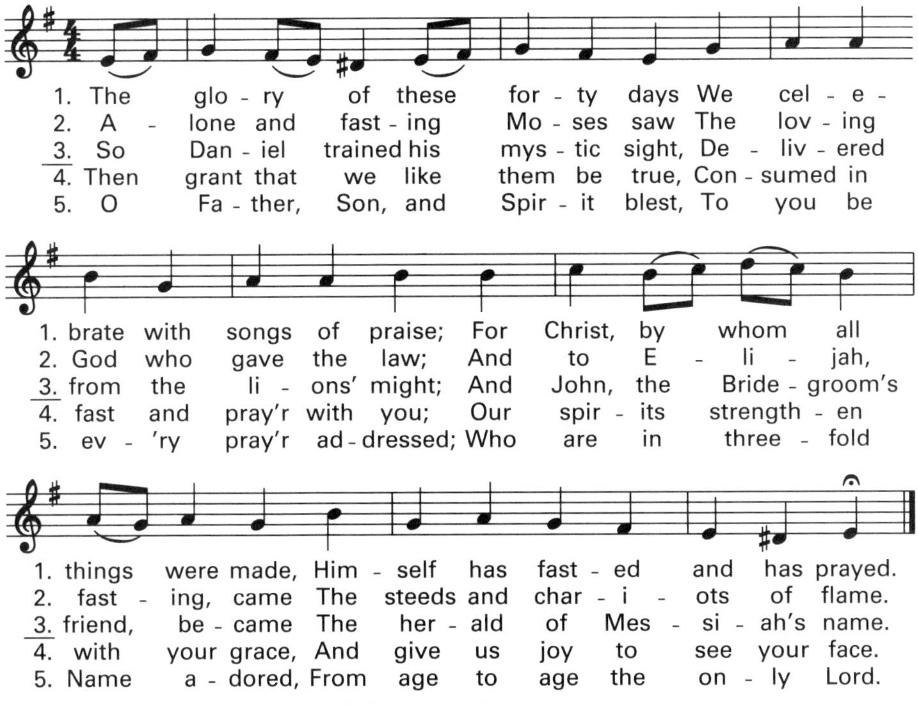

1. The glo - ry of these for - ty days We cel - e -
2. A - lone and fast - ing Mo - ses saw The lov - ing
3. So Dan - iel trained his mys - tic sight, De - liv - ered
4. Then grant that we like them be true, Con - sumed in
5. O Fa - ther, Son, and Spir - it blest, To you be

1. brate with songs of praise; For Christ, by whom all
2. God who gave the law; And to E - li - jah,
3. from the li - ons' might; And John, the Bride - groom's
4. fast and pray'r with you; Our spir - its strength - en
5. ev - 'ry pray'r ad - dressed; Who are in three - fold

1. things were made, Him - self has fast - ed and has prayed.
2. fast - ing, came The steeds and char - i - ots of flame.
3. friend, be - came The her - ald of Mes - si - ah's name.
4. with your grace, And give us joy to see your face.
5. Name a - dored, From age to age the on - ly Lord.

Text: LM; *Clarum decus jejunii*; St. Gregory the Great, ca. 540–604;
tr. fr. the *English Hymnal*, 1906; Maurice F. Bell, 1862–1947, alt.
Music: ERHALT UNS, HERR; J. Klug's *Geistliche Lieder*, Wittenberg, 1543; adapt. by Johann Sebastian Bach, 1685–1750, alt.

274 Transfigure Us, O Lord

Refrain

Trans - fig - ure us, O Lord, trans - fig - ure us, O Lord.
Break the chains that bind us; speak your heal - ing word, and
where you lead we'll fol - low. Trans - fig - ure us, O Lord.

Verses

1. Down from heights of glo - ry in - to the depths be - low, the
love of God self - emp - tied, the love of God to show. You
light the path be - fore us, the way that we must go.

2. Light for those in dark - ness, the hun - gry have their fill, glad
tid - ings for the hum - ble, the heal - ing of all ills; in
these we glimpse your glo - ry, God's prom - is - es ful - filled.

3. Par - don for the sin - ner, a shep - herd for the sheep, a
drink of liv - ing wa - ter for all who thirst and seek, and
feast - ing at your ta - ble, the low - ly and the least.

4. To the ho - ly cit - y, Je - ru - sa - lem, you go; your
face set toward the end - ing, the cross to be your throne.
Shall we jour - ney with you and share your pas - chal road?

to Refrain

Text: Based on Matthew 17:1–9; Mark 9:2–10; Luke 9:28b–36; Bob Hurd, b. 1950.
Music: Bob Hurd.

275 With the Lord

Verse 1
1. Out of the depths I cry to you, I cry to you, O Lord. Lord,
1. o-pen your ears and hear my voice, at-tend to the sound of my plea.

Refrain
With the Lord there is mer-cy and the full-ness of re-demp-tion, call to him in your tri-als, he will an-swer when-ev-er you call.
1, 3 to Vss 2, 4
call.
2 to Vs 3
call.
Final
call.
Verses 2, 4
2. If you O Lord, should mark our guilt, then, Lord, who could hope to sur-vive? But with you is found for-give-ness of sin, and mer-cy that we might re-vere you.
4. More than the sen-ti-nels wait for the dawn, let Is-ra-el wait for the Lord. For kind-ness is his, re-demp-tion for all, for-give-ness of sins for his peo-ple.
to Refrain
Verse 3
3. Trust in the Lord, count on his word, wait for the Lord, my soul. I will wait for the Lord all the days of my life as sen-ti-nels wait for the dawn.
to Refrain

Text: Based on Psalm 130; Michael Joncas, b. 1951,
Music: Michael Joncas,

276 SAVE YOUR PEOPLE

Refrain

Save your peo-ple, O Lord. Show us the way to come home. We have been wan-der-ing far from your love. Save your peo-ple, O Lord.

Verses

1. One thing I ask, O Lord, this I seek: to dwell for - ev - er in your house, that I may gaze on your love - li - ness all the days of my life.
2. For you will hide me in the shel - ter of your wings and from the ar - rows of my foes. You set me high on a moun-tain-top, saved me from my dis - tress.
3. Lis - ten, O Lord, to the sound of my call, for I ac - knowl - edge my of - fense. Wash me and I shall be pur - i - fied. I shall be whit - er than snow.
4. Thus will I bless you all the days of my life. Lift - ing my hands, I call your name: "O Lord, re - mem - ber your in - her - i - tance. Save your peo - ple, O Lord!"

to Refrain

Text: Based on Psalm 27; Jim Farrell, b. 1947.
Music: Jim Farrell.

277 LORD, WHO THROUGHOUT THESE FORTY DAYS

1. Lord, who through - out these for - ty days, For
2. As you with Sa - tan did con - tend, And
3. As you did hun - ger bear and thirst, So
4. And through these days of pen - i - tence, And
5. A - bide with us that when this life Of

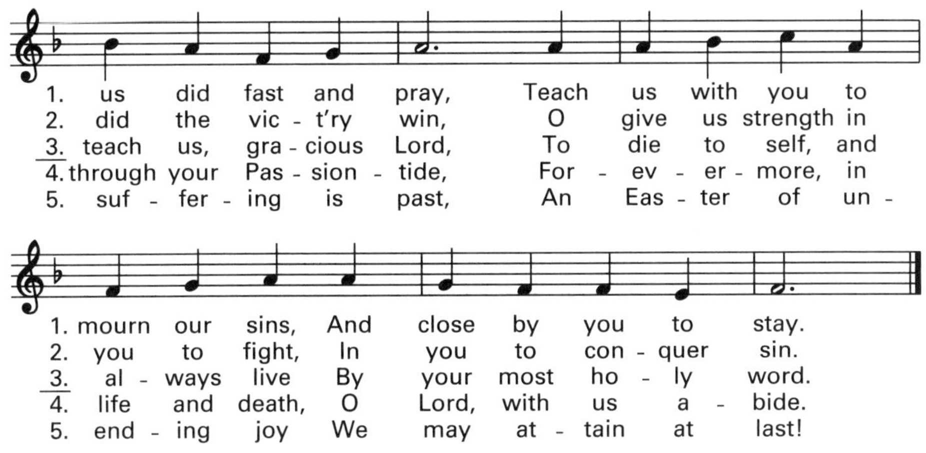
1. us did fast and pray, Teach us with you to
2. did the vic - t'ry win, O give us strength in
3. teach us, gra - cious Lord, To die to self, and
4. through your Pas - sion - tide, For - ev - er - more, in
5. suf - fer - ing is past, An Eas - ter of un -
1. mourn our sins, And close by you to stay.
2. you to fight, In you to con - quer sin.
3. al - ways live By your most ho - ly word.
4. life and death, O Lord, with us a - bide.
5. end - ing joy We may at - tain at last!

Text: CM; Claudia F. Hernaman, 1838–1898, alt.
Music: ST. FLAVIAN; *The Whole Psalmes in Foure Partes*, 1563; adapt. by Richard Redhead, 1820–1901.

Somebody's Knockin' at Your Door 278

1, 6. Some-bod - y's knock-in' at your door; Some-bod - y's knock-in' at your

1, 6. door; O sin - ner, why don't you an - swer? Some-bod - y's

1, 6. knock - in' at your door.

(Fine) Cantor

2. Knocks like Je - sus,
3. Can't you hear him?
4. Je - sus calls you,
5. Can't you trust him?

All

2-5. Some-bod - y's knock-in' at your door.

Cantor

2. Knocks like Je - sus,
3. Can't you hear him?
4. Je - sus calls you,
5. Can't you trust him?

All

2-5. Some-bod - y's knock-in' at your door. O sin - ner,

2-5. why don't you an-swer? Some-bod - y's knock-in' at your door.

Text and music: Spiritual.

279 SEEK THE LORD

Refrain

*a. Seek the Lord whose mercy abounds;
a. call aloud to God who is near.

**b. *Seek the Lord while he may be found;*
b. *call to him while he is still near.*

Verses 1-3

1a. Today is the day and now the proper hour to forsake our sinful lives and turn to the Lord.
2a. As high as the sky is above the earth, so high above our ways, the ways of the Lord.
3a. Open your heart to hear the voice of God, whose words, whose ways lead us to life.

1b. *Today is the day and now the proper hour to forsake our sinful lives and turn to the Lord.*
2b. *As high as the sky is above the earth, so high above our ways, the ways of the Lord.*
3b. *Finding the Lord, let us cling to him. His words, his ways lead us to life.*

to Refrain

Verse 4

4a. Someday we'll live in the house of God;
4b. *Someday we'll live in the house of God;*

4a. hearts full of praise for God's gracious love.
4b. *gaze on his face and praise his name.*

to Refrain

*Composer's revised text
**Original text

Text: Based on Isaiah 55:6–9; Roc O'Connor, SJ, b. 1949.
Music: Roc O'Connor, SJ.

Turn to Me

280

Refrain
Turn to me, O turn, and be saved, says the Lord, for
I am God; there is no oth-er, none be-
side me. I call your name.
3
Verse 1
1. I am God, who com-forts you; who are
1. you to be a-fraid of flesh that fades, is
1. made like the grass of the field, soon to with-er.
to Refrain
Verses 2, 3
2. Lis-ten to me, my peo-ple; give ear to
3. Lift up your eyes to the heav-ens, and look at the
2. me, my na-tion: a law will go forth from
3. earth down be-low. The heav-ens will van-ish like
2. me, and my jus-tice for a light to the peo-ple.
3. smoke, and the earth will wear out like a gar-ment.
to Refrain

Text: Based on Isaiah 45:22–23; 51:12, 4, 6; John Foley, S.J., b. 1939.
Music: John Foley, S.J.

281 FAITHFUL CROSS

Verses

1. Who shall dare to sing the prais - es Of the gal - lows
2. Might - y is the arm of Cae - sar Who to God's own
3. "Bet - ter one life than the na - tion," Ar - gue those who
4. Love's as - tound-ing trans - for - ma - tion Gilds the in - stru -
5. Lift - ed up, his heart laid o - pen, Robbed of breath, his

1. tree whose limbs Bore the car - pen - ter of Naz-'reth,
2. name pre - tends. Strong the i - ron of the ar - row,
3. plot and arm. Guard - ing their civ - i - li - za - tion:
4. ment of death, Love con - founds so - phis - ti - ca - tion,
5. bod - y torn, Still his arms re - call the rain - bow

1. Tree whose wood was borne by him? Sing as his dear
2. Strong - er still the oak that bends. Christ's the em - pire
3. Vi - o - lence and threats of harm. Thus are proph - ets'
4. Takes a - way the cyn - ic's breath. Ev - er shun - ning
5. Prom - is - ing a world re - born. Gaz - ing on the

1. blood and spir - it, Min - gling with the air and
2. un - like oth - ers, All must put a - way the
3. voic - es si - lenced. Priv - i - lege that fears its
4. pow'r and glo - ry, Love has stripped the cross of
5. cross, look up - ward, 'til his heart ar - rests the

1. earth, Make the tree a new cre - a - tion,
2. sword. Here the king be - comes the ser - vant.
3. loss Sum - mons ser - vants of the vio - lence,
4. shame, So God saved the hu - man sto - ry,
5. glance, And his arms di - rect us out - ward

1, 3 — 3 — 2, 4, 5

1. Re - cre - ate the u - ni - verse.
2. He who wash - es feet is 2. Lord.
3. Forg - es nails and builds the cross.
4. Tak - ing hu - man flesh and 4. name.
5. To the world, with heal - ing 5. hands.

Refrain
Ris-ing from the earth to heav-en, Stretched be-tween the mud and stars, Ter-ri-ble in pain and pur-pose, Beau-ti-ful the wood-en bars. Root-ed in the glades of E-den, Tree that shaped the sav-ing ark, Light your frail hu-man bur-den: He the light un-dimmed by dark.
5

The Children of Jerusalem 282

(Palm Sunday Processional)

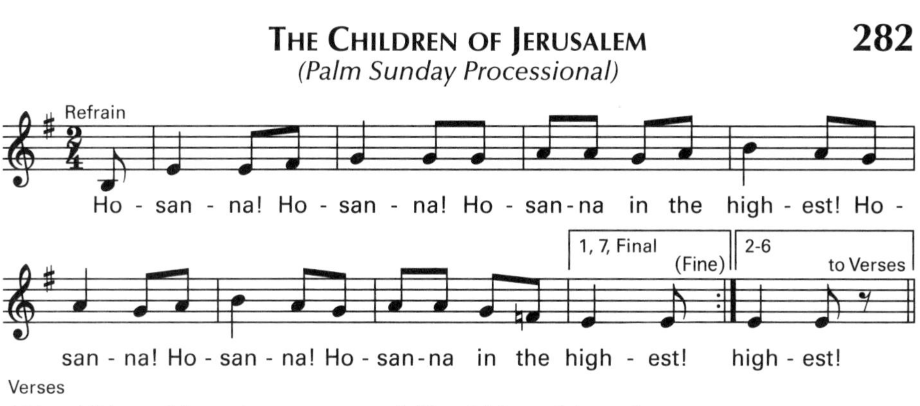
Refrain
Ho-san-na! Ho-san-na! Ho-san-na in the high-est! Ho-san-na! Ho-san-na! Ho-san-na in the high-est! high-est!
1, 7, Final
(Fine)
2-6
to Verses

Verses

1. The children of Jerusalem
they welcomed Christ the King;
they all went out to meet him
and loudly did they sing!

2. The children of Jerusalem
they welcomed Christ the King;
they carried olive branches
and loudly did they sing!

3. Hosanna! Hosanna!
Hosanna in the highest!
Hosanna! Hosanna!
Hosanna in the highest!

4. The children of Jerusalem
they welcomed Christ the King;
they spread their cloaks before him
and loudly did they sing!

5. The children of Jerusalem
they welcomed Christ the King;
proclaiming resurrection
and loudly did they sing!

283 Hosanna to the Son of David

Refrain

Ho - san - na to the Son of Da - vid! O blest is he, O blest is he who comes in the name of the Lord!

Verses

1. Re - joice, daugh - ter of Zi - on, in the One who brings great joy!
2. Re - joice, all who are thirst - ing for the streams of liv - ing joy!
3. Re - joice, all who are long - ing to be - hold the face of God!
4. Re - joice, all who are search - ing for the truth of ho - ly light!
5. Re - joice, all who are hop - ing for the reign of peace and love!
6. Re - joice, all who are wait - ing for the dawn of heav - en's light!
7. Re - joice, all who are call - ing on the name of God on high!
8. Re - joice, all who are hun - gry for the taste of liv - ing bread!

Sing praise, chil - 1-8. - dren of Ju - dah, for the Lord is close at hand!

to Refrain

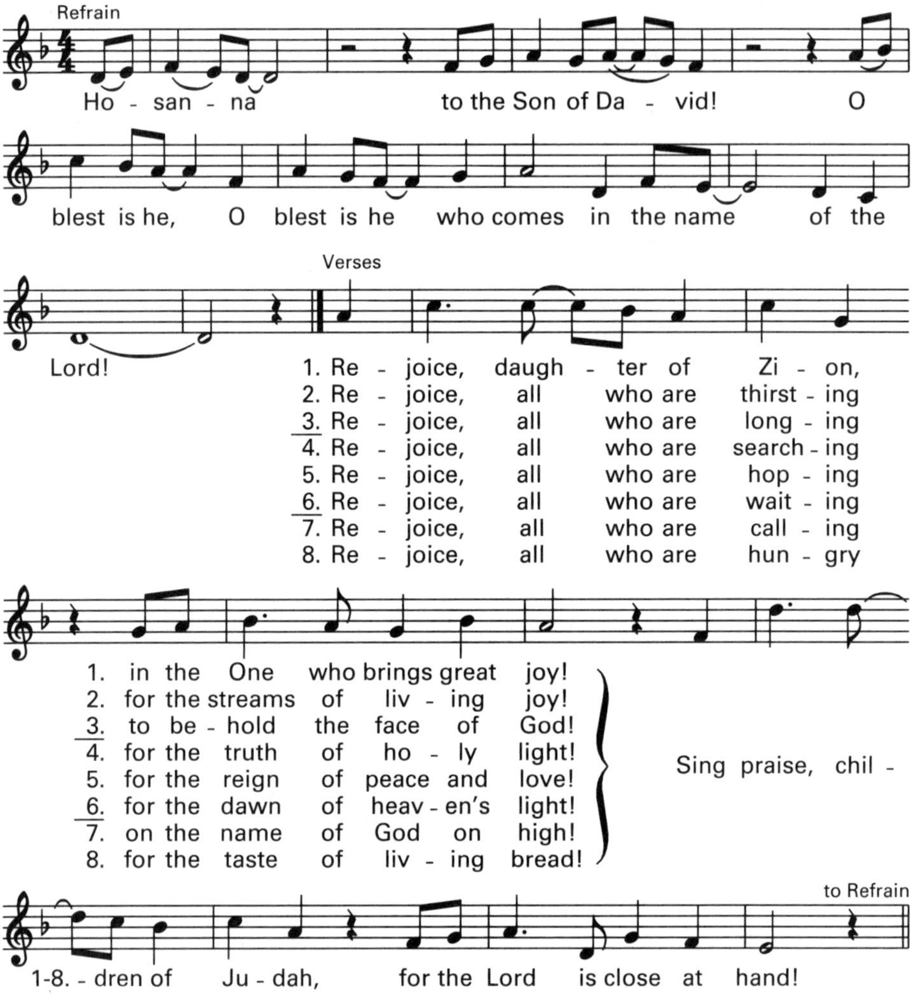

Text: Refrain based on Matthew 21:9; Dan Schutte, b. 1947.
Music: Dan Schutte.

284 All Glory, Laud, and Honor

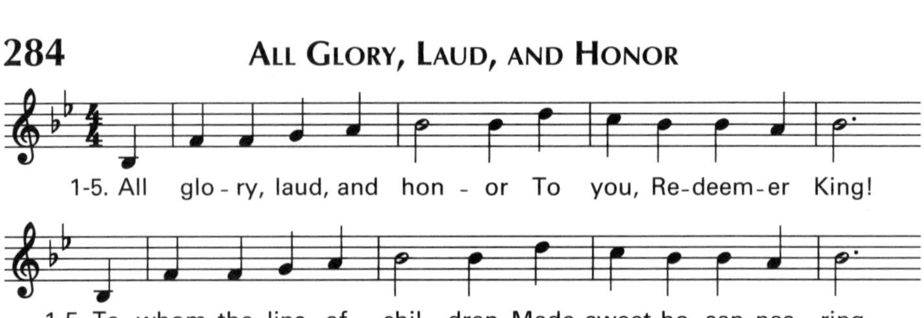
1-5. All glo - ry, laud, and hon - or To you, Re-deem-er King!
1-5. To whom the lips of chil - dren Made sweet ho-san-nas ring.

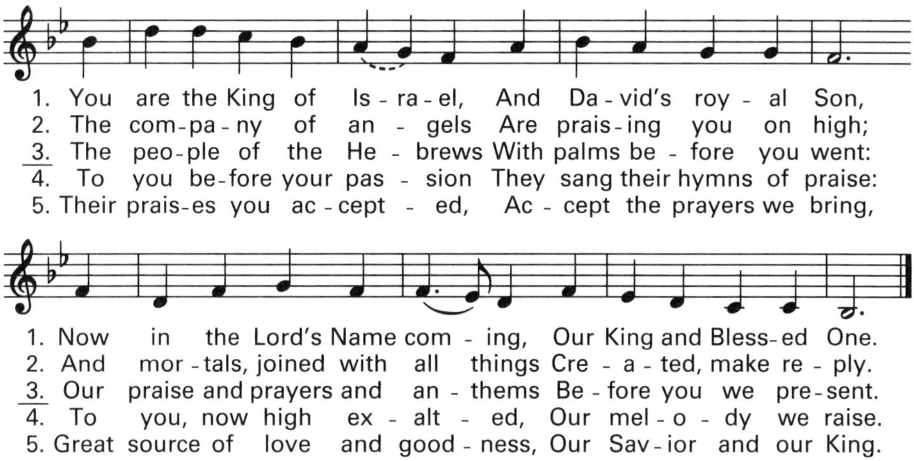

1. You are the King of Is - ra - el, And Da - vid's roy - al Son,
2. The com - pa - ny of an - gels Are prais - ing you on high;
3. The peo - ple of the He - brews With palms be - fore you went:
4. To you be - fore your pas - sion They sang their hymns of praise:
5. Their prais - es you ac - cept - ed, Ac - cept the prayers we bring,

1. Now in the Lord's Name com - ing, Our King and Bless - ed One.
2. And mor - tals, joined with all things Cre - a - ted, make re - ply.
3. Our praise and prayers and an - thems Be - fore you we pre - sent.
4. To you, now high ex - alt - ed, Our mel - o - dy we raise.
5. Great source of love and good - ness, Our Sav - ior and our King.

Text: 76 76 D; Theodulph of Orleans, ca. 760–821; tr. by John M. Neale, 1818–1866, alt.
Music: ST. THEODULPH; Melchior Teschner, 1584–1635.

Blessings on the King 285

Refrain *Ho - san - nah! Ho - san - nah! Bless - ings on the King! Ho - san - nah! Ho - san - nah! Son of God, we sing! Ho - san - nah! Ho - san - nah! Bless - ings on the King! We praise you, we bless you, our gifts to you we bring.*

Verses
1. Your peo - ple are gath - ered on this ho - ly day, to lay down be - fore you, branch - es on your way. We sing of your glo - ry as you en - ter in. Come now, Lord Je - sus, wash a - way our sin.
2. O Lord, you are King now, King of all the earth. The stars in the heav - ens shine on our re - birth. Your death and your ris - ing give to us new life. No long - er in dark - ness, now we have your light.
3. You are our broth - er, broth - er and friend, sent by the Fa - ther, all our hearts to mend. We pray now, Lord Je - sus, as you come to - day. Please guide us now with you as you go your way.
4. The meek and the low - ly gath - er now to sing; to sing out their prais - es to the hum - ble King. Yours is the King - dom of peace and joy and love. The Fa - ther has sent us his Spir - it from a - bove.

Text and music: Michael Lynch, b. 1945,

286 As I Have Done for You

Refrain

I, your Lord and Mas-ter, now be-come your ser-vant.

I who made the moon and stars will kneel to wash your feet.

This is my com-mand-ment: to love as I have loved you.

Kneel to wash each oth-er's feet as I have done for you.

Verses

1. All the world will know you are my dis - ci - ples
2. I must leave you now on - ly for a mo-ment.
3. I am like a vine, you are like the branch-es.
4. I have called you friends, now no long - er ser-vants.
5. You will weep for now while the world re - joic - es.
6. I will give you peace; this will be my bless-ing.

1. by the love that you of - fer, the kind - ness you
2. I must go to my Fa - ther to make you a
3. If you cling to my teach - ing you sure - ly will
4. What I told you in se - cret, the world longs to
5. But the tears of your sor - row will soon turn to
6. Though the world churns a - round you, I leave you my

1. show. You have heard the voice of God in the
2. home. On the day of my re - turn, I will
3. live. If you make your home in me, I will
4. know. There can be no great - er love than to
5. joy. As a moth - er cries in child-birth and her
6. peace. I have told you all these things that my

1. words that I have spo - ken. You be - held heav-en's
2. come to take you with me to the place I have
3. come to dwell with - in you. You can count on my
4. give your life for oth - ers. As the Fa - ther has
5. pain is turned to glad - ness, you will know great re -
6. peace may dwell with - in you. Let your faith be un -
to Refrain
1. glo - ry and have seen the face of God.
2. prom - ised where your joy will have no end.
3. mer - cy when you ask for what you need.
4. loved me, so I love you as my own.
5. joic - ing on the day of my re - turn.
6. shak - en and your hope be ev - er strong.

Text: Based on John 13—16; Dan Schutte, b. 1947.
Music: Dan Schutte.

287 JESU, JESU

Refrain

Je - su, Je - su, fill us with your love, show
us how to serve the neigh-bors we have from you.

Verses

1. Kneels at the feet of his friends, Si - lent - ly wash - es their
2. Neigh-bors are rich folk and poor, Var - ied in col - or and
3. These are the ones we should serve, These are the ones we should
4. Kneel at the feet of our friends, Si - lent - ly wash-ing their

to Refrain

1. feet, Mas - ter who pours out him - self for them.
2. race, Neigh-bors are near - by and far a - way.
3. love. All these are neigh-bors to us and you.
4. feet, This is the way we should live with you.

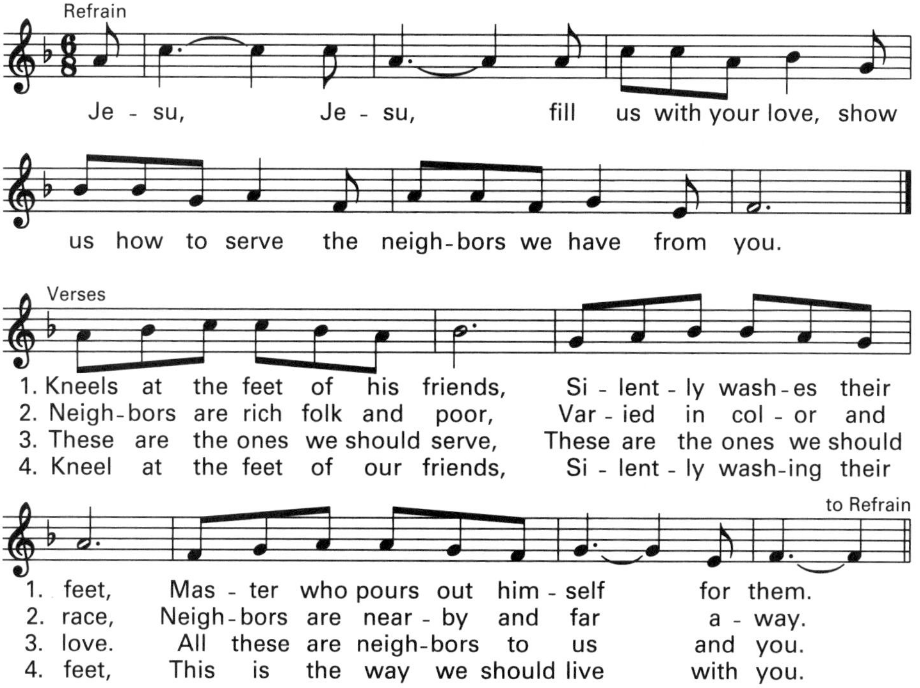

Note: Jesu is pronounced "yay-zoo."

Text: 779 with refrain; John 13:3–5; Ghanaian folk song; tr. by Tom Colvin, b. 1925.
Music: CHEREPONI; Ghanaian folk song; adapt. by Tom Colvin.

288 Where Charity and Love Prevail

1. Where char - i - ty and love pre - vail, There God is ev - er found;
2. With grate - ful joy and ho - ly fear God's char - i - ty we learn;
3. For - give we now each oth - er's faults As we our faults con - fess;
4. Let strife a - mong us be un - known, Let all con - ten - tion cease;
5. Let us re - call that in our midst Dwells God's be - got - ten Son;
6. No race nor creed can love ex - clude, If hon - ored be God's name;

1. Brought here to - geth - er by Christ's love, By love are we thus bound.
2. Let us with heart and mind and soul Now love God in re - turn.
3. And let us love each oth - er well In Chris - tian ho - li - ness.
4. Be God's the glo - ry that we seek, Be ours God's ho - ly peace.
5. As mem - bers of his bod - y joined, We are in Christ made one.
6. Our fam - i - ly em - brac - es all Whose Fa - ther is the same.

Text: CM; *Ubi Caritas*, 9th cent.; tr. by Omer Westendorf, 1916–1997.
Music: CHRISTIAN LOVE; Paul Benoit, OSB, 1893–1979.

289 Glory in the Cross

Holy Thursday
1. Let us ev - er glo - ry in the cross of Christ, our sal -
2. Let us make our jour - ney to the cross of Christ, who sur -
3. Let us tell the sto - ry of the cross of Christ as we
4. Let us stand to - geth - er at the cross of Christ where we

1. va - tion and our hope. Let us bow in hom - age to the
2. ren - dered glo - ry and grace to be - come a ser - vant of the
3. share this heav - en - ly feast. We be - come one bod - y in the
4. see God's bound - less love. We are saints and sin - ners who are

1. Lord of Life, who was bro - ken to make us whole. There is
2. great and small, that all peo - ple may know God's face. Though his
3. blood of Christ, from the great to the ver - y least. When we
4. joined by faith here on earth and in heav'n a - bove. Nei - ther

1. no great-er love, as bless-ed as this: to lay down one's
2. birth was di - vine, he knelt as a slave, to wash com-mon
3. eat of this bread, and drink of this cup, we hon - or the
4. wom - an nor man, not ser - vant or free, but one in the
3
1. life for a friend.
2. dust from our feet.
3. death of the Lord.
4. eyes of the Lord.
Let us ev - er glo-ry in the cross of Christ and the
Fine
1, 2
2
3
1-4. tri-umph of God's great love.

Good Friday

1. Let us ever glory in the cross of Christ
   who redeems us with his blood.
   Let us tell the story of the cross of Christ
   and the pow'r of his saving love.
   Like a lamb he was slain;
   he carried our shame,
   to show us the mercy of God.
   Let us ever glory in the cross of Christ
   and the triumph of God's great love.

2. Let us bring our burdens
   to the cross of Christ
   who has known our sorrow and tears.
   In the great compassion of
   the heart of Christ,
   God has walked in our hopes and fears.
   He was mocked and betrayed,
   deserted by friends, and banished
   to die among thieves.
   Let us ever glory in the cross of Christ
   and the triumph of God's great love.

3. Let us kneel in homage at
   the cross of Christ
   where we see God's human face.
   We behold the Maker of the sun and stars
   as he hangs on the throne of grace.
   As we share in his pain,
   his sorrow and shame,
   our hearts will be tested in fire.
   Let us ever glory in the cross of Christ
   and the triumph of God's great love.

Easter

1. Let us ever glory in the cross of Christ,
   our salvation and our hope.
   Let us bow in homage to the Lord of Life,
   who was broken to make us whole.
   There is no greater love, as blessed as this:
   to lay down one's life for a friend.
   Let us ever glory in the cross of Christ
   and the triumph of God's great love.

2. Let us ever glory in the cross of Christ
   who is risen from the grave.
   He will come in glory to receive our hearts
   at the dawn of the lasting day.
   For the trumpet will sound,
   the dead shall be raised,
   and death shall defeat us no more.
   Let us ever glory in the cross of Christ
   and the triumph of God's great love.

3. Let us raise our voices to the cross of Christ
   where the earth and heaven unite.
   God has wed creation on the tree of hope
   where the darkness becomes our light.
   Let us join in the dance of heaven and earth,
   give thanks for the goodness of God.
   Let us ever glory in the cross of Christ
   and the triumph of God's great love.

290 NO GREATER LOVE

Refrain

There can be no great - er love than to lay

down your life for a friend.

Verses

1. On the night on which our Sav - ior was be - trayed,
2. Then the Lord when he had eat - en with his friends,
3. "If I, your Lord and Teach - er, wash your feet,
4. "This is my com - mand - ment: love each oth - er;
5. "Let not your hearts be troub - led or a - fraid.
*6. Come, be - hold the cross on which our Sav - ior hung.
7. If you live, you live not on - ly for your - self;
8. All flesh is grass and beau - ty fad - ing;

1. the ___ Lord broke bread and passed it 'round:
2. be - gan to wash their feet and said:
3. then ___ you must wash each oth - er's feet.
4. as ___ I have loved you, you must do.
5. I ___ go be - fore you un - to death.
6. He ___ gave his life to set us free.
7. when you die, you die not for your - self.
8. ash - es to ash - es, dust to dust.

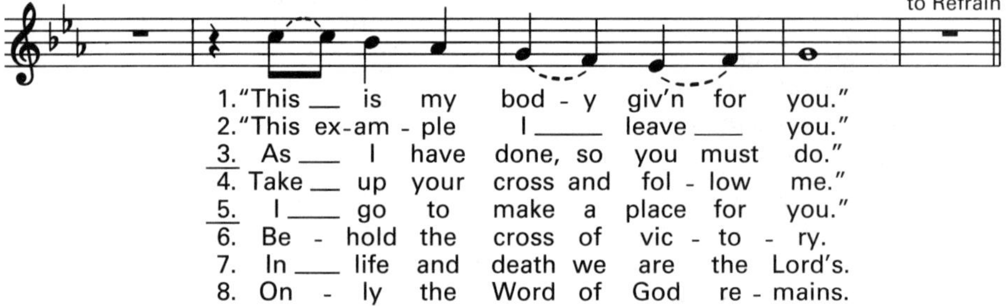
to Refrain
1. "This ___ is my bod - y giv'n for you."
2. "This ex - am - ple I ___ leave ___ you."
3. As ___ I have done, so you must do."
4. Take ___ up your cross and fol - low me."
5. I ___ go to make a place for you."
6. Be - hold the cross of vic - to - ry.
7. In ___ life and death we are the Lord's.
8. On - ly the Word of God re - mains.

*Verses 6–8: Good Friday

Text: Refrain, John 15:13; verses 1–5 for Holy Thursday, 1 Corinthians 11:23–24; John 13:4–5, 14–15, 34; 14:1–4; verses 6–8 for Good Friday, Good Friday Liturgy; Romans 14:7–8; Isaiah 40:6–8; adapt. by Tim Schoenbachler, b. 1952.
Music: Tim Schoenbachler.

291 PANGE, LINGUA, GLORIOSI/ SING, MY TONGUE, THE SAVIOR'S GLORY

*
1. Pan - ge, lin - gua, glo - ri - ó - si Cór - po - ris my - sté - ri - um
2. No - bis da - tus, no - bis na - tus Ex in - tá - cta Vír - gi - ne,
3. In su - pré - mae no - cte coe - nae, Ré - cum - bens cum frá - tri - bus,
4. Ver - bum ca - ro, pa - nem ve - rum Ver - bo car - nem éf - fi - cit:
**
5. Tan - tum er - go Sa - cra - mén - tum Ve - ne - ré - mur cér - nu - i:
6. Ge - ni - tó - ri, Ge - ni - tó - que Laus et ju - bi - lá - ti - o,
1. San - gui - nís - que pre - ti - ó - si, Quem in mun - di pré - ti - um
2. Et in mun - do con - ver - sá - tus, Spar - so ver - bi sé - mi - ne,
3. Ob - ser - vá - ta le - ge ple - ne Ci - bis in le - gá - li - bus,
4. Fit - que san - guis Chri - sti me - rum, Et si sen - sus dé - fi - cit,
5. Et an - tí - quum do - cu - mén - tum No - vo ce - dat rí - tu - i:
6. Sa - lus, ho - nor, vir - tus quo - que Sit et be - ne - dí - cti - o:
1. Fru - ctus ven - tris ge - ne - ró - si Rex ef - fú - dit gén - ti - um.
2. Su - i mo - ras in - co - lá - tus Mi - ro clau - sit ór - di - ne.
3. Ci - bum tur - bae du - o - dé - nae Se dat su - is má - ni - bus.
4. Ad fir - mán - dum cor sin - cé - rum So - la fi - des súf - fi - cit.
5. Prae - stet fi - des sup - ple - mén - tum Sén - su - um de - fé - ctu - i.
6. Pro - ce - dén - ti ab u - tró - que Com - par sit lau - dá - ti - o.

* 1. Sing, my tongue, the Savior's glory,
Of his flesh the mystery sing;
Of the Blood, all price exceeding,
Shed by our immortal King,
Destined for the world's redemption,
From a noble womb to spring.

2. Of a pure and spotless virgin
Born for us on earth below,
He, as man, with us conversing,
Stayed, the seeds of truth to sow;
Then he closed in solemn order
Wondrously his life of woe.

3. On the night of that last supper,
Seated with his chosen band,
He, the Paschal victim eating,
First fulfills the Law's command;
Then as food, to the disciples
Gives himself with his own hand.

4. Word made flesh, the bread of nature
By his word to flesh he turns;
Wine into his blood he changes:
What though sense no change discerns?
Only be the heart in earnest,
Faith its lesson quickly learns.

** 5. Down in adoration falling,
This great sacrament we hail;
Over ancient forms of worship
Newer rites of grace prevail;
Faith will tell us Christ is present,
When our human senses fail.

6. To the everlasting Father,
And the Son who made us free,
And the Spirit, God proceeding
From them each eternally,
Be salvation, honor, blessing,
Might and endless majesty.

*Verses 1–4 are repeated as necessary until the procession reaches the place of repose.

**Verses 5–6 are sung while the priest, kneeling, incenses the Blessed Sacrament. Then the Blessed Sacrament is placed in the tabernacle of repose.

Text: 87 87 87; *Pange lingua gloriosi* and *Tantum ergo*; St. Thomas Aquinas, 1227–1274; *Liber Hymnarius*, 1983; tr. by Edward Caswall, 1814–1878.
Music: ST. THOMAS (TANTUM ERGO); John F. Wade, 1711–1786.

292 DONDE HAY AMOR Y CARIDAD/ WHERE CHARITY AND LOVE ABOUND

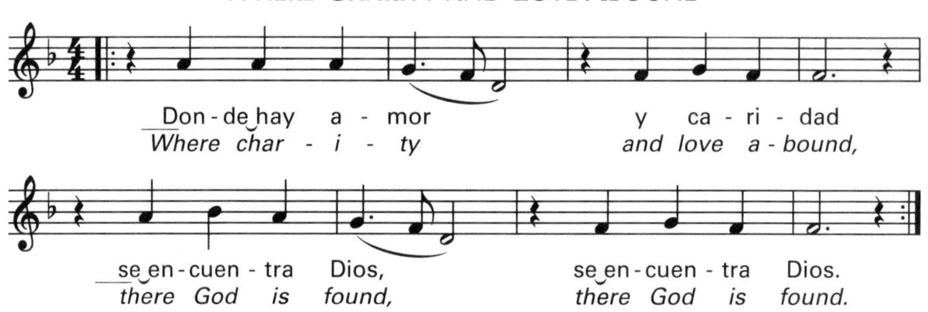
Don-de hay a - mor y ca - ri - dad
Where char - i - ty and love a - bound,
se en - cuen - tra Dios, se en - cuen - tra Dios.
there God is found, there God is found.

1. Tanto nos amó
   que Dios su Hijo nos mandó.
2. El que vive en el amor
   está en Dios y Dios en él.
3. No hay más grande amor
   que dar la vida por otro.
4. Ámense ustedes
   como yo los amé.

1. *God so loved the world*
   that he gave his only Son.
2. *All who abide in love,*
   abide in God and God in them.
3. *There is no greater love*
   than to lay down your life for friends.
4. *Love one another*
   as my love has been for you.

Text: Based on *Ubi Caritas*; John 3:16; 15:12–13; 1 John 4:16; Pedro Rubalcava, b. 1958.
Music: Pedro Rubalcava.

293 THE LORD JESUS

Refrain

The Lord Je - sus, af - ter eat-ing with his friends,
washed their feet and said to them: "Do you know what I, your
Lord, have done to you? I have giv - en you ex -
am - ple that so you al - so should do."

Verses

1. "You ___ are my friends: and you can have no great - er
2. "Peace I leave with you, my peace I give to all who
3. "I ___ am the vine and you, the branch: re - main in
4. "Those who come to me will nev - er thirst nor want for

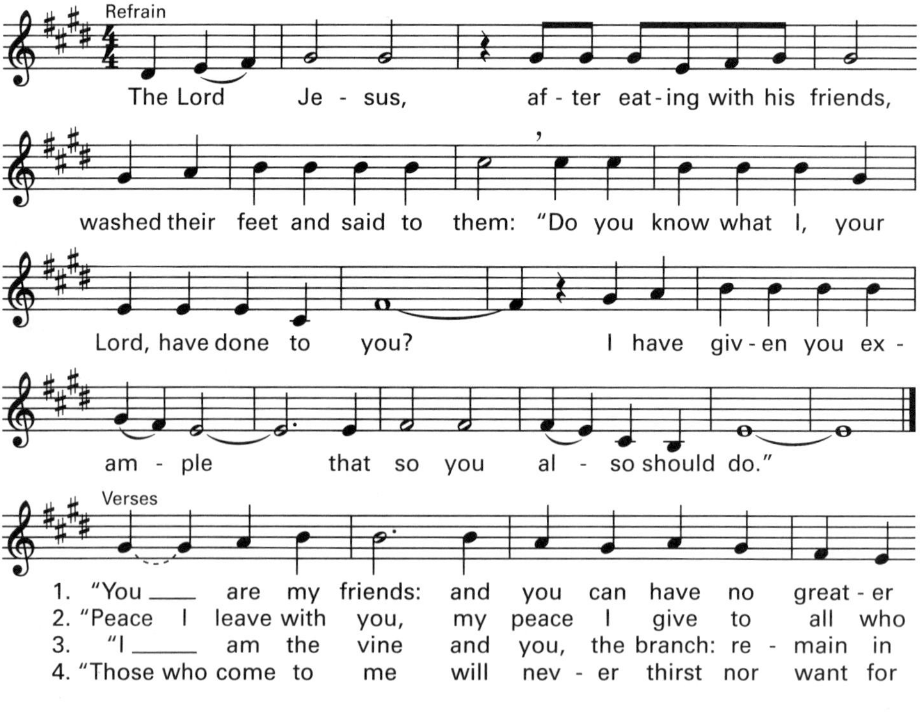

to Refrain
1. love than to give your life ___ for ___ your ___ friends."
2. live with ___ sin-cere love for ev - 'ry ___ one."
3. me and ___ you will bear a - bun - dant ___ fruit."
4. food, and ___ I will raise them up on the last day."

Text and music: Weston Priory, Gregory Norbet, OSB, b. 1940,

O Sacred Head 294

Verses 1, 2, 4

1. O Sa-cred Head, sur-round-ed by crown of pierc-ing thorn! O bleed-ing Head, so wound-ed, re-viled and put to scorn!
2. No come-li-ness or beau-ty your wound-ed face be-trays. Yet an-gel hosts a-dore you and trem-ble as they gaze.
4. Life-giv-ing love, em-pow'r us with cour-age bold and true to walk the road of jus-tice, and bear the cross with you, and bear the cross with you.

1 to Verse 2 · 2 to Verse 3 · Final

Verse 3

3. My sis-ter ren-dered voice-less, de-meaned and still in chains, my broth-er still ex-ploit-ed, im-ag-es of your pain.

to Verse 4

Text: Verses 1 & 2 ascr. to Bernard of Clairvaux, 1091–1153, alt.; verses 3 & 4, Bob Hurd, b. 1950,
Music: Bob Hurd,

295 BEHOLD THE LAMB OF GOD

Verse 1
1. Be-hold the Lamb of God, be-hold the
1. Lamb of God who car-ries our bur-den, who
1. knows our pain, who bears the sins of the world.
Refrain
Be-hold the Lamb of God, be-hold the
Lamb of God; Je - sus,
to Verses 2-4
Fine
Je - sus is the Lamb of God.
Verse 2
2. Sure-ly he has borne our grief and car-ried the
2. sor-rows of us all. Struck down in our stead, re-
to Refrain
2. ject-ed and scorned, and by his wounds we are healed.
Verse 3
3. Fa - ther, for-give them, they do not un-der-stand,
to Refrain
3. they do not un-der-stand what they do.

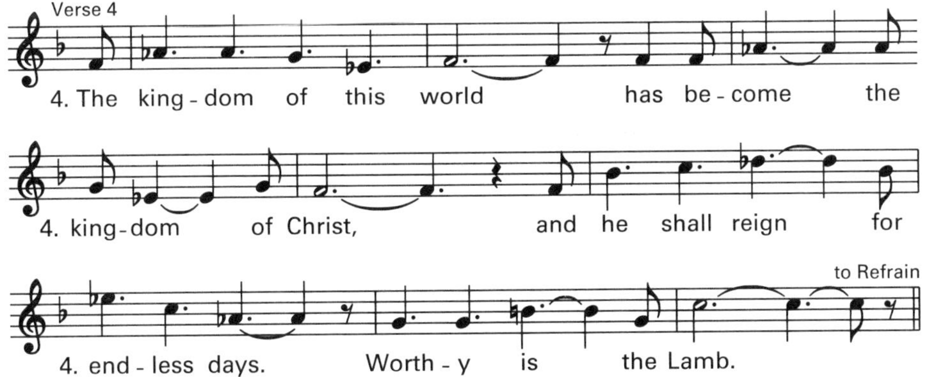
Verse 4
4. The king-dom of this world has be-come the
4. king-dom of Christ, and he shall reign for
4. end-less days. Worth-y is the Lamb.
to Refrain

Text: Based on John 1:29; Isaiah 53:4–5; Luke 23:34; Revelation 11:15; Bob Dufford, b. 1943.
Music: Bob Dufford.

Wood of the Cross 296

Refrain

Be-hold the wood of the cross, on which hung the Sav-ior of the world. O come, O come, let us wor-ship, let us a-dore.

Verses

1. O God, my God, why have you a-ban-doned me? Why have you for-sak-en me? Answer me, O God!
2. I am de-spised, re-ject-ed by my peo-ple. How could they for-get me? An-swer me, O God!
3. My bones are bro-ken. They pierce my hands and feet. Why have you a-ban-doned me? An-swer me, O God!
4. The jaws of death are clos-ing in up-on me. The wick-ed laugh and taunt me. An-swer me, O God!
5. You are en-throned in the ho-ly place. In you our fa-thers trust-ed. An-swer me, O God!

to Refrain

Text: Based on the Good Friday Liturgy; Psalm 22; Owen Alstott, b. 1947.
Music: Owen Alstott.

297 O Sacred Head, Surrounded

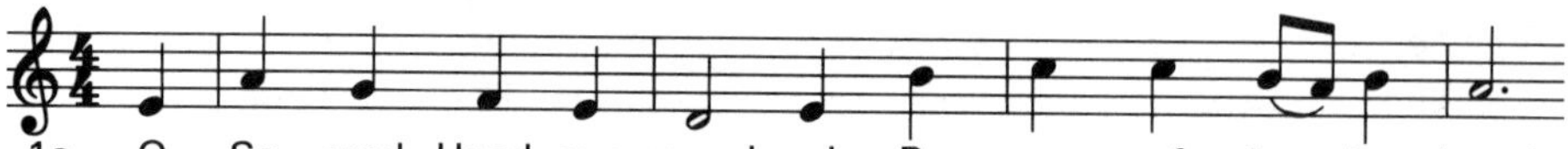

1a. O Sa - cred Head, sur - round - ed By crown of pierc - ing thorn!
2a. In this, your bit - ter pas - sion, Good Shep - herd, think of me
3a. What lan - guage shall I bor - row To thank you, dear - est friend,
*1b. O Sa - cred Head, sur - round - ed By crown of pierc - ing thorn!
2b. O Love, all love tran - scend - ing, O Wis - dom from on high!
3b. O Je - sus, we a - dore thee, Up - on the cross our King!

1a. O bleed - ing Head, so wound - ed, Re - viled and put to scorn!
2a. With your most kind com - pas - sion, Un - worth - y though I be:
3a. For this, your dy - ing sor - row, Your mer - cy with - out end?
1b. O bleed - ing Head, so wound - ed, Re - viled and put to scorn!
2b. O Truth, un - changed, un - chang - ing, Sur - ren - dered up to die!
3b. We hum - bly bow be - fore thee, And of thy vic - t'ry sing!

1a. The pow'r of death comes o'er you, The glow of life de - cays,
2a. Be - neath your cross a - bid - ing, For - ev - er would I rest,
3a. Lord, make me yours for - ev - er, A loy - al ser - vant true,
1b. No come - li - ness or beau - ty Thy wound - ed face be - trays,
2b. Was e'er a love so won - drous! That from his heav'n - ly throne
3b. Thy cross is our sal - va - tion, Our hope from day to day,

1a. Yet an - gel hosts a - dore you, And trem - ble as they gaze.
2a. In your dear love con - fid - ing, And with your pres - ence blest.
3a. And let me nev - er, nev - er Out - live my love for you.
1b. Yet an - gel hosts a - dore thee And trem - ble as they gaze.
2b. God should de - scend a - mong us To suf - fer for his own.
3b. Our peace and con - so - la - tion When life shall fade a - way.

*Alternate verses.

Text: 76 76 D; *Salve caput cruentatum*; ascr. to Bernard of Clairvaux, 1091–1153.
Verses 1, 2 tr. by Henry W. Baker, 1821–1877, alt.; verse 3 tr. by James W. Alexander, 1804–1859, alt.
Alternate verses: verse 1 tr. by Henry W. Baker, alt.; verse 2, Owen Alstott, b. 1947; verse 3, Owen Alstott, composite.

Music: PASSION CHORALE; Hans Leo Hassler, 1564–1612; adapt. by Johann Sebastian Bach, 1685–1750.

298 Behold the Wood

Refrain
Be - hold, be - hold the wood of the cross, on which is
hung our sal - va - tion. O come, let us a - dore.

Verses
1. Un - less a grain of wheat shall fall up - on the ground and die, it
2. And when my hour of glo - ry comes as all was meant to be,
3. For there can be no great - er love shown up - on this land than
4. My Fa - ther, if it be your plan, this cup might pass me by; yet
5. For sure - ly he has borne our tears, is wound - ed by our sin, and
6. My bod - y now is torn with pain, my friends have left and gone. O
to Refrain
1. shall re - main but a sin - gle grain and not give life.
2. you shall see me lift - ed up up - on a tree.
3. in the one who came to die that we might live.
4. let it hap - pen as you will if I must die.
5. yet he o - pens not his mouth that we might live.
6. lov - ing Fa - ther, take my life in - to your hands.

Text: Based on John 12:24, 32; 15:13; Good Friday Liturgy; Dan Schutte, b. 1947.
Music: Dan Schutte.

We Venerate Your Cross/ Tu Cruz Adoramos 299

*Refrain

We ven - er - ate your cross, *tu Cruz a - do - ra - mos, Se - ñor;* we praise your res - ur - rec - tion, *a - la - ba - mos tu re - su - rrec - ción.*

We wor - ship you, O Lord, *te glo - ri - fi - ca - mos, Se - ñor; de la Cruz nos ha ve - ni - do el go - zo,* through the cross you brought joy to the world.

*Verses available in accompaniment books.

Text: English fr. *The Roman Missal* © 1973, ICEL. All rights reserved. Used with permission.
Spanish fr. *Misal Romano* © 1975, Comisión Episcopal de Pastoral Litúrgica de la Conferencia del Episcopado Mexicano. All rights reserved. Sole US agent: US Conference of Catholic Bishops. Used with permission.
Music: Santiago Fernández, b. 1971, © 2004, Santiago Fernández. Published by OCP. All rights reserved.

300 WERE YOU THERE

1. Were you there when they cru - ci - fied my Lord?
2. Were you there when they nailed him to the tree?
3. Were you there when they pierced him in the side?
4. Were you there when the sun re - fused to shine?
5. Were you there when they laid him in the tomb?
6. Were you there when he rose up from the grave?
1. Were you there when they cru - ci - fied my Lord?
2. Were you there when they nailed him to the tree?
3. Were you there when they pierced him in the side?
4. Were you there when the sun re - fused to shine?
5. Were you there when they laid him in the tomb?
6. Were you there when he rose up from the grave?
1-6. Oh! Some - times it caus - es
1-6. me to trem - ble, trem - ble, trem - ble,
1. Were you there when they cru - ci - fied my Lord?
2. Were you there when they nailed him to the tree?
3. Were you there when they pierced him in the side?
4. Were you there when the sun re - fused to shine?
5. Were you there when they laid him in the tomb?
6. Were you there when he rose up from the grave?

Text: 10 10 14 10; Spiritual; *Old Plantation Hymns*, Boston, 1899.
Music: WERE YOU THERE; Spiritual; *Old Plantation Hymns*, Boston, 1899.

PIETÀ 301

Refrain
Come and see what I have done: I've giv - en my
on - ly Son. He lived for you, and he died for you.
Come and see.
Verses
3
1. Lamb __ of God,
2. Cre - a - tor of love,
to Refrain
1. Lamb __ of God, have mer - cy on us; for - give us, Lord.
2. source of all life, have mer - cy on us; for - give us, Lord.

Text and music: Tom Kendzia, b. 1954,

WHEN I SURVEY THE WONDROUS CROSS 302

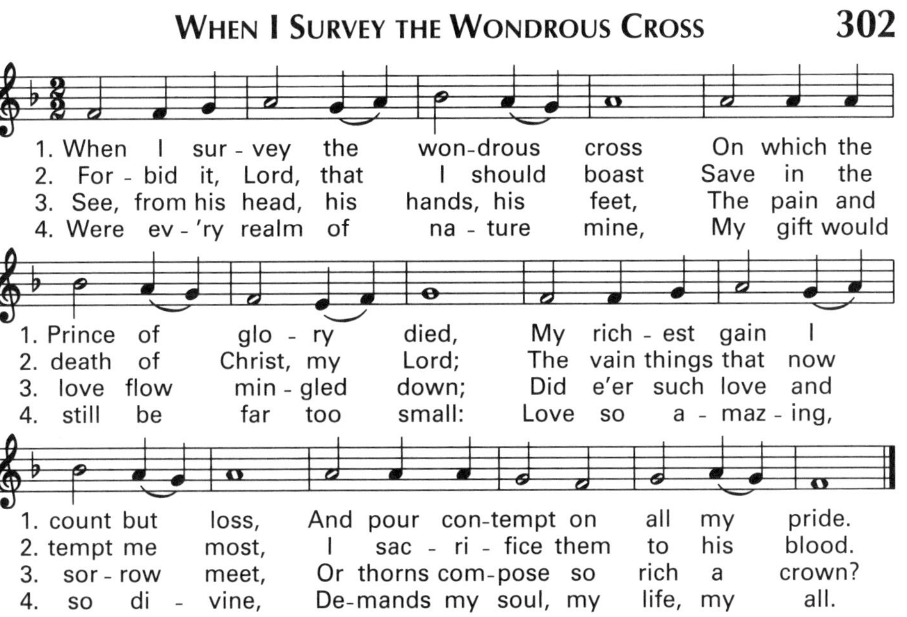
1. When I sur - vey the won - drous cross On which the
2. For - bid it, Lord, that I should boast Save in the
3. See, from his head, his hands, his feet, The pain and
4. Were ev - 'ry realm of na - ture mine, My gift would
1. Prince of glo - ry died, My rich - est gain I
2. death of Christ, my Lord; The vain things that now
3. love flow min - gled down; Did e'er such love and
4. still be far too small: Love so a - maz - ing,
1. count but loss, And pour con-tempt on all my pride.
2. tempt me most, I sac - ri - fice them to his blood.
3. sor - row meet, Or thorns com-pose so rich a crown?
4. so di - vine, De-mands my soul, my life, my all.

Text: LM; Isaac Watts, 1674–1748, alt.
Music: HAMBURG; Lowell Mason, 1792–1872.

303 CHRIST, BE OUR LIGHT

(Easter Vigil Text)

Verses
1. This is the night of new be - gin - nings. This is the
2. This is the night Christ our re - deem - er rose from the
3. Now will the fire kin - dled in dark - ness burn to dis -
4. Sing of the hope deep - er than dy - ing. Sing of the
5. In - to this world morn - ing is break - ing. All of God's
1. night when heav - en meets earth. This is the night
2. grave tri - um - phant and free, leav - ing the tomb of
3. pel the shad - ows of night. Star of the morn - ing,
4. pow'r strong - er than death. Sing of the love
5. peo - ple, lift up your voice. Cry out with joy,
1. filled with God's glo - ry, prom - ise of our new birth!
2. e - vil and dark - ness, emp - ty for all to see.
3. Je - sus our Sav - ior, you are the world's true light!
4. end - less as heav - en, dawn - ing through-out the earth.
5. tell out the sto - ry, all of the earth re - joice.
Refrain
Christ, be our light! Shine in our hearts.
Shine through the dark - ness. Christ, be our light!
Shine in your church gath - ered to - day.

Text and music: Bernadette Farrell, b. 1957,

I Saw Water Flowing 304

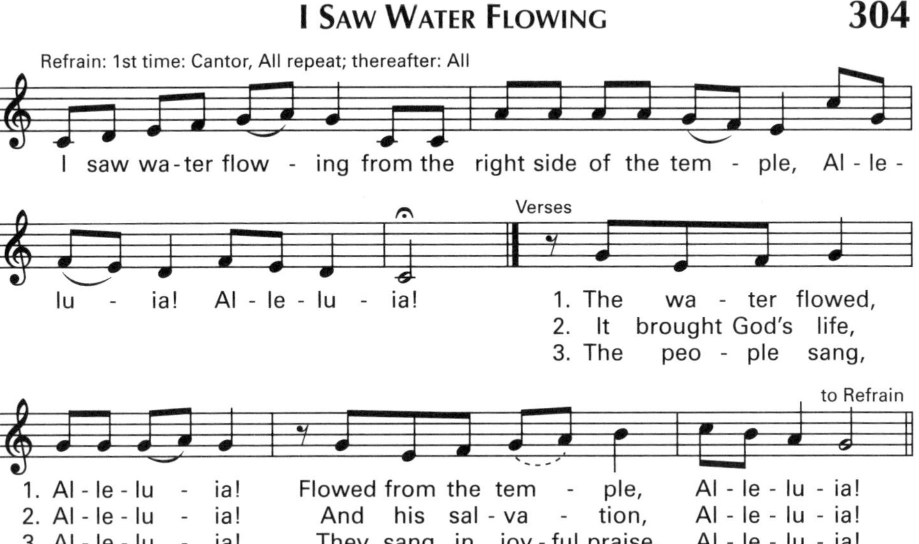
Refrain: 1st time: Cantor, All repeat; thereafter: All
I saw wa-ter flow - ing from the right side of the tem - ple, Al - le - lu - ia! Al - le - lu - ia!
Verses
1. The wa - ter flowed,
2. It brought God's life,
3. The peo - ple sang,
1. Al - le - lu - ia! Flowed from the tem - ple, Al - le - lu - ia!
2. Al - le - lu - ia! And his sal - va - tion, Al - le - lu - ia!
3. Al - le - lu - ia! They sang in joy - ful praise, Al - le - lu - ia!
to Refrain

Text: Based on Ezekiel 47:1–2, 9,
Music: Randall DeBruyn, b. 1947,

Litany of the Saints 305

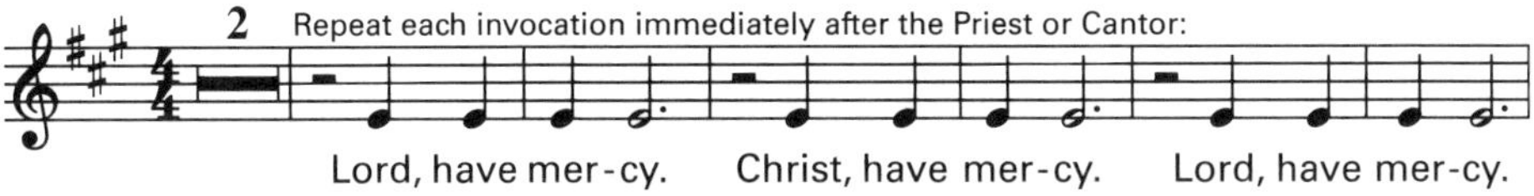

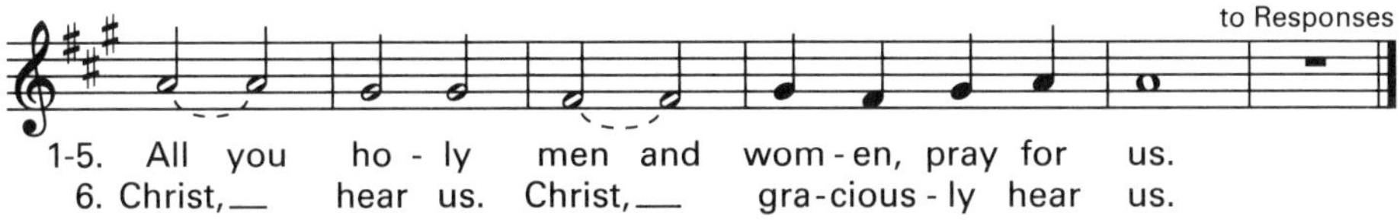

Repeat each invocation immediately after the Priest or Cantor:

Lord, have mer-cy. Christ, have mer-cy. Lord, have mer-cy.

Invocations

Responses: Sing 1-5 four times; 6 two times

(Saint Invocation) 1-4. pray for us.
("Lord, be merciful,") 5. Lord, de - liv - er us, we pray.
("Be merciful to us sinners.") 6. Lord, we ask you, hear our prayer.

1-4. pray for us.
5. Lord, de - liv - er us, we pray.
6. Lord, we ask you, hear our prayer.

1-5. All you ho - ly men and wom - en, pray for us.
6. Christ, hear us. Christ, gra-cious - ly hear us.

to Responses

Music: John D. Becker, b. 1953,

306 OUT OF DARKNESS

Refrain

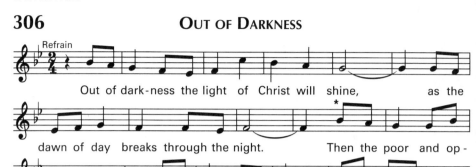

Out of dark-ness the light of Christ will shine, as the dawn of day breaks through the night. *Then the poor and op-pressed will cry out and be heard by the light that ris-es from the night.

Verses

1. Let the darkness flee from here.
   Put an end to sadness and fear.
   The hungry will eat, the sick will dance,
   the dead will live again.
2. This is the night, O holy of nights,
   the chains of death are destroyed.
   This is the light;
   the glory of God is raised to life again.
3. A single flame,
   a flicker of hope spreads like a sea of fire.
   Open the door, shout to the night:
   We will live again.

*Last time, repeat final phrase.

Text and music: Tom Kendzia, b. 1954, © 1998, Tom Kendzia. Published by OCP.

307 LITANY OF THE SAINTS

Cantors
All
Lord, have mer - cy. **Lord, have mer - cy.**
Christ, have mer - cy. **Christ, have mer - cy.**
Lord, have mer - cy. **Lord, have mer - cy.**

Cantors
All
Holy Mary, Mother of Gód, **pray for us.**
Saint Mích - ael,

Holy Angels of Gód,
Saint John the Báptist,
Saint Jóseph,
Saint Peter and Saint Pául,
Saint Ándrew,
Saint Jóhn,
Saint Mary Mágdalene,
Saint Stéphen,
Saint Ignatius of Ántioch,
Saint Láwrence,
Saint Perpetua and Saint Felícity,
Saint Ágnes,
Saint Grégory,
Saint Augústine,
Saint Athanásius,
Saint Básil,
Saint Mártin,
Saint Bénedict,
Saint Francis and Saint Dóminic,
Saint Francis Xávier,
Saint John Viánney,
Saint Catherine of Siéna,
Saint Teresa of Jésus,
All holy men and women, Saints of Gód,

Cantors — All

Lord, be mer-ci-ful, **Lord, de-liv-er us, we pray.**

Cantors — All

From àll é-vil, **Lord, de-liv-er us, we pray.**

From èverý sin,
From everlàsting déath,
By your Ìncarnátion,
By your Death and Rèsurréction,
By the outpouring of the
Hòly Spírit,

Cantors — All

Be merciful to us sin-ners, **Lord, we ask you, hear our prayer.**

If there are candidates to be baptized

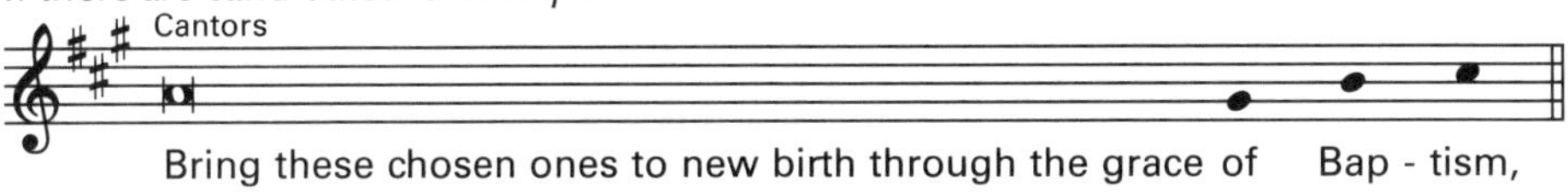

Cantors

Bring these chosen ones to new birth through the grace of Bap-tism,

All

Lord, we ask you, hear our prayer.

If there is no one to be baptized

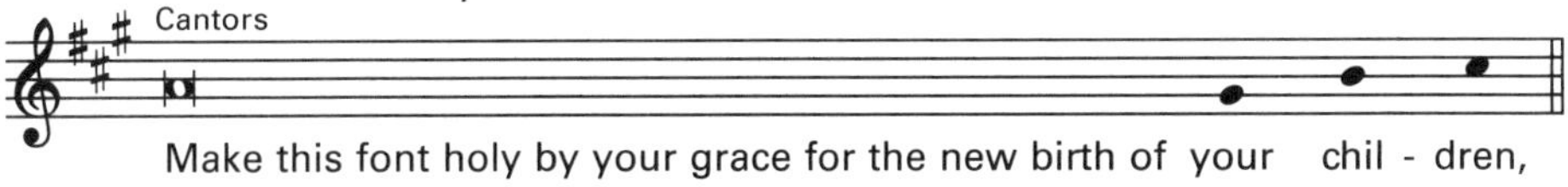

Cantors

Make this font holy by your grace for the new birth of your chil-dren,

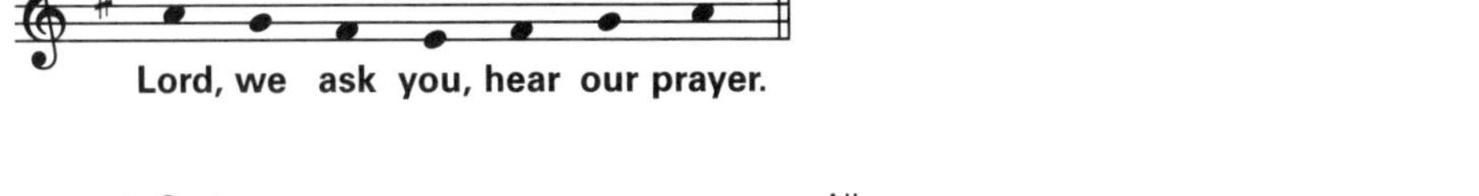
All
Lord, we ask you, hear our prayer.

Cantors
All
Jesus, Son of the liv-ing God, **Lord, we ask you, hear our prayer.**
Cantors, All repeat
Cantors, All repeat
Christ, hear us. Christ, gra-cious-ly hear us.

308 Our Paschal Sacrifice/ El Cordero Pascual

Refrain
Christ has be - come our pas - chal sac - ri - fice; al - le - lu - ia, al - le - lu - ia.
Cris - to, el Cor - de - ro Pas - cual, es in - mo - la - do; a - le - lu - ya, a - le - lu - ya.
Verses
1. Christ yes - ter - day and to - day,
2. All time be - longs to Christ,
3. May the light of the ris - en Christ dis -
4. In this ho - ly night tru - ly blessed,
1. Je - su - cris - to a - yer y hoy,
2. Y de Cris - to es la e - ter - ni - dad,
3. Que la luz de Cris - to glo - rio - so di -
4. Qué no - che tan di - cho - sa: se
to Refrain
1. Christ is the be - gin - ning and the end.
2. his be pow - er, glo - ry ev - er - more.
3. pel the dark - ness of our hearts and minds.
4. we are rec - on - ciled with God him - self.
1. Cris - to es el prin - ci - pio y el fin.
2. pa - ra él la glo - ria y el po - der.
3. si - pe las ti - nie - blas del te - mor.
4. u - ne lo hu - ma - no al mis - mo Dios.

*Last time, repeat final phrase.

Text: Refrain fr. Easter Vigil Communion Antiphon; 1 Corinthians 5:7–8. English refrain © 1973, ICEL. All rights reserved. Used with permission. English verses and all Spanish text by Eleazar Cortés, b. 1947, and Pedro Rubalcava, b. 1958, © 2007, Eleazar Cortés and Pedro Rubalcava. Published by OCP. All rights reserved.
Music: Eleazar Cortés and Pedro Rubalcava, © 2007, Eleazar Cortés and Pedro Rubalcava. Published by OCP. All rights reserved.

ALL SHALL BE WELL 309

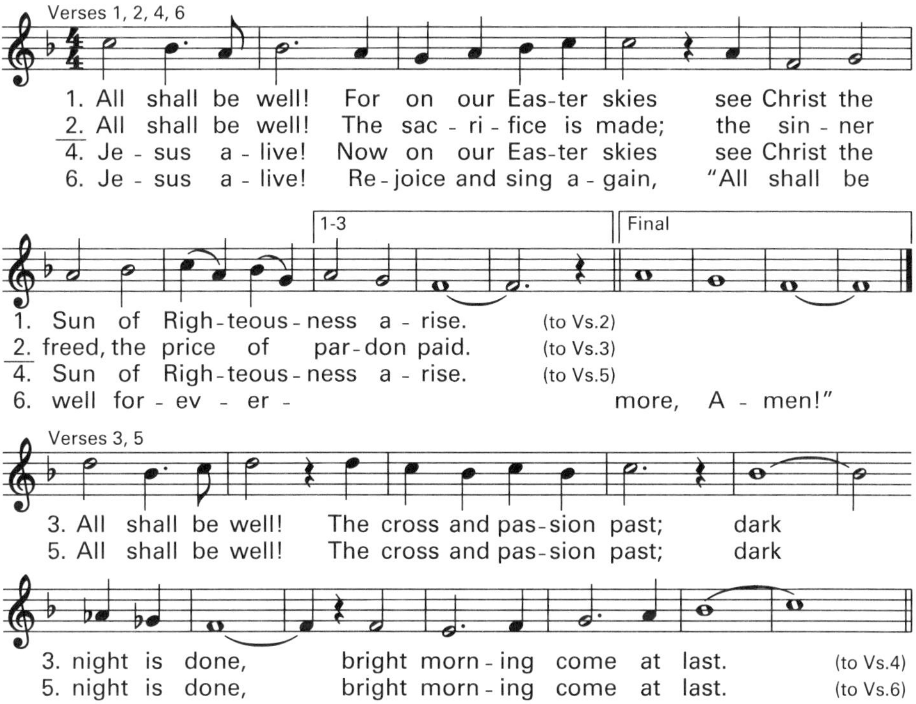

Verses 1, 2, 4, 6

1. All shall be well! For on our Eas-ter skies see Christ the
2. All shall be well! The sac - ri - fice is made; the sin - ner
4. Je - sus a - live! Now on our Eas-ter skies see Christ the
6. Je - sus a - live! Re - joice and sing a - gain, "All shall be

1-3 | Final

1. Sun of Righ-teous - ness a - rise. (to Vs.2)
2. freed, the price of par - don paid. (to Vs.3)
4. Sun of Righ-teous - ness a - rise. (to Vs.5)
6. well for - ev - er - more, A - men!"

Verses 3, 5

3. All shall be well! The cross and pas-sion past; dark
5. All shall be well! The cross and pas-sion past; dark

3. night is done, bright morn - ing come at last. (to Vs.4)
5. night is done, bright morn - ing come at last. (to Vs.6)

Text: Timothy Dudley-Smith, b. 1926,
Music: John Foley, SJ, b. 1939,

CHRISTIANS, TO THE PASCHAL VICTIM 310

(Easter Sequence)

Refrain: 1st time: Cantor, All repeat; thereafter: All
Chris-tians, to the Pas - chal Vic-tim of - fer your thank - ful
1: Repeat Ref.
2-4: to Verses
Final
prais - es! A - men. Al-le - lu - ia.

1. A Lamb the sheep redeems;
   Christ, who only is sinless,
   reconciles sinners to the Father. **(to Vs 2)**
2. Death and life have contended
   in that combat stupendous:
   The Prince of life, who died,
   reigns immortal. **(Ref.)**
3. Speak, Mary, declaring
   what you saw, wayfaring.
   "The tomb of Christ, who is living,
   the glory of Jesus' resurrection; **(to Vs 4)**
4. Bright angels attesting,
   the shroud and napkin resting.
   Yes, Christ my hope is arisen;
   to Galilee he goes before you." **(Ref.)**
5. Christ indeed from death is risen,
   our new life obtaining.
   Have mercy, victor King, ever reigning! **(Ref.)**

Text: Poetic Sequence for Easter, *Victimae paschali laudes*; fr. *The Roman Missal*
Music: Chant, Mode I (alt.); *Graduale Romanum*, 1974; adapt. and arr. by Ken Canedo, b. 1953, arr.

311 ALELUYA, ALELUYA

Estribillo

¡A - le - lu - ya! ¡A - le - lu - ya! ¡A - le - lu - ya!

Estrofas

1. ¡Cris - to Je - sús re - su - ci - tó! Can - tar que -
2. Ya las mu - je - res san - tas van a͜ un - gir el
3. La nue-va͜ un án - gel les da - rá: "Cris - to Je -
4. An - te la nue - va, Pe - dro͜ y Juan a - cu - den
5. Re - su - ci - ta - do, vi - si - tó a Mag - da -
6. A los a - pós - to - les des - pués, se mues - tra͜ y
7. To - más no͜ es - ta - ba͜ y se ne - gó a dar por
8. Je - sús ben - di - jo͜ a quien sin ver y sin du -
9. Los dos a - mi - gos de͜ E - ma - ús du - ran - te
10. Con go - zo can - te͜ al Sal - va - dor la re - di -

1. re - mos en su͜ ho - nor por - que͜ a la muer - te
2. cuer - po del Se - ñor y͜ a su se - pul - cro
3. sús re - su - ci - tó y͜ en su se - pul - cro
4. pres - tos al lu - gar. A Cris - to͜ en él no͜ en -
5. le - na͜ el Sal - va - dor, y͜ e - lla͜ a sus plan - tas
6. dí - ce - les: "Yo soy; mi - rad mis ma - nos
7. cier - to que͜ e - ra Él. Por fin lo vio y
8. dar cre - ye - ra͜ en Él. Ben - di - tos, pues, que -
9. la frac - ción del pan re - co - no - cie - ron
10. mi - da͜ hu - ma - ni - dad y͜ en Él con - fie - se͜ a

1. de - rro - tó. ¡A - le - lu - ya!
2. lle - ga - rán. ¡A - le - lu - ya!
3. ya ___ no͜ es - tá". ¡A - le - lu - ya!
4. con - tra - rán. ¡A - le - lu - ya!
5. se͜ a - rro - jó. ¡A - le - lu - ya!
6. y ___ mis pies". ¡A - le - lu - ya!
7. lo con - fe - só. ¡A - le - lu - ya!
8. rra - mos ser. ¡A - le - lu - ya!
9. a ___ Je - sús. ¡A - le - lu - ya!
10. su ___ Se - ñor. ¡A - le - lu - ya!

al Estribillo

Text: 888 with alleluias; attr. to Jean Tisserand, d. 1494; Spanish tr, anon.
Music: O FILII ET FILIAE; Chant, Mode II; *Airs sur les hymnes sacrez, odes et noëls*, 1623.

312 YE SONS AND DAUGHTERS

Refrain
Al - le - lu - ia! Al - le - lu - ia! Al - le - lu - ia!

Verses

1. Ye sons and daughters, let us sing! The King of heav'n, the glorious King, O'er death today rose triumphing. Alleluia!
2. That Easter morn, at break of day, The faithful women went their way To seek the tomb where Jesus lay. Alleluia!
3. An angel clad in white they see, Who sat, and spoke unto the three, "Your Lord has gone to Galilee." Alleluia!
4. That night the apostles met in fear; Amidst them came their Lord most dear, And said, "My peace be on all here." Alleluia!
5. When Thomas first the tidings heard, How they had seen the risen Lord, He doubted the disciples' word. Alleluia!
6. "My piercèd side, O Thomas, see; My hands, my feet, I show to thee; Not faithless, but believing be." Alleluia!
7. No longer Thomas then denied, He saw the feet, the hands, the side; "Thou art my Lord and God," he cried. Alleluia!
8. How blest are they who have not seen, And yet whose faith has constant been, For they eternal life shall win. Alleluia!
9. On this most holy day of days, To God your hearts and voices raise, In laud, and jubilee and praise. Alleluia!

to Refrain

Text: 888 with alleluias; attr. to Jean Tisserand, d. 1494; tr. by John M. Neale, 1818–1866, alt.
Music: O FILII ET FILIAE; Chant, Mode II; *Airs sur les hymnes sacrez, odes et noëls*, 1623.

Alleluia No. 1 313

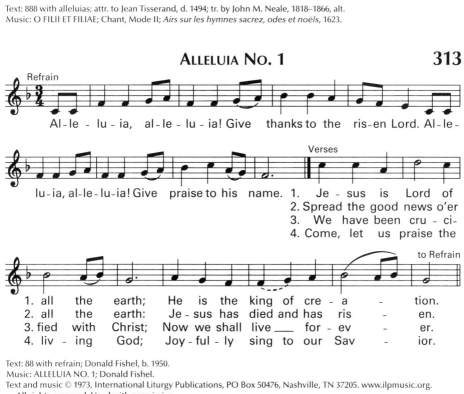

Refrain

Alleluia, alleluia! Give thanks to the risen Lord. Alleluia, alleluia! Give praise to his name.

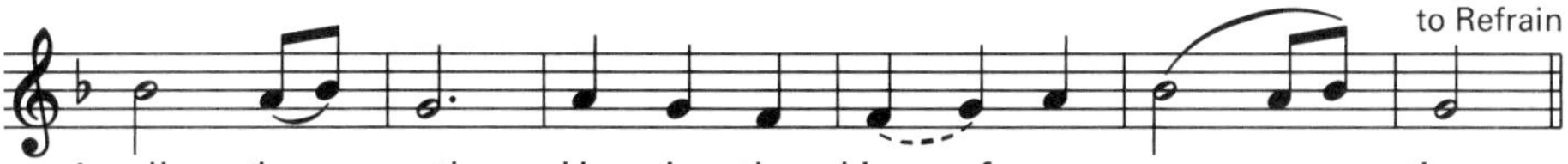

Verses

1. Jesus is Lord of all the earth; He is the king of creation.
2. Spread the good news o'er all the earth: Jesus has died and has risen.
3. We have been crucified with Christ; Now we shall live forever.
4. Come, let us praise the living God; Joyfully sing to our Savior.

to Refrain

Text: 88 with refrain; Donald Fishel, b. 1950.
Music: ALLELUIA NO. 1; Donald Fishel.

314 Alleluia! Love Is Alive

Verses
1. People of God, see the morning is new; rise from your sleeping and run to the tomb. Come and see! Come and see! He is alive! A grave that is empty, a promise fulfilled. God who was with us is here with us still. He is here! He is here! He is alive!
2. People of God, let your fear fall away. Your chains have been broken; abandon your shame. Lift your hearts! Lift your hearts! He is alive! Here now is mercy embracing your soul; here the fulfillment that once was foretold. It is true! It is true! He is alive!
3. People of God now rejoicing in Christ, carry your joy to the darkness of night. Tell the world! Tell the world! He is alive! Hear the good news of this glorious day, every heart singing as heaven proclaims: He is Lord! He is Lord! He is alive!
Refrain
Alleluia! Love is alive; conquered the grave and defeated the night. Alleluia! Love is alive! The Son has arisen for

all. Your peo - ple sing al - le - lu - ia!

JOIN IN THE DANCE 315

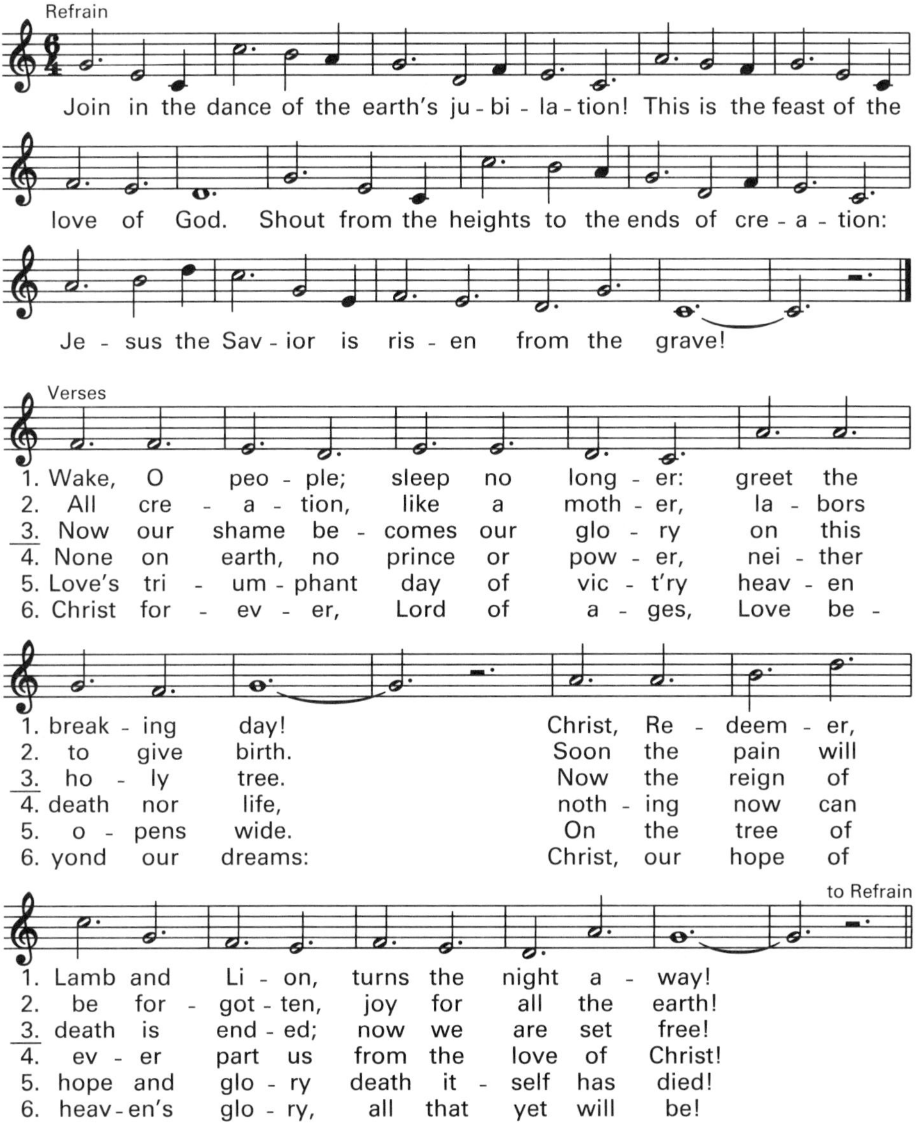

Refrain

Join in the dance of the earth's ju - bi - la - tion! This is the feast of the love of God. Shout from the heights to the ends of cre - a - tion: Je - sus the Sav - ior is ris - en from the grave!

Verses

1. Wake, O peo - ple; sleep no long - er: greet the break - ing day! Christ, Re - deem - er, Lamb and Li - on, turns the night a - way!
2. All cre - a - tion, like a moth - er, la - bors to give birth. Soon the pain will be for - got - ten, joy for all the earth!
3. Now our shame be - comes our glo - ry on this ho - ly tree. Now the reign of death is end - ed; now we are set free!
4. None on earth, no prince or pow - er, nei - ther death nor life, noth - ing now can ev - er part us from the love of Christ!
5. Love's tri - um - phant day of vic - t'ry heav - en o - pens wide. On the tree of hope and glo - ry death it - self has died!
6. Christ for - ev - er, Lord of a - ges, Love be - yond our dreams: Christ, our hope of heav - en's glo - ry, all that yet will be!

to Refrain

316 Behold the Glory of God

Refrain

Be-hold the glo-ry of God, the Day-Star a-ris-ing! Christ Je-sus shines on the earth with mer-cy en-dur-ing.

**Verses

1. Night of hope, night of glo-ry di-vine,
2. Dance for joy, all you an-gels of God;
3. Let the earth in its beau-ty re-joice,
4. Robed a-bout in the light of the day,
5. Bless-ed was the first fall from your grace;
6. O how won-drous the gift of your love,
7. O my God, you are wor-thy in-deed
8. God de-liv-ered our life from the snare
9. Through the fire and the wa-ter you led

1. dark-ness con-quered ev-er-more. Christ tri-um-phant
2. let the pow'rs of heav'n ex-ult. All cre-a-tion,
3. ra-diant as the morn-ing sky. Chains of death lie
4. let the Church take up its praise. Sa-cred walls re-
5. bless-ed was the fate-ful sin. Bless-ed more the
6. ten-der gift on our be-half: to re-deem a
7. to re-ceive our grate-ful song. We ac-claim the
8. with a strong and might-y hand, set us free from
9. with the dark-ness round a-bout. Death was near; the

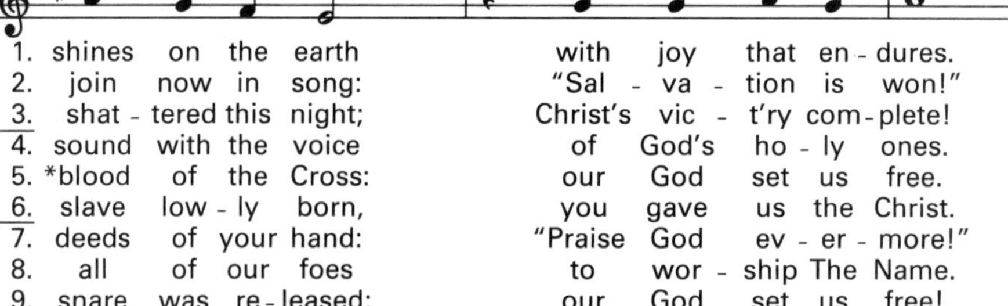
to Refrain
1. shines on the earth with joy that en-dures.
2. join now in song: "Sal-va-tion is won!"
3. shat-tered this night; Christ's vic-t'ry com-plete!
4. sound with the voice of God's ho-ly ones.
5. *blood of the Cross: our God set us free.
6. slave low-ly born, you gave us the Christ.
7. deeds of your hand: "Praise God ev-er-more!"
8. all of our foes to wor-ship The Name.
9. snare was re-leased; our God set us free!

*Verse 5 alt. text: vic-t'ry of Christ
**Additional verses are available in accompaniment books.

Alleluia! Alleluia! Let the Holy Anthem Rise 317

1. Al-le-lu-ia! Al-le-lu-ia! Let the ho-ly an-them rise, And the
2. Al-le-lu-ia! Al-le-lu-ia! Like the sun from out the wave, He has
3. Al-le-lu-ia! Al-le-lu-ia! Bless-ed Je-sus, make us rise From the

1. choirs of heav-en chant it In the tem-ple of the skies; Let the
2. ris-en up in tri-umph From the dark-ness of the grave. He's the
3. life of this cor-rup-tion To the life that nev-er dies. May your

1. moun-tains skip with glad-ness, And the joy-ful val-leys ring With ho-
2. splen-dor of the na-tions, He's the lamp of end-less day; He's the
3. glo-ry be our por-tion, When the days of time are past, And the

1. san-nas in the high-est To our Sav-ior and our King!
2. ver-y Lord of glo-ry Who is ris-en up to-day!
3. dead shall be a-wak-ened By the trum-pet's might-y blast!

Text: 87 87 D; Edward Caswall, 1814–1878.
Music: HOLY ANTHEM; *St. Basil's Hymnal*, 1889.

I Know That My Redeemer Lives 318

1. I know that my Re-deem-er lives! What joy the
2. He lives tri-um-phant from the grave; He lives e-
3. He lives to si-lence all my fears; He lives to
4. He lives, all glo-ry to his name! He lives my
1. blest as-sur-ance gives! He lives, he lives, who
2. ter-nal-ly to save; He lives in maj-es-
3. wipe a-way my tears; He lives to calm my
4. Sav-ior, still the same; What joy this blest as-
1. once was dead; He lives, my ev-er-liv-ing head!
2. ty a-bove; He lives to guide his church in love.
3. trou-bled heart; He lives all bless-ings to im-part.
4. sur-ance gives: I know that my Re-deem-er lives!

Text: LM; based on Job 19:25; Samuel Medley, 1738–1799, alt.
Music: DUKE STREET; John Hatton, ca. 1710–1793.

319 AT THE LAMB'S HIGH FEAST

1. At the Lamb's high feast we sing Praise to our vic - to - rious King, He has washed us in the tide Flow - ing from his o - pen side; Praise we him, whose love di - vine Gives his sa - cred Blood for wine, Gives his Bod - y for the feast, Christ the vic - tim, Christ the priest.
2. Where the Pas - chal blood is poured, Death's dark an - gel sheathes his sword; Is - rael's hosts tri - um - phant go Thru' the wave that drowns the foe. Praise we Christ, whose blood was shed, Pas - chal vic - tim, Pas - chal bread; With sin - cer - i - ty and love Eat we man - na from a - bove.
3. Eas - ter tri - umph, Eas - ter joy, Sin a - lone can this de - stroy; From sin's pow'r do thou set free Souls new - born, O Lord, in thee. Hymns of glo - ry, songs of praise, Fa - ther, un - to thee we raise: Ris - en Lord, all praise to thee With the Spir - it ev - er be.

Text: 77 77 D; *Ad regias Agni dapes;* Latin, 4th cent.; tr. by Robert Campbell, 1814–1868, alt.
Music: SALZBURG; Jakob Hintze, 1622–1702; adapt. by Johann Sebastian Bach, 1685–1750.

320 CHRIST, THE LORD, IS RISEN TODAY

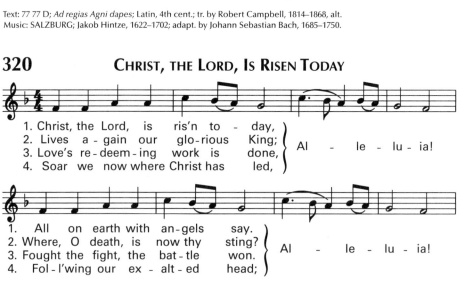

1. Christ, the Lord, is ris'n to - day, Al - le - lu - ia!
All on earth with an - gels say. Al - le - lu - ia!
2. Lives a - gain our glo - rious King; Al - le - lu - ia!
Where, O death, is now thy sting? Al - le - lu - ia!
3. Love's re - deem - ing work is done, Al - le - lu - ia!
Fought the fight, the bat - tle won. Al - le - lu - ia!
4. Soar we now where Christ has led, Al - le - lu - ia!
Fol - l'wing our ex - alt - ed head; Al - le - lu - ia!

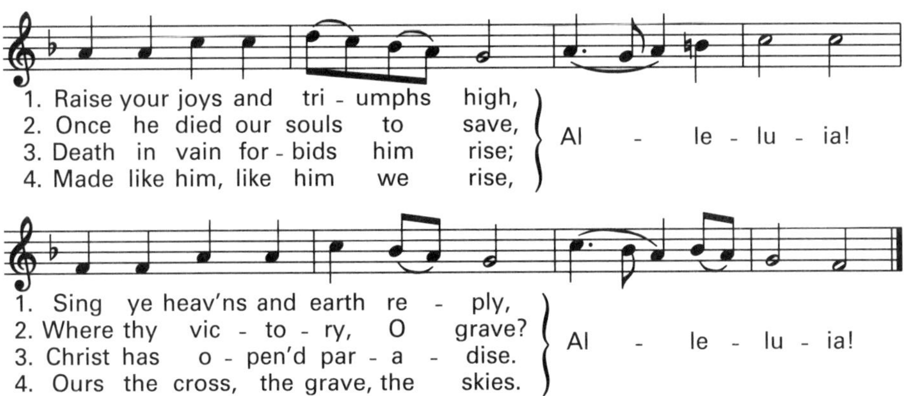
1. Raise your joys and tri - umphs high,
2. Once he died our souls to save,
3. Death in vain for - bids him rise;
4. Made like him, like him we rise,
Al - le - lu - ia!
1. Sing ye heav'ns and earth re - ply,
2. Where thy vic - to - ry, O grave?
3. Christ has o - pen'd par - a - dise.
4. Ours the cross, the grave, the skies.
Al - le - lu - ia!

Text: 77 77 with alleluias; Charles Wesley, 1707–1788, alt.
Music: LLANFAIR; Robert Williams, 1781–1821.

Alleluia! Alleluia! 321

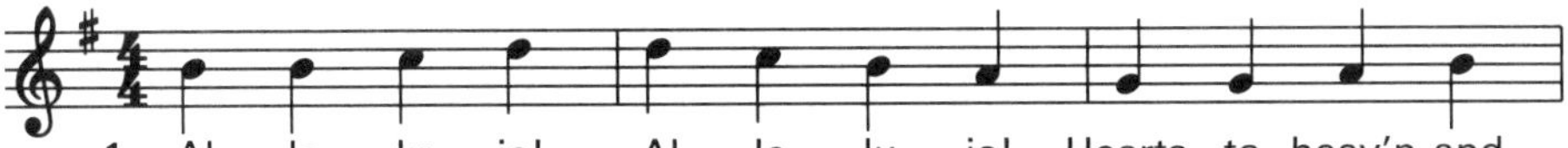

1. Al - le - lu - ia! Al - le - lu - ia! Hearts to heav'n and
2. Now the i - ron bars are bro - ken, Christ from death to
3. Al - le - lu - ia! Al - le - lu - ia! Glo - ry be to

1. voic - es raise; Sing to God a hymn of glad - ness,
2. life is born, Glo - rious life, and life im - mor - tal,
3. God on high; Al - le - lu - ia to the Sav - ior,

1. Sing to God a hymn of praise. He who on the
2. On this res - ur - rec - tion morn; Christ has tri-umphed,
3. Who has won the vic - to - ry; Al - le - lu - ia

1. cross as Sav - ior For the world's sal - va-tion bled, Je - sus
2. and we con-quer By his might - y en - ter-prise, We with
3. to the Spir - it, Font of love and sanc - ti - ty; Al - le-

1. Christ, the King of Glo - ry, Now is ris - en from the dead.
2. him to life e - ter - nal By his res - ur - rec - tion rise.
3. lu - ia! Al - le - lu - ia! To the Tri - une Maj - es - ty.

Text: 87 87 D; Christopher Wordsworth, 1807–1885, alt.
Music: HYMN TO JOY; Ludwig van Beethoven, 1770–1827; adapt. by Edward Hodges, 1796–1867.

322 LORD OF THE DANCE

Verses
1. I danced in the morn-ing when the world was be-gun, And I
2. I danced for the scribe and the Phar - i - see, But they
3. I danced on the Sab-bath and I cured the lame, The
4. I danced on a Fri-day when the sky turned black; It's
5. They cut me down and I leapt up high,
1. danced in the moon and the stars and the sun, And I
2. would not dance and they would-n't fol-low me; I
3. ho - ly peo - ple, they said it was a shame; They
4. hard to dance with the dev - il on your back; They
5. I am the life that-'ll nev-er, nev-er die, I'll
1. came down from heav-en and I danced on the earth, At
2. danced for the fish-er-men, for James and for John; They
3. whipped and they stripped and they hung me high, And they
4. bur - ied my bod-y and they thought I'd gone, But
5. live in you if you'll live in me;
1. Beth-le - hem I had my birth.
2. came with me and the dance went on.
3. left me there on a cross to die.
4. I am the dance and I still go on.
5. "I am the Lord of the Dance," said he.
Refrain
"Dance, then wher-ev-er you may be; I am the Lord of the Dance," said he. "I'll lead you all wher-ev-er you may be, I will lead you all in the
1-4
Dance," said he.
to Verses
Final
Dance," said he.

Text: Sydney B. Carter, 1915–2004.
Music: Shaker Melody, 19th cent.; adapt. by Sydney B. Carter.

323 RESUCITÓ/HE IS RISEN

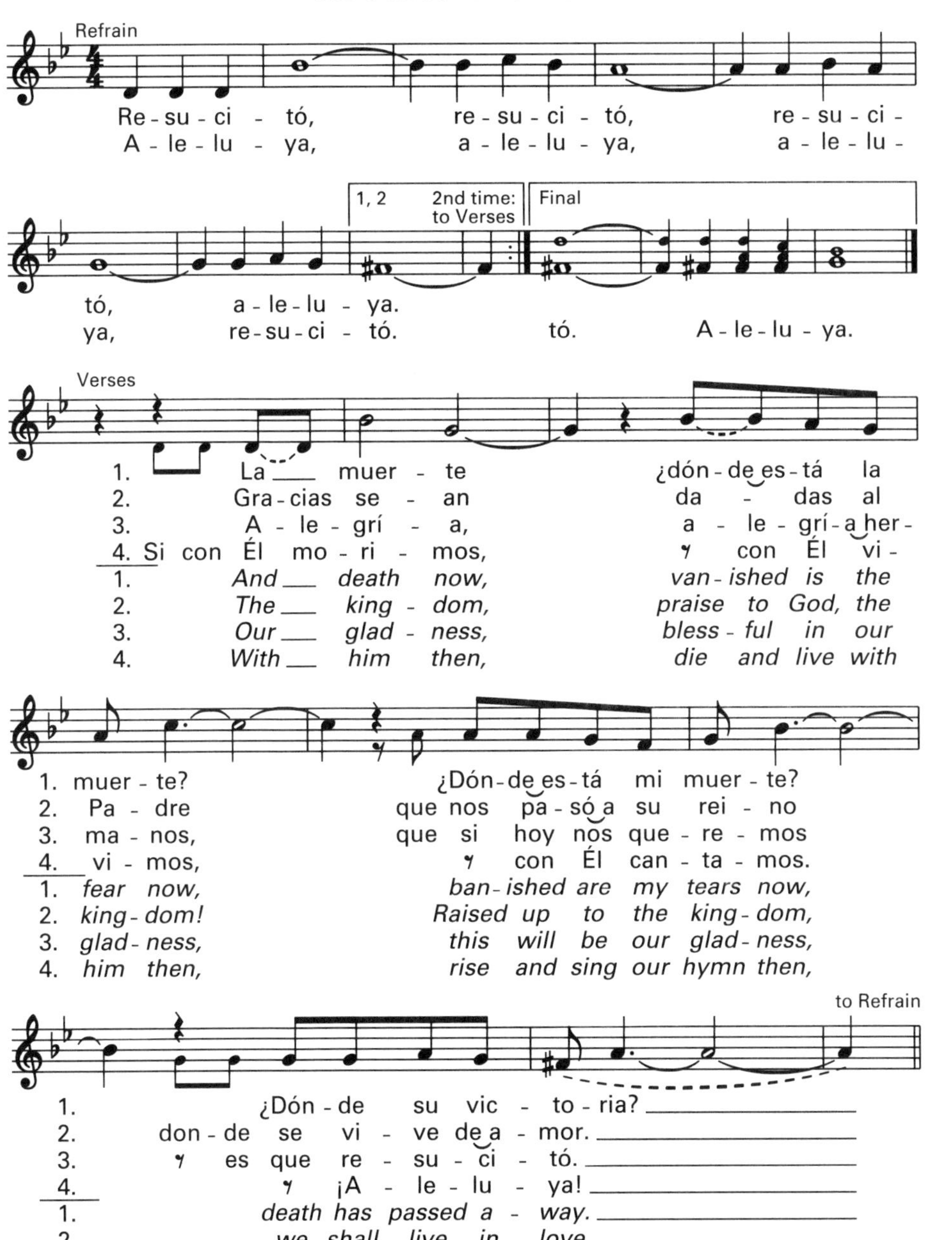
Refrain
Re - su - ci - tó, re - su - ci - tó, re - su - ci - tó, a - le - lu - ya.
A - le - lu - ya, a - le - lu - ya, a - le - lu - ya, re - su - ci - tó.
1, 2
2nd time: to Verses
Final
tó. A - le - lu - ya.
Verses
1. La muer - te ¿dón - de es - tá la muer - te? ¿Dón - de es - tá mi muer - te? ¿Dón - de su vic - to - ria?
2. Gra - cias se - an da - das al Pa - dre que nos pa - só a su rei - no don - de se vi - ve de a - mor.
3. A - le - grí - a, a - le - grí - a her - ma - nos, que si hoy nos que - re - mos es que re - su - ci - tó.
4. Si con Él mo - ri - mos, con Él vi - vi - mos, con Él can - ta - mos. ¡A - le - lu - ya!
1. And death now, van - ished is the fear now, ban - ished are my tears now, death has passed a - way.
2. The king - dom, praise to God, the king - dom! Raised up to the king - dom, we shall live in love.
3. Our glad - ness, bless - ful in our glad - ness, this will be our glad - ness, that he is a - live.
4. With him then, die and live with him then, rise and sing our hymn then, sing al - le - lu - ia.
to Refrain

Text: Spanish, Kiko Argüello; English tr., OCP.
Music: Kiko Argüello.

324 Roll Away the Stone

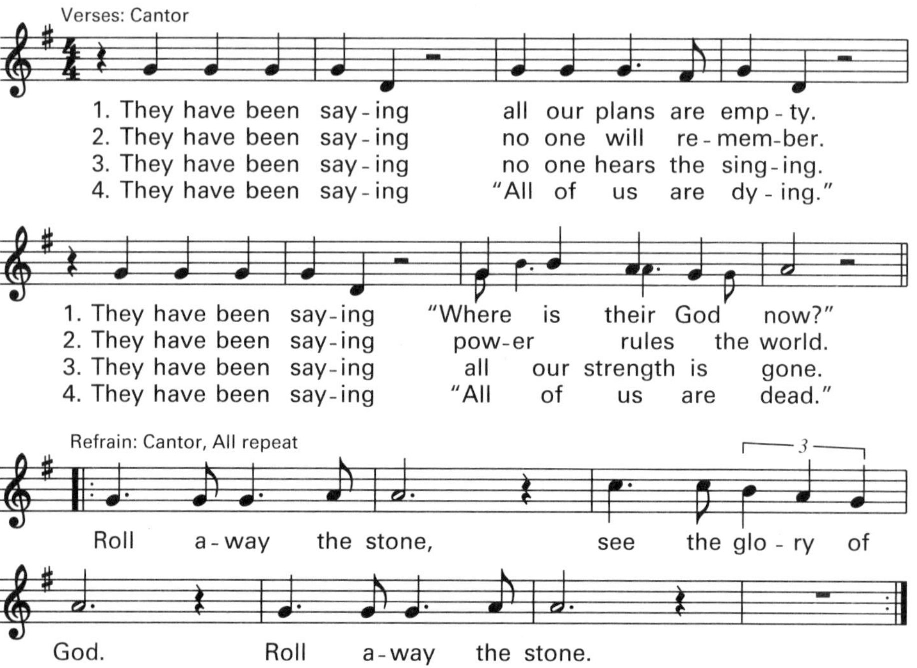
Verses: Cantor
1. They have been say-ing all our plans are emp-ty.
2. They have been say-ing no one will re-mem-ber.
3. They have been say-ing no one hears the sing-ing.
4. They have been say-ing "All of us are dy-ing."
1. They have been say-ing "Where is their God now?"
2. They have been say-ing pow-er rules the world.
3. They have been say-ing all our strength is gone.
4. They have been say-ing "All of us are dead."
Refrain: Cantor, All repeat
3
Roll a-way the stone, see the glo-ry of
God. Roll a-way the stone.

325 Let Us Sing and Be Glad/ And the Father Will Dance

Refrain

Let us sing and be glad! This is a time of joy!

(Original text) *And the Fa-ther will dance as on a day of joy.*

The Lord is ris-en to-day and re-news us by his love.

He will ex-ult o-ver you and re-new you by His love.

Verse 1

1. Shout for joy, all you, God's peo-ple. Sing a-

Shout for joy, all you, His peo-ple. Sing a-

1. loud and ex-ult with all your heart, for the

loud and ex-ult with all your heart, for the

to Refrain
1. Lord, our Bless - ed Sav - ior, lives!
Lord, your God, is in your midst.
Verse 2
2. We have no more e - vil to fear! We have
You have no more e - vil to fear. You have
2. no more e - vil to fear! We no long - er fear the
no more e - vil to fear. Do not let your hands fall
to Refrain
2. night for the Lord, our Bless - ed Sav-ior, lives!
limp, for the Lord, your God, is in your midst.
Verse 3
3. This is a new day; cre - a - tion danc - es for
And when the time comes I will res - cue the
3. joy! There is a new hope as peo-ple op-pressed find their
lame, and when the time comes I will gath - er the
3. voice. There is a new song; let ev - ery-one re -
strays, and when the time comes I will be your
3. joice! Let us o - pen our hearts to Je - sus Christ, our
guide. I will gath-er you in and give you re -
to Refrain
3. Light, who shines a - mong us.
nown a - mong all peo - ples.

Text: Based on Zephaniah 3:14–15, 15–17, 19–20; Carey Landry, b. 1944.
Music: Carey Landry.

326 This Is the Day

Refrain

This is the day that the Lord has made.
Let us be glad, and let us re-joice.
He has ris - en just as he said.
This is the day, al - le - lu - ia, this is the day.

1-3 to Verses

Final

This is the day, al - le - lu - ia, this is the day.

Verses 1, 2

1. Sing, O sing all the earth. Sing al - le - lu - ia. Go to the tomb, God has raised Je - sus up!
2. This light has cast off the dark - ness, the light of Je - sus will shine. All sad - ness and fear have been swept a - way!

2 to Refrain

Verse 3

3. The right hand of God has struck with pow - er.

3. The right hand of God is ex-alt - ed; and
3. we will live and sing praise to our God.
2
to Refrain

Text: Based on Psalm 118. Refrain
Verses, Tom Kendzia, b. 1954,
Music: Tom Kendzia,

Up from the Earth **327**

1. Up from the earth, and surg - ing like a wave,
2. Up from the cross, a bil - lion voic - es strain,
3. Up from the night, Christ Morn - ing - star a - wakes.
4. Up from the tomb of all the past con - ceals!
5. Cry to the cross where ty - rants work their dread!

1. Rise up, O Christ! Your God de - fies the grave!
2. Cry for a hand to lift them from their pain.
3. O what a light up - on earth's dark - ness breaks!
4. See how our God a bright - er day re - veals.
5. Shout to the tombs where par - ents mourn their dead!

1. Up from the earth push blade and leaf and stem.
2. Up from the cross, but scarred in limbs and side,
3. Up from the night, Christ sows his life like wheat,
4. Up from the tomb! Though death had bound us tight,
5. Sing to the earth, for God all new - ness gives!

1-4 to Vss 2-5 3

1. They rise for Christ, and we shall rise with them!
2. A wound - ed church brings heal - ing far and wide!
3. And death it - self lies fal - low at his feet!
4. Like Laz - a - rus, we stum - ble in - to light!
5. Al - le - lu - ia! Christ Lib - er - a - tor

Final

5. lives! Al - le - lu - ia! Christ Lib - er - a - tor lives!

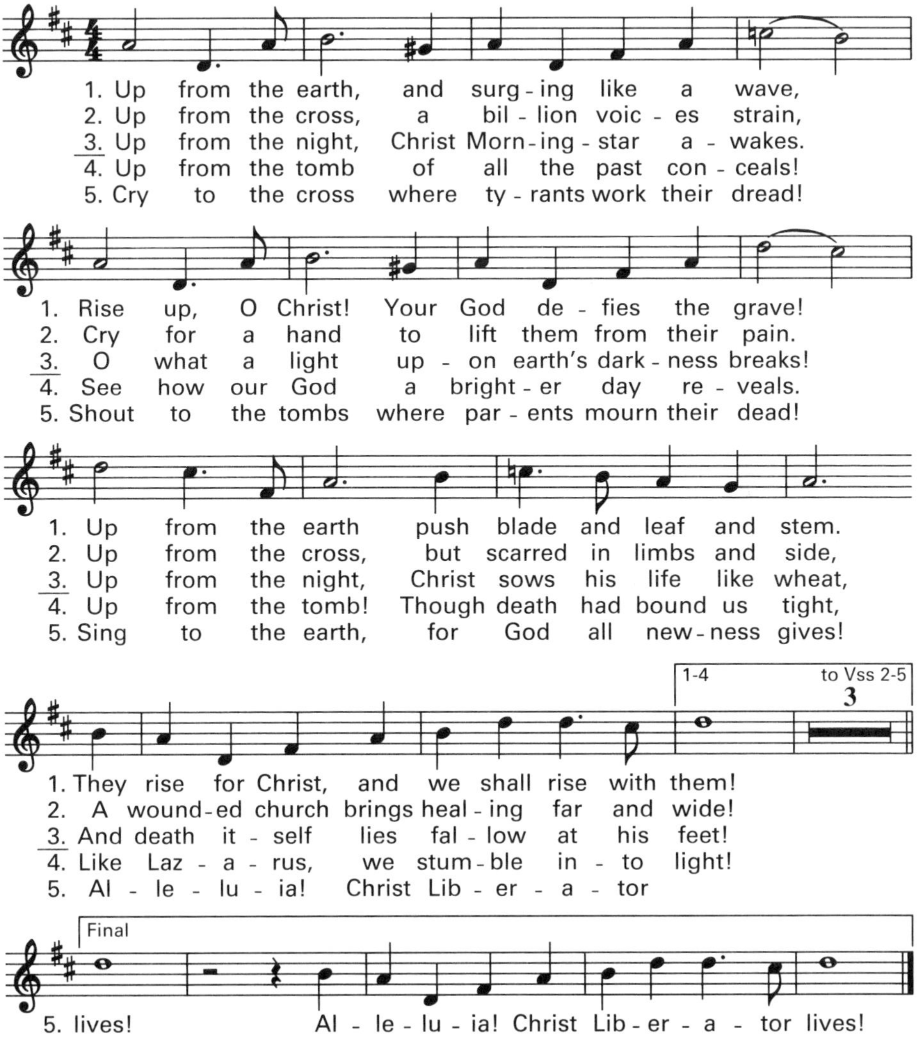

Text: 10 10 10 10; Rory Cooney, b. 1952.
Music: LIBERATOR; Rory Cooney.

328 NOW THE GREEN BLADE RISES

1. Now the green blade ris - es from the bur - ied grain,
2. In the grave they laid him, love by ha - tred slain,
3. Forth he came at Eas - ter, like the ris - en grain,
4. When our hearts are win - try, griev-ing, or in pain,

1. Wheat that in dark earth man - y days has lain;
2. Think - ing that he would nev - er wake a - gain,
3. He that for three days in the grave had lain;
4. Your touch can call us back to life a - gain,

1. Love lives a - gain, that with the dead has been:
2. Laid in the earth like grain that sleeps un - seen:
3. Raised from the dead, my liv - ing Lord is seen:
4. Fields of our hearts that dead and bare have been:

1-4. Love is come a - gain like wheat a - ris - ing green.

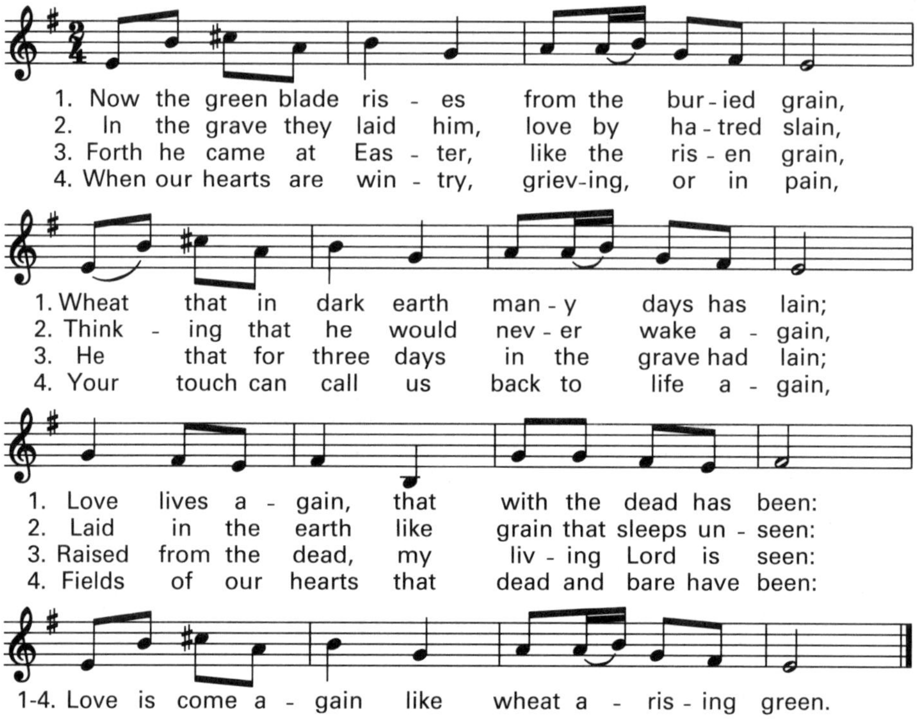

Text: 11 10 10 11; 'Now the green blade riseth' by J M C Crum, 1872–1958, [alt.].

Music: NOËL NOUVELET; trad. French melody.

329 I AM THE RESURRECTION

Refrain
I am the res - ur-rec - tion and the life;
all who be - lieve in me will nev - er die. I am the
res - ur-rec - tion and the life; all who be - lieve in me will
1-3
to Verses
Final
live a new life. live, will live a new life.

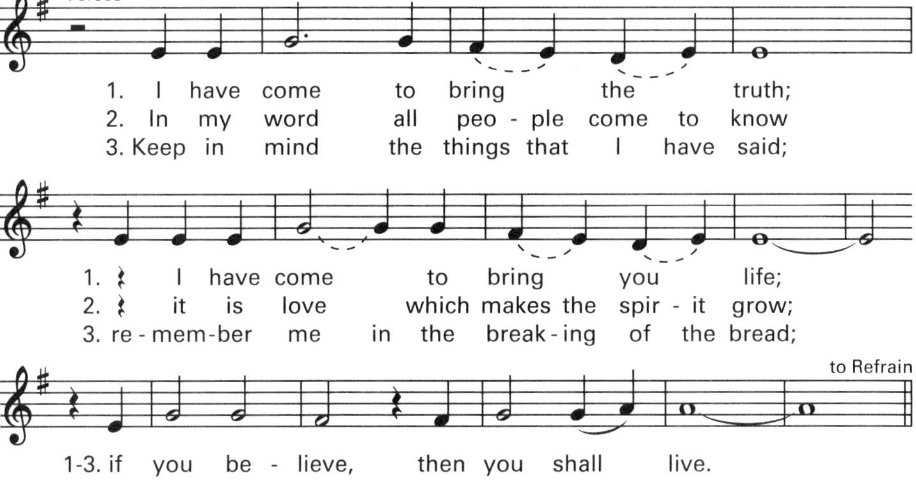
Verses
1. I have come to bring the truth;
2. In my word all peo - ple come to know
3. Keep in mind the things that I have said;
1. I have come to bring you life;
2. it is love which makes the spir - it grow;
3. re - mem - ber me in the break - ing of the bread;
to Refrain
1-3. if you be - lieve, then you shall live.

Text: Based on John 11:25–26; Ray Repp, b. 1942.
Music: Ray Repp.

JESUS CHRIST IS RISEN TODAY 330

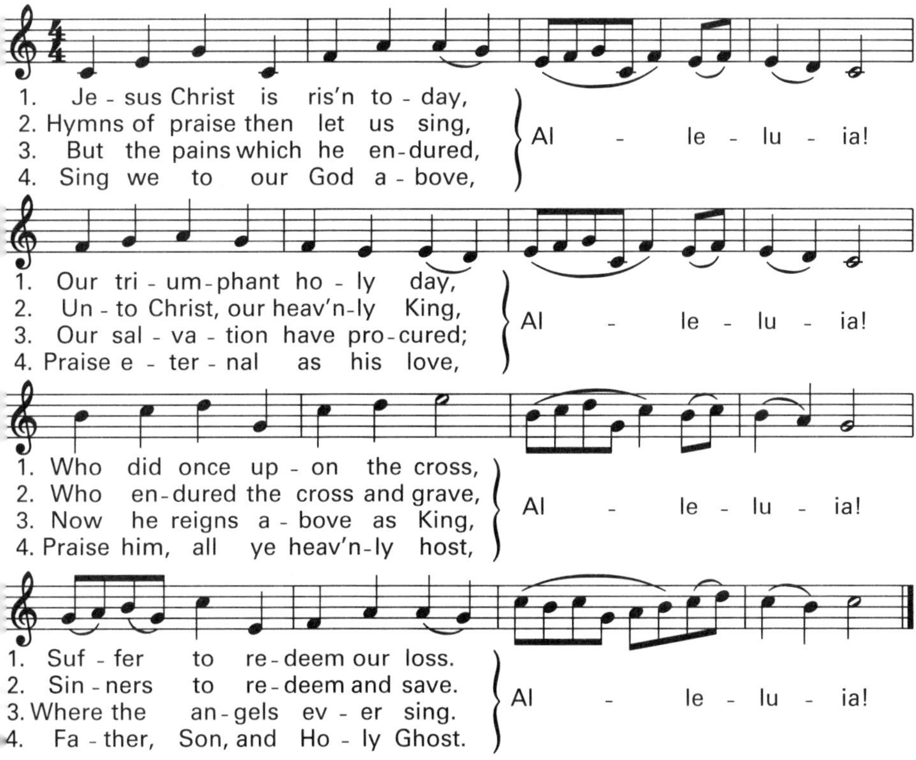

1. Je - sus Christ is ris'n to - day,
2. Hymns of praise then let us sing,
3. But the pains which he en - dured,
4. Sing we to our God a - bove,
Al - le - lu - ia!

1. Our tri - um - phant ho - ly day,
2. Un - to Christ, our heav'n - ly King,
3. Our sal - va - tion have pro - cured;
4. Praise e - ter - nal as his love,
Al - le - lu - ia!

1. Who did once up - on the cross,
2. Who en - dured the cross and grave,
3. Now he reigns a - bove as King,
4. Praise him, all ye heav'n - ly host,
Al - le - lu - ia!

1. Suf - fer to re - deem our loss.
2. Sin - ners to re - deem and save.
3. Where the an - gels ev - er sing.
4. Fa - ther, Son, and Ho - ly Ghost.
Al - le - lu - ia!

Text: 77 77 with alleluias; verse 1, Latin, 14th cent., para. in *Lyra Davidica*, 1708, alt.; verses 2–3, *The Compleat Psalmodist*, ca. 1750, alt.; verse 4, Charles Wesley, 1707–1788, alt.
Music: EASTER HYMN; later form of melody fr. *Lyra Davidica*, 1708.

331 This Day Was Made by the Lord

Refrain

This day was made by the Lord, let us re-joice, let us be glad.

let us re-joice in sal-va-tion!

Verses
Cantor

1. I thank you, your love is e-ternal, you have giv-en me life. All You have giv-en me life.
2. Your hand raised me up in tri-umph, you have giv-en me life. You have giv-en me life.
3. The stone which the build-ers re-ject-ed is the cor-ner-stone, is the cor-ner-stone.
4. You o-pened the gates of heav-en, you have giv-en me life. You have giv-en me life.
5. You are my strength and my Sav-ior, you have giv-en me life. You have giv-en me life.

1-5. I will pro-claim the won-ders you do!

to Refrain

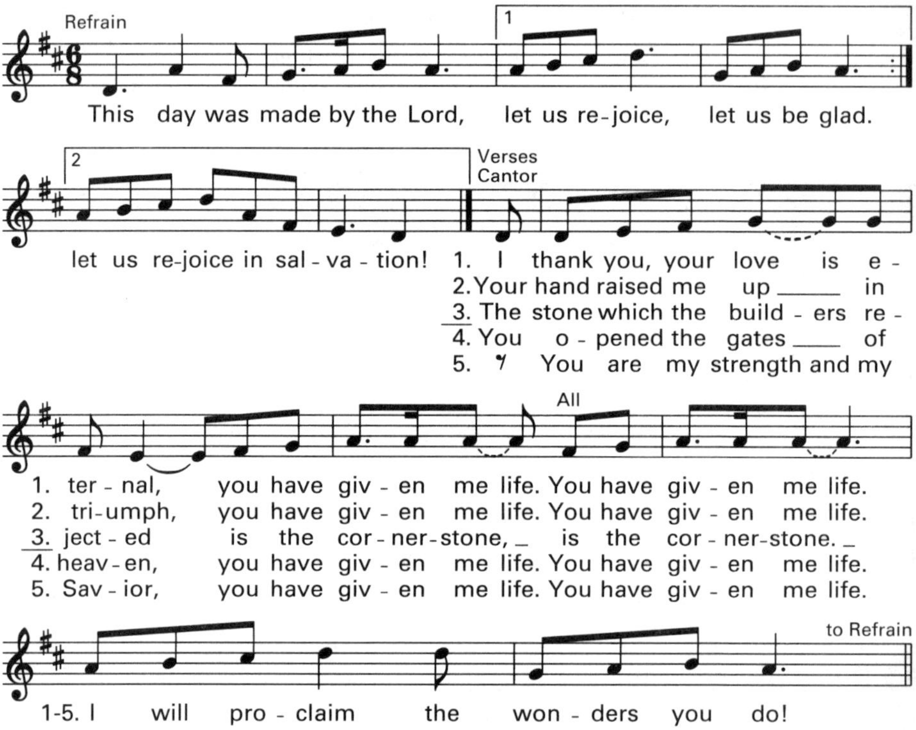

Text: Based on Psalm 118; Christopher Walker, b. 1947.
Music: Christopher Walker.

332 Two Were Bound for Emmaus

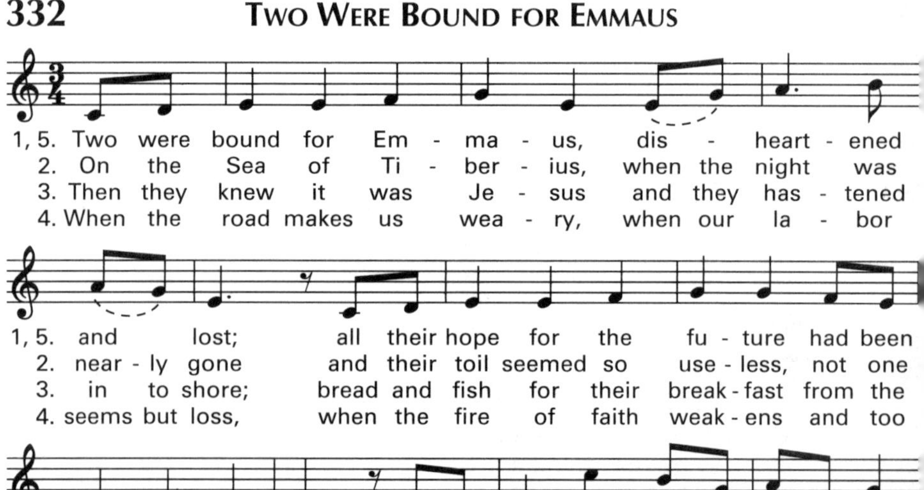
1, 5. Two were bound for Em-ma-us, dis-heart-ened and lost; all their hope for the fu-ture had been nailed to a cross. Love un-known then walked be-side them,
2. On the Sea of Ti-ber-ius, when the night was near-ly gone and their toil seemed so use-less, not one fish had they caught, from the shore the strang-er called to them:
3. Then they knew it was Je-sus and they has-tened in to shore; bread and fish for their break-fast from the hands of their Lord. "O Pe-ter, if you love me
4. When the road makes us wea-ry, when our la-bor seems but loss, when the fire of faith weak-ens and too high seems the cost, let the Church turn to its ris-en Lord,

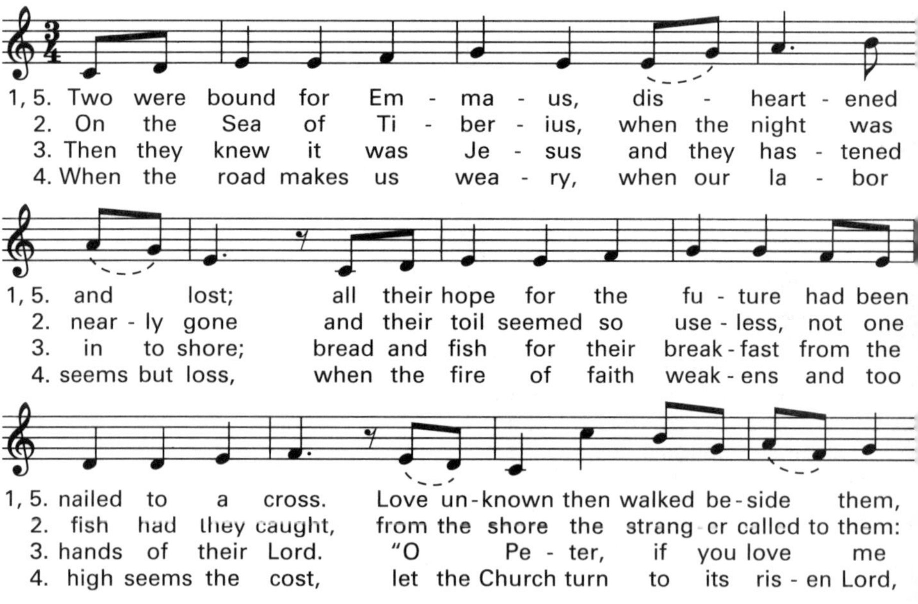

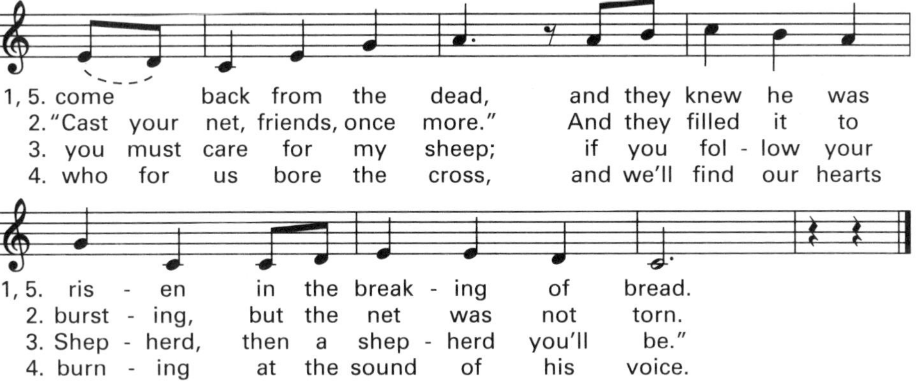
1, 5. come back from the dead, and they knew he was
2. "Cast your net, friends, once more." And they filled it to
3. you must care for my sheep; if you fol - low your
4. who for us bore the cross, and we'll find our hearts
1, 5. ris - en in the break - ing of bread.
2. burst - ing, but the net was not torn.
3. Shep - herd, then a shep - herd you'll be."
4. burn - ing at the sound of his voice.

Text: 11 13 13 13; based on Luke 24:13–35; John 21:1–19; Bob Hurd, b. 1950.
Music: KENMARE; Bob Hurd.

LET HEAVEN REJOICE 333

Refrain

Let heav-en re-joice and earth be glad; let all cre-a-tion sing. Let chil-dren pro-claim through ev-'ry land: "Ho-san-na to our King."

Verses 1-3

1. Sound the trum-pet in-to the night; the day of the Lord is near. Wake your peo-ple, lift your voice, pro-claim it to the world.
2. Rise in splen-dor; shake off your sleep; put on your robes of joy. And in the morn-ing you shall see the glo-ry of the Lord.
3. Raise your voic-es, be not a-fraid. Pro-claim it in ev-'ry land. Christ has died, but he has ris-en; he will come a-gain.

to Refrain

Verse 4

4. Sing a new song un-to the Lord, whose la-bor has led us to life. With grate-ful hearts and joy-ful danc-ing, play be-fore the Lord.

to Refrain

334 Christ, the Lord, Is Risen Today

1. Christ, the Lord, is ris'n to - day; Chris-tians, haste your
2. Christ, the Vic - tim un - de - filed, God and sin - ners
3. Say, O won - d'ring Ma - ry, say What you saw a -
4. Christ, who once for sin - ners bled, Now the first - born
1. vows to pay; Make your joy and prais - es known At the
2. re - con-ciled; When in strange and awe - some strife Met to -
3. long the way. "I be - held two an - gels bright, Emp - ty
4. from the dead, Throned in end - less might and pow'r, Lives and
1. Pas - chal Vic - tim's throne; For the sheep the Lamb has bled,
2. geth - er death and life; Chris - tians, on this hap - py day
3. tomb and wrap - pings white; I be - held the glo - ry bright
4. reigns for - ev - er - more. Hail, e - ter - nal Hope on high!
1. Sin - less in the sin - ner's stead; Christ, the Lord, is
2. Haste with joy your vows to pay; Christ, the Lord, is
3. Of the ris - en Lord of light; Christ, my hope, is
4. Hail, our King of Vic - to - ry! Hail, our Prince of
1. ris'n on high; Now he lives, no more to die!
2. ris'n on high; Now he lives, no more to die!
3. ris'n a - gain; Now he lives, and lives to reign!"
4. Life a - dored! Help and save us, gra - cious Lord!

Text: 77 77 D; *Victimae paschali laudes*; ascr. to Wipo of Burgundy, ca. 1000–1050; tr. by Jane E. Leeson, 1808–1881, alt.
Music: VICTIMAE PASCHALI; Würth's *Katholisches Gesangbuch*, 1859.

335 This Is the Day

Refrain: 1st time: Cantor, All repeat; thereafter: All

This is the day! This is the day! This is the day that the Lord has made! Let us re-joice!

(to Verses)
Let us re-joice! Let us re-joice and be glad!
Final time only
Let us re-joice and be glad!

Verses: Cantor

1. This is the day that the Lord has made.
Let us rejoice and be glad.

2. Give thanks to the Lord!
Our God is good.
Whose love endures forever.
Let all the children of Israel say:
God's love endures forever.

3. The right hand of God has struck with power.
The right hand of God is exalted.
I shall not die, but I shall live
and proclaim the works of the Lord!

4. The stone which the builders rejected
has become the foundation of our house!
By the Lord has this been done.
How wonderful to behold!

Text: Based on Psalm 118:1–2, 16–17, 22–23. Refrain
Verses, Bobby Fisher, b. 1952,
Music: Bobby Fisher,

THE STRIFE IS O'ER 336

Refrain

Al - le - lu - ia! Al - le - lu - ia! Al - le - lu - ia!

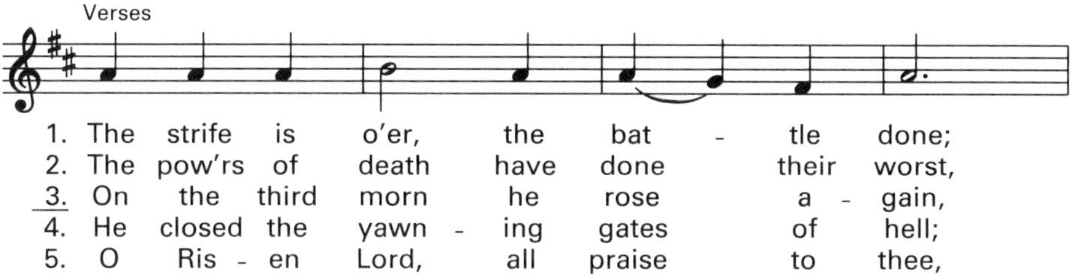

Verses

1. The strife is o'er, the bat - tle done;
2. The pow'rs of death have done their worst,
3. On the third morn he rose a - gain,
4. He closed the yawn - ing gates of hell;
5. O Ris - en Lord, all praise to thee,

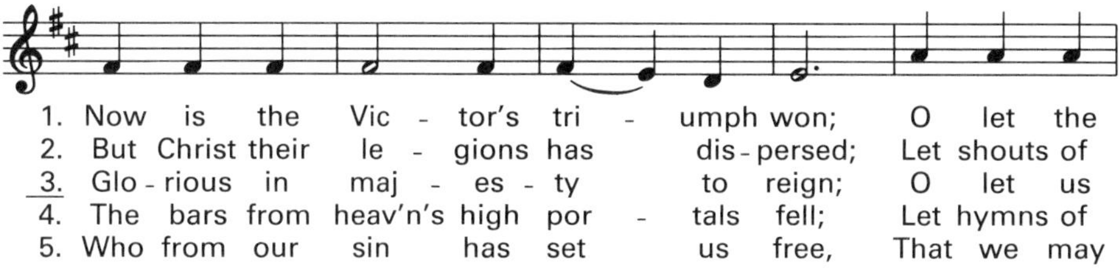

1. Now is the Vic - tor's tri - umph won; O let the
2. But Christ their le - gions has dis - persed; Let shouts of
3. Glo - rious in maj - es - ty to reign; O let us
4. The bars from heav'n's high por - tals fell; Let hymns of
5. Who from our sin has set us free, That we may

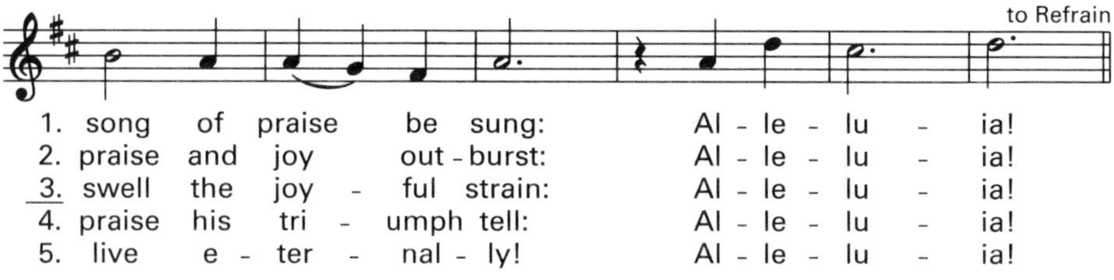

to Refrain

1. song of praise be sung: Al - le - lu - ia!
2. praise and joy out - burst: Al - le - lu - ia!
3. swell the joy - ful strain: Al - le - lu - ia!
4. praise his tri - umph tell: Al - le - lu - ia!
5. live e - ter - nal - ly! Al - le - lu - ia!

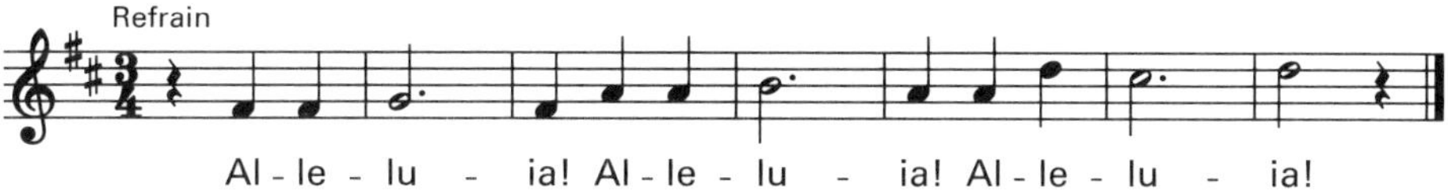

Text: 888 with alleluias; *Finita iam sunt praelia*; Latin, 12th cent.; tr. by Francis Pott, 1832–1909, alt.
Music: VICTORY; Giovanni Pierluigi da Palestrina, 1525–1594; adapt. by Willam H. Monk, 1823–1889.

337 Hail the Day That Sees Him Rise

1. Hail the day that sees him rise
2. There for him high tri-umph waits:
3. High-est heav'n its Lord re-ceives;
4. See! he lifts his hands a-bove.
5. Lord, though part-ed from our sight
6. There with you we shall re-main,
Al - le - lu - ia!
1. To his throne be-yond the skies;
2. Lift your heads, e-ter-nal gates;
3. Yet he loves the earth he leaves;
4. See! he shows the wounds of love.
5. Far be-yond the star-ry height,
6. Share the glo-ry of your reign,
Al - le - lu - ia!
1. Christ, the Lamb for sin-ners giv'n,
2. He has con-quered death and sin;
3. Though re-turn-ing to his throne,
4. Hark! his gra-cious lips be-stow,
5. Lift our hearts that we may rise
6. There your face un-cloud-ed view,
Al - le - lu - ia!
1. En-ters now the high-est heav'n!
2. Take the King of glo-ry in.
3. Still he calls the world his own.
4. Bless-ings on his church be-low.
5. One with you be-yond the skies:
6. Find our heav'n of heav'ns in you.
Al - le - lu - ia!

Text: 77 77 with alleluias; Charles Wesley, 1707–1788, and Thomas Cotterill, 1779–1823, alt.
Music: LLANFAIR; Robert Williams, 1781–1821.

One Sacrifice of Christ 338

1. One sac - ri - fice of Christ, one throne a - bove the heav -
2. One gaze we lift a - bove, where Love was drawn to heav -
3. One ban-quet rich - ly set for all God's ho - ly peo -
1. - ens. Christ has ris - en as he said, and will
2. - en. We stand watch - ful through the night for our
3. - ple. We will dine in joy and peace, and our
1. come to wake the dead. Christ will re - turn to set us free.
2. King to come in light, heirs to the glo - ry of the Lamb.
3. song will nev - er cease, prais - ing the Lamb up - on the throne.
1. One sac - ri - fice of love, one mes-sage for the na - tions:
2. One might-y Word of truth: Christ did a - rise in tri - umph.
3. One shout of joy we raise, one voice in ex - al - ta - tion.
1. Je - sus suf - fered, died and rose, and as - cend - ed to the
2. Now he sits up - on the throne; God's right hand is he a -
3. For in glo - ry Christ has gone, and in hope we now are
1, 2
1. throne. Christ will re - turn to save the world.
2. lone. Christ reigns in splen-dor o - ver all.
3. drawn to
Final
3. one sac-ri-fice of Christ, one sac-ri-fice of Christ.

339 Lord, You Give the Great Commission

1. Lord, you give the great com-mis-sion: "Heal the sick and
2. Lord, you call us to your ser-vice: "In my name bap-
3. Lord, you make the com-mon ho-ly: "This my bod-y,
4. Lord, you show us love's true mea-sure: "Fa-ther, what they
5. Lord, you bless with words as-sur-ing: "I am with you

1. preach the word." Lest the church ne-glect its mis-sion
2. tize and teach." That the world may trust your prom-ise,
3. this my blood." Let us all, for earth's true glo-ry,
4. do, for-give." Yet we hoard as pri-vate trea-sure
5. to the end." Faith and hope and love re-stor-ing,

1. And the gos-pel go un-heard, Help us wit-ness to your
2. Life a-bun-dant meant for each, Give us all new fer-vor,
3. Dai-ly lift life heav-en-ward, Ask-ing that the world a-
4. All that you so free-ly give. May your care and mer-cy
5. May we serve as you in-tend And, a-mid the cares that

1. pur-pose With re-newed in-teg-ri-ty:
2. draw us Clos-er in com-mu-ni-ty:
3. round us Share your chil-dren's lib-er-ty:
4. lead us To a just so-ci-e-ty:
5. claim us, Hold in mind e-ter-ni-ty:

With the Spir-it's

1-5. gifts em-pow'r us For the work of min-is-try.

Text: 87 87 D; Jeffery Rowthorn, b. 1934,
Music: ABBOT'S LEIGH; Cyril Vincent Taylor, 1907–1991,

340 Peace, My Friends

Refrain
Peace I leave with you, my friends. Sha-lom, my peace in
all you do. Peace I leave with you, my friends.

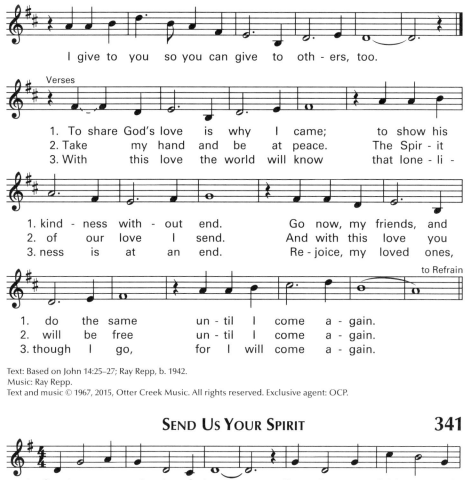

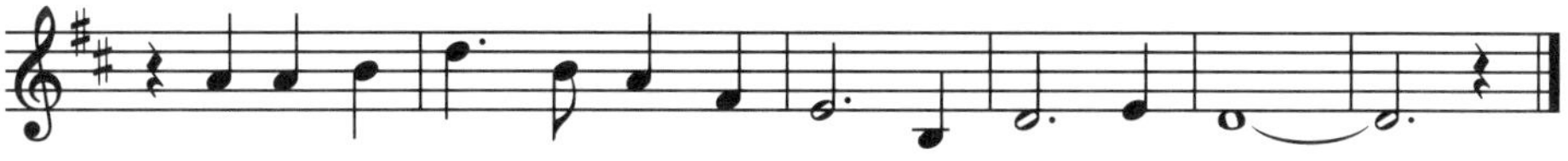

I give to you so you can give to others, too.

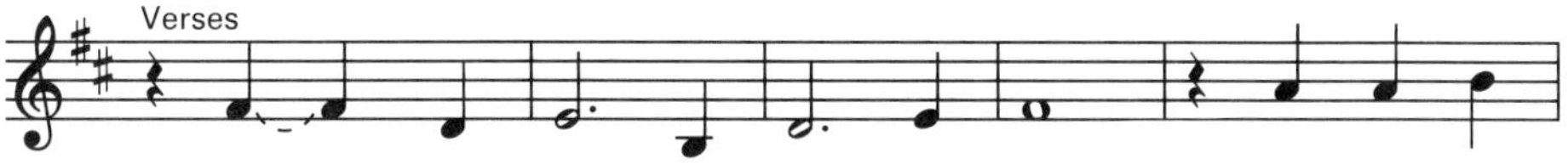

Verses

1. To share God's love is why I came; to show his kindness without end. Go now, my friends, and do the same until I come again.

2. Take my hand and be at peace. The Spirit of our love I send. And with this love you will be free until I come again.

3. With this love the world will know that loneliness is at an end. Rejoice, my loved ones, though I go, for I will come again.

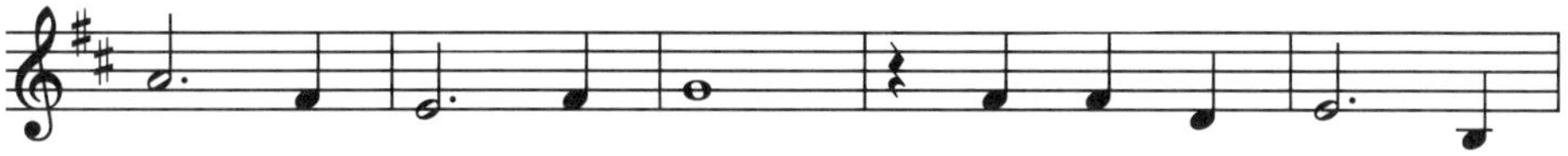

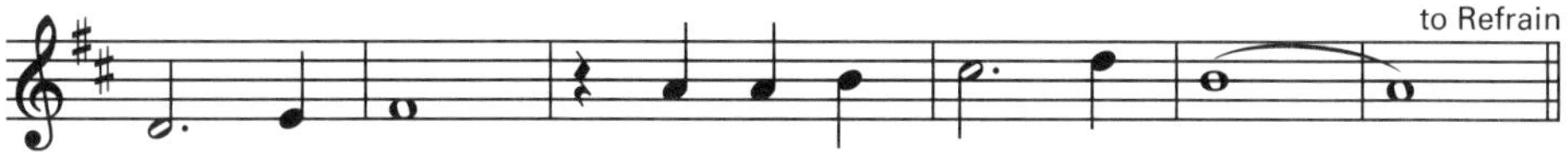

to Refrain

Text: Based on John 14:25–27; Ray Repp, b. 1942.
Music: Ray Repp.

SEND US YOUR SPIRIT 341

1. Send us your spir - it, O Lord. Eve - ning en - folds us and holds us too near. Wake the morn - ing light. Make our liv - ing bright. Shine on our dark-ness, O Lord.
2. Hold us with mer - cy, O Lord. Sor - row has spo - ken, has bro - ken our hearts. Clothe us in your care. Be the life we bear. Feed us and fill us, O Lord.
3. Teach us your wis - dom, O Lord. Shad-ows have cloud-ed, have crowd-ed our sight. Give us hearts that see. Set our lov-ing free. Hear us and help us, O Lord.
4. Send us good sum-mer, O Lord. Win - ters have chilled us, and stilled us too long. Give us love's own fire. Be our true de-sire. Send us your spir - it, O Lord.
2

Text: Inspired by *Veni, Sancte Spiritus*; Dan Schutte, b. 1947.
Music: Dan Schutte.

342 COME, O SPIRIT OF THE LORD

Verse 1

1. Bless the Lord, O my soul; O Lord, my God,
1. how great are you. The earth is full of your
1. won-ders, and your works un - fold be-fore our eyes.

Refrain

Come, O Spir - it of the Lord, and re - new the face of the
earth, O come, O Spir - it of the Lord,
and re - new the face of the earth.

to Verses

Verse 2

2. If you take a-way our breath we die,
2. and re-turn to dust. When you
2. send your Spir-it here a - gain, you cre - ate us and
2. you re-new the face of the earth.

to Refrain

Verse 3

3. May your glo - ry en - dure for - ev - er; may you be

3. glad in all your works. We will sing to you all our
to Refrain
3. days. We will praise you while we live.

Text: Based on Psalm 104; Tom Kendzia, b. 1954.
Music: Tom Kendzia.

HOLY SPIRIT, COME TO ME 343

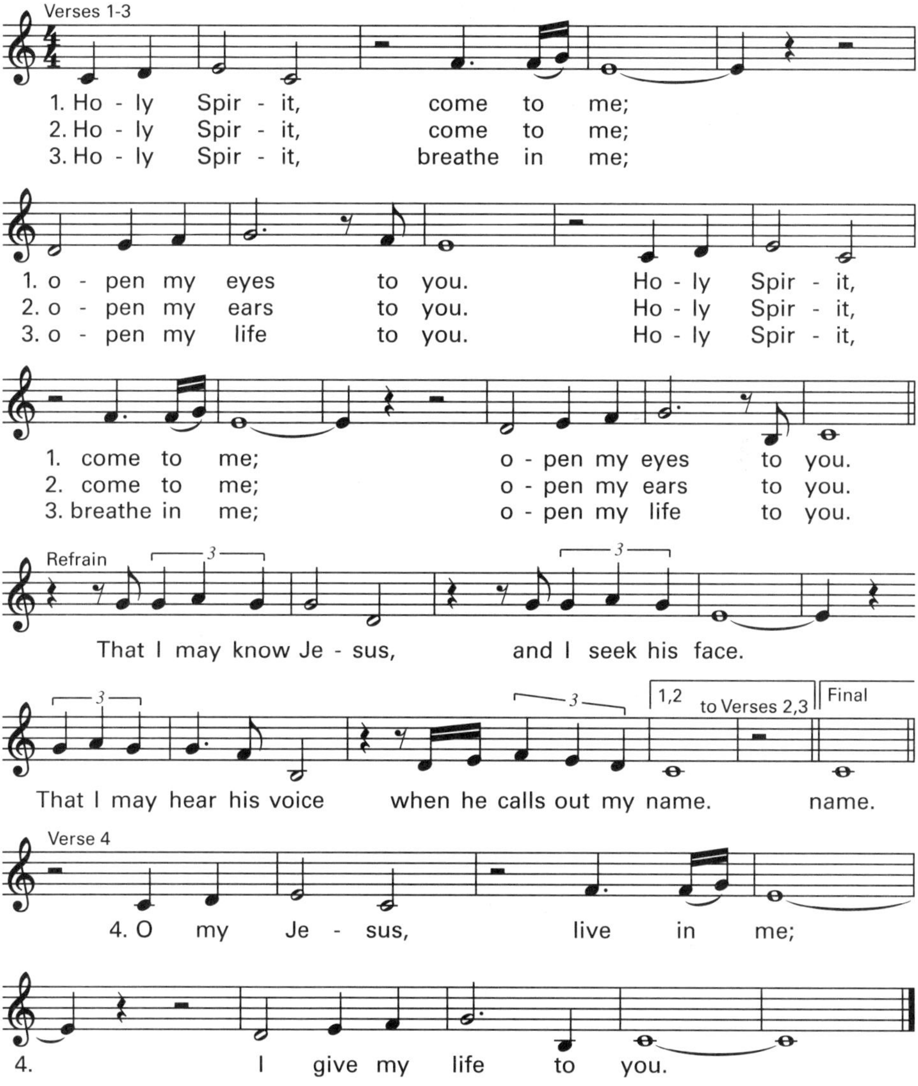

Verses 1-3

1. Holy Spirit, come to me; open my eyes to you. Holy Spirit, come to me; open my eyes to you.
2. Holy Spirit, come to me; open my ears to you. Holy Spirit, come to me; open my ears to you.
3. Holy Spirit, breathe in me; open my life to you. Holy Spirit, breathe in me; open my life to you.

Refrain

That I may know Jesus, and I seek his face. That I may hear his voice when he calls out my name.

1,2 to Verses 2,3

Final name.

Verse 4

4. O my Jesus, live in me; I give my life to you.

344 HOLY SPIRIT

Ostinato Refrain: All
Ho - ly Spir - it, come in - to our lives. Ho - ly Spir - it, make us tru - ly wise.
Verses: Cantor
1. Give us a spir - it of wis - dom, an un - der - stand - ing heart. Give us a spir - it of knowl - edge, and lead us to the truth.
2. Give us a spir - it of cour - age, and judg - ment that is wise. Give us a spir - it of rev - 'rence, of won - der and of awe.
3. Spir - it of love and com - pas - sion, give hope to all the poor. Spir - it of jus - tice and mer - cy, come o - pen ev - 'ry door.
4. Spir - it of all con - so - la - tion, O lift our hearts this day. Spir - it of all un - der - stand - ing, O help us know your way.
5. Spir - it of light and of wis - dom, O lift us from our sor - row. Spir - it of peace and for - give - ness, O help us face to - mor - row.
6. Spir - it of strength and of heal - ing, bend stub - born heart and will. Spir - it of trust and of car - ing, O melt us, warm our chill.
to Refrain

Text: Verses 1 & 2 based on Isaiah 11:2; verses 3–6 based on the Sequence for Pentecost; Ken Canedo, b. 1953.
Music: Ken Canedo.

SEND OUT YOUR SPIRIT

Refrain

Lord, send out your Spir - it; re - new the face of the earth.

Lord, send out your Spir - it; re - new the face of the earth.

6

Verses

1. You set the earth on its foun - da - tion firm, not to be moved ___ in all its days; clothed it with o - ceans and robed it in light: O bless the Lord, all you his works.
2. You sprang up springs run - ning down to the streams, wind - ing their ways through moun-tains and hills. Birds dwell in tree - tops where wa - ters run, send - ing their song in - to the world.
3. From sea to shore how your won - ders are seen, care - ful - ly planned in wis - dom and love. All of your world is a - bun - dant with life: O my ___ soul, bless you the Lord.
4. You reign down rains on the earth all be - low; or - chards bear fruit, ___ fields yield your grain. Earth, brown and fur - rowed, bears fruit in your gaze, giv - ing us bread; giv - ing us life.
5. He comes with bright wings a - wash - ing the world; all is made new in wa - ter and fire. Morn - ing a - ris - es a - new in the sky: God re - cre - ates in a new day.

to Refrain

2

Text: Based on Psalm 104. Refrain © 1969, ICEL. All rights reserved. Used with permission.
Verses, Tim Schoenbachler, b. 1952, © 1979, OCP. All rights reserved.
Music: Tim Schoenbachler, © 1979, OCP. All rights reserved.

346 SPIRIT, COME

Refrain

Spir - it, come, trans-form us. Come, be our breath, be our hope.

Spir - it, come, trans-form us. Come, be our breath, be our

1-5 to Vss. | Final

hope. Come, be our breath, be our hope.

Verses

1. Deep in the womb of our heart ______ re -
2. Draw us to share oth - ers' bur - dens,
3. You are the one who u - nites us in
4. Sing in our heart, be the danc - er,
5. Teach us to live with com - pas - sion, un -

to Refrain

1. veal ___ your pres-ence, O God.
2. heal-ing and lov - ing with truth.
3. striv-ing for jus - tice, for peace.
4. birth-ing our love as we grow.
5. fold - ing cre - a-tor's love.

Text and music: Gregory Norbet, b. 1940,

347 ENVÍA TU ESPÍRITU

Refrain
*En - ví-a tu Es-pí-ri-tu, en - ví-a tu Es-pí-ri-tu, en-
ví-a tu Es-pí-ri-tu, se-a re-no-va-da la faz de la tie-
- rra. Se-a re-no-va-da la faz de la tie - rra.

*Send out your Spirit, and renew the face of the earth.

Verses

1. *Spir - it of the liv - ing God, burn in our hearts,*
2. *Wind of prom - ise, wind of change, friend of the poor,*
3. *Breath of life and ho - li - ness, heal ev - 'ry wound,*

to Refrain

1. *and make us a peo - ple of hope and com-pas - sion.*
2. *em - pow - er your peo - ple to make peace and jus - tice.*
3. *and lead us be-yond ev - 'ry sin that di-vides us.*

Text: Based on Psalm 104:30 and *Veni, Sancte Spiritus*; Latin, 12th cent.; adapt. by Bob Hurd, b. 1950.
Music: Bob Hurd.

BY THE WAKING OF OUR HEARTS 348

Refrain
Verses

Refrain

By the wak-ing of our hearts, by the stir-ring of our souls,
may the Spir-it of God a-bide and bring us to-geth-er in Christ.

Verses

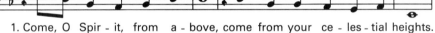

1. Come, O Spir - it, from a - bove, come from your ce - les - tial heights.
2. Come, O Sav - ior of the poor, come, O source of gifts en - sured.
3. In our la - bor, rest most sweet; grate - ful cool-ness in the heat.
4. Bend the stub-born heart and will, melt the fro - zen, warm the chill.
5. Grant us vir - tue's sure re - ward, may your gra-cious love be sent.

to Refrain

1. Come with your bless - ed light so ___ ra - diant bright.
2. Come with your gen - tle hope, so ___ won-drous and pure.
3. Con - sole our rest - less lives, by your com - fort, we seek.
4. Come guide our search-ing minds toward your prom - ise ful - filled.
5. Come with your peace and joy that shall nev - er end.

Text: Verses based on the Pentecost Sequence, *Veni, Sancte Spiritus*; Ricky Manalo, CSP, b. 1965.
Music: Ricky Manalo, CSP.

349 Pentecost Sequence

Verses 1, 2
1. Come, Ho - ly Spir - it, come! And from your ce - les - tial home
2. You, of com - fort - ers the best; You, the soul's most wel - come guest;
1. Shed a ray of light di - vine! Come, Fa - ther of the poor!
2. Sweet re - fresh - ment here be - low; In our la - bor, rest most sweet;
1. Come, source of all our store! Come, with - in our bos - oms shine.
2. Grate - ful cool - ness in the heat; So - lace in the midst of woe.
Verses 3-5
3. O most bless - ed Light di - vine, Shine with - in these hearts of yours,
4. Heal our wounds, our strength re - new; On our dry - ness pour your dew;
5. On the faith - ful, who a - dore And con - fess you, ev - er - more
3. And our in - most be - ing fill! Where you are not, we have naught,
4. Wash the stains of guilt a - way: Bend the stub - born heart and will;
5. In your sev'n - fold gift de - scend; Give them vir - tue's sure re - ward;
3. Noth - ing good in deed or thought, Noth - ing free from taint of ill.
4. Melt the fro - zen, warm the chill; Guide the steps that go a - stray.
5. Give them your sal - va - tion, Lord; Give them joys that nev - er end.
5. A - men, a - men. A - men, a - men. A - men, a - men.

Text: *Veni, Sancte Spiritus*; Poetic Sequence for Pentecost © 1964, The National Catholic Welfare Conference, Inc. (now US Conference of Catholic Bishops). All rights reserved. Used with permission.
Music: Tom Kendzia, b. 1954, © 2001, Tom Kendzia. Published by OCP. All rights reserved.

Veni Sancte Spiritus 350

Ostinato Refrain: All
Ve-ni San-cte Spi-ri-tus; Ve-ni San-cte Spi-ri-tus;
Ve-ni, ve-ni San-cte Spi-ri-tus; Ve-ni San-cte Spi-ri-tus.

Verses: Cantor

1. Holy Spirit, Lord of Light,
   radiance give from celestial height.
   Come, O Spirit of the poor,
   come now with treasures that endure:
   Light of all who live.

2. You of all consolers the best.
   You the soul's delightful guest;
   refreshing peace bestow.
   You in toil my comfort sweet.
   You coolness in the heat.
   You my solace in time of woe.

3. Light immortal, light divine;
   fire of love our hearts refine,
   our inmost being fill.
   Take your grace away
   and nothing pure in us will stay,
   all our good is turned to ill.

4. Heal our wounds, our strength renew,
   on our dryness pour your dew;
   wash guilt away,
   bend the stubborn heart,
   melt the frozen,
   warm the chill
   and guide the steps that go astray.

5. Seven-fold gifts on us be pleased to pour,
   who you confess and you adore;
   bring us your comfort when we die;
   give us life with you on high;
   give us joys, give us joys that never end.

Text: Latin, 12th cent. Verses based on the Pentecost Sequence, *Veni, Sancte Spiritus*;
adapt. by Christopher Walker, b. 1947,
Music: Christopher Walker,

The Spirit Is A-Movin' 351

Refrain
The Spir-it is a-mov-in' all o-ver, all o-ver this land.
Verses
1. Peo-ple are gath - er-in', the church is born; ___ the
2. Old ___ ones ___ are ___ dream-ing dreams, ___ and
3. Old ___ walls ___ are ___ fall - ing down, ___ and
4. Filled _ with the Spir-it, we are sent to serve. _ We are
5. The Spir - it fills ___ us ___ all with pow'r, ___ to
to Refrain
1. Spir-it is a-blow-in' on a world ___ re - born. ___
2. young _ men and wom - en ___ see ___ the ___ light. ___
3. peo-ple all o - ver are ___ speak-ing with each oth-er. ___
4. called _ out to-geth-er, we are called ___ to ___ work. ___
5. be ___ God's ___ wit-ness-es to all ___ we ___ meet. ___

Text and music: Carey Landry, b. 1944,

352 COME, HOLY GHOST

1. Come, Ho - ly Ghost, Cre - a - tor blest, And in our hearts take
2. O Com-fort - er, to thee we cry, Thou heav'n-ly gift of
3. Praise be to thee, Fa-ther and Son, And Ho - ly Spir - it,
1. up thy rest; Come with thy grace and heav'n-ly aid To fill the
2. God most high; Thou font of life and fire of love, And sweet a -
3. with them one; And may the Son on us be-stow The gifts that
1. hearts which thou hast made; To fill the hearts which thou hast made.
2. noint - ing from a - bove; And sweet a - noint - ing from a - bove.
3. from the Spir - it flow; The gifts that from the Spir - it flow.

Text: LM with repeat; *Veni, Creator Spiritus*; attr. to Rabanus Maurus, 776–856; tr. by Edward Caswall, 1814–1878, alt.
Music: LAMBILLOTTE; Louis Lambillotte, SJ, 1796–1855.

353 EVERYONE MOVED BY THE SPIRIT

Refrain

Ev-'ry-one moved by the Spir-it is a son and daugh-ter of God. Led by the fire of his love we will live in the light of the Lord. We will live in the light of the Lord.

Verses

1. Come, O Spir - it of Je - sus. Come in the pow-er of his name. Re-new the depths of our hearts.
2. Come, O Spir - it of Je - sus. Send forth the pow-er of your love. Re-new the face of the earth.

to Refrain

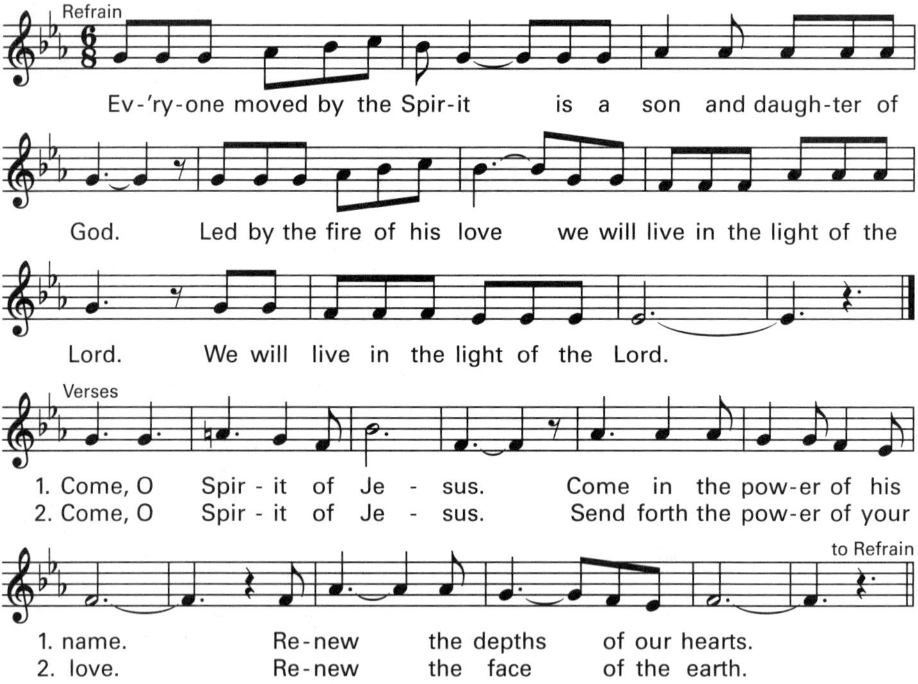

Text: Based on Romans 8; Carey Landry, b. 1944.
Music: Carey Landry.

ALL HAIL, ADORED TRINITY

354

1. All hail, a - dor - ed Trin - i - ty! All hail, e - ter - nal U - ni - ty! O God the Fa - ther, God the Son, And God the Spir - it, ev - er One.
2. Three per - sons praise we ev - er - more, One on - ly God our hearts a - dore: In thy sure mer - cy, ev - er kind, May we your strong pro - tec - tion find.
3. O Trin - i - ty! O U - ni - ty! Be pres - ent as we wor - ship thee; And with the songs that an - gels sing U - nite the hymns of praise we bring.

Text: LM; *Ave colenda Trinitas*, ca. 11th cent.; tr. by John D. Chambers, 1805–1893, alt.
Music: OLD HUNDREDTH; *Genevan Psalter*, 1551; attr. to Louis Bourgeois, ca. 1510–1561, alt.

ALL PRAISE AND GLAD THANKSGIVING

355

1. All praise and glad thanks - giv - ing To God the Fa - ther be: The Font of all things liv - ing, Who reigns e - ter - nal - ly.
2. Christ Je - sus, we a - dore you, The Son of God most high; With thanks we sing be - fore you, Who came for us to die.
3. O Ho - ly Spir - it, bless - ing To you who reign a - bove! Your won - drous gifts con - fess - ing, The Church sings forth your love!

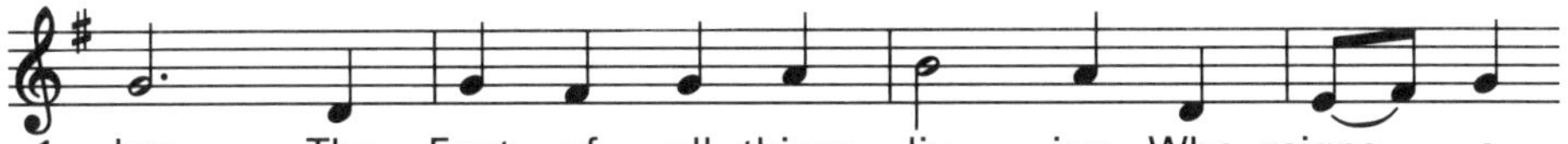

Praise to God for - ev - er be, 
1-3. One in life, in Per - sons three: Might - y God, 
1-3. sav - ing God, God e - ter - nal Trin - i - ty!

Text: 76 76 77 67; based on *Trisagion*, Greek, 5th cent.; Melvin Farrell, SS, 1930–1986, © 1976, OCP. All rights reserved.
Music: GOTT VATER SEI GEPRIESEN; *Limburg Gesangbuch*, 1838.

356 HYMN OF PRAISE

(Te Deum)

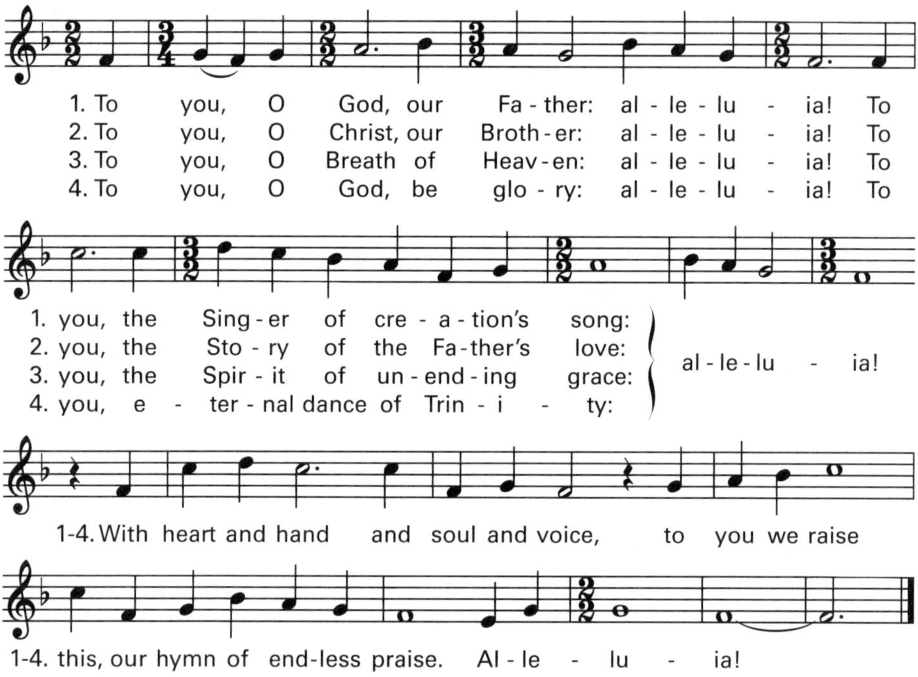

1. To you, O God, our Fa - ther: al - le - lu - ia! To
2. To you, O Christ, our Broth - er: al - le - lu - ia! To
3. To you, O Breath of Heav - en: al - le - lu - ia! To
4. To you, O God, be glo - ry: al - le - lu - ia! To

1. you, the Sing - er of cre - a - tion's song:
2. you, the Sto - ry of the Fa - ther's love:
3. you, the Spir - it of un - end - ing grace:
4. you, e - ter - nal dance of Trin - i - ty:

al - le - lu - ia!

1-4. With heart and hand and soul and voice, to you we raise

1-4. this, our hymn of end-less praise. Al - le - lu - ia!

Text: Inspired by *Te Deum laudamus*; 4th cent. Latin hymn.
Music: Based on chant *Regina Caeli*; Dan Schutte, b. 1947.

357 O GOD, ALMIGHTY FATHER

1. O God, al - might - y Fa - ther, Cre - a - tor of all
2. O Je - sus, Word in - car - nate, Re - deem - er most a -
3. O God, the Ho - ly Spir - it, Who lives with - in our
1. things, The heav - ens stand in won - der, While earth your
2. dored, All glo - ry, praise, and hon - or Be yours, O
3. soul, Send forth your light and lead us To our e -
1. glo - ry sings.
2. sov - 'reign Lord.
3. ter - nal goal.
O most ho - ly Trin - i - ty,

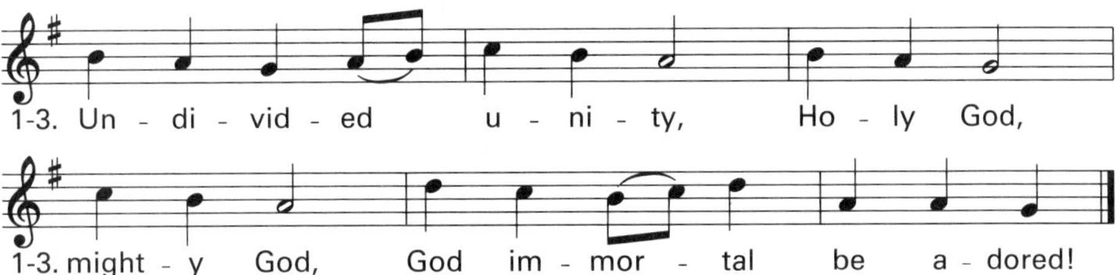
1-3. Un - di - vid - ed u - ni - ty, Ho - ly God,
1-3. might - y God, God im - mor - tal be a - dored!

Text: 76 76 77 67; anon.; tr. by Irvin Udulutsch, OFM, Cap., 1920–2010, alt.,
Music: GOTT VATER SEI GEPRIESEN; *Limburg Gesangbuch*, 1838.

Holy, Holy, Holy 358

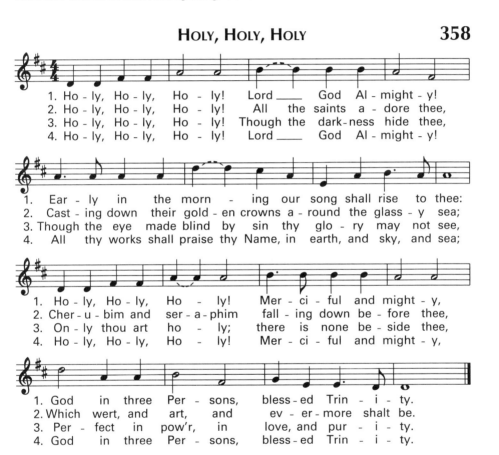

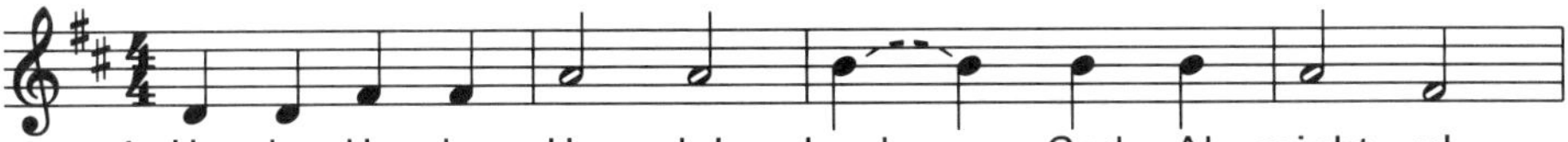

1. Ho - ly, Ho - ly, Ho - ly! Lord ___ God Al - might - y!
2. Ho - ly, Ho - ly, Ho - ly! All the saints a - dore thee,
3. Ho - ly, Ho - ly, Ho - ly! Though the dark - ness hide thee,
4. Ho - ly, Ho - ly, Ho - ly! Lord ___ God Al - might - y!

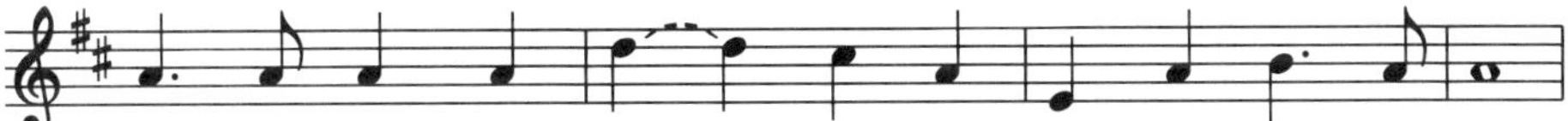

1. Ear - ly in the morn - ing our song shall rise to thee:
2. Cast - ing down their gold - en crowns a - round the glass - y sea;
3. Though the eye made blind by sin thy glo - ry may not see,
4. All thy works shall praise thy Name, in earth, and sky, and sea;

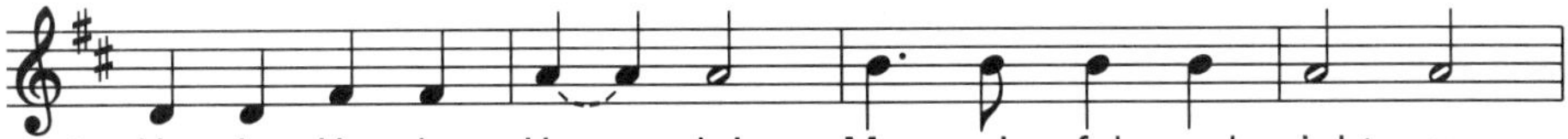

1. Ho - ly, Ho - ly, Ho - ly! Mer - ci - ful and might - y,
2. Cher - u - bim and ser - a - phim fall - ing down be - fore thee,
3. On - ly thou art ho - ly; there is none be - side thee,
4. Ho - ly, Ho - ly, Ho - ly! Mer - ci - ful and might - y,

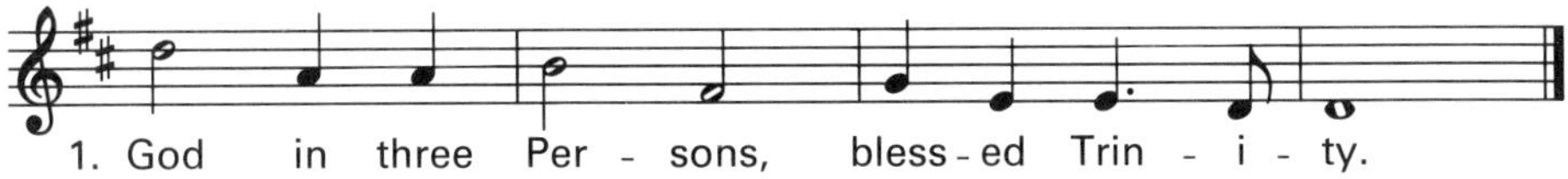

1. God in three Per - sons, bless - ed Trin - i - ty.
2. Which wert, and art, and ev - er - more shalt be.
3. Per - fect in pow'r, in love, and pur - i - ty.
4. God in three Per - sons, bless - ed Trin - i - ty.

Text: 11 12 12 10; Reginald Heber, 1783–1826, alt.
Music: NICAEA; John B. Dykes, 1823–1876.

359 COME NOW, ALMIGHTY KING

1. Come now, Al - might - y King, Help us your name to sing,
2. Come now, In - car - nate Word, Our just and might - y Lord,
3. Come, Ho - ly Com - fort - er, Your sa - cred wit - ness bear
4. To the great One in Three, E - ter - nal prais - es be
1. Help us to praise: Fa - ther, all glo - ri - ous, Ev - er vic -
2. Our prayer at - tend: Come, and your peo - ple bless, And give your
3. In this glad hour: To us your grace im - part, And rule in
4. For - ev - er - more! Your sov-'reign maj - es - ty May we in
1. to - ri - ous, Come, and reign o - ver us, An - cient of Days.
2. word suc - cess; Strength - en your righ - teous - ness, Sav - ior and Friend.
3. ev - 'ry heart! Nev - er from us de - part, Spir - it of pow'r.
4. glo - ry see, And to e - ter - ni - ty Love and a - dore!

Text: 66 4 666 4; anon., ca. 1757, alt.
Music: ITALIAN HYMN; Felice de Giardini, 1716–1796, alt.

360 TO JESUS CHRIST, OUR SOVEREIGN KING

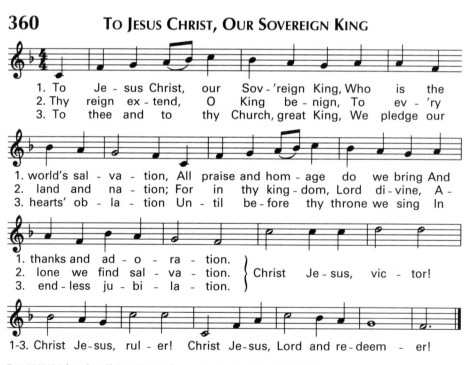

1. To Je - sus Christ, our Sov - 'reign King, Who is the
2. Thy reign ex - tend, O King be - nign, To ev - 'ry
3. To thee and to thy Church, great King, We pledge our

1. world's sal - va - tion, All praise and hom - age do we bring And
2. land and na - tion; For in thy king - dom, Lord di - vine, A -
3. hearts' ob - la - tion Un - til be - fore thy throne we sing In

1. thanks and ad - o - ra - tion.
2. lone we find sal - va - tion.
3. end - less ju - bi - la - tion.
Christ Je - sus, vic - tor!

1-3. Christ Je - sus, rul - er! Christ Je - sus, Lord and re - deem - er!

Text: 87 87 55 8; based on *Christus Vincit*, 8th cent.; Martin B. Hellriegel, 1891–1981,

Music: ICH GLAUB AN GOTT; *Mainz Gesangbuch*, 1870.

361 Alleluia! Sing to Jesus

1. Alleluia! sing to Jesus! His the scepter, his the throne;
Alleluia! his the triumph, His the victory alone;
Hark! the songs of peaceful Zion Thunder like a mighty flood;
Jesus out of ev'ry nation Has redeemed us by his blood.

2. Alleluia! not as orphans Are we left in sorrow now;
Alleluia! he is near us, Faith believes, nor questions how:
Though the cloud from sight received him, When the forty days were o'er,
Shall our hearts forget his promise? "I am with you evermore!"

3. Alleluia! Bread of Angels, Here on earth our food, our stay!
Alleluia! here the sinful Flee to you from day to day:
Intercessor, friend of sinners, Earth's redeemer, plead for me,
Where the songs of all the sinless Sweep across the crystal sea.

4. Alleluia! King eternal, You the Lord of lords we own;
Alleluia! born of Mary, Earth your footstool, heav'n your throne:
You within the veil have entered, Robed in flesh, our great high priest;
Here on earth both priest and victim In the Eucharistic feast.

5. Alleluia! Alleluia! Glory be to God on high;
Alleluia to the Savior Who has won the victory;
Alleluia to the Spirit, Font of love and sanctity;
Alleluia! Alleluia! To the triune majesty.

Text: 87 87 D; William C. Dix, 1837–1898, alt.
Music: HYFRYDOL; Rowland H. Prichard, 1811–1887.

362 CROWN HIM WITH MANY CROWNS

1. Crown him with man - y crowns, The Lamb up - on his
2. Crown him the Lord of life, Who tri - umphed o'er the
3. Crown him the Lord of love, Be - hold his hands and
4. Crown him the Lord of peace, Whose pow'r a scep - ter
5. Crown him the Lord of years, The ris - en Lord sub -
1. throne; Hark! how the heav'n - ly an - them drowns All
2. grave, And rose vic - to - rious in the strife For
3. side, Rich wounds yet vis - i - ble a - bove In
4. sways From pole to pole, that wars may cease, Ab -
5. lime, Cre - a - tor of the roll - ing spheres, The
1. mu - sic but its own. A - wake, my soul, and sing
2. those he came to save. His glo - ries now we sing,
3. beau - ty glo - ri - fied. No an - gel in the sky
4. sorbed in prayer and praise. His reign shall know no end,
5. Mas - ter of all time. All hail, Re - deem - er, hail!
1. Of him who set us free, And hail him as your
2. Who died and rose on high, Who died, e - ter - nal
3. Can ful - ly bear that sight, But down - ward bends his
4. And round his pierc - ed feet Fair flow'rs of Par - a -
5. For you have died for me; Your praise and glo - ry
1. heav'n - ly King Through all e - ter - ni - ty.
2. life to bring, And lives that death may die.
3. burn - ing eye At mys - ter - ies so bright.
4. dise ex - tend Their fra - grance ev - er sweet.
5. shall not fail Through - out e - ter - ni - ty.

Text: SMD; Revelation 19:12; verses 1, 3–5, Matthew Bridges, 1800–1894; verse 2, Godfrey Thring, 1823–1903, alt.
Music: DIADEMATA; George J. Elvey, 1816–1893.

JESUS, THE LORD

363

Refrain
Je - sus. Je - sus. Let all cre-
a - tion bend the knee to the Lord.
Verse 1
1. In him we live, we move and have our be - ing; In
1. him the Christ, in him the king! Je - sus, the Lord.
to Refrain
Verse 2
2. Though Son, he did not cling to
2. god - li - ness; but emp - tied him - self, be -
2. came a slave! Je - sus, the Lord.
to Refrain
Verse 3
3. He lived o - be - dient - ly his
3. Fa - ther's will ac - cept - ing his death, death on a
3. tree! Je - sus, the Lord.
to Refrain

Text: Based on the Jesus Prayer; Philippians 2:5–11; Acts 17:28; Roc O'Connor, SJ, b. 1949.
Music: Roc O'Connor, SJ.

364 ALL HAIL THE POWER OF JESUS' NAME

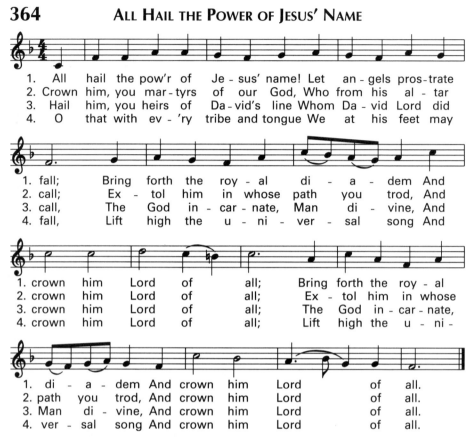

1. All hail the pow'r of Je - sus' name! Let an - gels pros - trate
2. Crown him, you mar - tyrs of our God, Who from his al - tar
3. Hail him, you heirs of Da - vid's line Whom Da - vid Lord did
4. O that with ev - 'ry tribe and tongue We at his feet may

1. fall; Bring forth the roy - al di - a - dem And
2. call; Ex - tol him in whose path you trod, And
3. call, The God in - car - nate, Man di - vine, And
4. fall, Lift high the u - ni - ver - sal song And

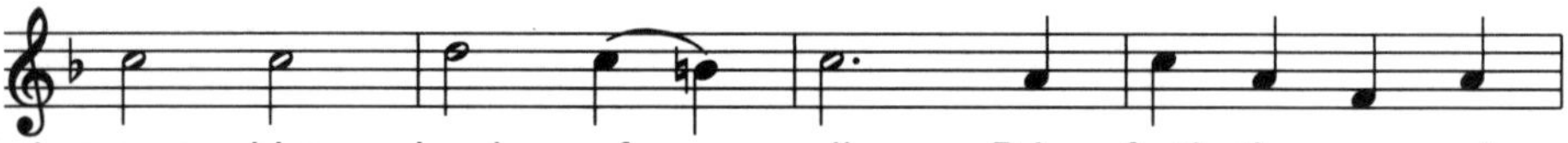

1. crown him Lord of all; Bring forth the roy - al
2. crown him Lord of all; Ex - tol him in whose
3. crown him Lord of all; The God in - car - nate,
4. crown him Lord of all; Lift high the u - ni -

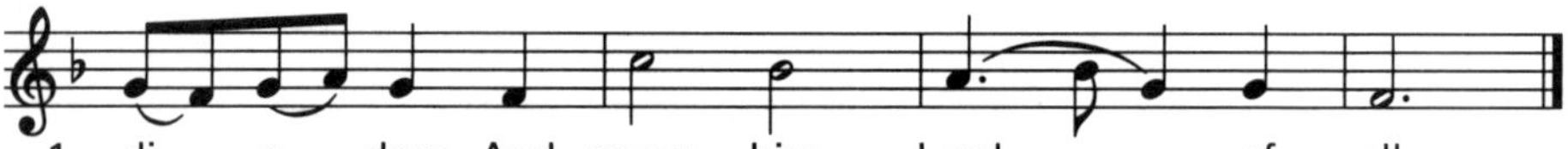

1. di - a - dem And crown him Lord of all.
2. path you trod, And crown him Lord of all.
3. Man di - vine, And crown him Lord of all.
4. ver - sal song And crown him Lord of all.

Text: 86 86 86; Edward Perronet, 1726–1792, alt.
Music: CORONATION; *Union Harmony*, 1793; Oliver Holden, 1765–1844.

365 HAIL, REDEEMER, KING DIVINE

Verses
1. Hail, re-deem-er, king di - vine! Priest and lamb, the throne is thine;
2. King of ev - er - last-ing might! Be to us e - ter - nal light,
1. King whose reign shall nev - er cease, Prince of ev - er - last-ing peace.
2. Till in peace each na - tion rings With thy prais-es, king of kings.

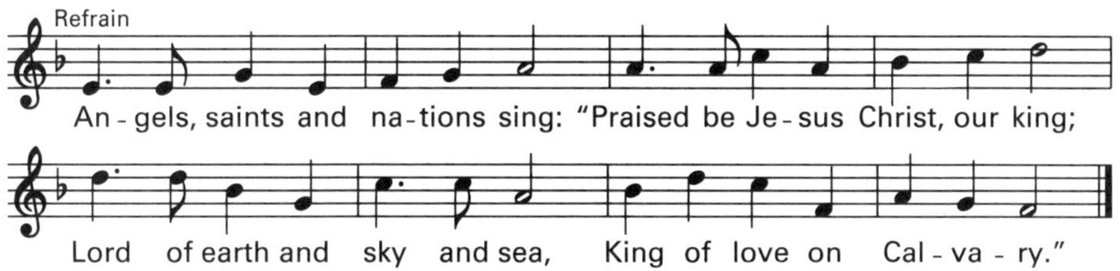
Refrain
An - gels, saints and na - tions sing: "Praised be Je - sus Christ, our king;
Lord of earth and sky and sea, King of love on Cal - va - ry."

Text: 77 77 with refrain; Patrick Brennen, 1877–1951, © Burns & Oates, Ltd. All rights reserved. Reproduced by permission of Continuum International Publishing Group, a Bloomsbury Company.
Music: ST. GEORGE'S WINDSOR; George J. Elvey, 1816–1893.

At the Name of Jesus 366

Refrain

At the name of Je - sus, ev - 'ry knee shall bow, ev - 'ry tongue confess him: King of glo - ry now. Je - sus is Lord, King of glo - ry now!

(last time only)

Verses

1. He ___ emp - tied him - self, as a slave, yet free, came in hu - man like - ness ___ for you and for me; in hu - man like - ness ___ for you and for me.
2. He ___ hum - bled him - self, and o - beyed God's will. On a cross he died ___ on Cal - va - ry's hill; for you and me he o - beyed ___ God's will.
3. God ex - alt - ed him, raised him up on high so a - bove all oth - ers ___ his name will not die; that name we hon - or ___ and glo - ri - fy.
4. Christ ___ Je - sus will come at the end of time, come with ju - bi - la - tion ___ to call ___ us home. Un - til that day you and I will pro - claim:

to Refrain

Text: Refrain, Caroline Maria Noel, 1817–1877. Verses based on Philippians 2; Christopher Walker, b. 1947, © 1995, Christopher Walker. Published by OCP. All rights reserved.
Music: Christopher Walker, © 1995, Christopher Walker. Published by OCP. All rights reserved.

JESUS CHRIST IS LORD

Refrain

Je - sus Christ is Lord.

Verses

1. He did not hold to his e - qual - i - ty with God, for he did emp - ty him - self to be as one of us, to be as one of us.
2. He chose the will of God through death up - on a cross, and God did raise___ him up, ex - alt - ing him on high, ex - alt - ing him on high.
3. And so God gave to him a name a - bove all names. May all in heav - en and earth pro - claim him now as Lord, pro - claim him now as Lord.

to Refrain

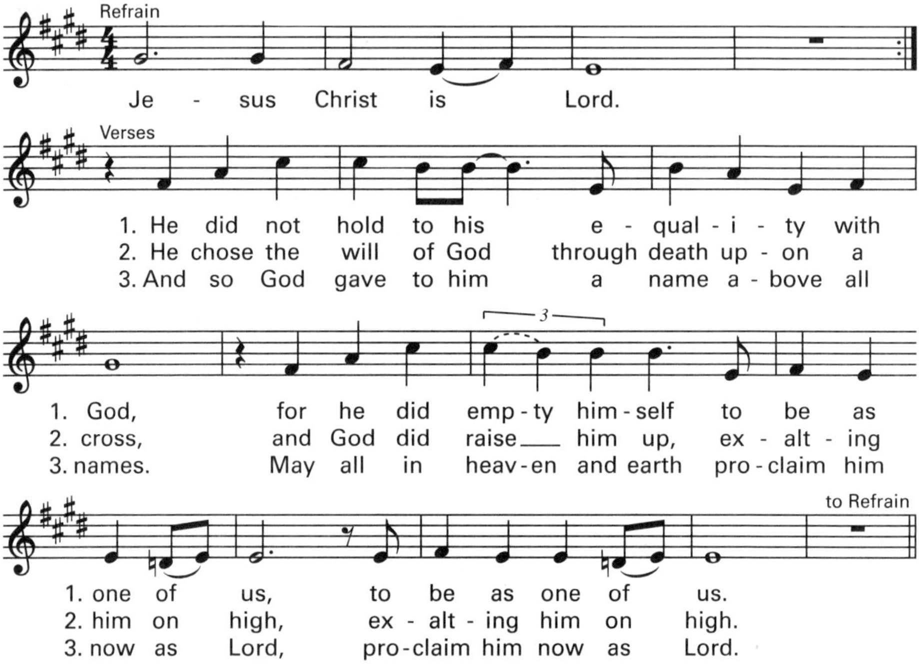

Text: Based on Philippians 2:6–11; Ken Canedo, b. 1953,

Music: Ken Canedo,

368 THE KING OF GLORY

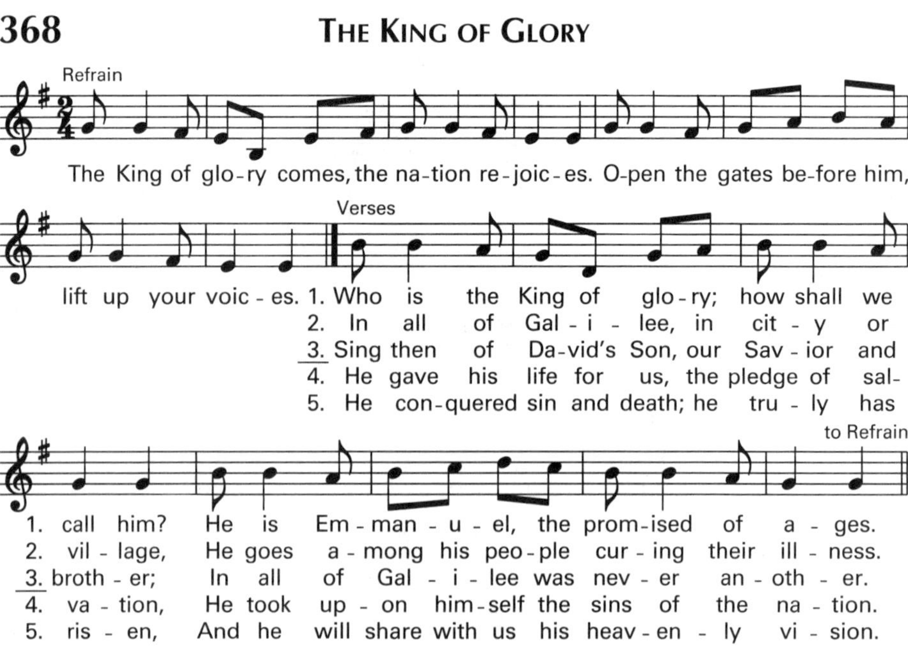
Refrain
The King of glo-ry comes, the na-tion re-joic-es. O-pen the gates be-fore him,
lift up your voic-es.
Verses
1. Who is the King of glo-ry; how shall we call him? He is Em-man-u-el, the prom-ised of a-ges.
2. In all of Gal-i-lee, in cit-y or vil-lage, He goes a-mong his peo-ple cur-ing their ill-ness.
3. Sing then of Da-vid's Son, our Sav-ior and broth-er; In all of Gal-i-lee was nev-er an-oth-er.
4. He gave his life for us, the pledge of sal-va-tion, He took up-on him-self the sins of the na-tion.
5. He con-quered sin and death; he tru-ly has ris-en, And he will share with us his heav-en-ly vi-sion.
to Refrain

Text: 12 12 with refrain; Willard F. Jabusch, b. 1930,
Music: KING OF GLORY; trad. Israeli folk song.

AVE MARIA 369

1. A - ve Ma - ri - a, gra - ti - a ple - na,
2. Be - ne - dic - ta, blest a - mong wom - en,
3. Sanc - ta Ma - ri - a, Ho - ly Ma - ry,
1. O ho - ly Ma - ry, full of grace;
2. be - ne - dic - tus, the child that you bore:
3. Ma - ter De - i, Moth - er of God:
1. Do - mi - nus te - cum, with you the Ho - ly One.
2. Je - sus the Sav - ior, God's love in - car - nate,
3. O - ra pro no - bis, pray for our faith - ful - ness
1. Such is your gift to know God in your
2. be - ne - dic - ta, deep wom - an of
3. all through the sea - sons of life with hope and with
1
to Verse 2
2
1. heart.
2. faith. A - ve Ma - ri -
2. a, A - ve, A - ve Ma - ri - a.
to Verse 3
Final
3. love. O - ra pro no - bis, pray for our faith - ful - ness
3. all through the sea - sons of life with hope and with love.

370 IMMACULATE MARY

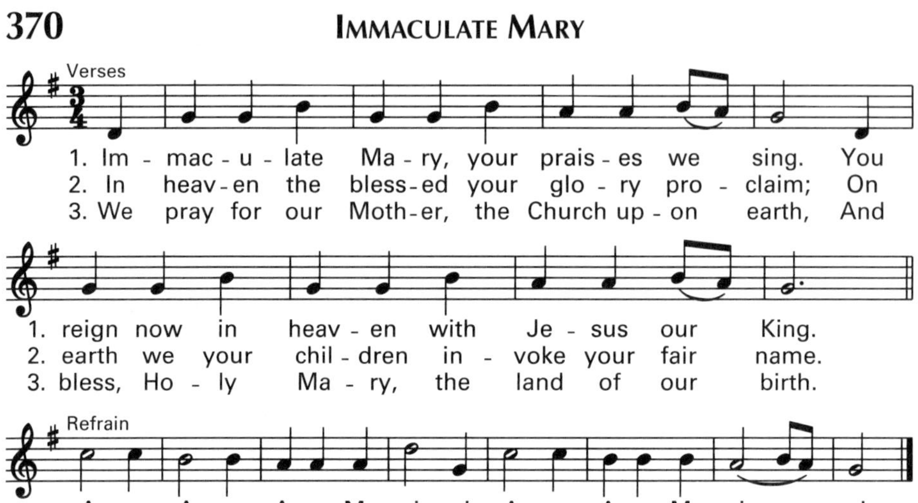
Verses
1. Im - mac - u - late Ma - ry, your prais - es we sing. You
2. In heav - en the bless - ed your glo - ry pro - claim; On
3. We pray for our Moth - er, the Church up - on earth, And
1. reign now in heav - en with Je - sus our King.
2. earth we your chil - dren in - voke your fair name.
3. bless, Ho - ly Ma - ry, the land of our birth.
Refrain
A - ve, A - ve, A-ve, Ma - ri - a! A - ve, A-ve, Ma - ri - a!

Text: 11 11 with refrain; anon. in *Parochial Hymn Book,* Boston, 1897;
rev. of *Hail Virgin of virgins* by Jeremiah Cummings, 1814–1866, alt.
Music: LOURDES HYMN; trad. Pyrenean melody, pub. Grenoble, 1882; alt. by Augustus Edmonds Tozer, 1857–1910.

371 DEL CIELO HA BAJADO

Estrofas

1. Del cie-lo ha ba - ja - do la Ma - dre de Dios. Can - te - mos el A - ve a su con-cep - ción.
2. Del ver - bo di - vi - no, de Cris - to Je - sús, San - tí - si - ma Ma - dre, Ma - rí - a, e-res tú.
3. Oh Vir-gen sin man-cha, oh Ma - dre de a - mor, El án - gel te o - frez - ca mi sa - lu - ta - ción.
4. Tú e - res el or - gu - llo de Dios cre - a - dor, Y el fru - to más dig - no de la re - den - ción.
5. Las gra-cias e - ma - nan del tro - no de Dios, Y to - das con - flu - yen en tu co - ra - zón.
6. La lu-na hu-mi - lla - da tus plan-tas be - só, Y el mun - do te a - do - ra ves - ti - da del _ sol.
7. Pues so - mos tus hi - jos, o - ye nues-tra voz; De - fién - de - nos siem - pre en la ten - ta - ción.

Estribillo

A - ve, a - ve, a - ve Ma-rí - a. A - ve, a - ve, a - ve Ma-rí - a.

Text: 11 11 with refrain; traditional.
Music: AVE DE LOURDES; trad. Pyrenean melody, pub. Grenoble, 1882.

HAIL MARY: GENTLE WOMAN 372

Intro: Cantor

Hail Mary, full of grace, the Lord is with you.
Blessed are you among women and
blest is the fruit of your womb, Jesus.

Holy Mary, Mother of God,
pray for us sinners now
and at the hour of death. Amen.

Refrain: All
Gen-tle wom-an, qui-et light, morn-ing star, so strong and bright, gen-tle Moth-er, peace-ful dove, teach us wis-dom; teach us love.
Verses: All
1. You were cho - sen by the Fa - ther; you were cho - sen for the Son. You were cho - sen from all wom-en and for wom-an, shin-ing one.
2. Bless-ed are you a-mong wom-en, blest in turn all wom-en, too. Bless-ed they with peace - ful spir-its. Bless-ed they with gen - tle hearts.
to Refrain

Text: Based on Luke 1:28, 42; Carey Landry, b. 1944.
Music: Carey Landry.

373 My Soul Magnifies the Lord

Refrain
My soul mag - ni-fies the Lord, and my spir - it re - joic - es in God my sav - ior; for he has done great things for me, and ho - ly is his name.
Verse 1
1. His mer - cy ex-tends to all who fear him. From
1. one gen-er - a-tion to the next, the hum-ble he ex-alts, but the
1. proud he casts down, and the hun-gry he fills with good things.
to Refrain
Verses 2, 3
2. For he has looked with fa - vor on his ser - vant and
3. The Lord has a plan for all his peo - ple, a
2. come to the help of Is - ra - el. He will not for - get the
3. plan to bring peace to ev - ery - one. Our God will be there in the
2. prom-ise of his mer - cy, the prom-ise he made to us all.
3. tri - al and the won-der, the joy of life he will bring.
to Refrain

Text: *Magnificat;* based on Luke 1:46–55. Refrain and verse 1, Charles B. Romer; verses 2–3, Paul Hillebrand, b. 1959.
Music: Charles B. Romer.

Song of Mary

374

1. Let us sing the prais-es of Ma-ry, daugh-ter of Da-vid's ho-ly line, she who heard the voice of an an-gel tell-ing the plan of God's de-sign, how in wis-dom's ho-ly sight she would moth-er heav-en's Christ.
2. Let us sing the prais-es of Ma-ry, cho-sen as bless-ed from the least, she who heard the song of the an-gels fill-ing the night with heav-en's peace. When the prom-ised time had come she gave birth to God's own Son.
3. Let us sing the prais-es of Ma-ry, wom-an of strong and stead-fast love. She who raised the Sav-ior of na-tions held in her arms the Son of God. She who knew the Fa-ther's grace taught her Son to know God's face.
4. Let us sing the prais-es of Ma-ry, pierced by the sword of sor-row's pain, she who saw the child of her lov-ing nailed on a cross to die in shame. Though his friends would flee in fear she re-mained for-ev-er near.
5. Let us sing the prais-es of Ma-ry, friend of the poor in ev-'ry age, she who saw her Son and her Sav-ior ris-en in glo-ry from the grave. Sin and death shall reign no more; Christ has o-pened heav-en's door.
1–5. Bless-ed be the name of Ma-ry, she who trust-ed the love of God.
2

Text: 98 98 77 88; Dan Schutte, b. 1947.
Music: SONG OF MARY; Dan Schutte.

375 Mary's Song

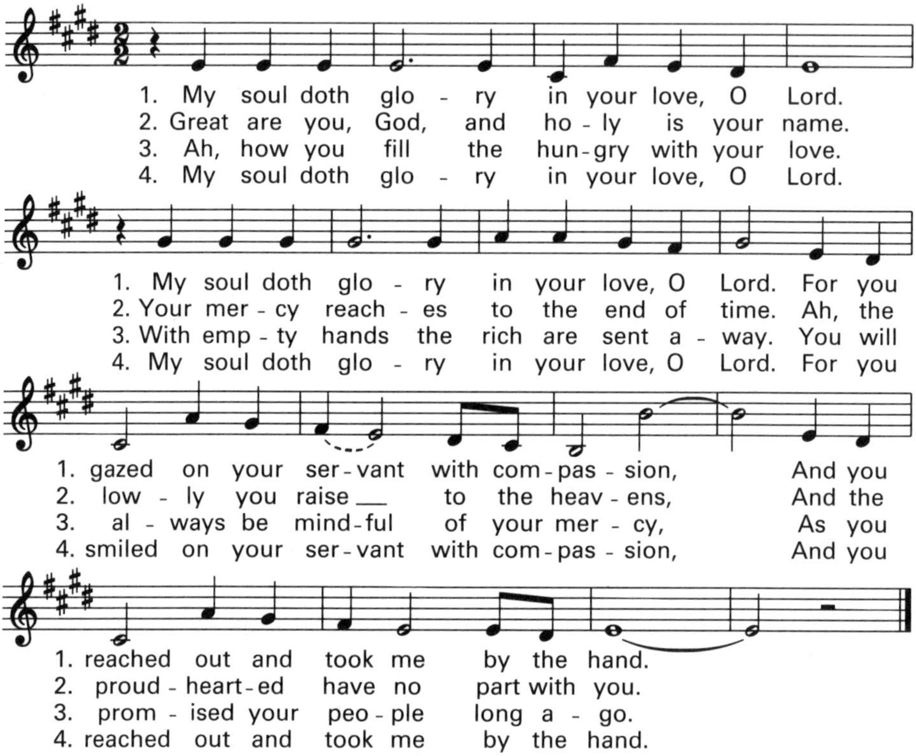

1. My soul doth glo - ry in your love, O Lord.
2. Great are you, God, and ho - ly is your name.
3. Ah, how you fill the hun-gry with your love.
4. My soul doth glo - ry in your love, O Lord.

1. My soul doth glo - ry in your love, O Lord. For you
2. Your mer - cy reach - es to the end of time. Ah, the
3. With emp - ty hands the rich are sent a - way. You will
4. My soul doth glo - ry in your love, O Lord. For you

1. gazed on your ser-vant with com-pas - sion, And you
2. low - ly you raise __ to the heav - ens, And the
3. al - ways be mind-ful of your mer - cy, As you
4. smiled on your ser-vant with com-pas - sion, And you

1. reached out and took me by the hand.
2. proud - heart-ed have no part with you.
3. prom - ised your peo - ple long a - go.
4. reached out and took me by the hand.

Text: *Magnificat;* based on Luke 1:46–55; Millie Rieth, 1940–2003.
Music: Millie Rieth.

376 Hail, Holy Queen

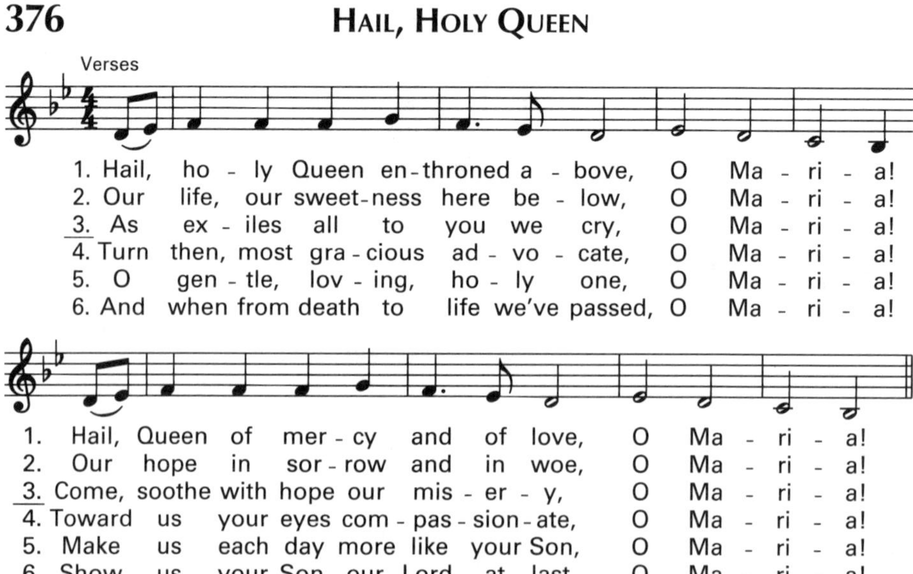
Verses
1. Hail, ho - ly Queen en-throned a - bove, O Ma - ri - a!
2. Our life, our sweet-ness here be - low, O Ma - ri - a!
3. As ex - iles all to you we cry, O Ma - ri - a!
4. Turn then, most gra - cious ad - vo - cate, O Ma - ri - a!
5. O gen - tle, lov - ing, ho - ly one, O Ma - ri - a!
6. And when from death to life we've passed, O Ma - ri - a!
1. Hail, Queen of mer - cy and of love, O Ma - ri - a!
2. Our hope in sor - row and in woe, O Ma - ri - a!
3. Come, soothe with hope our mis - er - y, O Ma - ri - a!
4. Toward us your eyes com - pas - sion - ate, O Ma - ri - a!
5. Make us each day more like your Son, O Ma - ri - a!
6. Show us your Son, our Lord, at last, O Ma - ri - a!

Refrain
Tri - umph, all ye cher - u - bim, Sing with us, ye
ser - a - phim! Heav'n and earth re - sound the hymn:
Sal - ve, sal - ve, sal - ve, Re - gi - na!

Text: 84 84 with refrain; *Salve, Regina, mater misericordiae*, ca. 1080;
verses 1, 2, 5 and refrain tr. anon. in *Roman Hymnal*, 1884; verses 3, 4, 6, para.
Music: SALVE REGINA COELITUM; Melchior Ludwig Herold, 1753–1810; *Choralmelodien zum Heiligen Gesänge*, 1808.

There Is Nothing Told 377

Verses

1-6. There is noth - ing told a - bout this wom - an, but that

1. she had once be - come en - gaged, and an an - gel ad -
2. she had brought in - to the world, in the land of Ju -
3. she had searched for three long days for her child who was
4. she at Ca - na was a guest, and that Je - sus changed
5. she was stand - ing by the cross when her son stretched his
6. she was one in prayer with those up - on whom tongues of

1. dressed her and said: "You are bless - ed a - mong all your kind."
2. de - a, her son; for some shep-herds have passed on this tale.
3. bus - y else-where, and her heart then did not un - der - stand.
4. wa - ter to wine, so that all might be - lieve who he was.
5. arms out on high, and met death with a thief on each side.
6. fire did de-scend, and the Spir - it bap - tized them with flame.

Refrain

On this day all earth and all par-a-dise join in nam - ing you
hap - py and blessed; Vir-gin Ma - ry, bless - ed are you.

Text: *Une femme dont on n'a rien dit*; Didier Rimaud, 1922–2003; tr. by Christopher Willcock, b. 1947,

Music: Christopher Willcock,

378 THE ANGEL GABRIEL FROM HEAVEN CAME

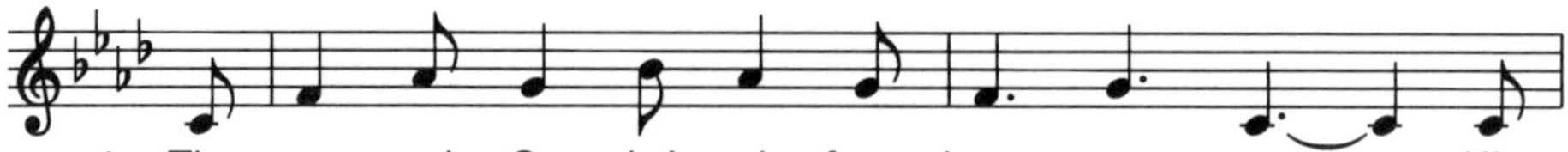

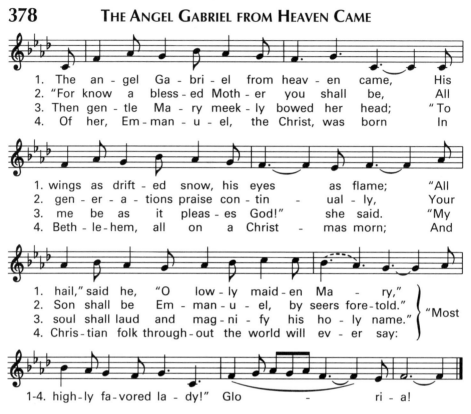

1. The an - gel Ga - bri - el from heav - en came, His
2. "For know a bless - ed Moth - er you shall be, All
3. Then gen - tle Ma - ry meek - ly bowed her head; "To
4. Of her, Em - man - u - el, the Christ, was born In

1. wings as drift - ed snow, his eyes as flame; "All
2. gen - er - a - tions praise con - tin - ual - ly, Your
3. me be as it pleas - es God!" she said. "My
4. Beth - le - hem, all on a Christ - mas morn; And

1. hail," said he, "O low - ly maid - en Ma - ry,"
2. Son shall be Em - man - u - el, by seers fore - told."
3. soul shall laud and mag - ni - fy his ho - ly name."
4. Chris - tian folk through - out the world will ev - er say:
"Most

1-4. high - ly fa - vored la - dy!" Glo - ri - a!

Text: 10 10 12 10; *Birjina gaztettobat zegoen*; trad. Basque carol; tr. by Sabine Baring-Gould, 1834–1924.
Music: GABRIEL'S MESSAGE; trad. Basque carol melody.

379 HOLY IS HIS NAME

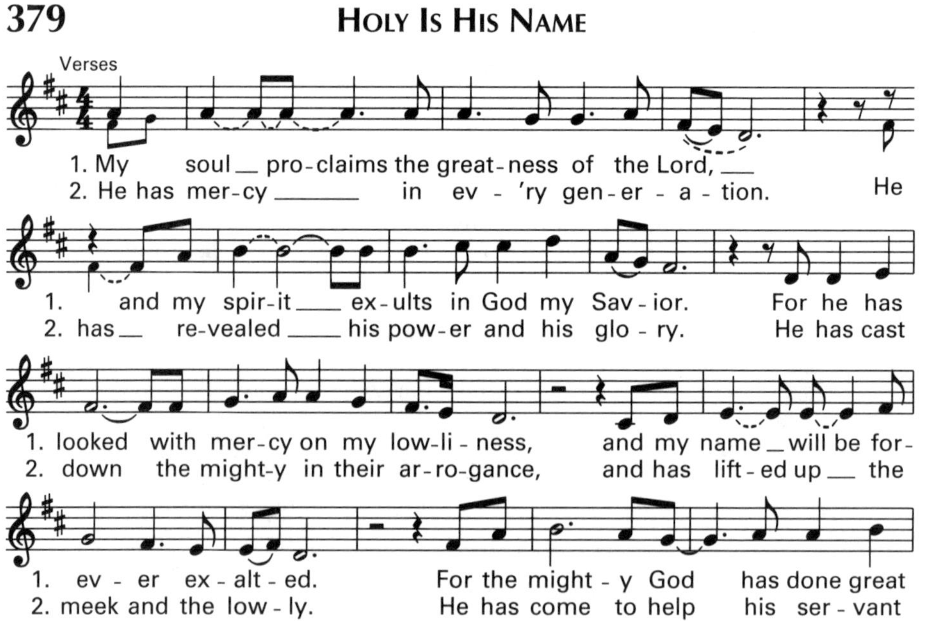
Verses
1. My soul __ pro - claims the great - ness of the Lord, __
2. He has mer - cy ______ in ev - 'ry gen - er - a - tion. He
1. and my spir - it ___ ex - ults in God my Sav - ior. For he has
2. has __ re - vealed ____ his pow - er and his glo - ry. He has cast
1. looked with mer - cy on my low - li - ness, and my name __ will be for -
2. down the might - y in their ar - ro - gance, and has lift - ed up __ the
1. ev - er ex - alt - ed. For the might - y God has done great
2. meek and the low - ly. He has come to help his ser - vant

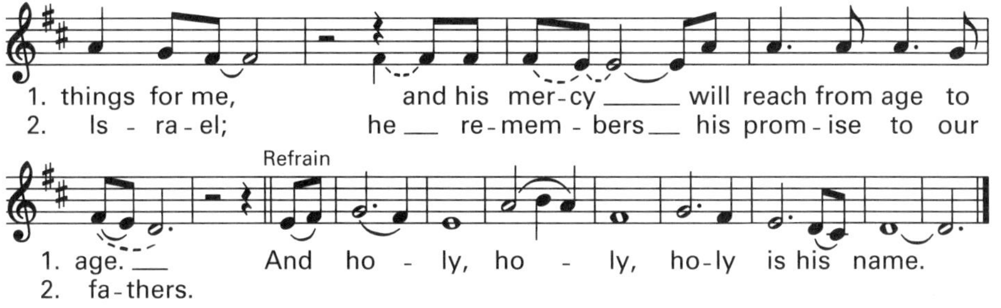
1. things for me, and his mer-cy ___ will reach from age to
2. Is - ra - el; he ___ re-mem - bers ___ his prom - ise to our
Refrain
1. age. ___ And ho - ly, ho - ly, ho-ly is his name.
2. fa-thers.

Text: *Magnificat;* based on Luke 1:46–55; John Michael Talbot, b. 1954.
Music: John Michael Talbot.

SING OF MARY 380

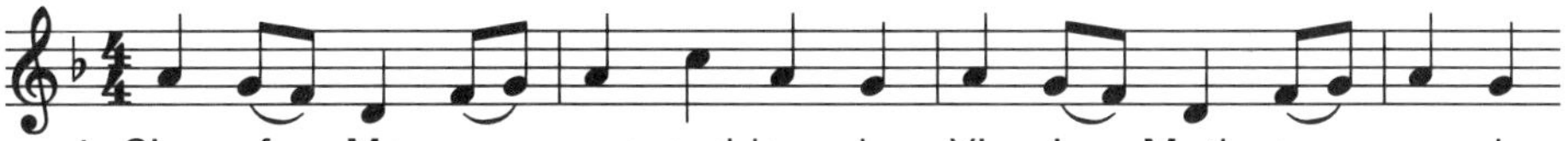

1. Sing of Ma - ry, pure and low - ly, Vir - gin Moth - er un - de -
2. Sing of Je - sus, son of Ma - ry, In the home at Naz - a -
3. Glo - ry be to God the Fa - ther; Glo - ry be to God the

1. filed. Sing of God's own Son most ho - ly, Who be - came her
2. reth. Toil and la - bor can - not wea - ry Love en - dur - ing
3. Son; Glo - ry be to God the Spir - it; Glo - ry to the

1. lit - tle child. Fair - est child of fair - est moth - er,
2. un - to death. Con - stant was the love he gave her,
3. Three in One. From the heart of bless - ed Ma - ry,

1. God the Lord who came to earth, Word made flesh, our
2. Though he went forth from her side, Forth to preach and
3. From all saints the song as - cends, And the Church the

1. ver - y broth - er, Takes our na - ture by his birth.
2. heal and suf - fer, Till on Cal - va - ry he died.
3. strain re - ech - oes Un - to earth's re - mot - est ends.

Text: 87 87 D; Roland F. Palmer, SSJE, 1891–1985,
Music: PLEADING SAVIOR; *Christian Lyre*, 1830.

381 TRANSFIGURATION

1. Je - sus, on the moun - tain peak, stands a - lone in glo - ry
2. Trem - bling at his feet we saw Mo - ses and E - li - jah
3. Swift the cloud of glo - ry came, God, pro-claim-ing in its
4. Je - sus is the cho - sen one, liv - ing hope of ev - 'ry
1. blaz - ing. Let us, if we dare to speak, join the
2. speak - ing. All the proph-ets and the law shout through
3. thun - der, Je - sus as the Son by name! Na - tions,
4. na - tion, hear and heed him, ev - 'ry - one; sing, with
1. saints and an - gels prais - ing.
2. them their joy - ful greet - ing:
3. cry a - loud in won - der:
4. earth and all cre - a - tion:
Praise and glo - ry,
*Al - le - lu - ia,
1-4. praise and glo - ry, praise and glo - ry to our Lord!
1-4. al - le - lu - ia, al - le - lu - ia!
1. Let us, if we dare to speak, join the saints and an - gels
2. All the pro-phets and the law shout through them their joy - ful
3. Je - sus as the Son by name: na - tions, cry a - loud in
4. Hear and heed him, ev - 'ry - one; sing with earth and all cre-
(Fine) Interlude
6
1. prais - ing.
2. greet - ing.
3. won - der.
4. a - tion.

*Outside the season of Lent.

TRANSFIGURATION

382

Refrain
We behold the splendor of God shining on the face of Jesus. We behold the splendor of God shining on the face of the Son.
Verse 1
1. And oh, how his beauty transforms us, the wonder of presence abiding. Transparent hearts give reflection of Tabor's light within, of Tabor's light within.
to Refrain
Verse 2
2. Jesus, Lord of Glory, Jesus, beloved Son. Oh, how good to be with you; how good to share your light, how good to share your light.
to Refrain

383 Take Up Our Cross

Verses
1. Be-hold the wood that bears our name;
2. We em-brace the sac - ri - fice,
1. be - hold the nails that hold our sin.
2. and walk the path we can - not see.
1. The tree from which sal - va - tion blooms;
2. The bur - dens of this world made light;
1. the death by which we're born a - gain.
2. by blood and thorn we are re - deemed.
Refrain
We take up our cross and fol - low him; we
lay down our lives that we might live. We
car - ry the hope of Christ with-in; we take up our cross
and fol - low him.
1, Final
(Fine)
to Verse 2
2
2
to Bridge
3

Bridge

Lift him high, lift him high; let his name be glorified.
Lift him high, lift him high; let his name be glorified. **(to Refrain)**

LIFT HIGH THE CROSS

384

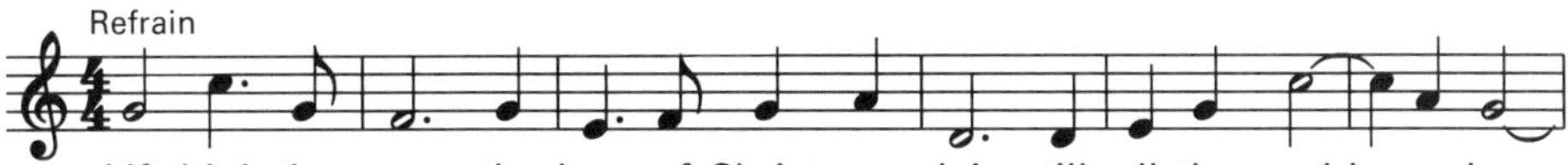
Refrain
Lift high the cross, the love of Christ pro-claim till all the world a-dore

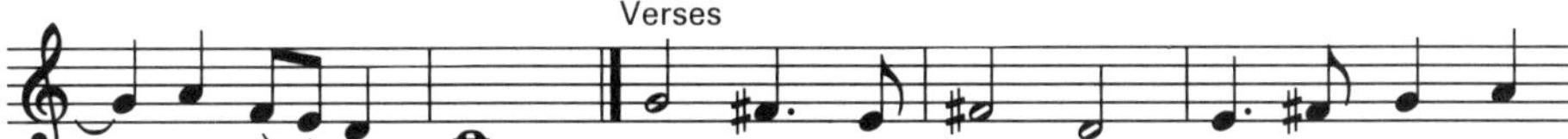
Verses
his sa-cred name.
1. Led on their way by this tri-um-phant
2. Each new-born ser-vant of the Cru-ci-
3. O Lord, once lift-ed on the glo-rious
4. So shall our song of tri-umph ev-er

to Refrain
1. sign, The hosts of God in con-quering ranks com-bine.
2. fied Bears on the brow the seal of him who died.
3. tree, As thou hast prom-ised, draw the world to thee.
4. be: Praise to the Cru-ci-fied for vic-to-ry!

Text: 10 10 with refrain; based on 1 Corinthians 1:18; George W. Kitchin, 1827–1912; alt. by Michael R. Newbolt, 1874–1956.
Music: CRUCIFER; Sydney H. Nicholson, 1875–1947.

COME NOW, AND PRAISE THE HUMBLE SAINT 385

1. Come now, and praise the hum-ble saint Of
2. The Ar-chi-tect's high mir-a-cles He
3. For him there was no glo-ry here, No
4. But now with-in the Fa-ther's grace Where
1. Da-vid's house and line, The car-pen-ter whose
2. saw, and what was done; The Vir-gin's spouse, the
3. crown or mar-tyr's fame; For him there was the
4. saints and an-gels throng, Be-side his spouse, be-

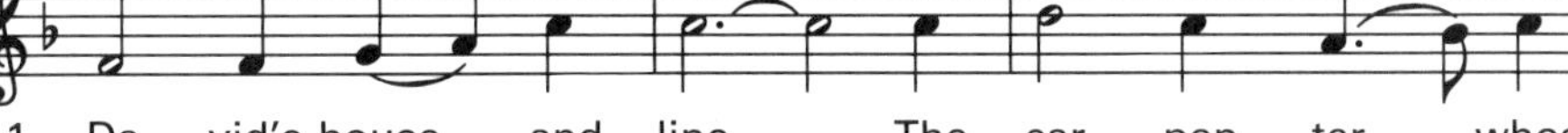
1. life ful-filled Our gra-cious God's de-sign.
2. guard-ian of Great Da-vid's great-er Son.
3. pa-tient life Of faith and hum-ble name.
4. fore the Son, He joins the heav'n-ly song.

Text: CM; George W. Williams, b. 1922,
Music: LAND OF REST; trad. American melody.

386 Blessed Feasts of Blessed Martyrs

1. Bless - ed feasts of bless - ed mar - tyrs, Ho - ly wom - en,
2. Faith pre - vail - ing, hope un - fail - ing, Lov - ing Christ with
3. There - fore, all that reign in glo - ry, Faith - ful heirs with

1. ho - ly men, With our love and ad - mi - ra - tion, Greet we
2. sin - gle heart, Thus they, glo - rious and vic - to - rious, Brave - ly
3. Christ on high, Join to ours your sup - pli - ca - tion When be -

1. your re - turn a - gain. Wor - thy deeds they wrought, and won - ders,
2. bore the mar - tyr's part, By con - tempt of ev - 'ry an - guish,
3. fore Christ we draw nigh, Pray - ing that, this life com - plet - ed,

1. Wor - thy of the name they bore; We, with joy - ful
2. By un - yield - ing bat - tle done; Vic - tors at the
3. All its fleet - ing mo - ments past, By Christ's grace we

1. praise and sing - ing, Hon - or them for ev - er - more.
2. last, they tri - umph, With the host of an - gels one.
3. may be wor - thy Of e - ter - nal bliss at last.

Text: 87 87 D; *O beata beatorum*, 11th cent.; tr. by John M. Neale, 1818–1866, alt.
Music: IN BABILONE; *Oude en Nieuwe Hollantse Boerenlieties en Contredansen*, ca. 1710.

387 Saints of God

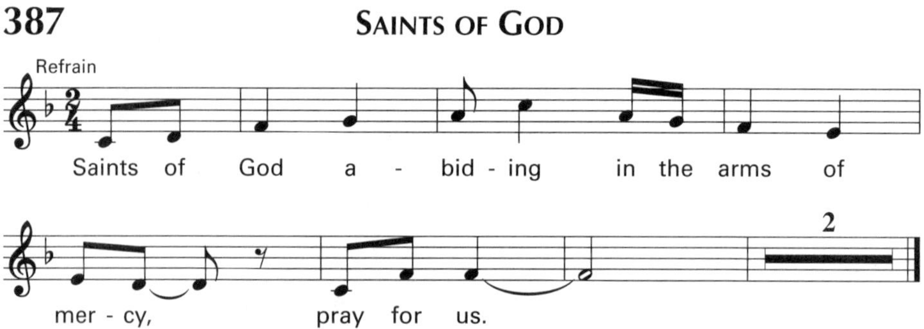
Refrain
Saints of God a - bid - ing in the arms of
mer - cy, pray for us.
2

Verses
1. I saw the souls of the saints be-neath the al - tar,
2. I saw a mul - ti - tude from ev - 'ry land and peo - ple
3. Since e - ven now this cloud of wit - ness - es sur-rounds us,
1. slain for bear - ing wit - ness to God's Word,
2. wor - ship - ing be - fore the throne of grace,
3. let us cast a - side the weight of sin,
to Refrain
1. and each one was robed in white.
2. where all tears are washed a - way.
3. so with them we may run the race.

Text: Based on Revelation 6:9–11; 7:9, 17; Hebrews 12:1; Bob Hurd, b. 1950.
Music: Bob Hurd.

388 For All the Saints

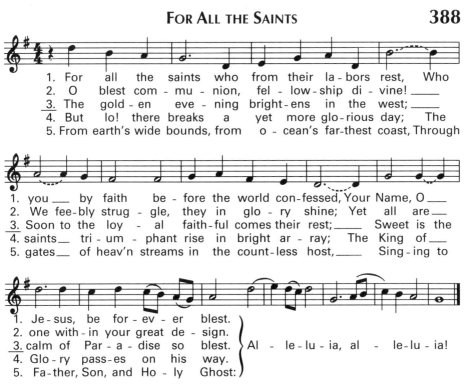

1. For all the saints who from their la - bors rest, Who
2. O blest com - mu - nion, fel - low - ship di - vine!
3. The gold - en eve - ning bright - ens in the west;
4. But lo! there breaks a yet more glo - rious day; The
5. From earth's wide bounds, from o - cean's far - thest coast, Through

1. you by faith be - fore the world con - fessed, Your Name, O
2. We fee - bly strug - gle, they in glo - ry shine; Yet all are
3. Soon to the loy - al faith - ful comes their rest; Sweet is the
4. saints tri - um - phant rise in bright ar - ray; The King of
5. gates of heav'n streams in the count - less host, Sing - ing to

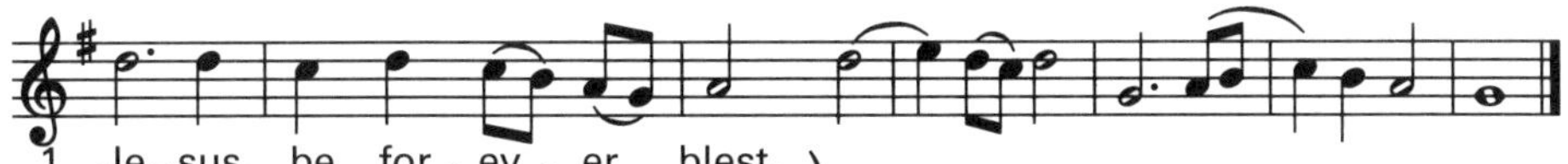

1. Je - sus, be for - ev - er blest.
2. one with - in your great de - sign.
3. calm of Par - a - dise so blest.
4. Glo - ry pass - es on his way.
5. Fa - ther, Son, and Ho - ly Ghost:

Al - le - lu - ia, al - le - lu - ia!

Text: 10 10 10 with alleluias; William W. How, 1823–1897, alt.
Music: SINE NOMINE; *English Hymnal*, 1906; Ralph Vaughan Williams, 1872–1958.

389 HOLY PATRON, THEE SALUTING

Verses

1. Holy patron, thee saluting Here we meet, with hearts sincere; Blest Saint Joseph, all uniting, Call on thee to hear our prayer.
2. Thou who faithfully attended Him whom heav'n and earth adore; Who with pious care defended Mary, Virgin ever pure.
3. May our fervent pray'rs ascending, Move thee for our souls to plead; May thy smile of peace descending, Benedictions on us shed.
4. Through this life, O watch around us! Fill with love our ev'ry breath, And, when parting fear surrounds us, Guide us through the toils of death.

Refrain

Happy saint, in bliss adoring Jesus, Savior of humankind, Hear thy children thee imploring, May we thy protection find.

Text: 87 87 with refrain; American, ca. 1843; anon.
Music: PLEADING SAVIOR; *Christian Lyre*, 1830.

390 YE WATCHERS AND YE HOLY ONES

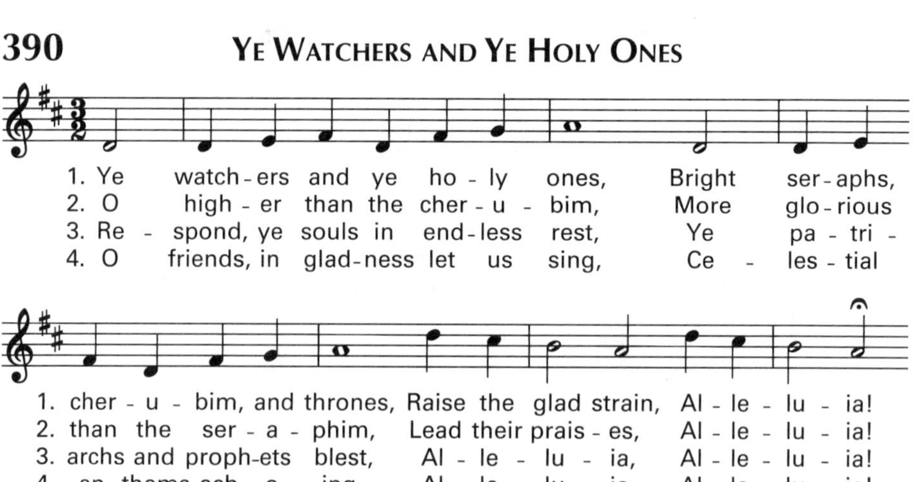

1. Ye watch-ers and ye ho-ly ones, Bright ser-aphs,
2. O high-er than the cher-u-bim, More glo-rious
3. Re-spond, ye souls in end-less rest, Ye pa-tri-
4. O friends, in glad-ness let us sing, Ce-les-tial
1. cher-u-bim, and thrones, Raise the glad strain, Al-le-lu-ia!
2. than the ser-a-phim, Lead their prais-es, Al-le-lu-ia!
3. archs and proph-ets blest, Al-le-lu-ia, Al-le-lu-ia!
4. an-thems ech-o-ing, Al-le-lu-ia, Al-le-lu-ia!

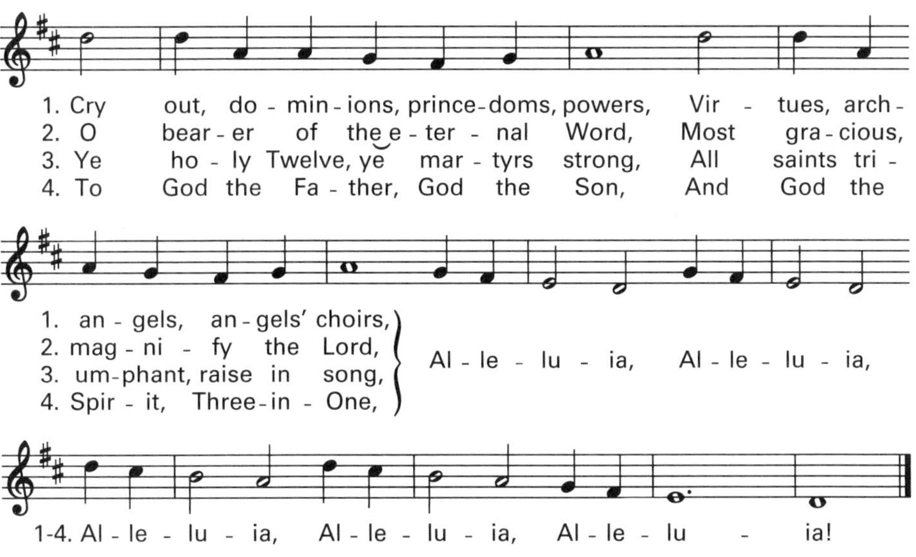
1. Cry out, do - min - ions, prince-doms, powers, Vir - tues, arch -
2. O bear - er of the e - ter - nal Word, Most gra - cious,
3. Ye ho - ly Twelve, ye mar - tyrs strong, All saints tri -
4. To God the Fa - ther, God the Son, And God the
1. an - gels, an - gels' choirs,
2. mag - ni - fy the Lord,
3. um-phant, raise in song,
4. Spir - it, Three-in - One,
Al - le - lu - ia, Al - le - lu - ia,
1-4. Al - le - lu - ia, Al - le - lu - ia, Al - le - lu - ia!

Text: LM with alleluias; *English Hymnal*, 1906; John A. Riley, 1858–1945.
Music: LASST UNS ERFREUEN; *Auserlesene Catholische Geistliche Kirchengesänge*, Cologne, 1623.

RITUAL MUSIC

BAPTIZED IN WATER

391

1. Bap-tized in wa - ter, Sealed by the Spir - it, Cleansed by the
2. Bap-tized in wa - ter, Sealed by the Spir - it, Dead in the
3. Bap-tized in wa - ter, Sealed by the Spir - it, Marked with the
1. blood of Christ our King: Heirs of sal - va - tion, Trust-ing his
2. tomb with Christ our King: One with his ris - ing, Freed and for -
3. sign of Christ our King: Born of one Fa - ther, We are his
1. prom - ise, Faith - ful - ly now God's praise we sing.
2. giv - en, Thank-ful - ly now God's praise we sing.
3. chil - dren, Joy - ful - ly now God's praise we sing.

Text: 55 8 D; Michael Saward, 1932–2015,
Music: BUNESSAN; trad. Gaelic melody.

392 ENTER THE JOURNEY

Refrain
En - ter the jour - ney. Come to the song. By God you are cho-sen, by name you are called to fol - low the vi - sion, car - ry the cross. En - ter the jour - ney of faith as the fam - 'ly of God.
2
Verses
All
Cantor
1. En - ter the jour - ney, the way may be long.
2. En - ter the jour - ney, though lost and un - sure.
3. En - ter the jour - ney, though dark is the way.
4. En - ter the jour - ney, the old and the young.
All
Cantor
1. En - ter the jour - ney, yet we are made strong.
2. En - ter the jour - ney, God's peace will be yours.
3. En - ter the jour - ney, do not be a - fraid,
4. En - ter the jour - ney, the king - dom is won.
1. God's spir - it will guide us, God's gifts will un - fold.
2. And all who are thirst - ing be filled with God's grace.
3. for God's great com - pas - sion will give you new sight.
4. By faith now u - nit - ed, as ser - vants we come.
All
En - ter the jour - ney of hope!
En - ter the jour - ney of faith!
En - ter the jour - ney of light!
En - ter the jour - ney of love!
to Refrain

Text and music: Mark Friedman, b. 1952, and Janet Vogt, b. 1953,

PUT ON CHRIST 393

Verses 1, 2: Cantor (or All)
1. We have come to this feast, called by love
2. We be-come what we share: Bread of Life,
1. for love, keep-ing mem-'ry of the Lord.
2. Je-sus, blessed and bro-ken for the world.
Refrain: All
Put on Christ. Put on Christ. Come to the wa-ters of
ev-er-last-ing life. Put on Christ. Put on
Christ. Walk in the free-dom of the chil-dren.
of God. God. God.
1 to Verse 2
2 to Verse 3
Final
Verse 3: Cantor (or All)
3. We have seen God's sav - ing love in an earth - ly
3. time and place: God's own glo - ry in a
3. hu - man face.
to Refrain

Text and music: Bob Hurd, b. 1950, © 1991, Bob Hurd. Published by OCP.

394 Down to the River to Pray

As I went down to the riv-er to pray, stud-y-ing a-bout that
good old way and who shall wear the star - ry crown— Good Lord,
show me the way! O *sis-ters, let's go down. Let's go down, come on
down. O *sis-ters, let's go down, down to the riv-er to pray.

*brothers, fathers, mothers, sinners

Text and music: American folk song; *"The Good Old Way,"* attr. to George H. Allan, fr. *Slave Songs of the United States*, 1867.

395 We Have Been Baptized in Christ

Refrain

We have been bap - tized in Christ. It is he that we have put on. We who are washed in this wa - ter have hope of e - ter - nal life.

Verse 1

1. We are a new cre - a - tion; in Christ we have been clothed. We are all mem - bers of God's ho - ly peo - ple, for we have been giv - en new birth.

to Refrain

Verse 2
2. We re-ceived the light of Christ; we keep it burn - ing
2. bright-ly. We seek to walk al - ways as chil-dren of light,
to Refrain
2. with his flame a-live in our hearts.

WADE IN THE WATER 396

Ostinato Refrain: 1st time: Cantor, All repeat; thereafter: All

Wade in the wa-ter, wade in the wa-ter, chil-dren now.
Wade in the wa-ter, God's gon-na trou-ble the wa - ter.

*Verses: Sung over Refrain

1. John __ was a-preach-in' by the shores of Jor - dan stream: __ "Re - pent __ of your sins and let the wa - ter wash you clean." __
2. Je-sus came to be bap-tized by John; and when it was done __ a voice __ from the heav-ens said: __ "This __ is my be - lov-ed Son."
3. "My __ fa - vor rests up - on him," said a voice from a - bove. __ The crowd __ saw the Spir - it in the form of a snow - white dove. __
4. Come __ to the riv - er where the liv - ing wa - ters rise: __ if you want to fol - low Je - sus, you must come __ and be bap - tized. __

to Refrain
O,

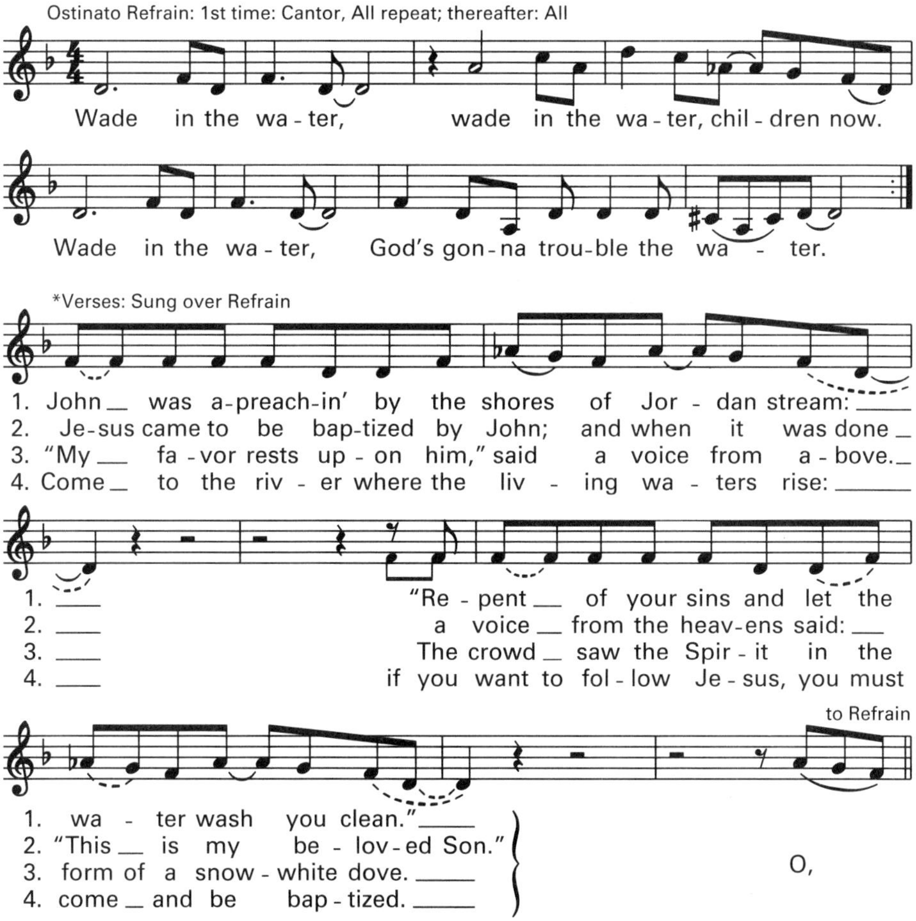

*Additional verses available in accompaniment books.

397 GIVE ME EARS TO LISTEN

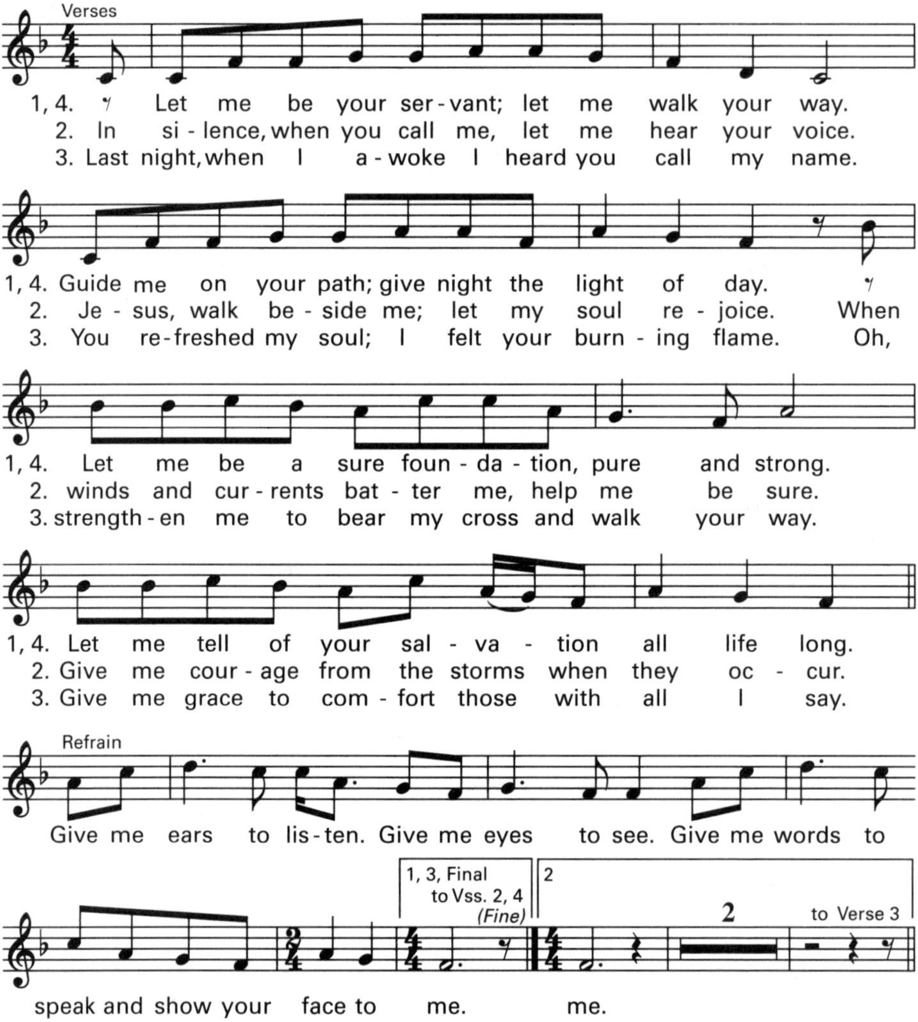

Verses

1, 4. Let me be your ser - vant; let me walk your way.
2. In si - lence, when you call me, let me hear your voice.
3. Last night, when I a - woke I heard you call my name.

1, 4. Guide me on your path; give night the light of day.
2. Je - sus, walk be - side me; let my soul re - joice. When
3. You re-freshed my soul; I felt your burn - ing flame. Oh,

1, 4. Let me be a sure foun - da - tion, pure and strong.
2. winds and cur - rents bat - ter me, help me be sure.
3. strength - en me to bear my cross and walk your way.

1, 4. Let me tell of your sal - va - tion all life long.
2. Give me cour - age from the storms when they oc - cur.
3. Give me grace to com - fort those with all I say.

Refrain

Give me ears to lis - ten. Give me eyes to see. Give me words to speak and show your face to me. me.

1, 3, Final to Vss. 2, 4 *(Fine)* | 2 | to Verse 3

Text and music: Timothy R. Smith, b. 1960, © 2005, Timothy R. Smith.
Published by Spirit & Song®, a division of OCP.

398 FLOW RIVER FLOW

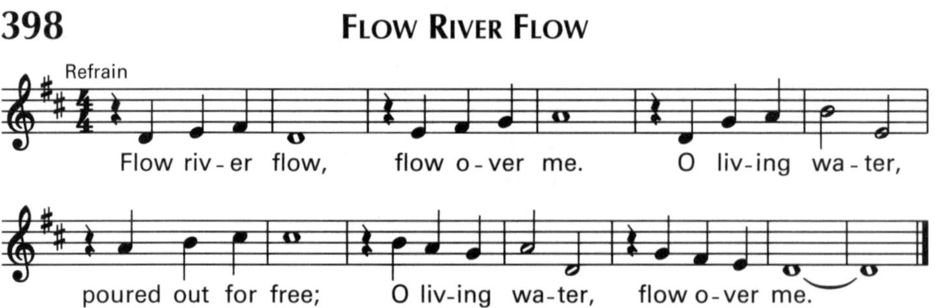
Refrain
Flow riv - er flow, flow o - ver me. O liv - ing wa - ter,
poured out for free; O liv - ing wa - ter, flow o - ver me.

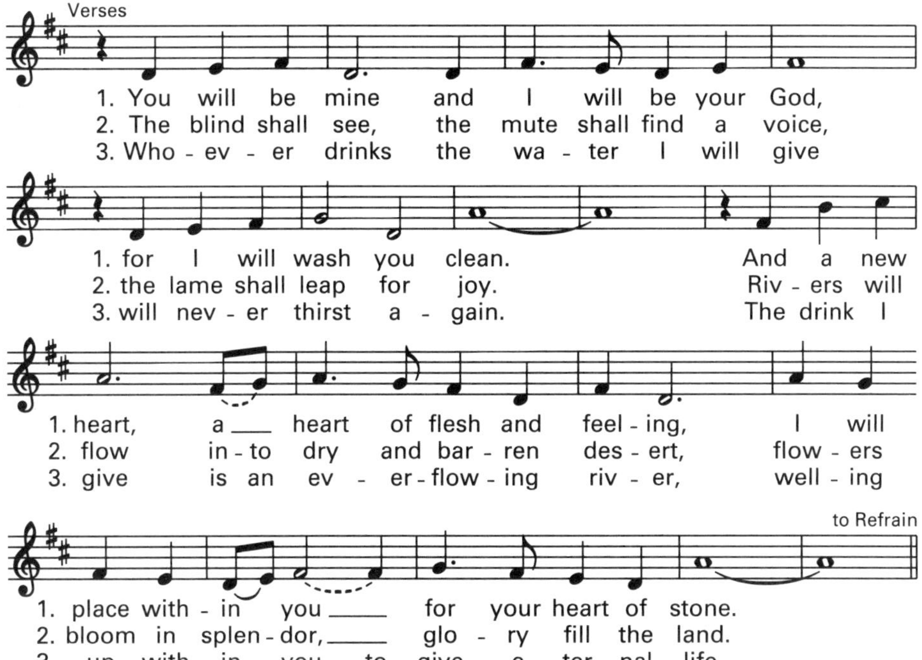
Verses
1. You will be mine and I will be your God,
2. The blind shall see, the mute shall find a voice,
3. Who - ev - er drinks the wa - ter I will give
1. for I will wash you clean. And a new
2. the lame shall leap for joy. Riv - ers will
3. will nev - er thirst a - gain. The drink I
1. heart, a heart of flesh and feel - ing, I will
2. flow in - to dry and bar - ren des - ert, flow - ers
3. give is an ev - er - flow - ing riv - er, well - ing
to Refrain
1. place with - in you for your heart of stone.
2. bloom in splen - dor, glo - ry fill the land.
3. up with - in you to give e - ter - nal life.

Text: Based on Ezekiel 11:19, 20; Isaiah 35:1–6; John 4:7–15; Bob Hurd, b. 1950.
Music: Bob Hurd.

O Breathe on Me, O Breath of God 399

1. O breathe on me, O Breath of God, Fill
2. O breathe on me, O Breath of God, Un -
3. O breathe on me, O Breath of God, My
4. O breathe on me, O Breath of God, So
1. me with life a - new, That I may love the
2. til my heart is pure; Un - til my will is
3. will to yours in - cline, Un - til this self - ish
4. I shall nev - er die, But live with you the
1. things you love, And do what you would do.
2. one with yours, To do and to en - dure.
3. part of me Glows with your fire di - vine.
4. per - fect life For all e - ter - ni - ty.

Text: CM; Edwin Hatch, 1835–1889, alt.
Music: ST. COLUMBA; trad. Irish melody.

400 WATER OF LIFE

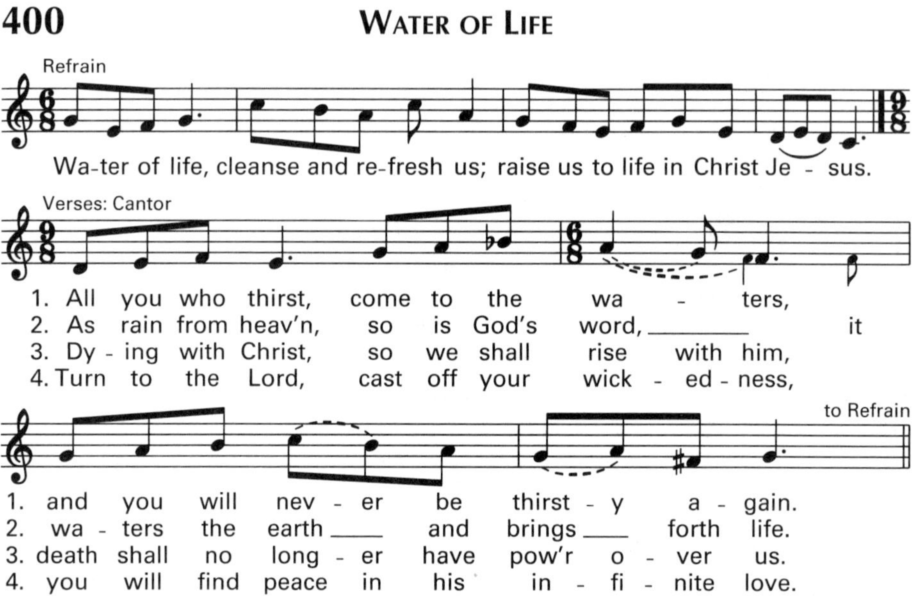
Refrain
Wa-ter of life, cleanse and re-fresh us; raise us to life in Christ Je - sus.
Verses: Cantor
1. All you who thirst, come to the wa - ters,
2. As rain from heav'n, so is God's word, ___ it
3. Dy - ing with Christ, so we shall rise with him,
4. Turn to the Lord, cast off your wick - ed - ness,
to Refrain
1. and you will nev - er be thirst - y a - gain.
2. wa - ters the earth ___ and brings ___ forth life.
3. death shall no long - er have pow'r o - ver us.
4. you will find peace in his in - fi - nite love.

Text and music: Stephen Dean, b. 1948,

401 ONE LORD

Refrain

There is one Lord, there is one faith, there is one Fa-ther of us all; and through his Son, who came to save us, there is one God liv-ing in us all.

Verses

1. We are one bod - y in the Lord; we are all the peo-ple of his love.
2. We are one spir - it of new life; we are all u - nit - ed in the Lord.
3. There is one liv - ing hope in us: we are called to ev - er - last-ing life.
4. There is one foun-tain of re - birth bless-ing us with wa-ters of new life.
5. Let us be wor-thy of his call; let us seek each oth - er in our God.

to Refrain

Text: Based on Ephesians 4:1–6; Scott Soper, b. 1961.
Music: Scott Soper.

You Have Called Us 402

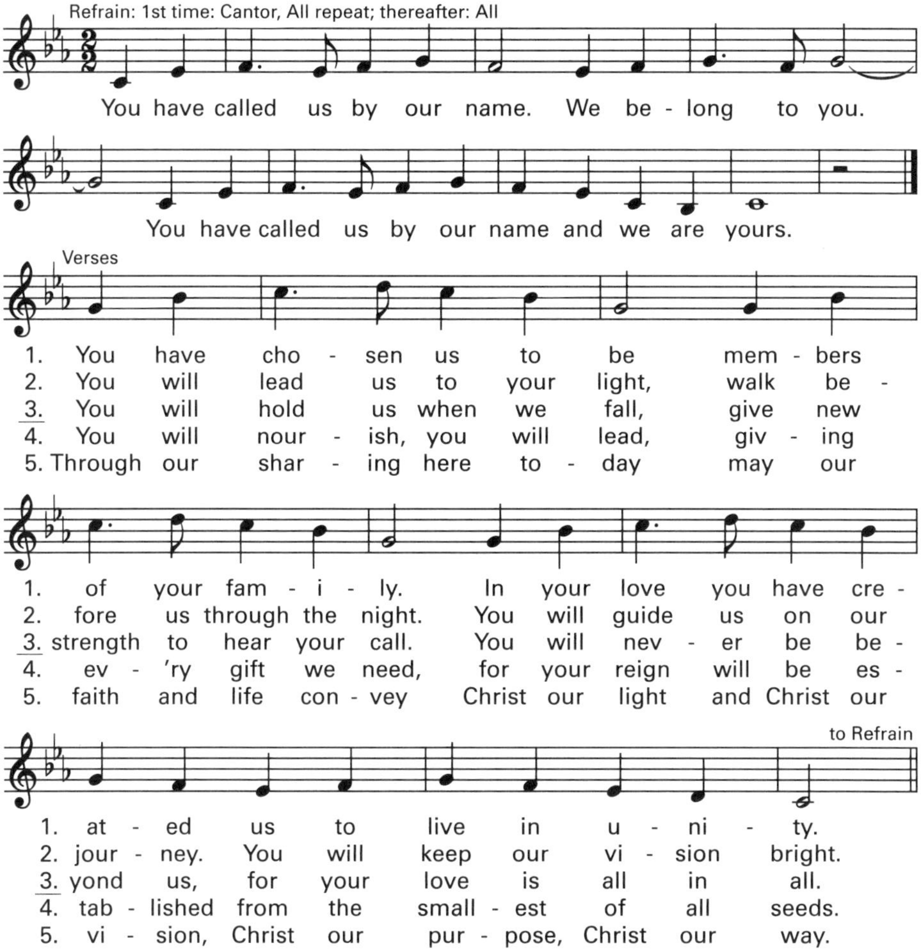

Refrain: 1st time: Cantor, All repeat; thereafter: All

You have called us by our name. We be - long to you.
You have called us by our name and we are yours.

Verses

1. You have cho - sen us to be mem - bers of your fam - i - ly. In your love you have cre - at - ed us to live in u - ni - ty.
2. You will lead us to your light, walk be - fore us through the night. You will guide us on our jour - ney. You will keep our vi - sion bright.
3. You will hold us when we fall, give new strength to hear your call. You will nev - er be be - yond us, for your love is all in all.
4. You will nour - ish, you will lead, giv - ing ev - 'ry gift we need, for your reign will be es - tab - lished from the small - est of all seeds.
5. Through our shar - ing here to - day may our faith and life con - vey Christ our light and Christ our vi - sion, Christ our pur - pose, Christ our way.

to Refrain

Signing of the Senses 403

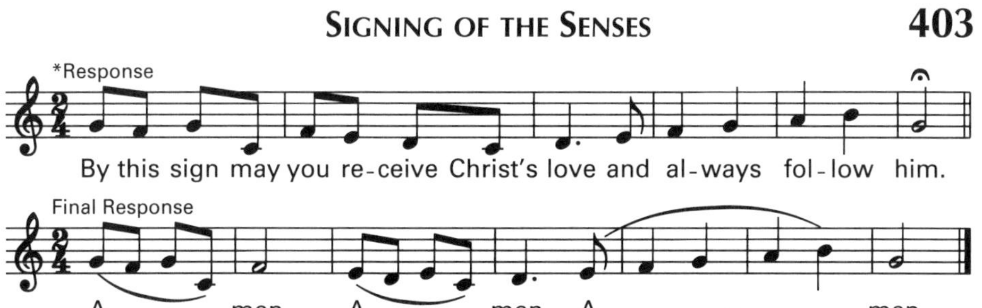
*Response
By this sign may you re-ceive Christ's love and al-ways fol-low him.
Final Response
A - men. A - men. A - men.

*Verses available in accompaniment books.

404 River of Glory

Refrain

Riv - er of glo - ry, springs of our birth, flood of God's rich - es poured on the earth. We are born from the dark-ness and clothed in the light! We are bathed in the glo - ry of

1-4 God! to Verses

Final God, bathed in the glo - ry of God!

Verses

1. Foun - tain of mer - cy, grace flow - ing free, streams of sal - va - tion, spill - ing with love from a tree!
2. Here there is ha - ven, heal - ing and health, joy for the ask - ing, love in a - bun - dance of wealth!
3. Bread for our jour - ney God will pro - vide. Hope for all a - ges, Je - sus, com - pan - ion and guide!
4. Dark - ness is ban - ished, night turned a - way. Christ is our sun - light, lift - ing and lead - ing our way!

to Refrain

405 We Belong to You

Refrain
We be-long to you, O Lord of our long-ing, We be-long to you.
In our dai-ly liv-ing, dy - ing and ris-ing We be-long to you.

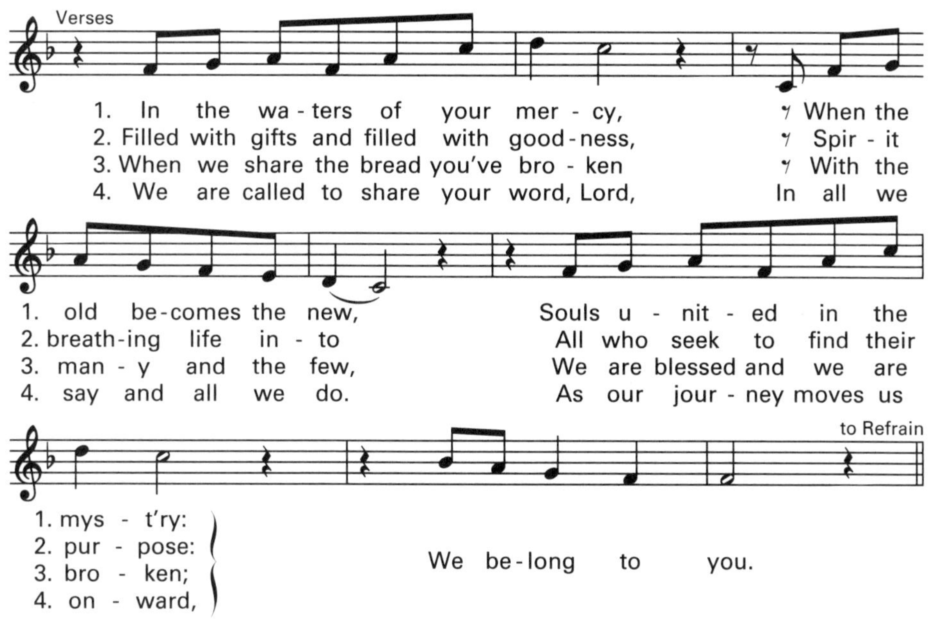
Verses
1. In the wa - ters of your mer - cy, When the
2. Filled with gifts and filled with good - ness, Spir - it
3. When we share the bread you've bro - ken With the
4. We are called to share your word, Lord, In all we
1. old be - comes the new, Souls u - nit - ed in the
2. breath - ing life in - to All who seek to find their
3. man - y and the few, We are blessed and we are
4. say and all we do. As our jour - ney moves us
to Refrain
1. mys - t'ry:
2. pur - pose:
3. bro - ken;
4. on - ward,
We be - long to you.

Text: Victoria Thomson, b. 1969, © 2006, Victoria Thomson.
Published by Spirit & Song®, a division of OCP. All rights reserved.
Music: Trevor Thomson, b. 1971, © 2006, Trevor Thomson.
Published by Spirit & Song®, a division of OCP. All rights reserved.

Agua de Vida/Water of Life 406

*Refrain: All
A - gua de vi - da, san - to re - cuer - do;
Wa - ter of life, ho - ly re - mind - er;
u - ne y re - nue - va al cuer - po de Cris - to.
touch - ing, re - new - ing the bod - y of Christ.
1
2
al cuer - po de Cris - to.
the bod - y of Christ.

*Verses available in accompaniment books.

Text and music: *Misa del Pueblo Inmigrante;* Jaime Cortez, b. 1963, © 1994, Jaime Cortez.
Published by OCP. All rights reserved.

407 Come to the River

Refrain
Come, O come, come to the riv - er
flow - ing from the bod - y of Christ.
We'll go down, deep in the wa - ter,
*
but in the Lord we shall a - rise.
Verses
1. Washed in wa - ters of re-birth,
2. Priest - ly peo - ple are ___ we,
3. Blest are those ___ who ___ thirst
4. Let us walk ___ in the light
5. Those who sow ___ in ___ tears
to Refrain
1. we have put on Christ Je - sus.
2. sealed and sent by the Spir - it.
3. for the reign of God's jus - tice.
4. of God's ho - ly prom - ise.
5. reap the har - vest re - joic - ing.

*Repeat last phrase final time.

Text and music: *Mass of Glory;* Bob Hurd, b. 1950,

HOLY SPIRIT, COME NOW/SANTO ESPÍRITU, VEN 408

Refrain
Ho - ly Spir - it, come, Ho - ly Spir -
Ven, Es - pí - ri - tu, San - to Es - pí -
1
2 to Verses
(Fine)
- it, come now, come now.
- ri - tu, ven, oh ven.
Verses
1. Oh, the sweet - ness of your mer - cy and grace!
2. In the faith we share, flow - ing from truth,
3. With the rev - 'rence of the Lord, love is shown.
1. La dul - zu - ra de tu gra - cia y bon - dad
2. En la fe que vie - ne de tu ver - dad,
3. Que mos - tre - mos la pre - sen - cia de Dios,
1. Bring us true wis - dom right here in this place.
2. bring us the knowl - edge that brings us to you.
3. Serv - ing each oth - er, God's pres - ence is known.
1. nos a - li - men - ta en es - te lu - gar.
2. ven, a - com - pa - ña nues - tro ca - mi - nar.
3. a - man - do a to - dos y de co - ra - zón,
1. Bring a glim - mer of the depth of God's will.
2. Through the dark - ness of de - spair and of fear,
3. Oh, the good - ness and the glo - ry of God!
1. Hoy nos mues - tras la vo - lun - tad
2. En el mie - do, en la os - cu - ri - dad,
3. y can - te - mos la glo - ria de Dios,
to Refrain
1. Bring un - der - stand - ing; God's plan be ful - filled.
2. give us the cour - age to know you are here.
3. Hearts o - ver - flow - ing with won - der and awe.
1. del Dios e - ter - no, su plan ce - les - tial.
2. que des - cu - bra - mos que a - quí es - tás.
3. lle - nos de go - zo y ad - mi - ra - ción.

409 Dismissal of the Catechumens and the Elect

Refrain: All
May the word of God strength-en you. May the word of God
nour-ish you. May the word of God com-fort you all your life.
Optional Verses: Cantor/Choir/All
to Refrain
1. May it be your light in dark-ness __ as you walk the path of faith.
2. May it lead you to the free-dom __ of the love that calls your name.
3. May it set your hearts on fire ______ to be faith-ful to God's voice.

Text and music: *Celtic Mass;* Christopher Walker, b. 1947, © 1996, Christopher Walker.

410 Come Home

Verse 1

1. I, your God, am wait-ing, a - wait - ing
1. your re - turn. Like a moth - er or fa - ther
1. wait-ing, long-ing for a child's re - turn.

Refrain

Come home, come home, for love is wait-ing there. In the
still - ness we will hear God's voice: Come home, be rec - on -

1, 2 to Verses 2, 3

ciled.

Final

ciled. Come home. Come home. Come home.

Verse 2

2. And if you, O God, should mark our guilt, then

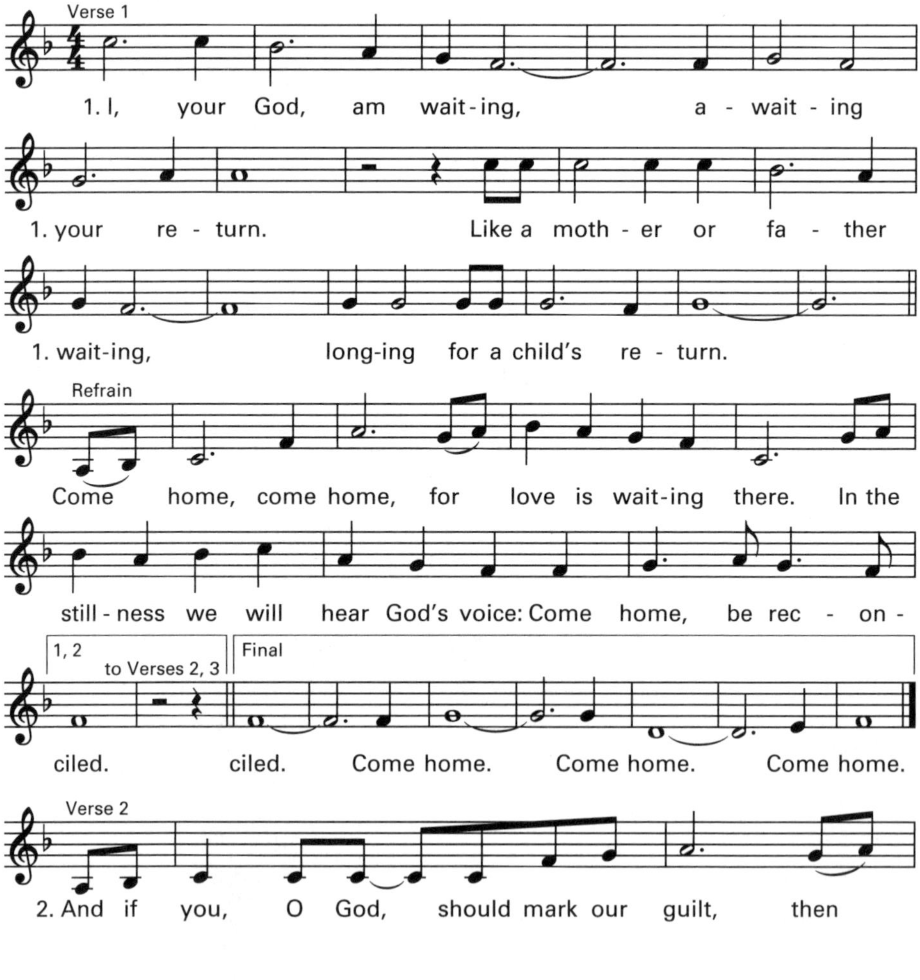

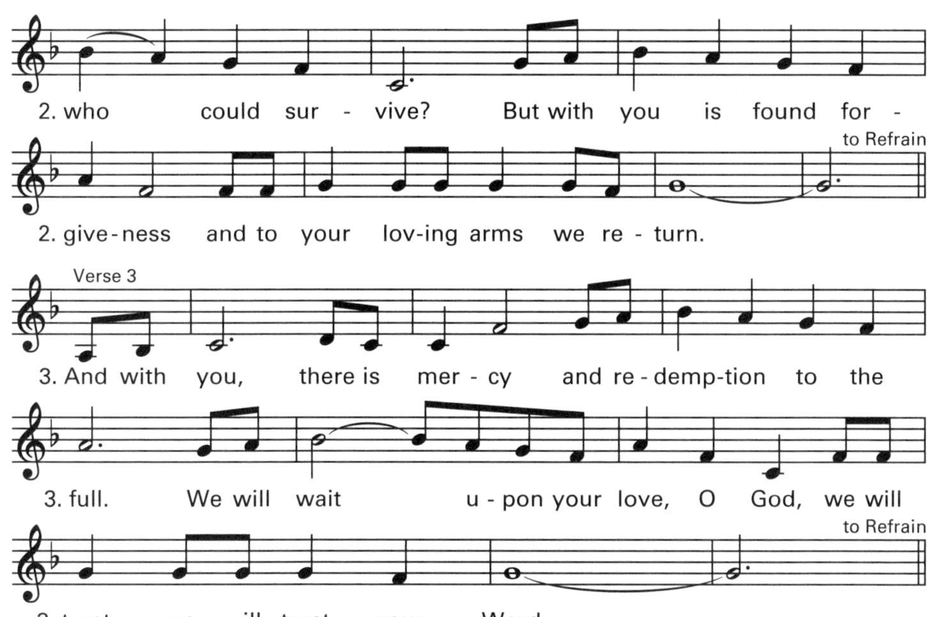
2. who could sur - vive? But with you is found for -
2. give-ness and to your lov-ing arms we re - turn.
to Refrain
Verse 3
3. And with you, there is mer - cy and re-demp-tion to the
3. full. We will wait u - pon your love, O God, we will
3. trust, we will trust your Word.
to Refrain

Text: Based on Luke 15:11–24; Psalm 130:3–6; Carey Landry, b. 1944.
Music: Carey Landry.

HOSEA 411

Verses
1. Come back to me with all your heart. Don't let
Trees do bend, though straight and tall; so must
2. The wil-der-ness will lead you to your
In - teg - ri - ty and jus - tice with ten-der-
3. You shall sleep se - cure with peace; faith-ful-
1. fear keep us a - part.
we to oth - ers' call.
2. heart where I will speak.
ness you shall know.
3. ness will be your joy.
Refrain
Long have I wait-ed for your
com-ing home to me and liv-ing deep-ly our new life.

Text: Based on Hosea; Weston Priory, Gregory Norbet, OSB, b. 1940.
Music: Weston Priory, Gregory Norbet, OSB.

412 RETURN TO THE LORD YOUR GOD

Refrain
Re - turn to the Lord your God. Re - turn to the
Lord your God. When you have grown emp - ty and
1-3
to Verses
wea - ry with e - vil, re - turn to the Lord your God.
3. Come
Final
God. Re - turn to the Lord your God.
Verse 1
1. Take with you words from your sor - row. Call on the
1. sounds of your grief. Let go of the gods that your
to Refrain
1. fears have fash-ioned, and lean on the Lord who can save.
Verse 2
2. Break up the fields that lie bar - ren. It is time to
2. seek the Lord. O sow your-selves with seeds of
to Refrain
2. mer - cy, and reap a har - vest of jus - tice.

Verse 3
3. back to me with all your heart. Come back, O faith - less
3. peo - ple! For how could I ev - er a - ban - don
to Refrain
3. you, or turn from the work of my heart?

Text: Based on Hosea 14:2ff, 10:12, 11:8; Joel 2:12; Bob Dufford, SJ, b. 1943.
Music: Bob Dufford, SJ.

Loving and Forgiving **413**

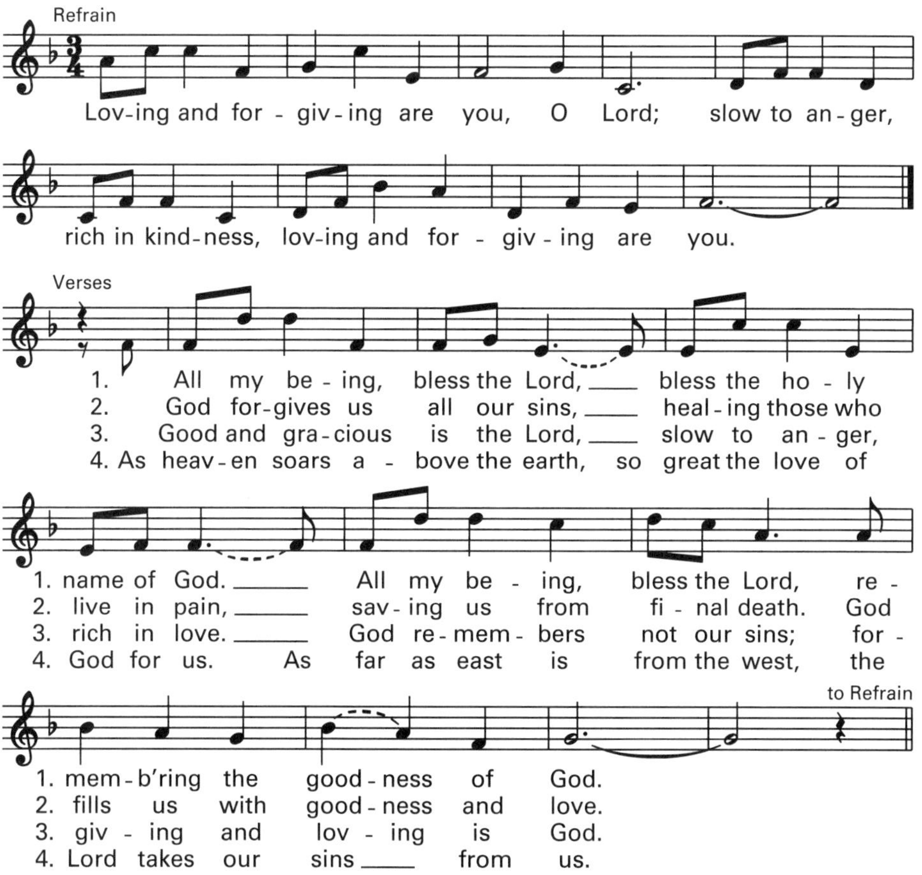

Refrain

Lov-ing and for - giv-ing are you, O Lord; slow to an-ger,
rich in kind-ness, lov-ing and for - giv - ing are you.

Verses

1. All my be - ing, bless the Lord, ___ bless the ho - ly name of God. ___ All my be - ing, bless the Lord, re - mem-b'ring the good-ness of God.
2. God for-gives us all our sins, ___ heal-ing those who live in pain, ___ sav-ing us from fi - nal death. God fills us with good-ness and love.
3. Good and gra-cious is the Lord, ___ slow to an - ger, rich in love. ___ God re-mem - bers not our sins; for - giv - ing and lov - ing is God.
4. As heav-en soars a - bove the earth, so great the love of God for us. As far as east is from the west, the Lord takes our sins ___ from us.

to Refrain

Text: Based on Psalm 103:8, 1–2, 3–4, 8–10, 11–12; Scott Soper, b. 1961.
Music: Scott Soper.

414 Softly and Tenderly Jesus Is Calling

Verses

1. Soft - ly and ten - der - ly Je - sus is call - ing, call - ing for
2. Why should we tar - ry when Je - sus is plead - ing, plead - ing for
3. O for the won - der - ful love he has prom - ised, prom - ised for

1. you and for me; see, on the por - tals he's
2. you and for me? Why should we lin - ger and
3. you and for me! Though we have sinned, he has

1. wait - ing and watch - ing, watch - ing for you and for me.
2. heed not his mer - cies, mer - cies for you and for me?
3. mer - cy and par - don, par - don for you and for me.

Refrain

Come home, come home, you who are

wea - ry, come home;

ear - nest - ly, ten - der - ly,

Je - sus is call - ing, call - ing for you to come home!

Text: 11 7 11 7 with refrain; Will L. Thompson, 1847–1909, alt.
Music: THOMPSON; Will L. Thompson.

415 You Alone

Refrain
You a-lone are ho - ly, you a-lone are Lord. You a-lone are
wor-thy to be hon-ored and a - dored. Mer-cy you have
giv-en, kind-ness you have shown. Love is you a - lone.

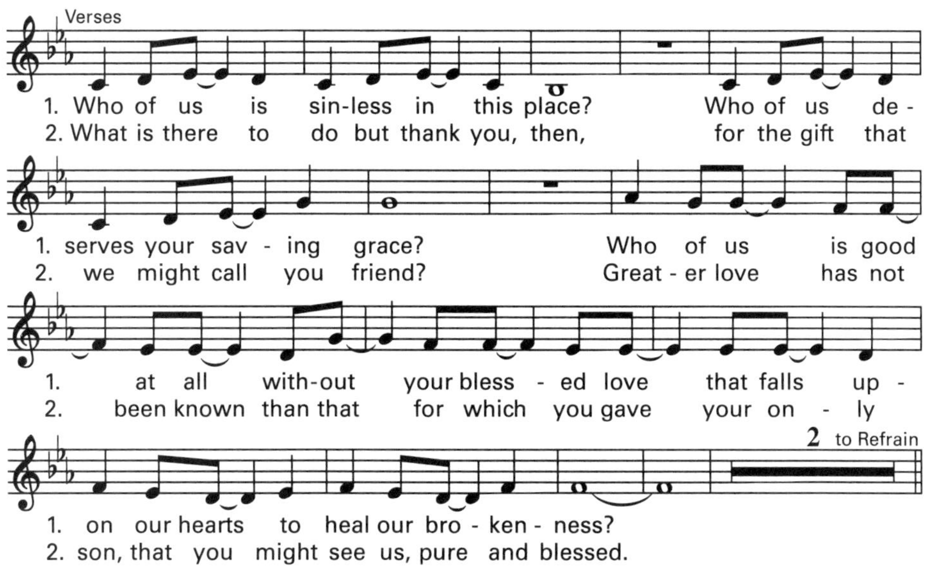
Verses
1. Who of us is sin-less in this place? Who of us de - serves your sav - ing grace? Who of us is good at all with-out your bless - ed love that falls up - on our hearts to heal our bro - ken - ness?
2. What is there to do but thank you, then, for the gift that we might call you friend? Great - er love has not been known than that for which you gave your on - ly son, that you might see us, pure and blessed.
2
to Refrain

PARDON YOUR PEOPLE 416

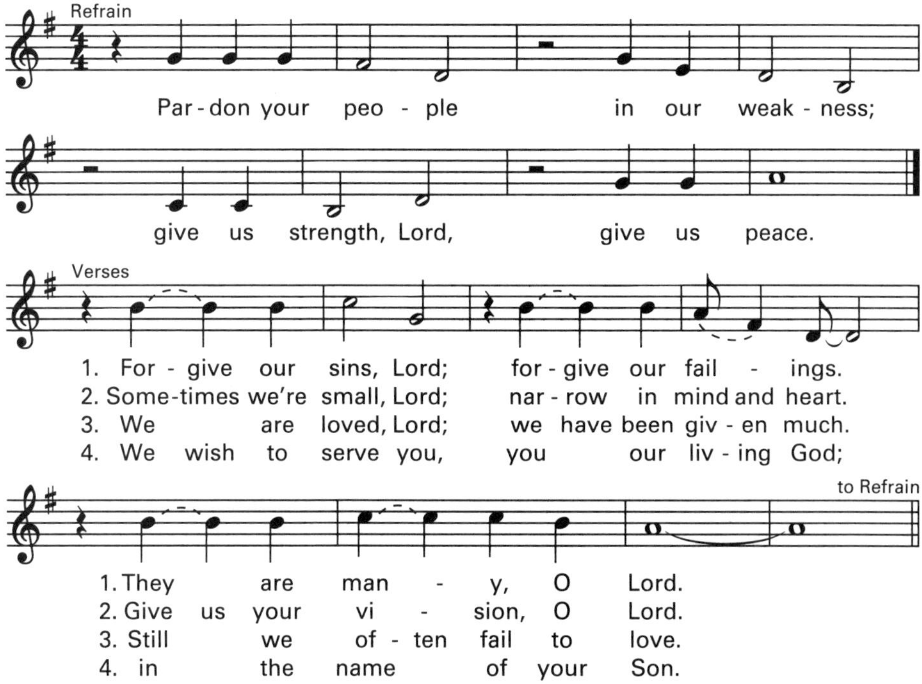

Refrain

Par - don your peo - ple in our weak - ness; give us strength, Lord, give us peace.

Verses

1. For - give our sins, Lord; for - give our fail - ings. They are man - y, O Lord.
2. Some-times we're small, Lord; nar - row in mind and heart. Give us your vi - sion, O Lord.
3. We are loved, Lord; we have been giv - en much. Still we of - ten fail to love.
4. We wish to serve you, you our liv - ing God; in the name of your Son.

to Refrain

417 REMEMBER YOUR LOVE

Refrain
Re-mem-ber your love and your faith-ful-ness, O Lord. Re-
mem-ber your peo-ple and have mer-cy on us, Lord.
Verses
1. The Lord is my light and my sal - va - tion,
2. If you dwelt, O Lord, up - on our sin - ful - ness,
3. O Lord, hear the sound of my call
4. As sen - ti - nels wait up - on the day - light,
5. Be - fore all the moun-tains were be - got - ten
1. whom should I fear? The Lord is my
2. then who could stand? But with you there is
3. and an - swer me. My heart cries
4. wait for the Lord. I trust in your
5. and earth took shape, e - ven then, O
to Refrain
1. life and my ref - uge, when I call God hears.
2. mer - cy and for - give - ness and a guid - ing hand.
3. out for your pres - ence; it is you I seek.
4. kind - ness and re - demp - tion; and your faith - ful word.
5. Lord, you were our ref - uge through-out ev - 'ry age.

Text: Based on Psalms 25, 27, 90, 130; Mike Balhoff, b. 1946.
Music: Darryl Ducote, b. 1945, and Gary Daigle, b. 1957.

Show Us Your Mercy 418

Refrain: 1st time: Cantor/All; thereafter: All
In times of trou-ble, God, come to our aid.
Show us your mer-cy, come save!
(All)
In times of trou-ble, God, come to our aid. Show us your mer-cy, come save!
1-3
to Verses
Final
save! Show us your mer-cy, come save!
Verses
1. We live se-cure in the shel-ter of God, safe in the fold of God's wings. We will pro-claim the great-ness of God, the rock of sal-va-tion God brings.
2. Lost and a-fraid, we're nev-er a-lone, God watch-es o-ver our lives. Walk-ing our path and light-ing our way, guard-ing us day and by night.
3. All of our lives we look to our God. We will lie safe in God's care. God is our rock. In God we can trust all of our trou-bles to bear.
to Refrain

Text: Based on Psalm 91; Mark Friedman, b. 1952.
Music: Mark Friedman.

419 BE STILL, MY SOUL

1. Be still, my soul— the Lord is on thy side!
2. Be still, my soul— thy God doth un - der - take
3. Be still, my soul— the hour is has - t'ning on
1. Bear pa - tient - ly the cross of grief or pain;
2. To guide the fu - ture as he has the past;
3. When we shall be for - ev - er with the Lord,
1. Leave to thy God to or - der and pro - vide—
2. Thy hope, thy con - fi - dence let noth - ing shake—
3. When dis - ap - point - ment, grief, and fear are gone,
1. In ev - 'ry change he faith - ful will re - main.
2. All now mys - te - rious shall be bright at last.
3. Sor - row for - got, love's pur - est joys re-stored.
1. Be still, my soul— thy best, thy heav'n - ly friend
2. Be still, my soul— the waves and winds still know
3. Be still, my soul— when change and tears are past,
1. Through thorn - y ways leads to a joy - ful end.
2. His voice who ruled them while he dwelt be - low.
3. All safe and bless - ed we shall meet at last.

Text: 10 10 10 10 10 10; Katharina von Schlegel; in *Neue Sammlung Geistlicher Lieder*, 1752; tr. by Jane Borthwick, 1813–1897.
Music: FINLANDIA; Jean Sibelius, 1865–1957.

HOLY DARKNESS 420

Refrain
Ho-ly dark-ness, bless-ed night, heav-en's an-swer
hid-den from our sight. As we a-wait you, O God of
si-lence, we em-brace your ho-ly night.
Verses 1-3
1. I have tried you in fires of af-flic-tion; I have
2. I have taught you the price of com-pas-sion; you have
3. Were you there when I raised up the moun-tains? Can you
1. taught your soul to grieve. In the bar-ren soil of your
2. stood be-fore the grave. Though my love can seem like a
3. guide the morn-ing star? Does the hawk take flight when you
to Refrain
1. lone-li-ness, there I will plant my seed.
2. rag-ing storm, this is the love that saves.
3. give com-mand? Why do you doubt my pow'r?
Verses 4, 5
4. In your deep-est hour of dark-ness I will
5. As the watch-man waits for morn-ing, and the
4. give you wealth un-told. When the si-lence stills your
5. bride a-waits her groom, so we wait to hear your
to Refrain
4. spir-it, will my rich-es fill your soul.
5. foot-steps as we rest be-neath your moon.

Text: Inspired by St. John of the Cross, 1542–1591; Dan Schutte, b. 1947.
Music: Dan Schutte.

421 LAY YOUR HANDS

Refrain

Lay your hands gent - ly up - on us.

Let their touch ren - der your peace.

Let them bring your for - give - ness and heal - ing.

Lay your hands gent - ly, lay your hands.

Verse 1

1. You were sent to free the bro - ken heart - ed.

1. You were sent to give sight to the blind.

1. You de - sire to heal all our ill - ness - es.

1. Lay your hands gent - ly, lay your hands.

to Refrain

Verse 2

2. Lord, we come to you through one an - oth - er.

2. Lord, we come to you in our need.

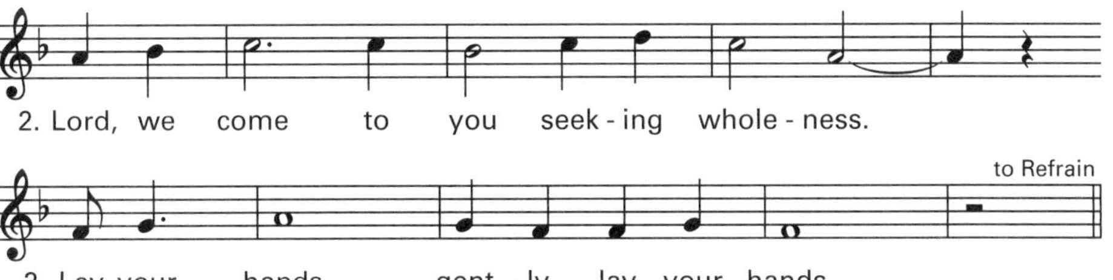
2. Lord, we come to you seek - ing whole - ness.
to Refrain
2. Lay your hands gent - ly, lay your hands.

Text: Based on Isaiah 61:1; Carey Landry, b. 1944.
Music: Carey Landry.

Healing River of the Spirit 422

1. Heal - ing riv - er of the Spir - it, Bathe the
2. Well - spring of the heal - ing Spir - it, Stream that
3. Liv - ing stream that heals the na - tions, Make us

1. wounds that liv - ing brings. Plunge our pain, our sin, our
2. flows to bring re - lease, As we gain our selves, our
3. chan - nels of your pow'r. All the world is torn by

1. sad - ness Deep be - neath your sa - cred springs.
2. sen - ses, May our lives re - flect your peace.
3. con - flict; Wars are rag - ing at this hour.

1. Wea - ry from the rest - less search - ing That has
2. Grate - ful for the flood that heals us, May your
3. Sav - ing Spir - it, move a - mong us, Guide our

1. lured us from your side, We dis - cov - er in your
2. church en - act your grace. As we meet both friend and
3. wind - ing hu - man course, Till we find our way to -

1. pres - ence Peace the world can - not pro - vide.
2. strang - er, May we see our Sav - ior's face.
3. geth - er, Flow - ing home - ward to our Source.

Text: 87 87 D; Ruth C. Duck, b. 1947; fr. *Circles of Care*, © 1996, The Pilgrim Press. All rights reserved. Used with permission.
Music: BEACH SPRING; *The Sacred Harp*, 1844.

423 O JESUS, HEALER OF WOUNDED SOULS

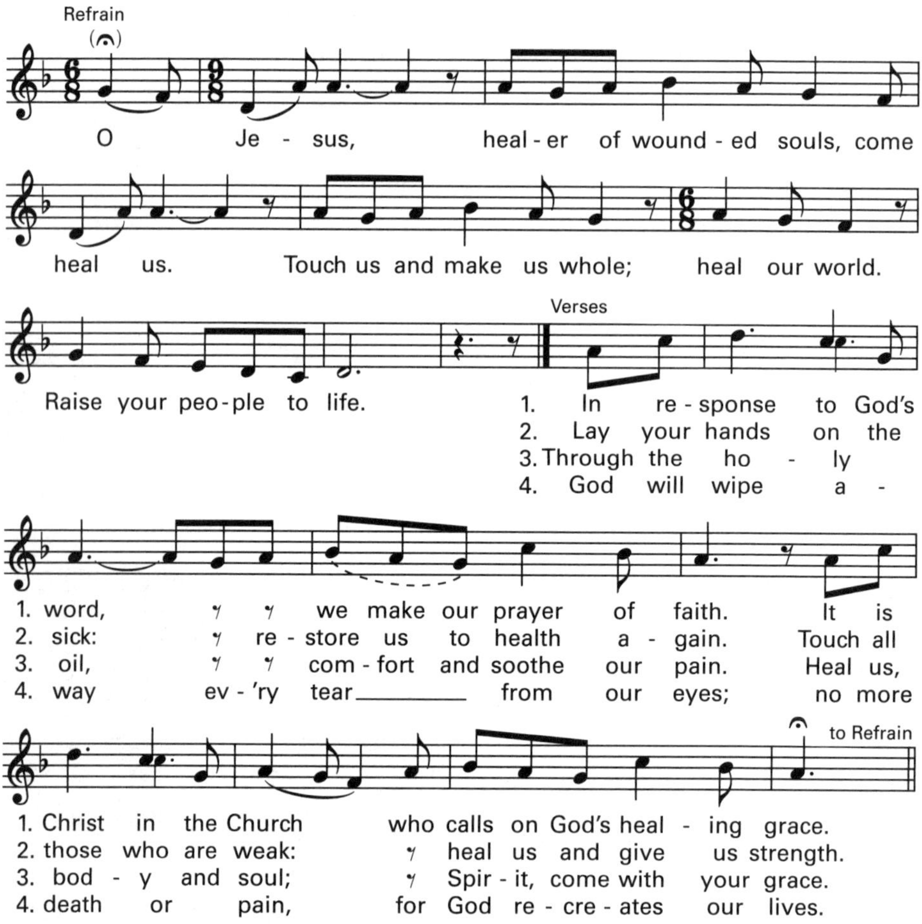

Refrain

O Je - sus, heal - er of wound - ed souls, come heal us. Touch us and make us whole; heal our world. Raise your peo - ple to life.

Verses

1. In re - sponse to God's word, we make our prayer of faith. It is Christ in the Church who calls on God's heal - ing grace.
2. Lay your hands on the sick: re - store us to health a - gain. Touch all those who are weak: heal us and give us strength.
3. Through the ho - ly oil, com - fort and soothe our pain. Heal us, bod - y and soul; Spir - it, come with your grace.
4. God will wipe a - way ev - 'ry tear from our eyes; no more death or pain, for God re - cre - ates our lives.

to Refrain

424 PRECIOUS LORD, TAKE MY HAND

1. Pre - cious Lord, take my hand, Lead me on, let me
2. When my way grows drear, Pre - cious Lord, lin - ger
3. When the dark - ness ap - pears And the night draws
1. stand; I am tired, I am weak, I am worn;
2. near, When my life is al - most gone;
3. near, And the day is past and gone,

1. Through the storm, through the night, Lead me on to the light:
2. Hear my cry, hear my call, Hold my hand lest I fall:
3. At the riv - er I stand, Guide my feet, hold my hand:
1-3. Take my hand, pre-cious Lord, lead me home.

Text: Irregular; Thomas A. Dorsey, 1899–1993.
Music: PRECIOUS LORD; Thomas A. Dorsey.

Healing Waters

425

Refrain

Heal-ing wa-ters, flow o-ver me. Mer-cy's wa-ter, re-new-ing me. Mer-cy's o-cean, trans-form-ing me. Heal-ing wa-ter, re-new me.

Verses

1. Re - new my heart, O God, come change my hard - ened heart, come fill my hard-ened heart with mer - cy. You are the wa - ter of life. You are the breath of heav-en, come fill my hard-ened heart with mer-cy, Lord.

2. Wash me in wa-ters of love; cleanse me and pur - i - fy me, for on - ly you can cleanse me, Lord. Wash o - ver me, O Lord. Re - fresh my thirst - y soul for you a - lone can make me ho - ly, Lord.

to Refrain

426 BLESSED BE (DIVINE PRAISES)

Verse 1
1. Bless-ed be God. Bless-ed be his Ho - ly Name.
1. Bless-ed be Je-sus Christ, true God and true Man.
1. Bless - ed be the Name of Je - sus,
1. his most Sa-cred Heart, his most Pre-cious Blood.
Refrain
Bless-ed be, bless-ed be, bless-ed be the Lord.
Bless-ed be, bless-ed be, bless-ed be the Lord.
to Verses
Verse 2
2. Bless-ed be Je - sus in the most Ho - ly
2. Sac-ra - ment of the Al - tar. Bless-ed be
2. the Ho-ly Spir - it. Bless-ed be the Par - a - clete.
to Refrain
Verse 3
3. Bless-ed be the great Moth - er of God,
3. Mar - y most ho - ly. Bless-ed be her
3. ho - ly and Im - mac-u-late Con-cep - tion.
to Verse 4

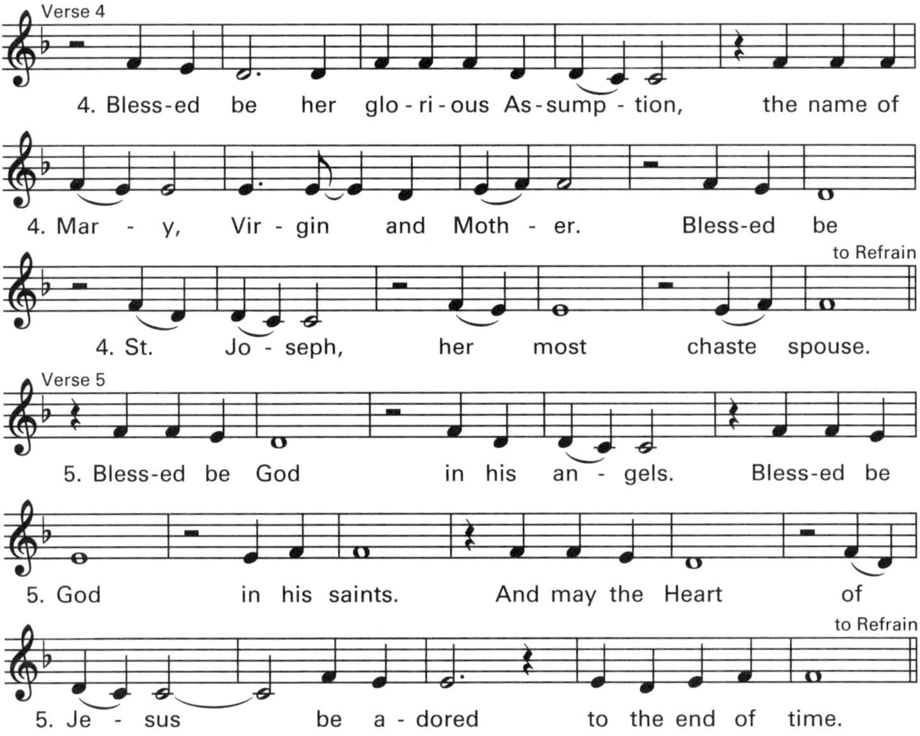

Verse 4

4. Bless-ed be her glo-ri-ous As-sump-tion, the name of
4. Mar-y, Vir-gin and Moth-er. Bless-ed be
4. St. Jo-seph, her most chaste spouse.

to Refrain

Verse 5

5. Bless-ed be God in his an-gels. Bless-ed be
5. God in his saints. And may the Heart of
5. Je-sus be a-dored to the end of time.

to Refrain

Text: Verses, *The Divine Praises*. Refrain, Josh Blakesley, b. 1976, and Sarah Hart, b. 1968,

Music: Josh Blakesley and Sarah Hart,

O Saving Victim/O Salutaris Hostia 427

1. O sav-ing Vic-tim, o-pen wide The gate of
2. To your great name be end-less praise, Im-mor-tal
1. *O sa-lu-tá-ris Hó-sti-a, Quae cae-li*
2. *U-ni tri-nó-que Dó-mi-no Sit sem-pi-*
1. heav'n to us be-low, Our foes press on from
2. God-head, One in Three; Grant us, for end-less
1. *pan-dis ó-sti-um: Bel-la pre-munt ho-*
2. *tér-na gló-ri-a, Qui vi-tam si-ne*
1. ev-'ry side; Your aid sup-ply, your strength be-stow.
2. length of days, In our true na-tive land to be.
1. *stí-li-a, Da ro-bur fer au-xí-li-um.*
2. *tér-mi-no No-bis do-net in pá-tri-a.*

Text: LM; *O Salutaris*; St. Thomas Aquinas, 1227–1274; tr. by Edward Caswall, 1814–1878, alt.
Music: DUGUET; attr. to Abbé Dieudonne Duguet, 1794–1849.

428 Songs of the Angels

Refrain
May songs of the an-gels wel-come you and guide you a-long your way. May the smiles of the mar-tyrs greet your own as dark-ness turns in-to day. Ev-ery fear will be un-done and death will be no more, as songs of the an-gels bring you home be-fore the face of God.
Verse 1
1. From the depths I cry to you, O Lord. Hear the sound of my pleading, for my soul longs for you, O Lord, like the watch-man longs for day.
to Refrain
Verse 2
2. I know that my Re-deem-er lives and he shall stand, shall stand up-on the earth. And I shall see, and I shall see.
to Refrain

Verse 3
3. Be - hold, I tell you a mys-t'ry. We shall all be
3. changed, for the trum-pet shall sound, the dead be raised in the
to Refrain
3. vic-t'ry, the glo - ry of our God.

Text: Refrain based on *In Paradisum*; verses based on Psalm 130:1, 6; Job 19:25ff; 1 Corinthians 15:31–52; Bob Dufford, SJ, b. 1943.
Music: Bob Dufford, SJ.

Go Forth 429

Refrain

Go forth, Chris-tian soul, from this world in the name of God. Go forth, go forth, beau - ti - ful one.

Verses

1,3. Fly a - way with the an - gels, with the aid
2. Fly a - way to the Sav - ior; fly a - way

1,3. of the ho - ly ones, to the place where tears are washed
2. to the Sav - ior's side, to the place where mer - cy reigns,

1,3. a - way, to the place where love a - bides.
2. to the place where love a - bides.

to Refrain

Text and music: Trevor Thomson, b. 1971, © 2008, Trevor Thomson.

430 How Lovely Is Your Dwelling Place

Refrain
O how love-ly is your dwell-ing place, dwell-ing of the Lord of hosts!
How we long for your house, O Lord,
sing-ing out a song of joy to the liv - ing God!
Verses
1. E - ven spar - rows find a home with you, and swal-lows lay their young to rest. Bless-ed are those who dwell in you and sing your praise, O God!
2. Bless'd are those who find their strength in you, whose hearts are high-ways for your will. Bring-ing joy to those a - round them, they go from strength to strength.
3. Hear our prayer, O Lord God of hosts; re - ceive our lives in - to your hands! Look in - to the hearts of those you love and grant us all we need!
4. For one day with - in your house ex - ceeds a thou-sand spent a - way from you. We would rath - er serve with- in your house than wealth and pow'r re - ceive.
5. For our God pro - tects us from all harm; he gives his fa - vor and his love. All good things will come to those who love the Lord, and walk with him.
to Refrain

I Know That My Redeemer Lives 431

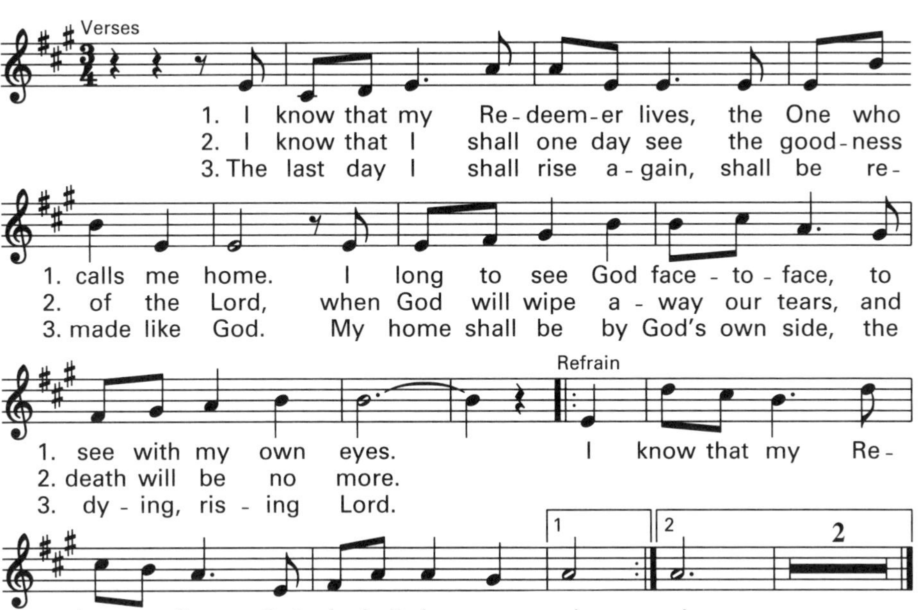
Verses
1. I know that my Re-deem-er lives, the One who
2. I know that I shall one day see the good-ness
3. The last day I shall rise a-gain, shall be re-
1. calls me home. I long to see God face-to-face, to
2. of the Lord, when God will wipe a-way our tears, and
3. made like God. My home shall be by God's own side, the
1. see with my own eyes.
2. death will be no more.
3. dy-ing, ris-ing Lord.
Refrain
I know that my Re-
deem-er lives, that I shall rise a-gain. gain.
1
2
2

Text: Based on Job 19; Psalm 27; Isaiah 25; Scott Soper, b. 1961.
Music: Scott Soper.

May the Angels 432

1, 2. May the an-gels lead you, lead you in-to par-a-dise.
1, 2. May the mar-tyrs wel-come you, wel-come you to heav-en.
1. Peace will be yours now in the Ho-ly Cit-y.
2. One day we'll see you in the New Je-ru-sa-lem.
1, 2. May the an-gels lead you, lead you in-to par-a-dise.

Text: Based on *In Paradisum*; adapt. by Tom Kendzia, b. 1954.
Music: *Silzcna Panienka*; trad. Polish melody; adapt. by Tom Kendzia.

433 I, THE LORD

Refrain

I, the Lord, am with you, al - ways by your side.

Come and take my hand, for I will lead you home. Fol-low

me, fol-low me.

1, 2 — 2 — to Verses

Final

Fol-low me, fol-low me.

Verse 1

1. I am the res - ur - rec-tion, and I am the life; if

1. you be-lieve in me, you shall live for - ev - er.

to Refrain

Verse 2

2. You shall have new life and live it to the full.

2. Turn your sor-row in - to joy, for life has just be - gun.

to Refrain

Text: Based on John 6:35–58; Tom Kendzia, b. 1954.
Music: Tom Kendzia.

434 KEEP IN MIND

Refrain
Keep in mind that Je-sus Christ has died for us and is ris - en from the

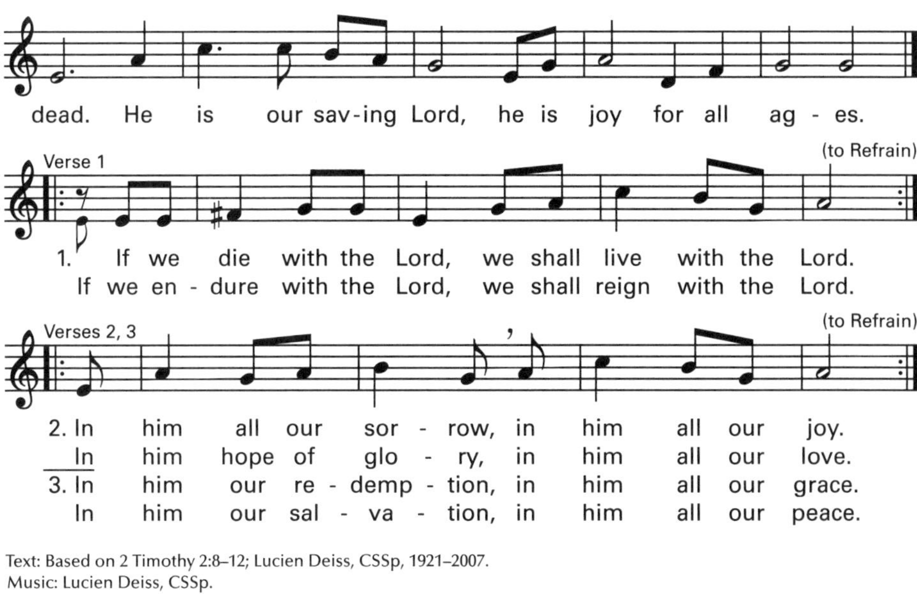
dead. He is our sav-ing Lord, he is joy for all ag - es.
Verse 1
(to Refrain)
1. If we die with the Lord, we shall live with the Lord.
If we en - dure with the Lord, we shall reign with the Lord.
Verses 2, 3
(to Refrain)
2. In him all our sor - row, in him all our joy.
In him hope of glo - ry, in him all our love.
3. In him our re - demp - tion, in him all our grace.
In him our sal - va - tion, in him all our peace.

Text: Based on 2 Timothy 2:8–12; Lucien Deiss, CSSp, 1921–2007.
Music: Lucien Deiss, CSSp.

435 Give Me Jesus

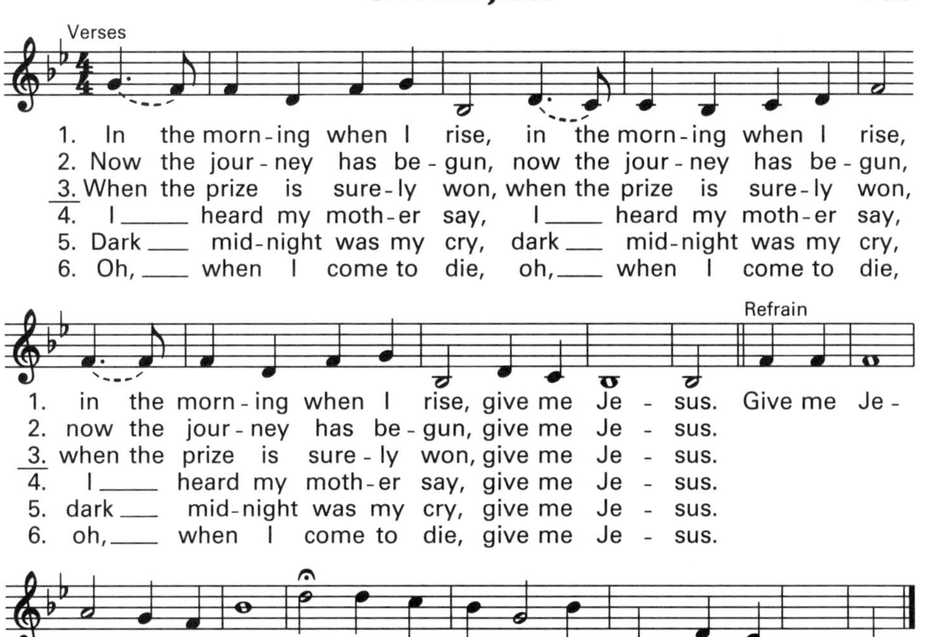
Verses
1. In the morn-ing when I rise, in the morn-ing when I rise,
2. Now the jour - ney has be - gun, now the jour - ney has be - gun,
3. When the prize is sure - ly won, when the prize is sure - ly won,
4. I ___ heard my moth - er say, I ___ heard my moth - er say,
5. Dark ___ mid-night was my cry, dark ___ mid-night was my cry,
6. Oh, ___ when I come to die, oh, ___ when I come to die,
Refrain
1. in the morn - ing when I rise, give me Je - sus. Give me Je -
2. now the jour - ney has be - gun, give me Je - sus.
3. when the prize is sure - ly won, give me Je - sus.
4. I ___ heard my moth - er say, give me Je - sus.
5. dark ___ mid-night was my cry, give me Je - sus.
6. oh, ___ when I come to die, give me Je - sus.
sus, give me Je - sus. You may have all this world. Give me Je - sus.

Text: Verses 1, 4–6 and refrain, Spiritual. Verses 2–3, James Hansen, b. 1937,

Music: Spiritual.

436 MY SOUL IS THIRSTING

Refrain

My soul is thirst-ing for you, my God. When shall I see him face to face? face?

Verses

1. Like the deer that yearns for wa - ter,
2. Why am I so trou - bled?
3. May the Lord show con - stant love by day,

1. my soul is yearn - ing for you, my God.
2. 𝄾 I will put my hope in you, my God.
3. 𝄾 so that I may sing his praise by night.

1. My soul is thirst-ing for the God of my life.
2. 𝄾 Once a - gain I will praise him.
3. 𝄾 For the Lord is my de - fend - er.

1. When shall I see you face to face?
2. He is my sav - ior and my God.
3. He is the God of my life.

to Refrain

Text: Based on Psalm 42; Grayson Warren Brown, b. 1948.
Music: Grayson Warren Brown.

437 IN PARADISUM/MAY ANGELS GUIDE YOU

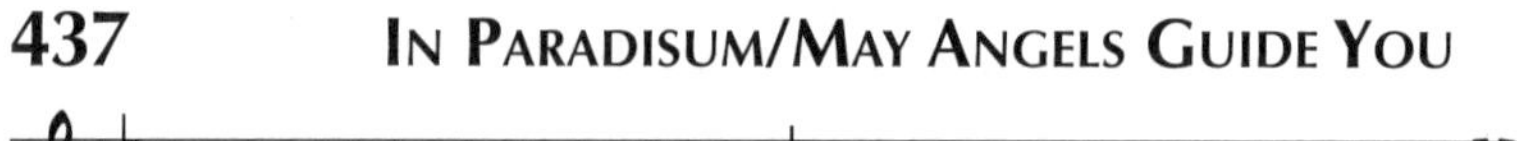

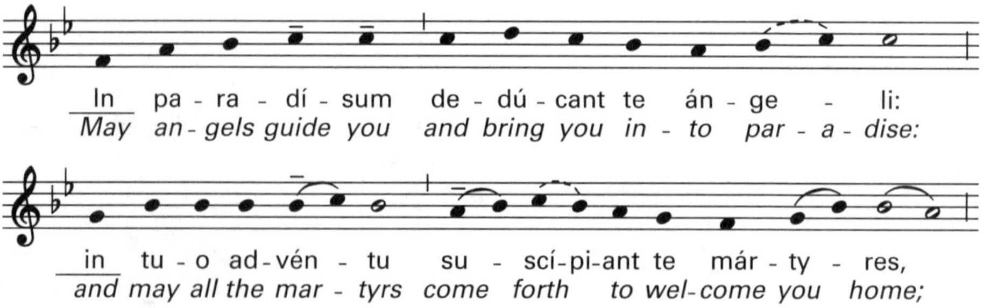

In pa - ra - dí - sum de - dú - cant te án - ge - li:
May an - gels guide you and bring you in - to par - a - dise:

in tu - o ad - vén - tu su - scí - pi - ant te már - ty - res,
and may all the mar - tyrs come forth to wel - come you home;

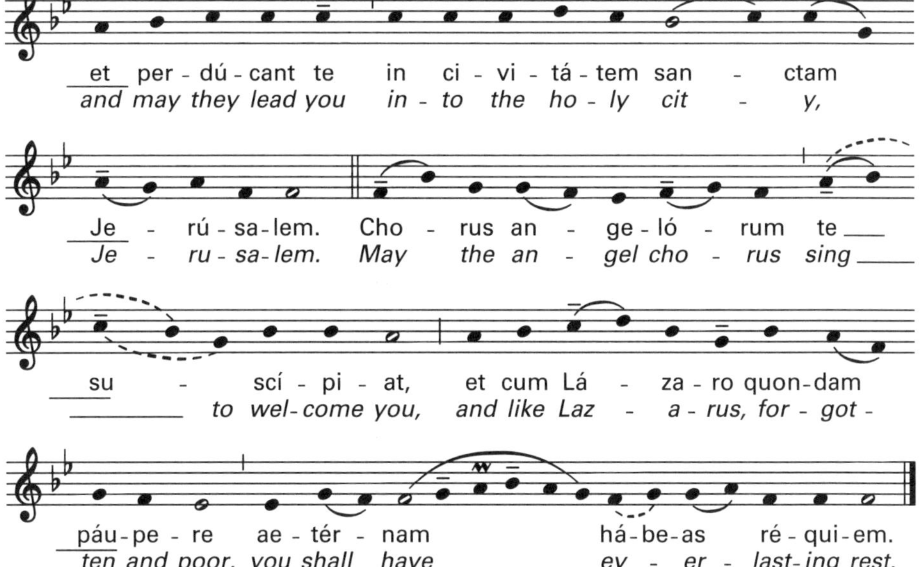
et per - dú - cant te in ci - vi - tá - tem san - ctam
and may they lead you in - to the ho - ly cit - y,
Je - rú - sa - lem. Cho - rus an - ge - ló - rum te
Je - ru - sa - lem. May the an - gel cho - rus sing
su - scí - pi - at, et cum Lá - za - ro quon - dam
to wel - come you, and like Laz - a - rus, for - got -
páu - pe - re ae - tér - nam há - be - as ré - qui - em.
ten and poor, you shall have ev - er - last - ing rest.

Text: *In paradisum* and *Chorus angelorum*; Latin, 11th cent.; English tr. by Owen Alstott, b. 1947,

Music: Chant, Mode VII and Mode VIII.

Song of Farewell 438

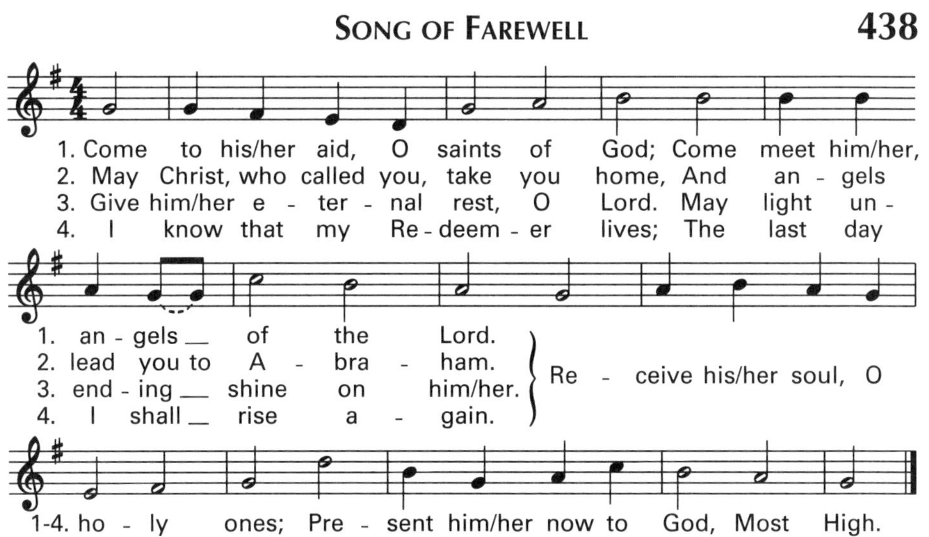
1. Come to his/her aid, O saints of God; Come meet him/her,
2. May Christ, who called you, take you home, And an - gels
3. Give him/her e - ter - nal rest, O Lord. May light un -
4. I know that my Re - deem - er lives; The last day
1. an - gels of the Lord.
2. lead you to A - bra - ham.
3. end - ing shine on him/her.
4. I shall rise a - gain.
Re - ceive his/her soul, O
1-4. ho - ly ones; Pre - sent him/her now to God, Most High.

Text: LM; *Subvenite sancti Dei*; *Requiem aeternam*; *Credo quod Redemptor*; tr. by Dennis C. Smolarski, SJ, b. 1947,

Music: OLD HUNDREDTH; *Genevan Psalter*, 1551; attr. to Louis Bourgeois, ca. 1510–1561, alt.

439 O LOVING GOD

Verses
1. O lov-ing God, we send your daugh-ter home to you,
(son)
2. O lov-ing God, have mer-cy and for-give-ness
1. home to a place of ev-er-last-ing love, to join there
2. up-on your ser-vant's now de-part-ed soul, and may your
1. with the an-gel choirs and bless-ed saints, and to be-
2. grace and love en-fold her/him ev-er-more, so she/he may
Refrain
1. hold your glo-rious ho-ly face.
2. dwell in par-a-dise at last.
Re-ceive her/his soul and
let e-ter-nal light shine, e-ter-nal light for-ev-er on her/his
soul, so she/he may be for-ev-er in your dwell-ing place,
and be at rest in peace un-til we meet her/him there.

Text: 12 10 12 10 with refrain; Paulette M. McCoy, b. 1953, © 2004, Paulette M. McCoy.
Published by OCP. All rights reserved.
Music: LONDONDERRY AIR; fr. *The Ancient Music of Ireland*, 1855.

PARABLE 440

Refrain
3

1-4. To ev-'ry thing there is a sea-son; a time to be born

1-4. and a time to die. 1, 4. A time to plant and a time for har-vest;
2. A time to speak and a time for si-lence;
3. A time for joy and a time for griev-ing;

1-3
to Vss.
4, Final
Fine
Verses
3

1, 4. a time to meet and a time to part. 4. part. 1. A sow-er went
2. a time to wound and a time to heal. 2. Noth-ing can
3. a time to seek and a time to lose. 3. God's word is

3
3

1. out to sow the seed. Some of it fell up-on the path, some fell on
2. grow in bar-ren soil; bri-ars and ra-vens take their toll; still there is
3. like the far-mer's seed, root-ed in joy-ful, lov-ing hearts, grow-ing like

3
to Refrain

1. shal-low, rock-y soil, and some a-mong chok-ing thorns.
2. grain a hun-dred-fold, from seed that took root and grew.
3. grain in fer-tile ground, a har-vest that o-ver-flows.

Text: Based on Ecclesiastes 3:1–9; Matthew 13:4–8; M.D. Ridge.
Music: M.D. Ridge.

RESTLESS IS THE HEART 441

*Refrain
Rest-less is the heart un-til it comes to rest in you. All the
3
earth, all the earth shall re-mem-ber and re-turn to our God.

*Verses available in accompaniment books.

Text based on Psalm 90:1–2, 4–6, 12, 14; Bernadette Farrell, b. 1957.
Music: Bernadette Farrell.

442 Song of Farewell

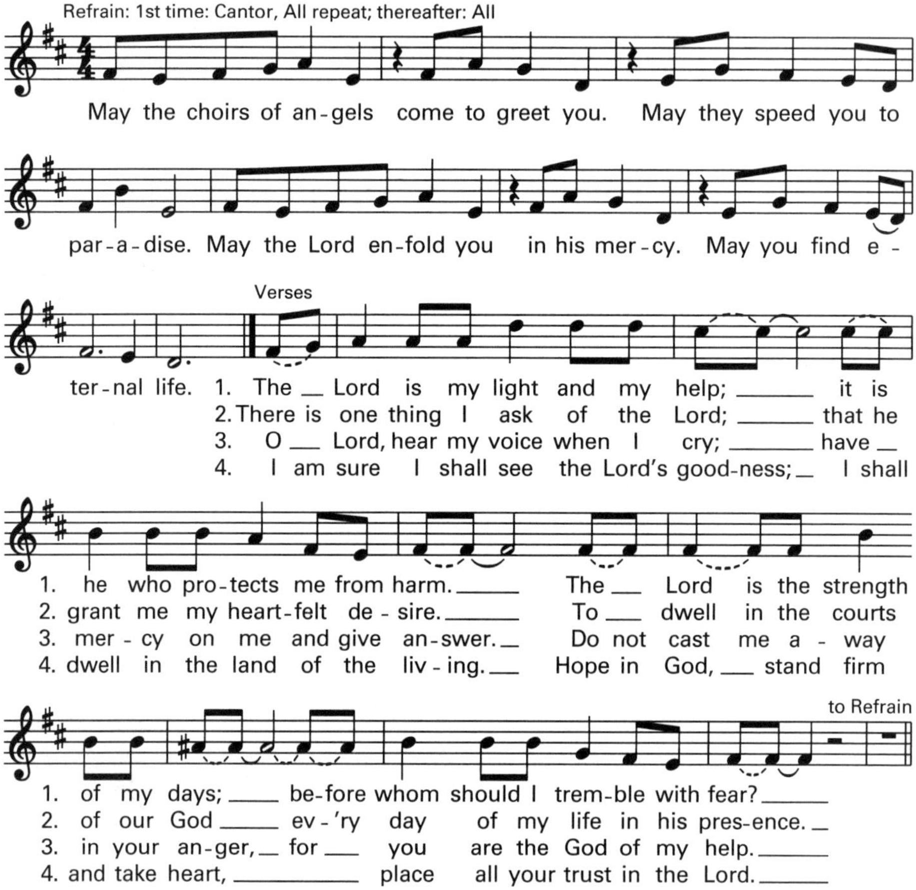

Refrain: 1st time: Cantor, All repeat; thereafter: All

May the choirs of an-gels come to greet you. May they speed you to par-a-dise. May the Lord en-fold you in his mer-cy. May you find e-ter-nal life.

Verses

1. The Lord is my light and my help; it is he who protects me from harm. The Lord is the strength of my days; before whom should I tremble with fear?
2. There is one thing I ask of the Lord; that he grant me my heart-felt de-sire. To dwell in the courts of our God ev-'ry day of my life in his pres-ence.
3. O Lord, hear my voice when I cry; have mer-cy on me and give an-swer. Do not cast me a-way in your an-ger, for you are the God of my help.
4. I am sure I shall see the Lord's good-ness; I shall dwell in the land of the liv-ing. Hope in God, stand firm and take heart, place all your trust in the Lord.

to Refrain

Text: Refrain based on *In Paradisum*; verses based on Psalm 27; Ernest Sands, b. 1949.
Music: Ernest Sands.

443 The Lord Is My Light

Verses
1. The Lord is my light, my help, my sal-va-tion. Why should I fear? With God I fear
2. There is one thing I ask of the Lord that I long for: all of my days with God to be
3. I know I will live to see the Lord's good-ness; now, in this life, I'm sure I will

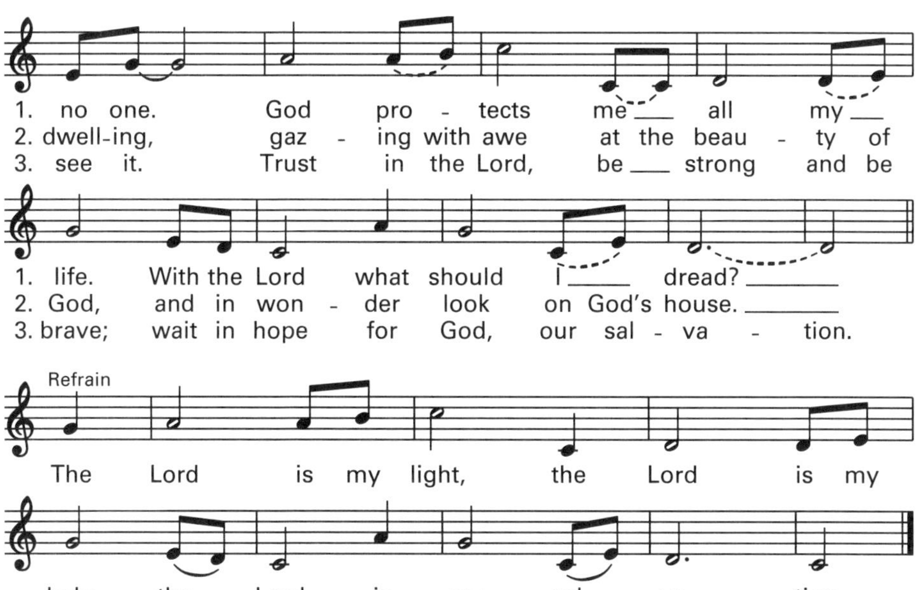
1. no one. God pro - tects me all my
2. dwell-ing, gaz - ing with awe at the beau - ty of
3. see it. Trust in the Lord, be strong and be
1. life. With the Lord what should I dread?
2. God, and in won - der look on God's house.
3. brave; wait in hope for God, our sal - va - tion.
Refrain
The Lord is my light, the Lord is my
help, the Lord is my sal - va - tion.

Text: Based on Psalm 27; Christopher Walker, b. 1947.
Music: Christopher Walker.

Yes, I Shall Arise 444

Refrain
Yes, I shall a-rise! I shall gaze up-on the love-li-ness of God for-ev-er-more.
Verses
1. One thing I ask of the Lord, this I seek: to
2. Day af - ter day I seek the house of the Lord.
3. Yearn - ing and pin - ing for the courts of the Lord, my
4. Thus will I go in - to the al - tar of God, the
5. Hap - py are they who place their trust in the Lord, for
to Refrain
1. dwell in the house of the Lord all the days of my life.
2. When shall I en - ter and see, see the face of my God?
3. flesh and my spir - it cry out for the God of my life.
4. God of my glad-ness and joy, giv - ing thanks on the harp.
5. they shall in - her - it the prize; theirs is life with-out end!

Text: Based on Psalms 27 and 43; Owen Alstott, b. 1947,
Music: Owen Alstott,

445 Go in Peace

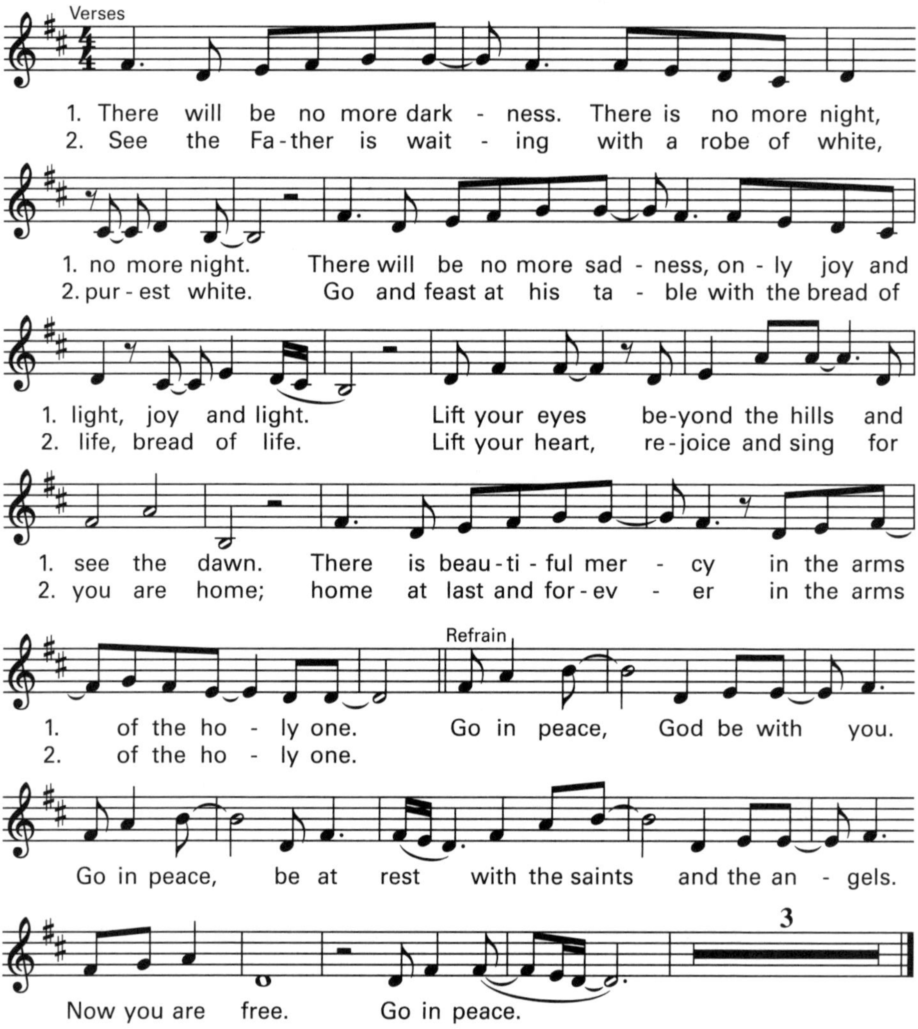

Verses

1. There will be no more darkness. There is no more night,
no more night. There will be no more sadness, only joy and
light, joy and light. Lift your eyes beyond the hills and
see the dawn. There is beautiful mercy in the arms
of the holy one.

2. See the Father is waiting with a robe of white,
purest white. Go and feast at his table with the bread of
life, bread of life. Lift your heart, rejoice and sing for
you are home; home at last and forever in the arms
of the holy one.

Refrain

Go in peace, God be with you.
Go in peace, be at rest with the saints and the angels.
Now you are free. Go in peace.

Text and music: Sarah Hart, b. 1968, and Dwight Liles, b. 1957,

446 Where There Is Love

Refrain
Where there is love, there is God. The love of
God has gath-ered us to - geth-er; Al - le - lu - ia.

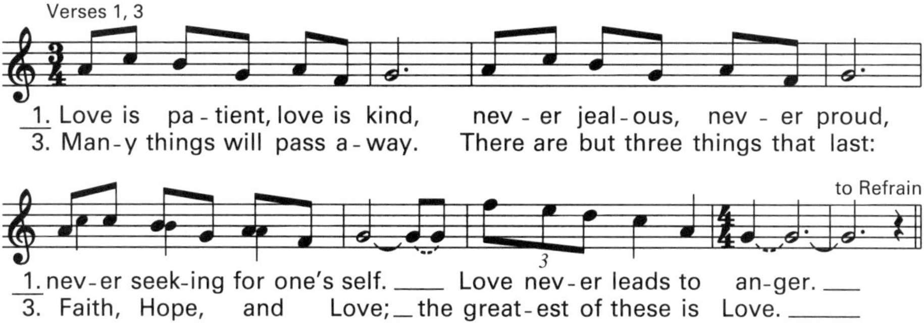

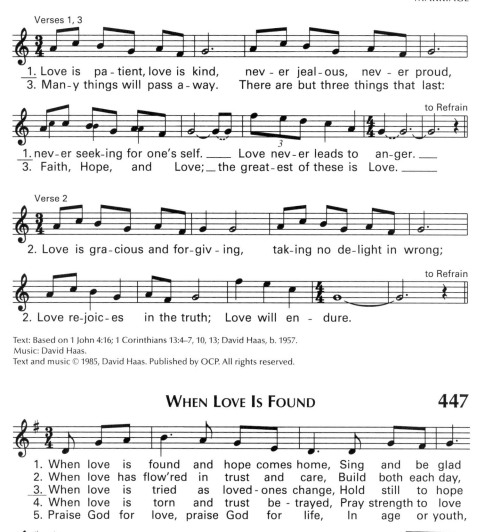

Verses 1, 3

1. Love is pa - tient, love is kind, nev - er jeal - ous, nev - er proud,
3. Man - y things will pass a - way. There are but three things that last:

to Refrain

1. nev - er seek - ing for one's self. ___ Love nev - er leads to an - ger. ___
3. Faith, Hope, and Love; _ the great - est of these is Love. ______

Verse 2

2. Love is gra - cious and for - giv - ing, tak - ing no de - light in wrong;

to Refrain

2. Love re - joic - es in the truth; Love will en - dure.

Text: Based on 1 John 4:16; 1 Corinthians 13:4–7, 10, 13; David Haas, b. 1957.
Music: David Haas.

When Love Is Found 447

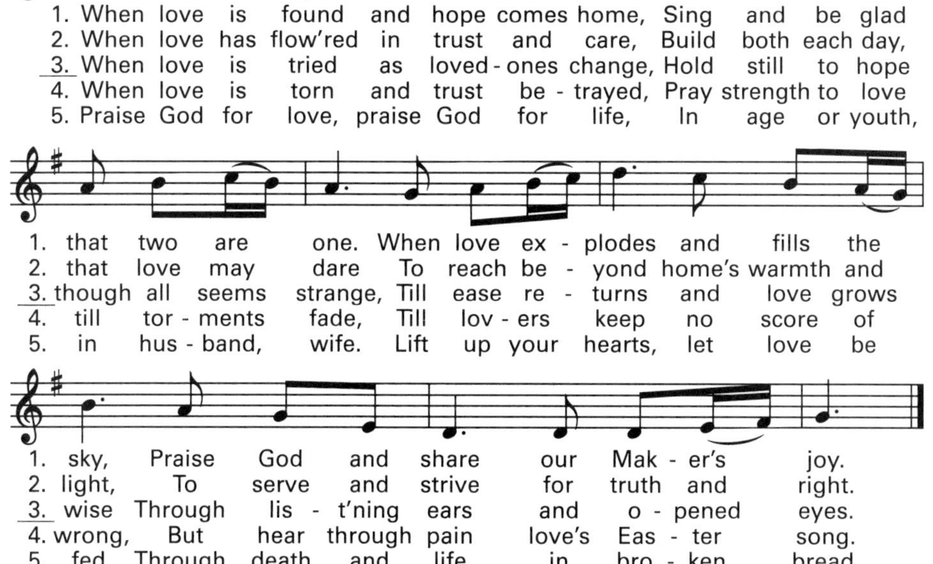
1. When love is found and hope comes home, Sing and be glad
2. When love has flow'red in trust and care, Build both each day,
3. When love is tried as loved - ones change, Hold still to hope
4. When love is torn and trust be - trayed, Pray strength to love
5. Praise God for love, praise God for life, In age or youth,
1. that two are one. When love ex - plodes and fills the
2. that love may dare To reach be - yond home's warmth and
3. though all seems strange, Till ease re - turns and love grows
4. till tor - ments fade, Till lov - ers keep no score of
5. in hus - band, wife. Lift up your hearts, let love be
1. sky, Praise God and share our Mak - er's joy.
2. light, To serve and strive for truth and right.
3. wise Through lis - t'ning ears and o - pened eyes.
4. wrong, But hear through pain love's Eas - ter song.
5. fed Through death and life in bro - ken bread.

Text: LM; Brian Wren, b. 1936, © 1983, Hope Publishing Co. All rights reserved. Used with permission.
Music: O WALY WALY; trad. English melody.

448 Hear Us Now, Our God and Father

1. Hear us now, our God and Fa - ther, Send your Spir - it from a-
2. Give them joy to light - en sor - row! Give them hope to bright - en
3. May the grace of Christ, our Sav - ior, And the Fa-ther's bound-less

1. bove On this Chris - tian man and wom - an Who here
2. life! Go with them to face the mor - row, Stay with
3. love, With the Ho - ly Spir - it's fa - vor Rest up -

1. make their vows of love! Bind their hearts in true de - vo - tion
2. them in ev - 'ry strife. As your Word has prom - ised, ev - er
3. on them from a - bove. Thus may they a - bide in un - ion

1. End - less as the sea - shore's sands, Bound - less as the
2. Fill them with your strength and grace, So that each may
3. With each oth - er and the Lord, And pos - sess in

1. deep - est o - ceans, Blest and sealed by your own hands.
2. serve the oth - er Till they see you face to face.
3. sweet com - mu - nion Joys which earth can - not af - ford.

Text: 87 87 D; verses 1–2, Harry N. Huxhold, 1922–2006, © 1978, *Lutheran Book of Worship*. All rights reserved.
Used with permission of Augsburg Fortress. Verse 3, John Newton, 1725–1807, alt.
Music: HYFRYDOL; Rowland H. Prichard, 1811–1887.

449 Like a Seal on Your Heart

Refrain
Set me like a seal on your heart, like a seal on your
arm. Set me like a seal on your heart. How
right it is to love you.
Verse 1
1. For love is strong - er than death, strong - er

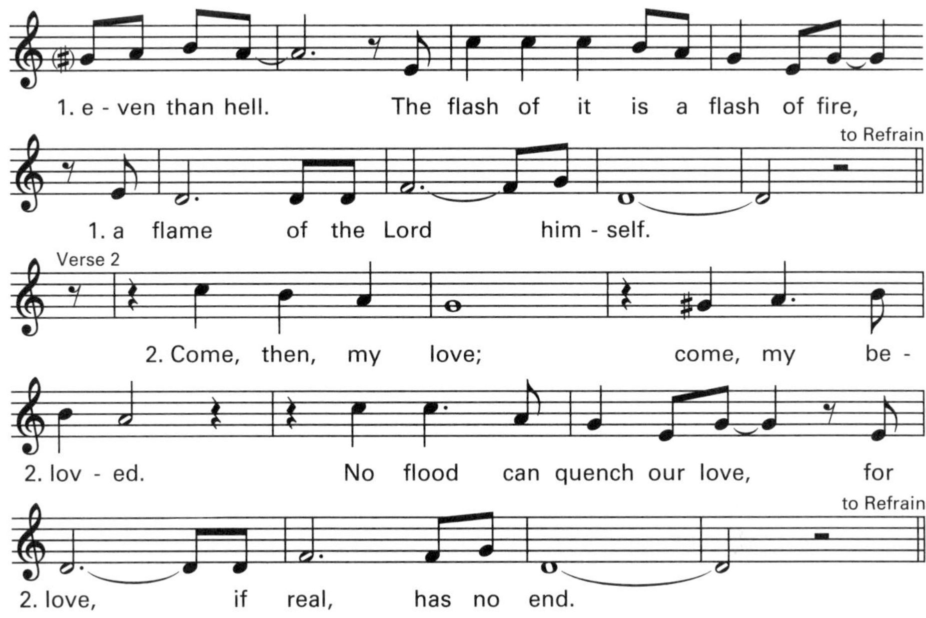
1. e - ven than hell. The flash of it is a flash of fire,
to Refrain
1. a flame of the Lord him - self.
Verse 2
2. Come, then, my love; come, my be -
2. lov - ed. No flood can quench our love, for
to Refrain
2. love, if real, has no end.

Text: Based on Song of Songs 8; Carey Landry, b. 1944.
Music: Carey Landry.

MAY GOD BLESS YOU

450

Refrain

May God bless you with his love, al-ways fill you with his love; may he hold you in the hol-low of his hand. For the Lord is with you in good-ness and love; may his light shine out in your heart.

Verses

1. Hap-py are they who re-flect his faith, seek-ing a depth with-out bound.
2. Bless-ed are they who re-flect his hope, find-ing a strength with-out bound.
3. Joy-ful are they who re-flect his love, liv-ing a gift with-out bound.
4. Ra-diant are they who re-flect his life, bond-ing their love with the Word.

to Refrain

1. Lord, it is good that we are here to see that faith which oth-ers have found.
2. Lord, it is good that we are here to see that hope which oth-ers have found.
3. Lord, it is good that we are here to see that love which oth-ers have found.
4. Lord, it is good that we are here to share that life with one ___ ac - cord.

451 LOVE NEVER FAILS

Refrain

Love is pa-tient, love is kind, love is not jeal-ous or rude. Love does not seek its own glo-ry. Love finds in e-vil no joy. Love be-lieves, love hopes and en-dures. Love nev-er fails.

1: to Verse 1
2: to Verse 2
3: to Bridge

Verse 1

1. I can speak the tongues of ev-'ry na-tion. I can sing with the el-o-quence of the an-gels. I can do all these things, but if I have not love I am noth-ing but a clang-ing cym-bal.

to Refrain

Verse 2

2. I can com-pre-hend all knowl-edge. I can have faith to move the might-y moun-tains. I can do all these things, but if I have not love I am noth-ing, noth-ing at all.

to Refrain

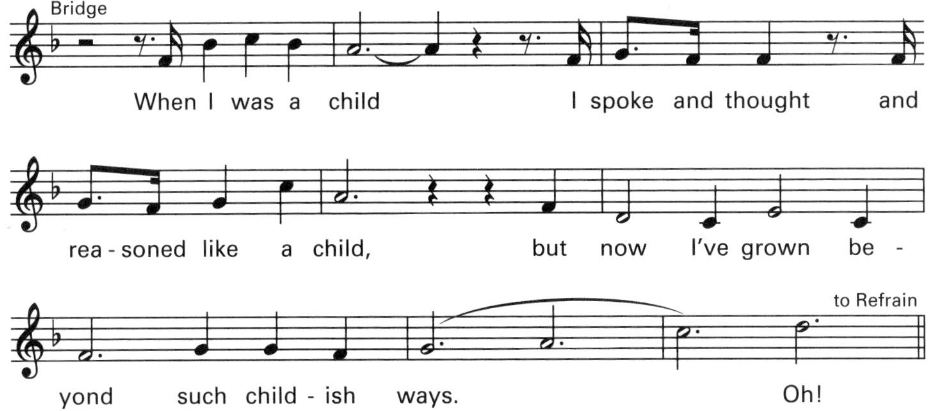
Bridge
When I was a child I spoke and thought and
rea - soned like a child, but now I've grown be -
yond such child - ish ways. Oh!
to Refrain

Text: Based on 1 Corinthians 13:1–2, 4–8b, 11; Ken Canedo, b. 1953, and Jesse Manibusan, b. 1958.
Music: Ken Canedo and Jesse Manibusan.

Wherever You Go 452

Verse 1

1. Wher-ev-er you go I shall go. Wher-ev-er you live
1. so shall I live. Your peo-ple will be my peo -
1. ple, and your God will be my God too.

2

Verse 2

2. Wher-ev-er you die I shall die, and there shall
2. I be bur-ied be-side you. We will be to-geth-er for-
2. ev - er, and our love will be the gift of our life.

Text: Based on Ruth 1:16, 17; Weston Priory, Gregory Norbet, OSB, b. 1940.
Music: Weston Priory, Gregory Norbet, OSB.

453 WHERE LOVE IS FOUND

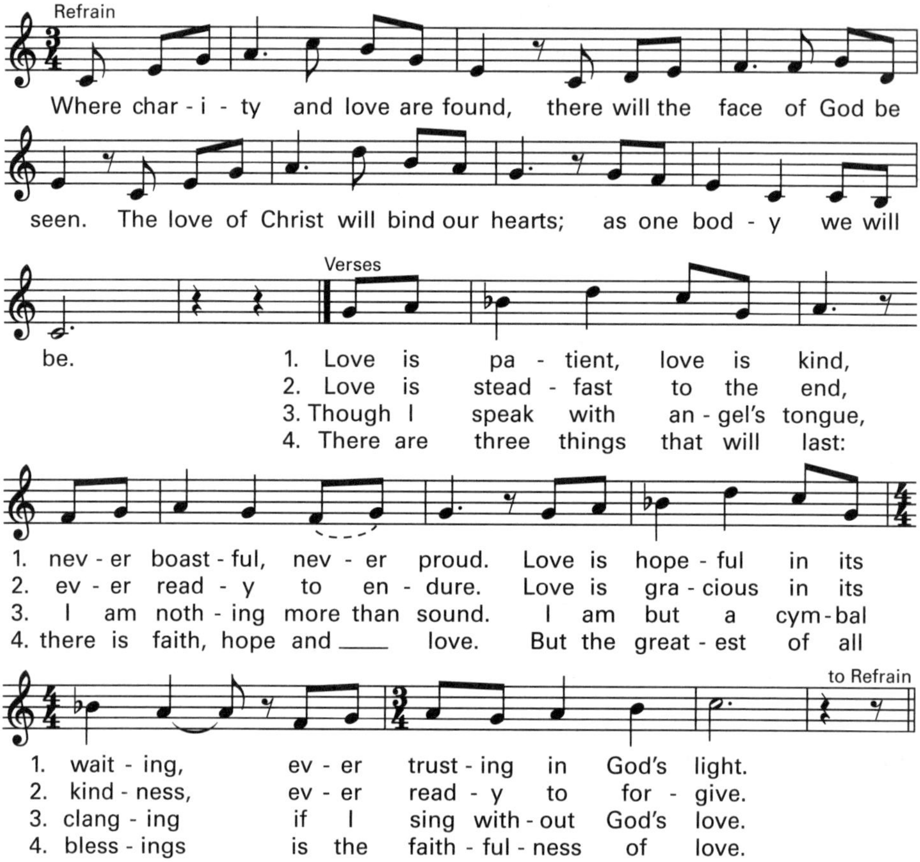

Refrain

Where char - i - ty and love are found, there will the face of God be seen. The love of Christ will bind our hearts; as one bod - y we will be.

Verses

1. Love is pa - tient, love is kind, nev - er boast - ful, nev - er proud. Love is hope - ful in its wait - ing, ev - er trust - ing in God's light.
2. Love is stead - fast to the end, ev - er read - y to en - dure. Love is gra - cious in its kind - ness, ev - er read - y to for - give.
3. Though I speak with an - gel's tongue, I am noth - ing more than sound. I am but a cym - bal clang - ing if I sing with - out God's love.
4. There are three things that will last: there is faith, hope and ___ love. But the great - est of all bless - ings is the faith - ful - ness of love.

to Refrain

Text: Based on the Latin chant *Ubi Caritas*, 9th cent.; 1 Corinthians 13:1–7, 13; Dan Schutte, b. 1947.
Music: Dan Schutte.

454 SET ME AS A SEAL

Refrain
Set me as a seal on your heart. Set me as a
seal on your soul. For strong as death is love, un-yield-ing
as the grave. Noth - ing will quench its flame,

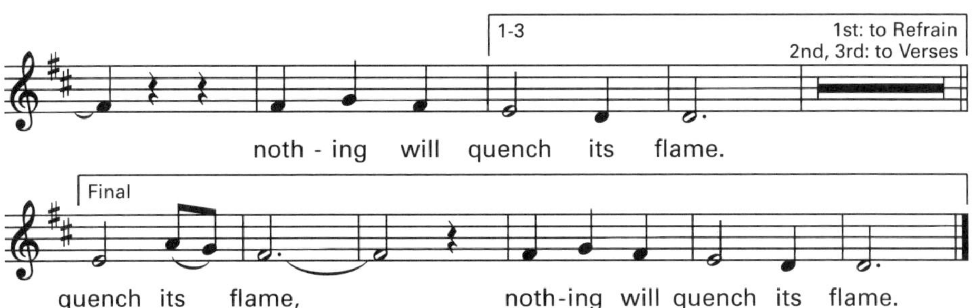
1-3
1st: to Refrain
2nd, 3rd: to Verses
noth - ing will quench its flame.
Final
quench its flame, noth-ing will quench its flame.

Verse 1

Kiss me, my love,
that your name be on my lips.
You intoxicate my being
with the fragrance of your presence.
How beautiful you are, my darling.
Show me your face,
let me hear your voice,
sweet as the dew in the early morn,
like a lily among the thorns. **(to Refrain)**

Verse 2

I looked for you, the one my heart loves;
I looked for you, but did not find you.
Searched through the night
until I rested in your sight.
Now I will never let you go.
'Cause you have stolen my heart,
my sister, my bride;
you've stolen my heart
with one glance of your eyes.
Your lips so sweet, adorned with honey.
My hands, they drip with myrrh. **(to Refrain)**

Text: Based on Song of Songs 8:6–7; Matt Maher, b. 1974.
Music: Matt Maher.

General Music for Worship

Gather Us Together 455

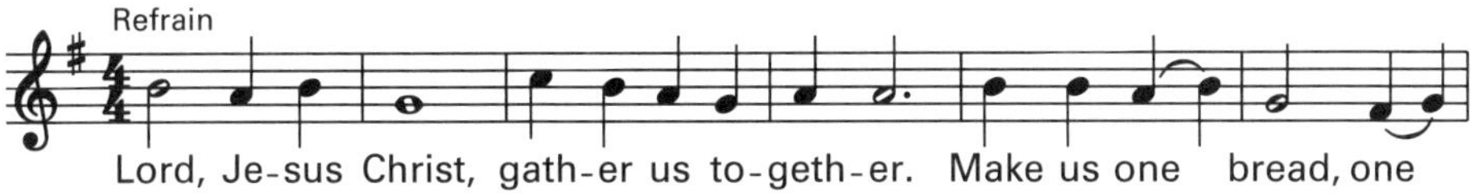

Refrain

Lord, Je-sus Christ, gath-er us to-geth-er. Make us one bread, one bod-y in your love.

Verses

1. Gath-er your peo - ple, who long to be one, one with you, O Lord, in truth and love.
2. We do pro-claim you the Sav-ior of all, Lord of all the earth and sea and sky.
3. For-give our fail - ings, cre - ate us a - new. Speak your words of peace in - to our hearts.
4. In - to your hands, Lord, we place all our cares, trust - ing in your love which nev - er fails.
5. With-in your tem - ple your prais-es we sing. Glo - rious is your name o'er all the earth.

to Refrain

456 All People That on Earth Do Dwell

1. All peo - ple that on earth do dwell, Sing to the
2. Know that the Lord is God in - deed; With - out our
3. O en - ter then his gates with praise; Ap - proach with
4. For why? the Lord our God is good: His mer - cy
5. To Fa - ther, Son, and Ho - ly Ghost, The God whom

1. Lord with cheer - ful voice; Him serve with mirth, his
2. aid he did us make; We are his folk, he
3. joy his courts un - to; Praise, laud, and bless his
4. is for ev - er sure; His truth at all times
5. heav'n and earth a - dore, From us and from the

1. praise forth tell, Come we be - fore him, and re - joice.
2. does us feed, And for his sheep he does us take.
3. Name al - ways, For it is seem - ly so to do.
4. firm - ly stood, And shall from age to age en - dure.
5. an - gel host Be praise and glo - ry ev - er - more.

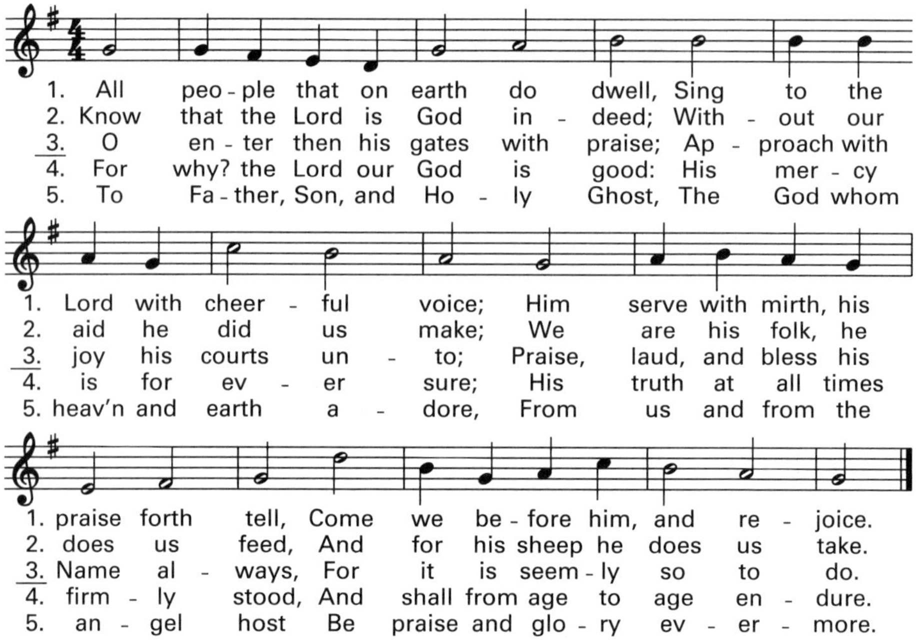

Text: LM; based on Psalm 100; William Kethe, d. ca. 1594, alt.
Music: OLD HUNDREDTH; *Genevan Psalter,* 1551; attr. to Louis Bourgeois, ca. 1510–1561, alt.

457 Come, Now Is the Time to Worship

Verse

Come, now is the time to wor - ship. Come,
Come, just as you are to wor - ship. Come,

now is the time to give your heart.
just as you are be-fore your God. Come.

Bridge

One day ev-ery tongue will con-fess you are God. One day ev-ery

knee will bow. Still the great-est trea-sure re-mains

for those who glad - ly choose you now.

to Verse

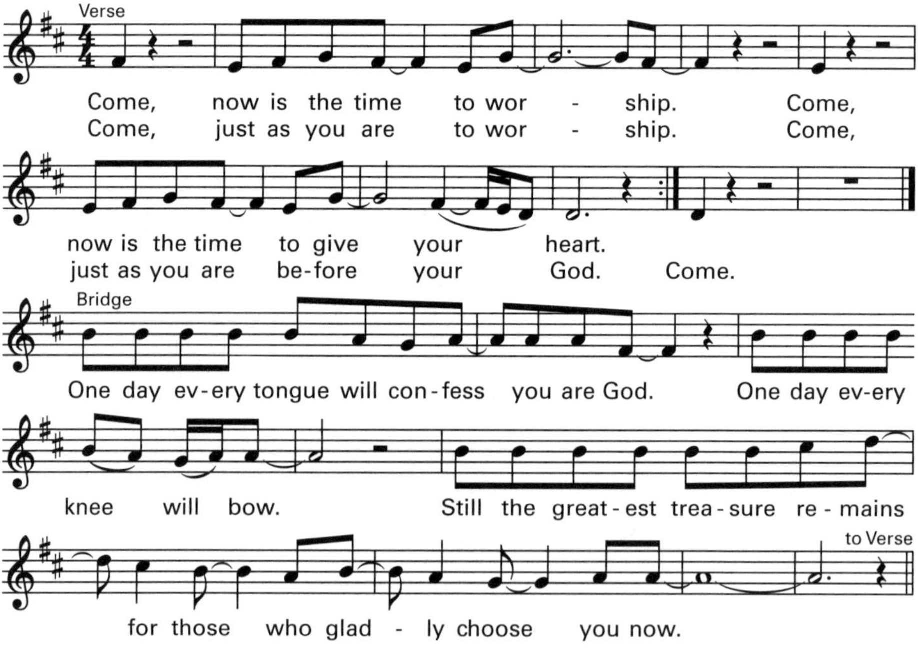

Text and music: Brian Doerksen, b. 1965,

Come to the Feast/Ven al Banquete 458

Refrain
Bilingual Ven, ven al ban - que - te. Ven a la fies - ta de Dios.
Spanish Ven, ven al ban - que - te. Ven a la fies - ta de Dios.
English Come, come to the ban - quet. Come, __ come to the feast.
Here the hun-gry find plen - ty, here the thirst-y shall drink. __
Los que tie - nen ham - bre y sed se - rán __ sa - cia - dos.
Here the hun-gry find plen - ty, here the thirst-y shall drink, __
Ven a la ce - na de Cris - to, come __ to __ the feast.
Ven a la ce - na de Cris - to, ven a la fies-ta de Dios.
here at the sup - per of Je - sus, come __ to __ the feast.
*
Verses
1. Like the child whose fish - es and loaves fed the mul - ti -
__ ¿Quién le pue - de dar de co - mer a la mul - ti -
2. 'Til the seed is giv - en to earth, it is just one
__ Hay que dar - se a __ mo - rir pa - ra co - se -
3. In the strang - er by __ our side, in the least and
Los de - sam - pa - ra - dos ven - drán a par - tir el
1. tude, in the Lord the lit - tle we have,
__ tud? Con Je - sús, al com - par - tir lo
2. grain; but once sown its death brings new birth, the
__ char, las se - mi - llas de li - ber - tad y
3. last, in the thirst for jus - tice we share,
pan y ve - rán su dig - ni - dad de
to Refrain
1. bro - ken and shared, be - comes a - bun - dant food.
__ po - co que hay, re - ci - bi - mos ple - ni - tud.
2. har - vest is rich; what's lost is raised a - gain.
__ re - su - rrec - ción, la pro - me - sa de vi - vir.
3. Christ __ is here in the break - ing of the bread.
nue - vo en Je - sús, Sal - va - dor y Buen Pas - tor.

*Last time, repeat final phrase.
Se repite la última vez.

Text: Bob Hurd, b. 1950, Pia Moriarty, b. 1948, and Jaime Cortez, b. 1963.
Music: Bob Hurd.

459 Our God Is Here

Verses

1. Here in this time, here in this place,
2. Here in the Word, God is re-vealed,

1. here we are stand - ing face to face. Here in our hearts,
2. here where the wound - ed can be healed. Here in our hearts,

1. here in our lives, our God is here. Here for the bro -
2. here in our lives, our God is here. Here we be-come

1. - ken, here for the strong, here in this tem - ple we be-long.
2. what we re-ceive, here in this Eu - cha-ris-tic feast.

1. Here in our hearts, here in our lives, our God is here.
2. We are his bod - y, liv-ing as one; our God is here.

Refrain

And we cry: "Ho-ly! Ho-ly! Ho-ly are you!" We cry:
"Ho-ly! Ho-ly! Ho-ly and true!" A-men, we do be-lieve
our God is here. Our God is here.

Text and music: Chris Muglia, b. 1971, © 2001, Chris Muglia.
Published by Spirit & Song®, a division of OCP.

460 Gather the People

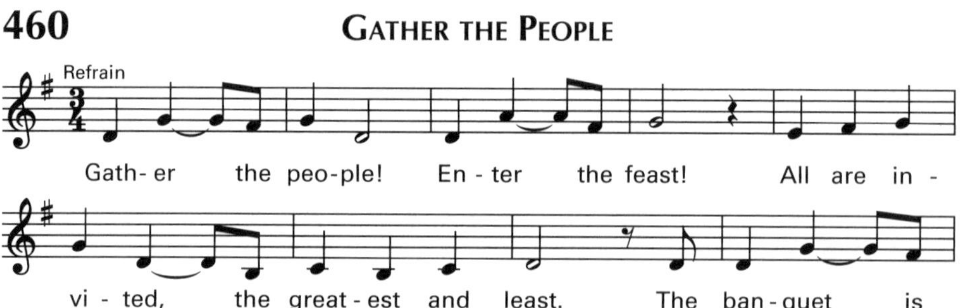
Refrain
Gath-er the peo-ple! En-ter the feast! All are in -
vi - ted, the great-est and least. The ban-quet is

read - y, now to be shared. Join in the heav - en - ly
feast that God has pre - pared.
(Fine)
5
to Verses
Verses
1. A - round this ta - ble we dine as kin, be -
2. A - round this ta - ble we tell great tales, the
3. A - round this ta - ble God's boun - ty falls on
4. A - round this ta - ble God's mer - cy flows to
5. A - round this ta - ble new hope is born, the
6. A - round this ta - ble God's heal - ing flows to
7. A - round this ta - ble God's peace will reign in
8. A - round this ta - ble our hearts re - joice in
9. A - round this ta - ble God's jus - tice reigns in
10. A - round this ta - ble God's low - ly ones are
1. lov - ed fam - 'ly of God. We
2. won - drous sto - ries of grace. We
3. all who hun - ger and thirst. We
4. hearts im - pris - oned by shame. We
5. flame of faith in our hearts. We
6. all the wound - ed and worn. We
7. hearts im - pris - oned by fear. We
8. love that's strong - er than death. We'll
9. hearts that la - bor for peace. We
10. clothed in splen - dor and grace. We
1. share the Bod - y of Christ, the Lord. Here we be -
2. hold the mem - 'ry of Christ, the Lord. So we be -
3. drink the full - ness of Christ, the Lord. So we be -
4. know com - pas - sion in Christ, the Lord. Let us be -
5. find our cour - age in Christ, the Lord, till we be -
6. join the suf - f'rings of Christ, the Lord, as we be -
7. live in free - dom through Christ, the Lord, as we be -
8. rise in glo - ry with Christ, the Lord. Then we be -
9. breathe the spir - it of Christ, the Lord, till we be -
10. share the ban - quet of Christ, the Lord. Here we be -
1-10. come what we eat.
2
to Refrain

461 Come to Us

1. Come to me, come to us, you who are bur-dened.
2. Come to me, come to us, pil - grim or strang - er,
3. Come to me, come to us, bro - ken or build - ing,
1. Come to the word, and come to the meal.
2. look - ing for change, or chal - lenge, or light.
3. come with your chil-dren, your choic - es, your chains.
1. Come with-out ques - tion or pres - sure or price:
2. We are the peo - ple whose call - ing is care,
3. All are in - vit - ed to friend-ship or rest, to
1, 2
1. come, be em-braced by the bod - y of Christ.
2. bear - ers of mer - cy, nour-ished in prayer.
3. share in our strug - gle, our call and our
Final
3. quest, to share in our strug-gle, our call
3. and our quest.

462 What Is This Place

1. What is this place, where we are meet-ing? On - ly a house, the
2. Words from a - far, stars that are fall - ing. Sparks that are sown in
3. And we ac - cept bread at his ta - ble, Bro - ken and shared, a

1. earth its floor. Walls and a roof, shel - ter - ing peo - ple, Win-dows for
2. us like seed: Names for our God, dreams, signs and won-ders Sent from the
3. liv-ing sign. Here in this world, dy - ing and liv - ing, We are each

1. light, an o - pen door. Yet it be-comes a bod - y that lives When
2. past are all we need. We in this place re - mem-ber and speak A-
3. oth - er's bread and wine. This is the place where we can re - ceive What
1. we are gath - ered here, And know our God is near.
2. gain what we have heard: God's free re - deem - ing word.
3. we need to in - crease: Our jus - tice and God's peace.

Text: 98 98 9 66; Huub Oosterhuis, b. 1933; tr. by David Smith, b. 1933.
Music: KOMT NU MET ZANG; trad. Dutch hymn; Valerius' *Nederlandtsche Gedenckclank*, Haarlem, 1626.

Table of Plenty 463

Refrain

Come to the feast of heav-en and earth! Come to the ta - ble of plen - ty! God will pro-vide for all that we need, here at the ta - ble of plen - ty.

Verses

1. O come and sit at my ta - ble where saints and sin - ners are friends. I wait to wel-come the lost and lone - ly to share the cup of my love.
2. O come and eat with-out mon-ey; come to drink with - out price. My feast of glad-ness will feed your spir - it with faith and full - ness of life.
3. My bread will ev - er sus - tain you through days of sor - row and woe. My wine will flow like a sea of glad-ness to flood the depths of your soul.
4. Your fields will flow - er in full-ness; your homes will flour - ish in peace. For I, the giv - er of home and har-vest, will send my rain on the soil.

to Refrain

464 HERE AT THIS TABLE

Refrain
Come and be filled here at this ta-ble.
Food for all who hun-ger and drink for all who thirst.
Drink of his love, wine of sal - va - tion.
*Final time: repeat from here
You shall live for - ev-er in Je - sus Christ the Lord.
Verses 1, 2, 4
1. You who la - bor for jus - tice, you who la - bor for peace, you who stead - y the plow in the field of the Lord,
2. You with lives full of pain, you who sor-row and weep, you, be - lov - ed of Christ, come to him, come to him!
4. You, the a - ged a - mong us, ho - ly, faith-ful and wise, may the wis - dom you share form our lives and our world!
to Refrain
Verses 3, 5
3. Chil - dren of ev - 'ry col - or in ev - 'ry land, you are his own, he gath-ers you gent - ly.
5. Let each wom - an and man learn from the strang-er; we're not so dif-f'rent and so much u - nites us.

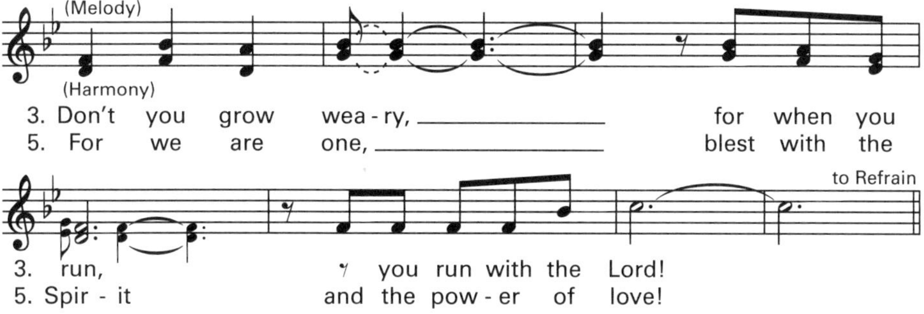
(Melody)
(Harmony)
3. Don't you grow wea-ry, for when you
5. For we are one, blest with the
to Refrain
3. run, you run with the Lord!
5. Spir-it and the pow-er of love!

Note: Previously published versions incorrectly showed the harmony part in Verses 3 & 5 as the melody.

Text and music: Janèt Sullivan Whitaker, b. 1958, and Max Whitaker, b. 1986,

Gather Your People 465

Refrain

Gath-er your peo-ple, O Lord. Gath-er your peo-ple, O Lord. One bread, one bod-y, one spir-it of love. Gath-er your peo-ple, O Lord.

Verses

1. Draw us forth to the ta-ble of life: broth-ers and sis-ters, each of us called to walk in your light.
2. We are parts of the bod-y of Christ, need-ing each oth-er, each of the gifts the Spir-it pro-vides.
3. No more harm on the moun-tain of God; swords in-to plow-shares. Free us, O Lord, from hard-ness of heart.
4. Wash us, Lord, in the wa-ters of life; wa-ters of mer-cy, wa-ters of hope that flow from your side.

2 to Refrain

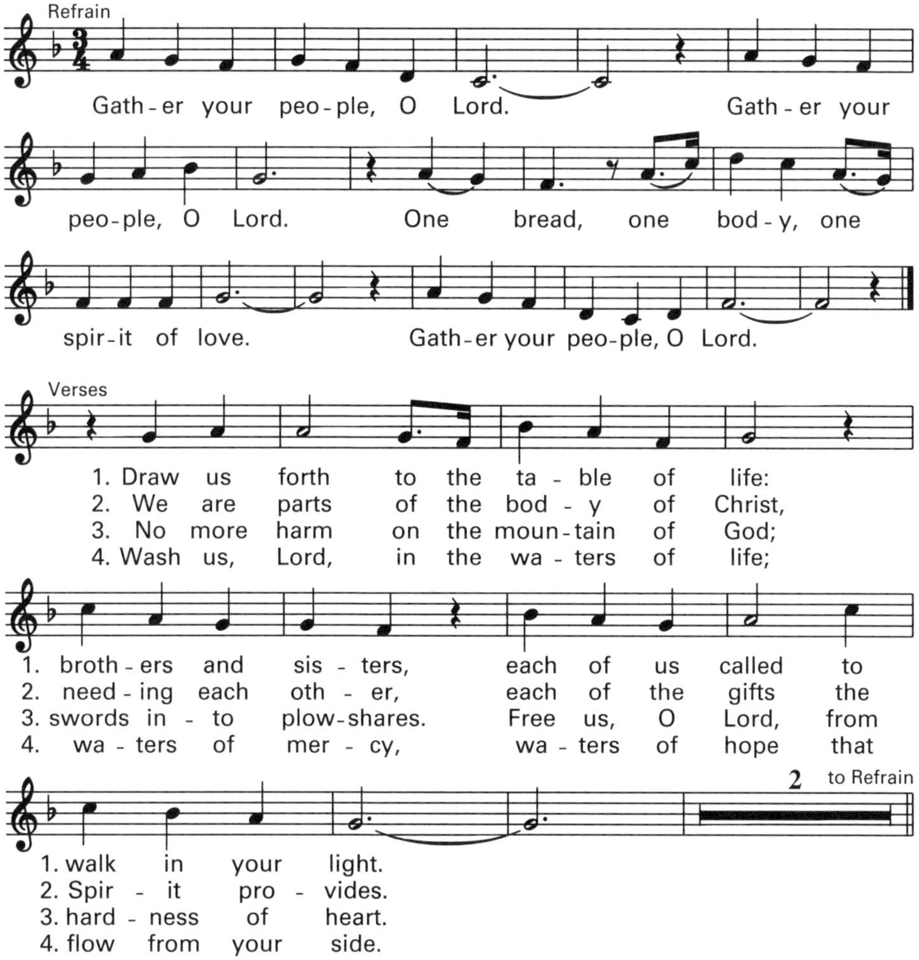

Text: Based on 1 Corinthians 12; Isaiah 2:3–4; 11:9; Bob Hurd, b. 1950.
Music: Bob Hurd.

466 O Love of God/Amor de Dios

Refrain
O love of God, gath-er us, a - mor de
Dios, haz-nos u - no,
*that we may share the
gifts we are giv-en;
**pa - ra cons-tru - ir
la co - mu - ni - dad,
pa - ra cons-tru -
ir la co - mu - ni - dad.
Verses
1. En el a - gua de vi - da nos con-ver -
In the liv - ing wa - ter we have be -
2. Hay di - ver - sos do - nes, pe - ro un
Man - y gifts of the Spir - it, but the same
3. Haz-nos u - na fa - mi - lia que se
Make us all one fam - 'ly; bring us to -
to Refrain
1. ti - mos en cuer - po del Se - ñor.
come one bod - y in the Lord.
2. só - lo Dios que nos ins - pi - ra.
God who works them in us all.
3. u - ne por o - bras de tu a - mor.
geth - er to do the works of love.

*para que compartamos los dones que hemos recibido
**for the upbuilding of the community

Text: Based on 1 Corinthians 12:4–6, 12–13; Bob Hurd, b. 1950, Pia Moriarty, b. 1948, Ana Victoria Demezas, b. 1958, and Jaime Cortez, b. 1963.
Music: Bob Hurd.

In This Place

467

Verses
1. We are all hun-gry peo-ple, we need shel-ter and strength. We are one in our hurt-ing, we are one in our pain. In our suf-f'ring and sad-ness, we are saved by the grace
2. All our lives are a Mys-t'ry; we see not where they lead. We are asked now to trust you and we know we must be-lieve. As our feet be-come Christ's feet, we go forth with the grace
3. Though the world may tell us to look at our-selves, we reach out to an-oth-er where suf-fer-ing dwells. As our hands be-come Christ's hands, we are healed by the grace
4. In the bread that is bro-ken is the Christ that re-stores. As we take, now re-ceive him, we find love ev-er-more. As the bread be-comes Bod-y, we are filled with the grace
of the pow-er and the
1-4. Spir-it that is here in this place.
Refrain
We are gath-ered at ta-ble as one in the Lord.
(*to-geth-er)
We are gath-ered as peo-ple who are liv-ing the Word. Our hearts and our spir-its are nur-tured by grace. It is Je-sus who fills us. He is here in this place.

*Alternate text

Text: Victoria Thomson, b. 1969, © 1996, Victoria Thomson.

Music: Trevor Thomson, b. 1971, © 1996, Trevor Thomson.

468 Lead Us to the Water

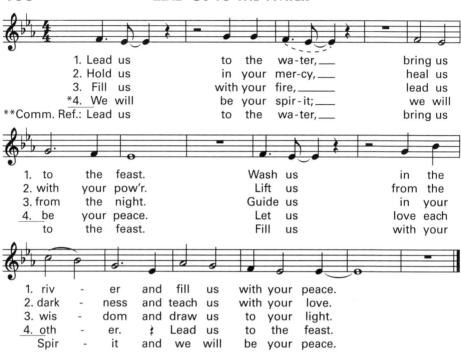

1. Lead us to the water, bring us to the feast. Wash us in the river and fill us with your peace.
2. Hold us in your mercy, heal us with your pow'r. Lift us from the darkness and teach us with your love.
3. Fill us with your fire, lead us from the night. Guide us in your wisdom and draw us to your light.
*4. We will be your spirit; we will be your peace. Let us love each other. Lead us to the feast.

**Comm. Ref.: Lead us to the water, bring us to the feast. Fill us with your Spirit and we will be your peace.

*Dismissal verse
**Communion verses available in accompaniment books

Text: Tom Kendzia, b. 1954,
Music: Tom Kendzia and Gary Daigle, b. 1957,

469 Now as We Gather

Verses
1. Now as we gath - er, God's cho-sen peo - ple, in - to one bod - y, in - to one place; here we shall tell of our own sal - va - tion, here we shall see our God face to face.
2. Now as we sing our song of sal - va - tion, there are no strang-ers in this ho - ly place; here we shall wel - come all with com-pas-sion, here we shall see our God face to face.
3. Here we shall break the bread of our prom-ise, here we shall share the wine of God's grace; here we shall feed from God's ho - ly ta - ble, here we shall see our God face to face.
4. A - ges have gone and a - ges will fol - low; peo-ple of ev - 'ry na - tion and race join us to greet the One who is ris - en, here we shall see our God face to face.

Refrain
God be a-mong us as we draw near, shar-ing the sign of
love and of prom-ise. Wine of our sor-row, bread of our joy,
Lord, God, be here a-mong us now.
4

Let Us Go to the Altar 470

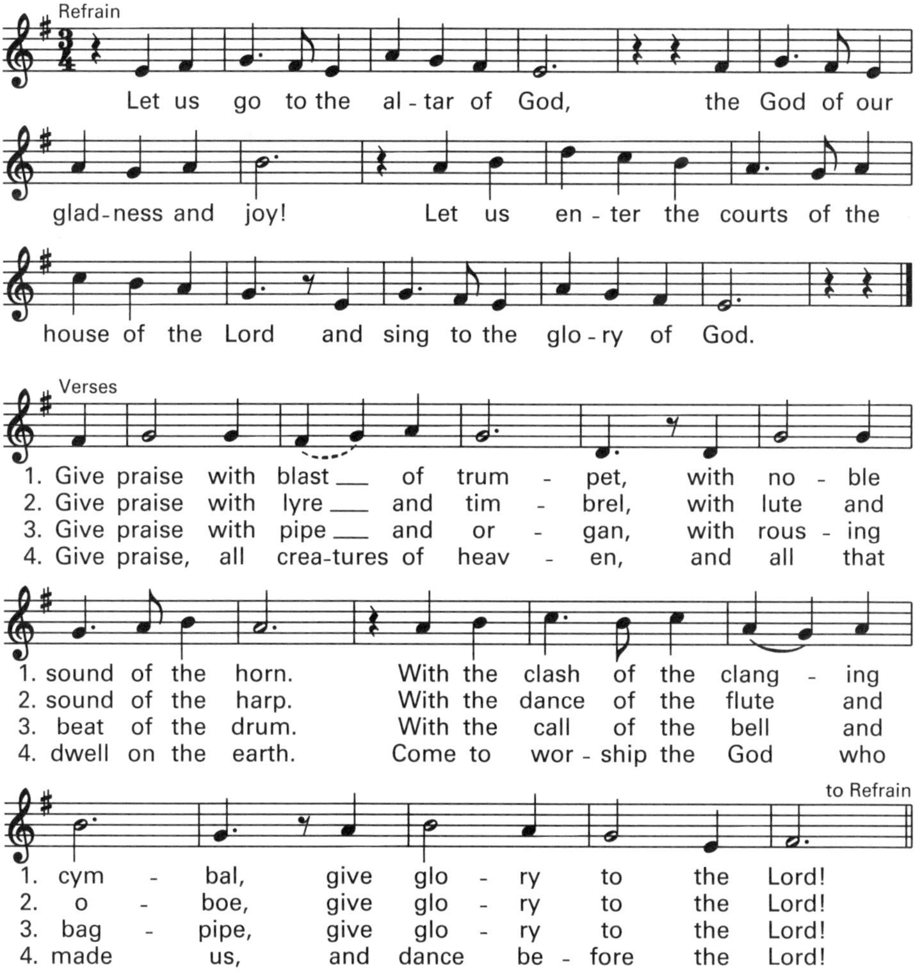

Refrain

Let us go to the al-tar of God, the God of our glad-ness and joy! Let us en-ter the courts of the house of the Lord and sing to the glo-ry of God.

Verses

1. Give praise with blast of trum-pet, with no-ble sound of the horn. With the clash of the clang-ing cym-bal, give glo-ry to the Lord!
2. Give praise with lyre and tim-brel, with lute and sound of the harp. With the dance of the flute and o-boe, give glo-ry to the Lord!
3. Give praise with pipe and or-gan, with rous-ing beat of the drum. With the call of the bell and bag-pipe, give glo-ry to the Lord!
4. Give praise, all crea-tures of heav-en, and all that dwell on the earth. Come to wor-ship the God who made us, and dance be-fore the Lord!

to Refrain

Text: Based on Psalms 42 and 150; Dan Schutte, b. 1947.
Music: Dan Schutte.

471 Gather Us In

1. Here in this place new light is stream-ing, now is the
2. We are the young— our lives are a mys - t'ry, we are the
3. Here we will take the wine and the wa - ter, here we will
4. Not in the dark of build-ings con - fin - ing, not in some
1. dark - ness van-ished a - way, See in this space our
2. old— who yearn for your face, We have been sung through-
3. take the bread of new birth, Here you shall call your
4. heav - en, light years a - way, but here in this place the
1. fears and our dream-ings, brought here to you in the light of this
2. out all of his - t'ry, called to be light to the whole hu-man
3. sons and your daugh-ters, call us a - new to be salt for the
4. new light is shin - ing, now is the King - dom, now is the
1. day. Gath-er us in — the lost and for - sa - ken, Gath-er us
2. race. Gath-er us in — the rich and the haugh-ty, Gath-er us
3. earth. Give us to drink the wine of com - pas-sion, Give us to
4. day. Gath-er us in and hold us for ev - er, Gath-er us
1. in — the blind and the lame; Call to us now, and we shall a -
2. in — the proud and the strong; Give us a heart so meek and so
3. eat the bread that is you; Nour-ish us well, and teach us to
4. in and make us your own; Gath - er us in— all peo-ples to -
1. wa-ken, we shall a - rise at the sound of our name.
2. low - ly, give us the cour-age to en - ter the song.
3. fash-ion lives that are ho - ly and hearts that are true.
4. geth-er, fire ___ of love in our flesh and our bone.

COME, WORSHIP THE LORD

472

Refrain
Come, and wor-ship the Lord, for we are his peo - ple, the
flock that he shep-herds. Al - le - lu - ia.
Verses 1, 2
1. Come, let us sing to the Lord, and shout with joy ___ to the
2. Come, let us bow down and wor-ship, bend-ing the knee be-fore the
1. rock who saves us. Let us come with thanks-giv - ing,
2. Lord our ma - ker. For we are his peo-ple,
to Refrain
2
1. and sing joy - ful songs to the Lord. ________
2. we are the flock that he shep-herds. __
Verse 3
3. The Lord is God, the might-y God, the great king o'er
3. all oth-er gods. He holds in his hands the depths of the earth and the
3. high-est moun-tains as well. He made the sea, it be-longs now to
to Refrain
2
3. him; the dry land, too, was formed by his hand.

Text: Based on Psalm 95; John Michael Talbot, b. 1954.
Music: John Michael Talbot.

473 As We Gather at Your Table

1. As we gath - er at your Ta - ble, As we lis - ten to your
2. Turn our wor - ship in - to wit - ness In the sac - ra - ment of
3. Gra - cious Spir - it, help us sum - mon Oth - er guests to share that

1. Word, Help us know, O God, your pres - ence: Let our
2. life; Send us forth to love and serve you, Bring - ing
3. feast Where tri - um - phant Love will wel - come Those who

1. hearts and minds be stirred. Nour - ish us with sa - cred
2. peace where there is strife. Give us, Christ, your great com -
3. had been last and least. There no more will en - vy

1. sto - ry Till we claim it as our own; Teach us
2. pas - sion To for - give as you for - gave; May we
3. blind us Nor will pride our peace de - stroy, As we

1. through this ho - ly ban - quet How to make Love's vic - t'ry known.
2. still be - hold your im - age In the world you died to save.
3. join with saints and an - gels To re - peat the sound - ing joy.

Text: 87 87 D; Carl P. Daw, Jr., b. 1944, © 1989, Hope Publishing Co. All rights reserved. Used with permission.
Music: NETTLETON; J. Wyeth's *Repository of Sacred Music, Part II*, 1813.

474 The God of All Grace

Refrain
The God of all grace has blessed us this day, all of cre -
a - tion joins us in praise; lift - ing our voic - es, lift - ing our
hearts to the glo - ry of God for - ev - er!

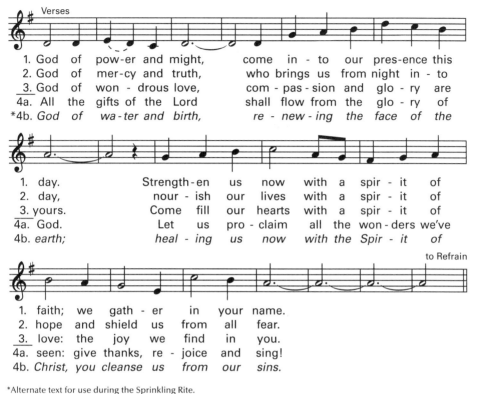

Verses

1. God of pow-er and might, come in - to our pres-ence this
2. God of mer-cy and truth, who brings us from night in - to
3. God of won - drous love, com - pas - sion and glo - ry are
4a. All the gifts of the Lord shall flow from the glo - ry of
*4b. *God of wa-ter and birth, re - new - ing the face of the*

1. day. Strength-en us now with a spir - it of
2. day, nour - ish our lives with a spir - it of
3. yours. Come fill our hearts with a spir - it of
4a. God. Let us pro - claim all the won - ders we've
4b. *earth; heal - ing us now with the Spir - it of*

to Refrain

1. faith; we gath - er in your name.
2. hope and shield us from all fear.
3. love: the joy we find in you.
4a. seen: give thanks, re - joice and sing!
4b. *Christ, you cleanse us from our sins.*

*Alternate text for use during the Sprinkling Rite.

Text and music: Ricky Manalo, CSP, b. 1965,

SHEPHERD OF SOULS 475

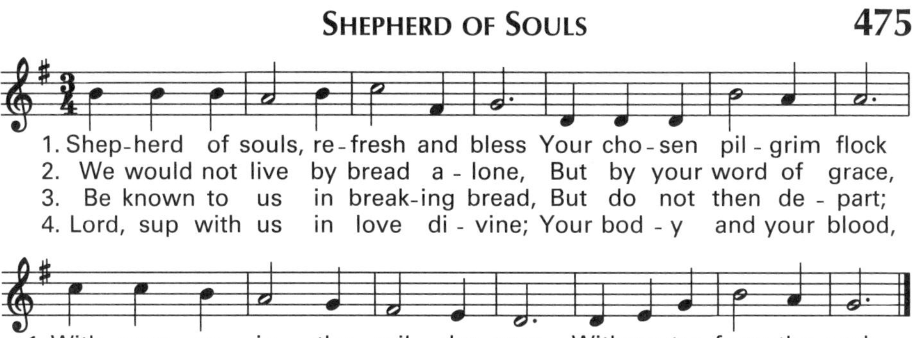
1. Shep-herd of souls, re-fresh and bless Your cho-sen pil - grim flock
2. We would not live by bread a - lone, But by your word of grace,
3. Be known to us in break-ing bread, But do not then de - part;
4. Lord, sup with us in love di - vine; Your bod - y and your blood,
1. With man - na in the wil - der-ness, With wa-ter from the rock.
2. In strength of which we trav - el on To our a - bid - ing place.
3. Sav - ior, a - bide with us, and spread Your ta-ble in our heart.
4. That liv - ing bread, that heav'n-ly wine, Be our im - mor - tal food.

Text: CM; verses 1, 2, James Montgomery, 1771–1854; verses 3, 4, anon.
Music: ST. AGNES; John B. Dykes, 1823–1876.

476 LORD, WHO AT THY FIRST EUCHARIST

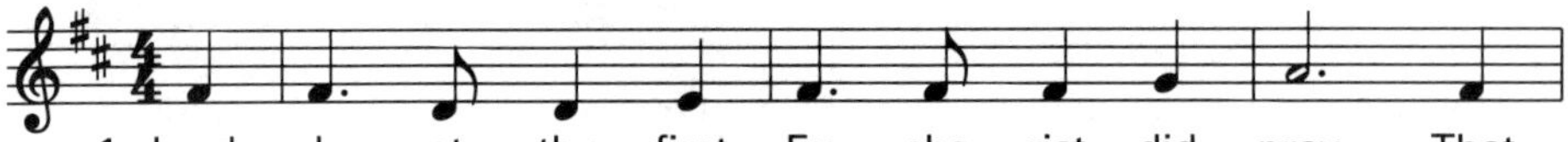

1. Lord, who at thy first Eu - cha - rist did pray That
*1. *At that first Eu - cha - rist be - fore you died, O*
2. For all thy Church, O Lord, we in - ter - cede; Make
3. We pray thee, too, for wan - d'rers from thy fold; O
4. So, Lord, at length when sac - ra - ments shall cease, May

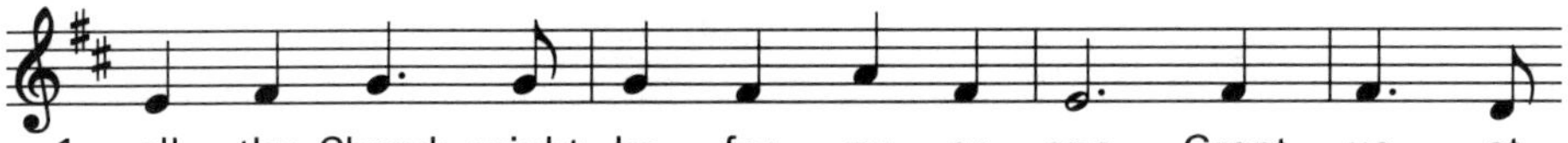

1. all thy Church might be for - ev - er one, Grant us at
1. *Lord, you prayed that all be one in you; At this our*
2. thou our sad di - vi - sions soon to cease; Draw us the
3. bring them back, Good Shep-herd of the sheep, Back to the
4. we be one with all thy Church a - bove, One with thy

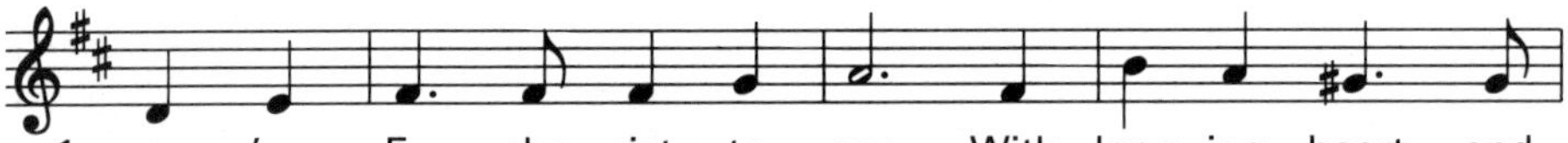

1. ev - 'ry Eu - cha - rist to say With long-ing heart and
1. *Eu - cha - rist a - gain pre - side, And in our hearts your*
2. near - er each, to each we plead, By draw-ing all to
3. faith which saints be-lieved of old, Back to the Church which
4. saints in one un - bro - ken peace, One with thy saints in

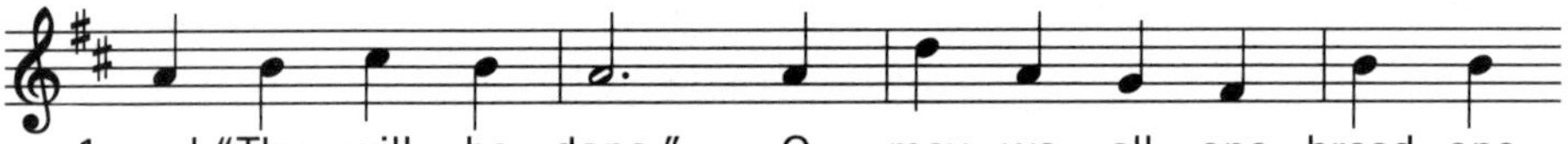

1. soul, "Thy will be done." O may we all one bread, one
1. *law of love re - new. O may we all one bread, one*
2. thee, O Prince of Peace; Thus may we all one bread, one
3. still that faith doth keep; Soon may we all one bread, one
4. one un-bound-ed love; More bless-ed still in peace and

1. bod - y be, Through this blest Sac - ra - ment of U - ni - ty.
1. *bod - y be, Through this blest Sac - ra - ment of U - ni - ty.*
2. bod - y be, Through this blest Sac - ra - ment of U - ni - ty.
3. bod - y be, Through this blest Sac - ra - ment of U - ni - ty.
4. love to be One with the Trin - i - ty in U - ni - ty.

*Alternate version of Verse 1.

Text: 10 10 10 10 10 10; William H. Turton, 1859–1938.
Music: UNDE ET MEMORES; William H. Monk, 1823–1889, alt.

477 SEE US, LORD, ABOUT YOUR ALTAR

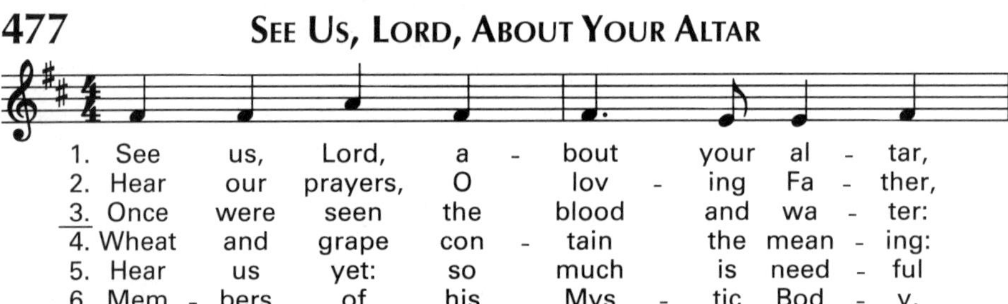
1. See us, Lord, a - bout your al - tar,
2. Hear our prayers, O lov - ing Fa - ther,
3. Once were seen the blood and wa - ter:
4. Wheat and grape con - tain the mean - ing:
5. Hear us yet: so much is need - ful
6. Mem - bers of his Mys - tic Bod - y,

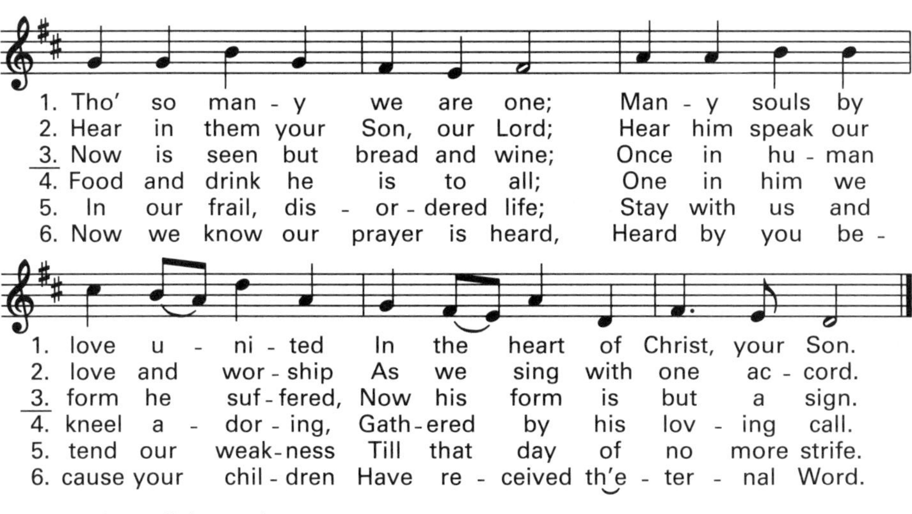
1. Tho' so man - y we are one; Man - y souls by
2. Hear in them your Son, our Lord; Hear him speak our
3. Now is seen but bread and wine; Once in hu - man
4. Food and drink he is to all; One in him we
5. In our frail, dis - or - dered life; Stay with us and
6. Now we know our prayer is heard, Heard by you be -
1. love u - ni - ted In the heart of Christ, your Son.
2. love and wor - ship As we sing with one ac - cord.
3. form he suf - fered, Now his form is but a sign.
4. kneel a - dor - ing, Gath - ered by his lov - ing call.
5. tend our weak - ness Till that day of no more strife.
6. cause your chil - dren Have re - ceived th'e - ter - nal Word.

Text: 87 87; John Greally, b. 1934, alt.
Music: DRAKES BROUGHTON; Edward Elgar, 1857–1934.

BREAD OF LIFE **478**

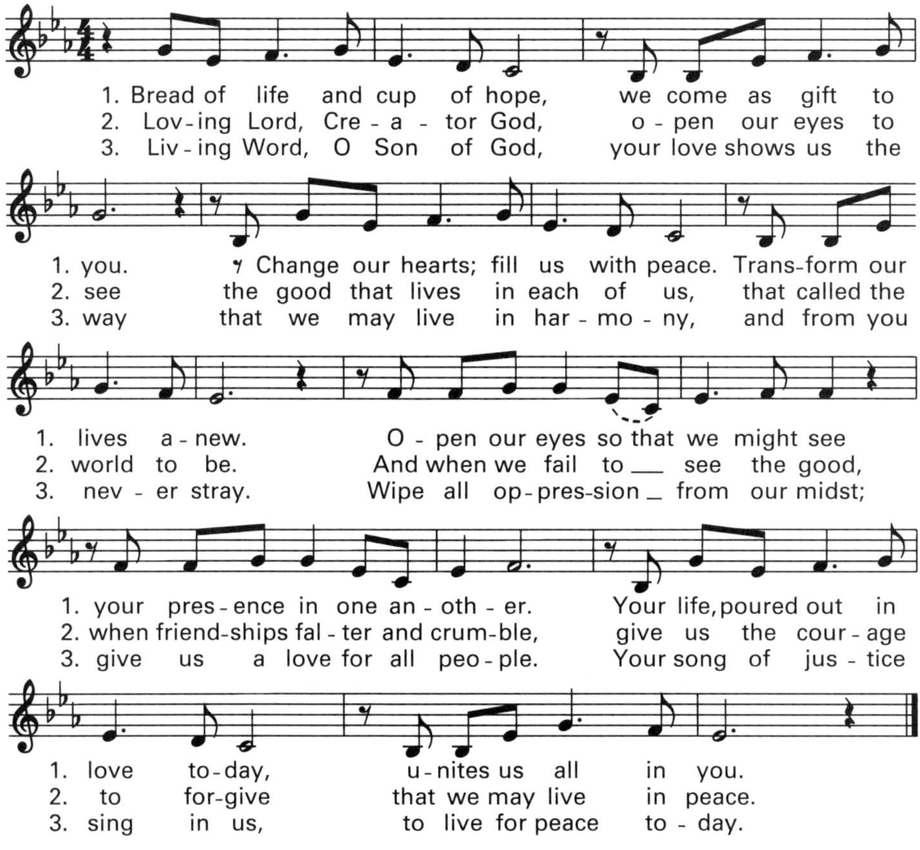

1. Bread of life and cup of hope, we come as gift to
2. Lov - ing Lord, Cre - a - tor God, o - pen our eyes to
3. Liv - ing Word, O Son of God, your love shows us the

1. you. Change our hearts; fill us with peace. Trans-form our
2. see the good that lives in each of us, that called the
3. way that we may live in har - mo - ny, and from you

1. lives a - new. O - pen our eyes so that we might see
2. world to be. And when we fail to __ see the good,
3. nev - er stray. Wipe all op - pres - sion _ from our midst;

1. your pres - ence in one an - oth - er. Your life, poured out in
2. when friend-ships fal - ter and crum-ble, give us the cour - age
3. give us a love for all peo - ple. Your song of jus - tice

1. love to - day, u - nites us all in you.
2. to for - give that we may live in peace.
3. sing in us, to live for peace to - day.

Text and music: Bobby Fisher, b. 1952,

479 Amén. El Cuerpo de Cristo

Refrain: All
A - mén. El Cuer - po de Cris-to. A - mén. La San-gre del Se - ñor. Eat - ing your bod - y,
drink - ing your blood, we be - come what we re - ceive. A - mén. A - mén.
Verses: Cantor
1. A - mén. We re - member your dy - ing and your ris - ing. A - mén.
2. A - mén. Now we of - fer the sac - ri - fice you gave us. A - mén.
3. A - mén. Lord, you make us one bod - y and one spir - it. A - mén.
4. A - mén. We find you when we serve the poor and low - ly. A - mén.
5. A - mén. We look for - ward to your re - turn in glo - ry. A - mén.
1. Y con - ti - go, Se - ñor, re - su - ci - ta - mos. A - mén.
2. Te o - fre - ce - mos, Se - ñor, to - do lo que so - mos. A - mén.
3. En tu cuer - po, Se - ñor, un pue - blo san - to. A - mén.
4. A ti mis - mo ser - vi - mos en los po - bres. A - mén.
5. Es - pe - ra - mos el día de tu ve - ni - da. A - mén.
to Refrain

Translation of Spanish text

Refrain Amen. The Body of Christ.
Amen. The Blood of the Lord.

Verses
1. And with you, Lord, we rise.
2. We offer you, Lord, all that we are.
3. In your body, Lord, a holy people.
4. You yourself we serve in the poor.
5. We hope for the day of your coming.

Traducción de la letra en inglés

Estribillo Cuando comemos tu cuerpo y bebemos tu sangre nos convertimos en lo que recibimos.

Estrofas
1. Recordamos tu muerte y resurrección.
2. Ofrecemos el sacrificio que Tú nos diste.
3. Tú, Señor, nos haces un solo cuerpo y un solo espíritu.
4. Cuando servimos a los pobres y a los humildes te encontramos a ti.
5. Anhelamos tu regreso en la gloria.

Text and music: John Schiavone, b. 1947,

As We Remember

Refrain

As we re-mem-ber, we are be-com-ing; what we see bro-ken, we hope to be. Show us your mer-cy, show us your mer-cy, your mer-cy, harsh and love-ly as the sea.

Verses 1, 2, 4, 5, 7, 8

1. Wind-fall of way-bread scat-tered on sand, lav-ished by love we can-not un-der-stand.
2. Pass-o-ver Lamb, slain and con-sumed that we be slaves not to tempt-er nor tomb.
4. No one re-joic-es or suf-fers a-lone: meal of the spir-it brings man-y to one.
5. Each has been washed, each is a-noint-ed, ser-vant and heal-er and proph-et ap-point-ed.
7. Cup of for-give-ness, bread of our peace; chil-dren come home to a Fa-ther's em-brace.
8. Feast of be-long-ing, feast for the lost; ban-quet e-ter-nal where Christ is the host.

to Refrain

Verses 3, 6, 9, 10

3. Here are our hearts marked with blood of the lamb: death will pass o-ver God's peo-ple a-gain.
6. Tem-ple not built by mus-cle and bone; house of the heart that God's peo-ple call home.
9. Christ in the meal to which we are called points toward the cross and be-yond in-to God.
10. Love of the Fa-ther, Spir-it of Christ, fill-ing your own with the gift of your life.

to Refrain

481 Ang Katawan ni Kristo/ Behold, the Body of Christ

Verses
1. In the pres-ence of our God, as we gath-er here in
We have come to break the bread; we have come to share our
2. When we gath-er in our homes, through our prayers and our
In the house-hold of the Lord, where we come to share the
3. In the pres-ence of our God, by the jus-tice that is
1. Christ, feel the Spir-it breathe up-on us, the
lives. Let us bring these fruits to the ta-ble, the
2. meals, we are fed and nour-ished to-geth-er, our
meal, we are fed the words of our Sav-ior, one
3. shown, we will build a king-dom to-geth-er; the
1, 3
2, 4, 5
1. breath of life, graced and di-vine.
love of God, yours and 1. mine!
2. fam-i-lies, bro-ken and blessed.
fam-i-ly, strength-ened and 2. healed.
3. love of Christ giv-en to 3. all!
Refrain
Ang ka-ta-wan ni Kris-to, ang ka-ta-wan ni Kris-to.
Be-hold, the Bod-y of Christ! Je-sus, our Sav-ior and Life!
Re-joice, O Peo-ple of God! We are the Bod-y of
1, 2
1st time: to Verse 2
2nd time: to Bridge
3, Final
(Fine)
Christ! Christ! Be-
Bridge
Is not the meal that we bless and share a com-mu-nion in the life of

to Verse 3
3
Christ? One bread, one bless-ing, one cup make us one bod-y in our Lord.
Refrain
Bread of life, hope of the world, Je-sus Christ, our broth-er:
feed us now, give us life, lead us to one an-oth-er.
Verses
1. As we pro-claim your death, as we re-call your life, we re-
2. The bread we break and share was scat-tered once as grain: just as
3. We eat this liv-ing bread, we drink this sav-ing cup: sign of
4. Hold us in u-ni-ty, in love for all to see; that the
5. You are the bread of peace, you are the wine of joy, bro-ken
to Refrain
1. mem-ber your prom-ise to re-turn a-gain.
2. now it is gath-ered, make your peo-ple one.
3. hope in our bro-ken world, source of last-ing love.
4. world may be-lieve in you, God of all who live.
5. now for your peo-ple, poured in end-less love.
Alternate Verses: for Advent/Christmas
Adv. 1. Be with your peo-ple, Lord, send us your sav-ing Word: Je-sus
Adv. 2. Bring to our world of fear the truth we long to hear: Je-sus
Chr. 1. A child is born for us, a son is giv'n to us, In our
Chr. 2. With our own eyes we see, with our own ears we hear The sal-
Chr. 3. You are the hope of all, our prom-ise and our call, Ra-diant
to Refrain
1. Christ, light of glad-ness, come a-mong us now.
2. Christ, hope of a-ges, come to save us now.
1. midst, Christ, our Lord and God comes as one who serves.
2. va-tion of all the world, God's in-car-nate Word.
3. light in our dark-ness, truth to set us free.

Text: Ricky Manalo, CSP, b. 1965, and Pia de Leon, © 2003, Ricky Manalo, CSP, and Pia de Leon. Published by OCP. All rights reserved.
Music: Ricky Manalo, CSP, © 2003, Ricky Manalo, CSP. Published by OCP. All rights reserved.

BREAD OF LIFE 482

Text and music: Bernadette Farrell, b. 1957, © 1982, 1987, Bernadette Farrell. Published by OCP. All rights reserved.

483 Bread for the World

Refrain: All
Bread for the world: a world of hun - ger. Wine for all peo - ples: peo - ple who thirst. May we who eat be bread for oth - ers. May we who drink pour out our love.
Verses: Cantor
1. Lord Je - sus Christ, you are the bread of life, bro - ken to reach and heal the wounds of hu - man pain. Where we di - vide your peo - ple, you are wait - ing there on bend - ed knee to wash our feet with end - less care.
2. Lord Je - sus Christ, you are the wine of peace, poured in - to hearts once bro - ken and where dry - ness sleeps. Where we are tired and wea - ry, you are wait - ing there to be the way which beck - ons us be - yond de - spair.
3. Lord Je - sus Christ, you call us to your feast, at which the rich and pow'r - ful have be - come the least. Where we sur - vive on oth - ers in our hu - man greed, you walk a - mong us beg - ging for your ev - 'ry need.
to Refrain

BREAD OF ANGELS 484

1. Bread of an - gels, we re - ceive you; with us
2. Cup of Mer - cy o - ver - flow - ing, fill us
3. Word in - car - nate, dwell with - in us; pierce our
4. Though un - wor - thy, we re - ceive you, sac - ra -

1. now a - bide. Pre - cious Je - sus, man - na of
2. with your grace; wine of pas - sion, O Son be -
3. hard - ened hearts. Ten - der Je - sus, Love so
4. ment di - vine. Bread of an - gels, ac - cept our

1. a - ges, with us now re - side.
2. got - ten, we flee to your em - brace.
3. gen - tle, nev - er let us part.
4. prais - es, let your glo - ry shine!

1. *Pa - nis an - gé - li-cus fit pa - nis hó - mi - num,*
2. *O res mi - rá - bi - lis man - dú - cat Dó - mi - num,*
3. *Te, tri - na Dé - i - tas ú - na - que, pó - sci - mus,*
4. *Per tu - as sé - mi-tas duc nos quo tén - di - mus,*

1, 3

1. *Dat pa - nis cáe - li-cus fi - gú - ris tér - mi - num.*
3. *Sic nos tu ví - si - ta, si - cut te có - li - mus.*

2, Final
2. Pau - per, Pau - per, ser - vus, et hú - mi - lis.
4. lu - cem, Ad lu - cem quam in - há - bi - tas.

Text: English, Curtis Stephan, b. 1973,
Latin, *Panis angelicus* by St. Thomas Aquinas, 1227–1274.
Music: Curtis Stephan,

485 Bread of Heaven

Refrain
Bread of heav - en, Sav - ior bro - ken, cup of life out-poured; we your peo - ple thirst and hun - ger.
Come re-new us, Lord; come re-new us, Lord.
1, 2: to Verses
3: to Bridge
Verses
1. From the moun-tain, bless - ing spo-ken where we came to pray; with the sim - ple truth be-fore us: love them in my name; love them in my name.
2. From the gar - den dark with sor-row, from the tears you wept, bloomed the flow - er of sal - va - tion: new life born of death, new life born of death.
3. From the tomb that could not hold you in the dark of night, broke the morn - ing of re-demp - tion, rais - ing us to life, rais - ing us to life.
to Refrain
Bridge
From the hill where love was lift - ed on the heav-y wood, flow the blood and streams of mer - cy where your Moth - er stood, where your Moth - er stood.
Interlude
7 to Verse 3

Text and music: Jesse Manibusan, b. 1958, and Sarah Hart, b. 1968,

Draw Near

486

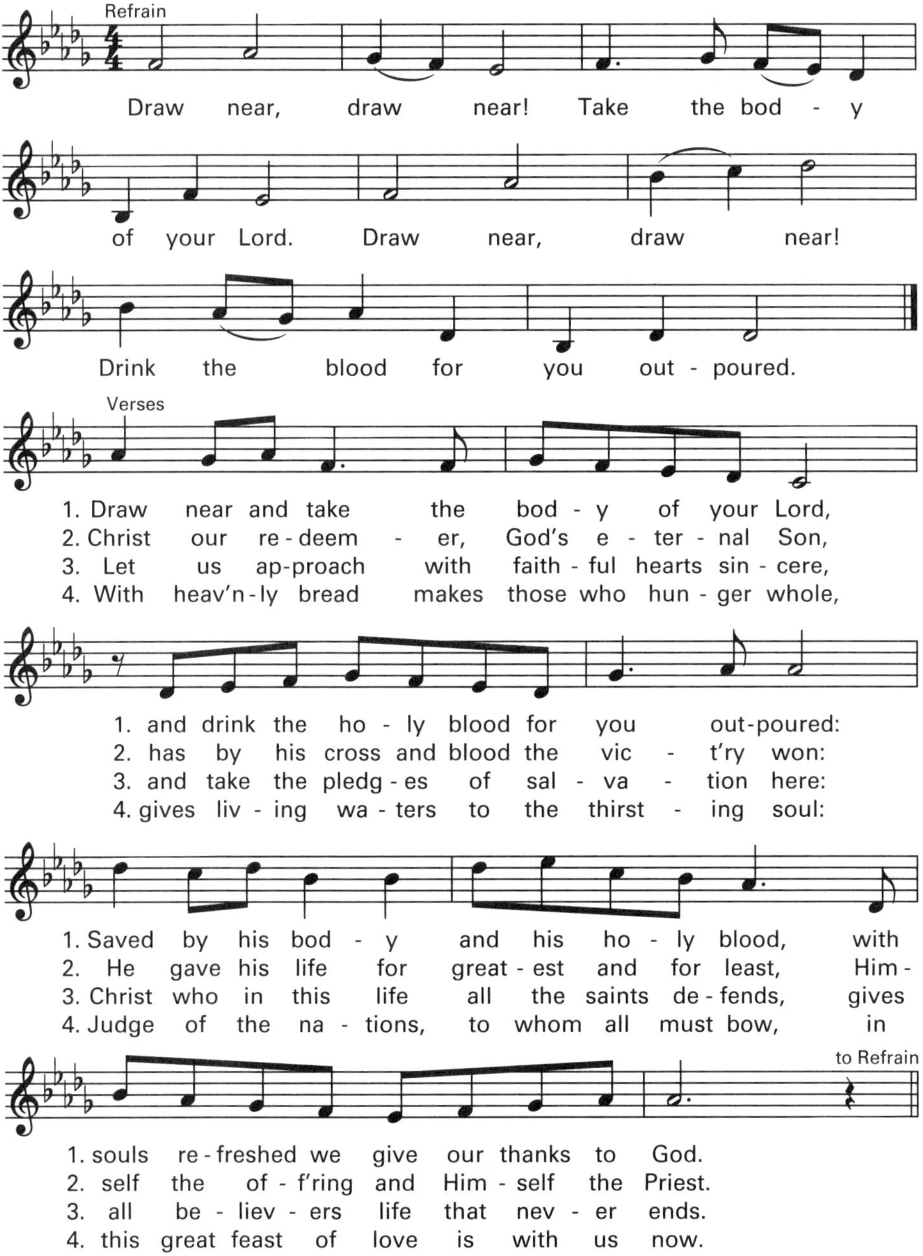

Refrain
Draw near, draw near! Take the bod - y
of your Lord. Draw near, draw near!
Drink the blood for you out - poured.
Verses
1. Draw near and take the bod - y of your Lord,
2. Christ our re - deem - er, God's e - ter - nal Son,
3. Let us ap-proach with faith - ful hearts sin - cere,
4. With heav'n-ly bread makes those who hun - ger whole,
1. and drink the ho - ly blood for you out-poured:
2. has by his cross and blood the vic - t'ry won:
3. and take the pledg - es of sal - va - tion here:
4. gives liv - ing wa - ters to the thirst - ing soul:
1. Saved by his bod - y and his ho - ly blood, with
2. He gave his life for great - est and for least, Him -
3. Christ who in this life all the saints de - fends, gives
4. Judge of the na - tions, to whom all must bow, in
to Refrain
1. souls re - freshed we give our thanks to God.
2. self the of - f'ring and Him - self the Priest.
3. all be - liev - ers life that nev - er ends.
4. this great feast of love is with us now.

Text: *Sancti, venite, Christi corpus sumite,* 7th cent.; tr. by John M. Neale, 1818–1866, alt.
Music: Steven R. Janco, b. 1961, © 1992, World Library Publications, wlpmusic.com.

487 GIFT OF FINEST WHEAT

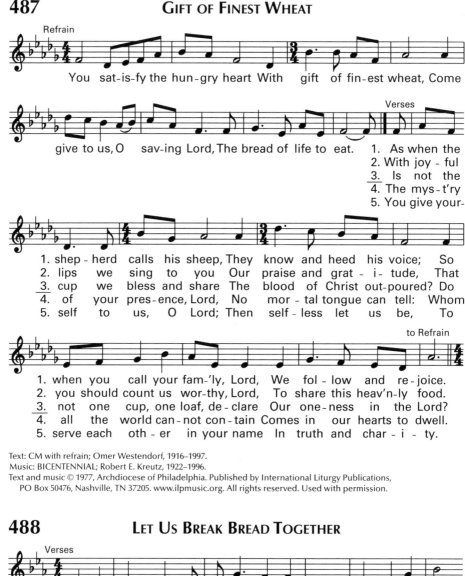

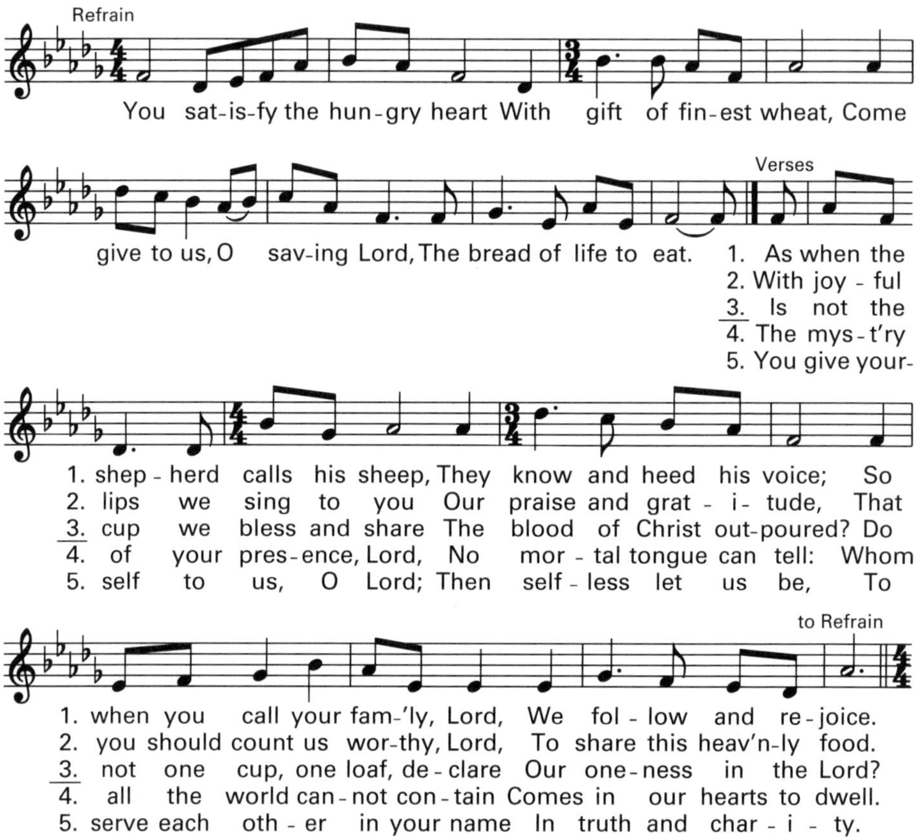

Refrain

You sat-is-fy the hun-gry heart With gift of fin-est wheat, Come give to us, O sav-ing Lord, The bread of life to eat.

Verses

1. As when the shep - herd calls his sheep, They know and heed his voice; So when you call your fam-'ly, Lord, We fol - low and re - joice.
2. With joy - ful lips we sing to you Our praise and grat - i - tude, That you should count us wor-thy, Lord, To share this heav'n-ly food.
3. Is not the cup we bless and share The blood of Christ out-poured? Do not one cup, one loaf, de - clare Our one - ness in the Lord?
4. The mys - t'ry of your pres-ence, Lord, No mor - tal tongue can tell: Whom all the world can - not con - tain Comes in our hearts to dwell.
5. You give your - self to us, O Lord; Then self - less let us be, To serve each oth - er in your name In truth and char - i - ty.

to Refrain

Text: CM with refrain; Omer Westendorf, 1916–1997.
Music: BICENTENNIAL; Robert E. Kreutz, 1922–1996.

488 LET US BREAK BREAD TOGETHER

Verses
1. Let us break bread to-geth-er on our knees; Let us break bread to-geth-er on our knees;
2. Let us drink wine to-geth-er on our knees; Let us drink wine to-geth-er on our knees;
3. Let us praise God to-geth-er on our knees; Let us praise God to-geth-er on our knees;
Refrain
When I fall on my knees,

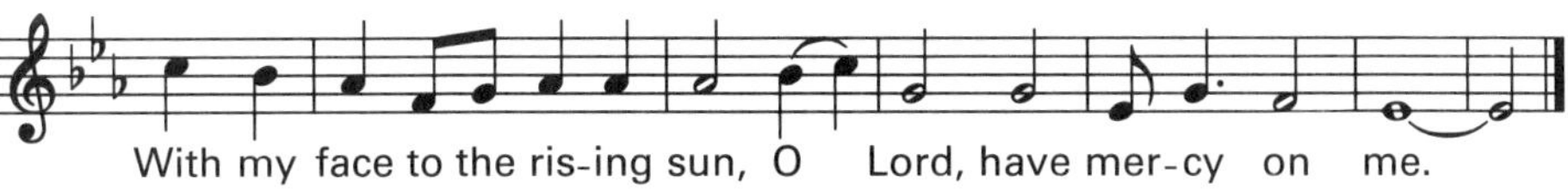
With my face to the ris-ing sun, O Lord, have mer-cy on me.

Text: 10 10 with refrain; Spiritual.
Music: LET US BREAK BREAD; Spiritual.

In the Breaking of the Bread 489

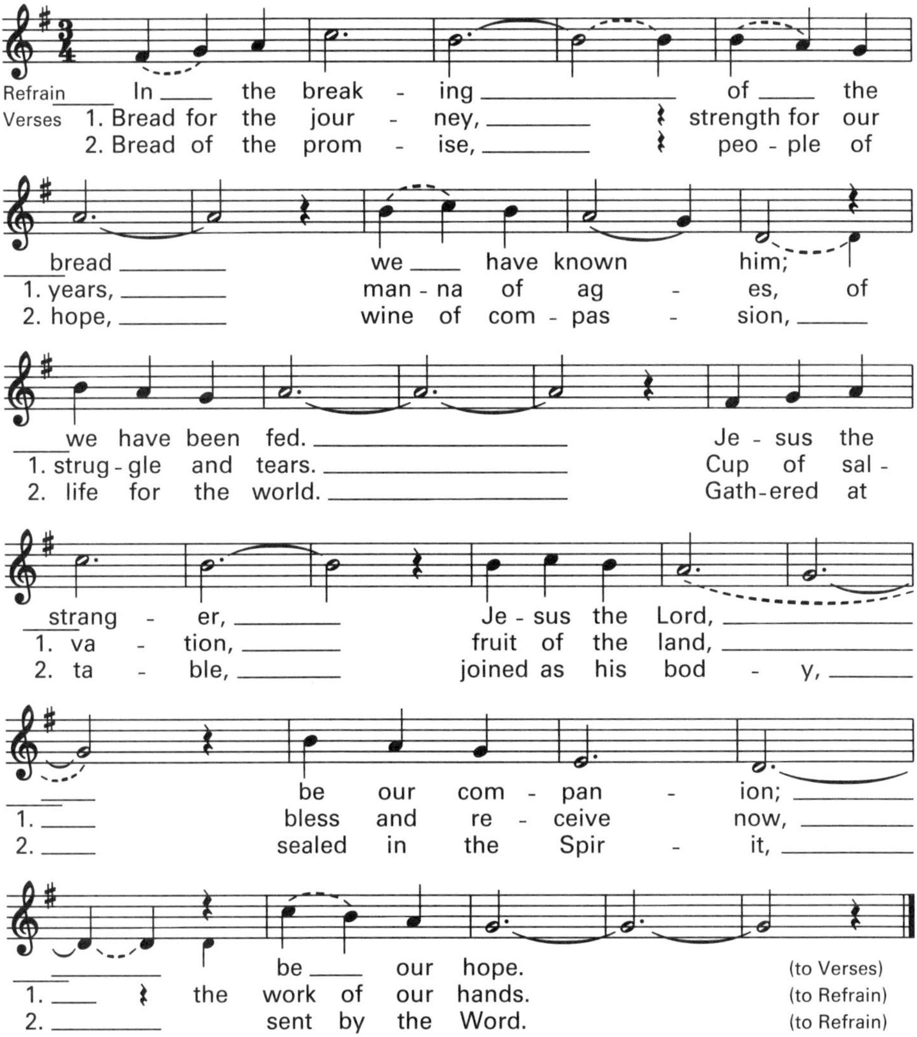

Refrain In the break - ing of the bread we have known him; we have been fed. Je - sus the strang - er, Je - sus the Lord, be our com - pan - ion; be our hope. (to Verses)

Verses
1. Bread for the jour - ney, strength for our years, man - na of ag - es, of strug - gle and tears. Cup of sal - va - tion, fruit of the land, bless and re - ceive now, the work of our hands. (to Refrain)
2. Bread of the prom - ise, peo - ple of hope, wine of com - pas - sion, life for the world. Gath-ered at ta - ble, joined as his bod - y, sealed in the Spir - it, sent by the Word. (to Refrain)

Text: Based on Luke 24:13–35; Acts 2:42; Bob Hurd, b. 1950, and Michael Downey,

Music: Bob Hurd,

490 BREAD OF LIFE

Refrain

I myself am the bread of life. You and I are the bread of life, taken and blessed, broken and shared by Christ that the world might live.

1-3 to Verses | Final live.

That the world might live. That the world might live.

Verses

1. This bread is spirit, gift of the Maker's love, and we who share it know that we can be one:
2. Here is God's kingdom given to us as food. This is our body, this is our blood:
3. Lives broken open, stories shared aloud, become a banquet, a shelter for the world:

a living sign of God in Christ.

to Refrain

Text and music: Rory Cooney, b. 1952, © 1987, OCP. All rights reserved.

491 TO BE YOUR BREAD

Refrain
To be your bread now, be your wine now, Lord, come and change us
to be a sign of your love. Blest and bro-ken, poured and flow-ing,
gift that you gave us, to be your bod-y once a-gain.

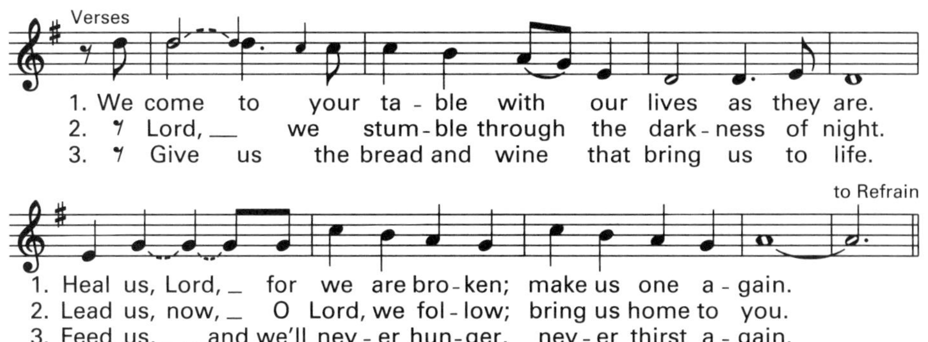
Verses
1. We come to your ta - ble with our lives as they are.
2. Lord, we stum - ble through the dark - ness of night.
3. Give us the bread and wine that bring us to life.
to Refrain
1. Heal us, Lord, for we are bro - ken; make us one a - gain.
2. Lead us, now, O Lord, we fol - low; bring us home to you.
3. Feed us, and we'll nev - er hun - ger, nev - er thirst a - gain.

BEHOLD THE LAMB 492

Verses

1. Those who were in the dark are thank - ful for the sun - light; we who live, we who die are grate - ful for his gift, thank - ful for his love.
2. Peace - ful now, those whose hearts are blessed with un - der - stand - ing of the wheat, of the wine u - nit - ed with his word and the love we share.
3. Gen - tle one, Child of God, join with us at this ta - ble. Bless our lives; nour - ish all who hun - ger for this feast; shel - ter them with peace.
4. Lord of all, give us light. De - liv - er us from e - vil. Make us one; be our shield. Make still the winds that blow; cra - dle us with love.

Refrain

Be - hold, be - hold the Lamb of God. All who eat, all who drink shall live; and all, all who dwell in God shall come to know his glo - ry.

Text: Refrain based on John 1:29; Martin Willett, b. 1960.
Music: Martin Willett.

493 I Am the Bread of Life

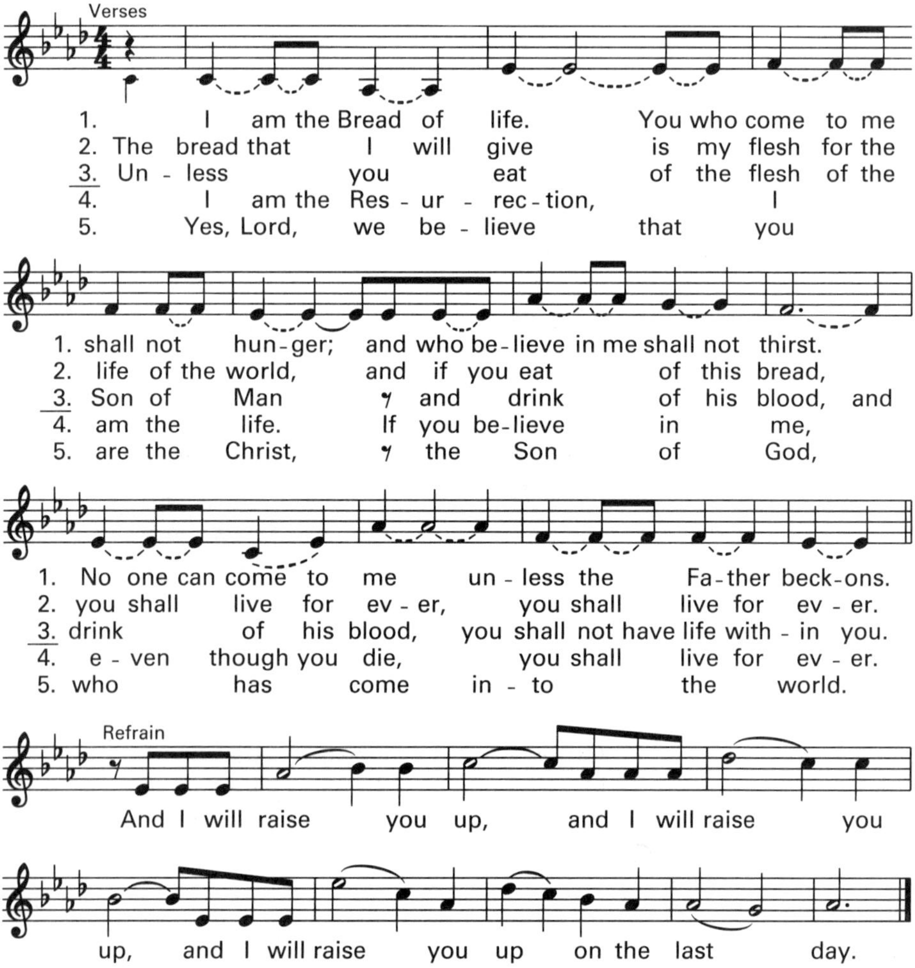

Verses

1. I am the Bread of life. You who come to me shall not hun-ger; and who be-lieve in me shall not thirst. No one can come to me un-less the Fa-ther beck-ons.
2. The bread that I will give is my flesh for the life of the world, and if you eat of this bread, you shall live for ev-er, you shall live for ev-er.
3. Un-less you eat of the flesh of the Son of Man and drink of his blood, and drink of his blood, you shall not have life with-in you.
4. I am the Res-ur-rec-tion, I am the life. If you be-lieve in me, e-ven though you die, you shall live for ev-er.
5. Yes, Lord, we be-lieve that you are the Christ, the Son of God, who has come in-to the world.

Refrain

And I will raise you up, and I will raise you up, and I will raise you up on the last day.

Text: John 6:35, 44, 51, 53–54; 11:25–27; Suzanne Toolan, RSM.
Music: Suzanne Toolan, RSM.

494 Look Beyond

Refrain
Look be-yond the bread you eat; see your Sav-ior and your Lord.
Look be-yond the cup you drink; see his love poured out as blood.

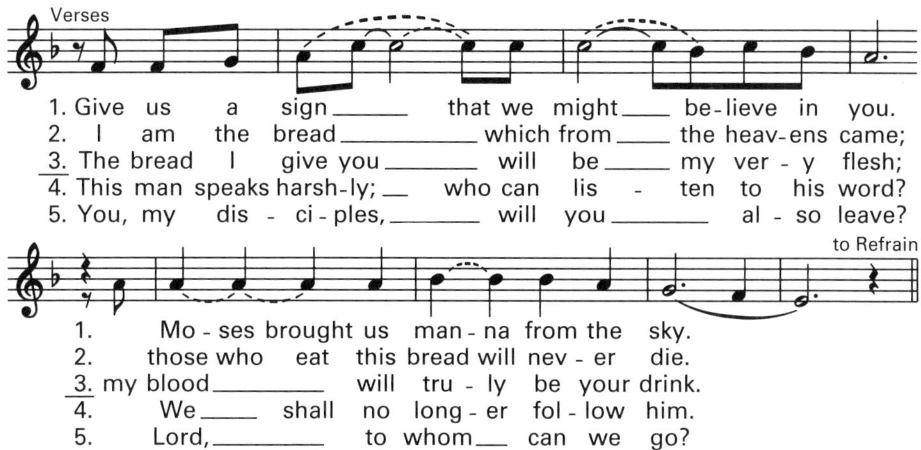
Verses
1. Give us a sign that we might be-lieve in you.
2. I am the bread which from the heav-ens came;
3. The bread I give you will be my ver - y flesh;
4. This man speaks harsh-ly; who can lis - ten to his word?
5. You, my dis - ci - ples, will you al - so leave?
to Refrain
1. Mo - ses brought us man - na from the sky.
2. those who eat this bread will nev - er die.
3. my blood will tru - ly be your drink.
4. We shall no long - er fol - low him.
5. Lord, to whom can we go?

I Am the Living Bread 495

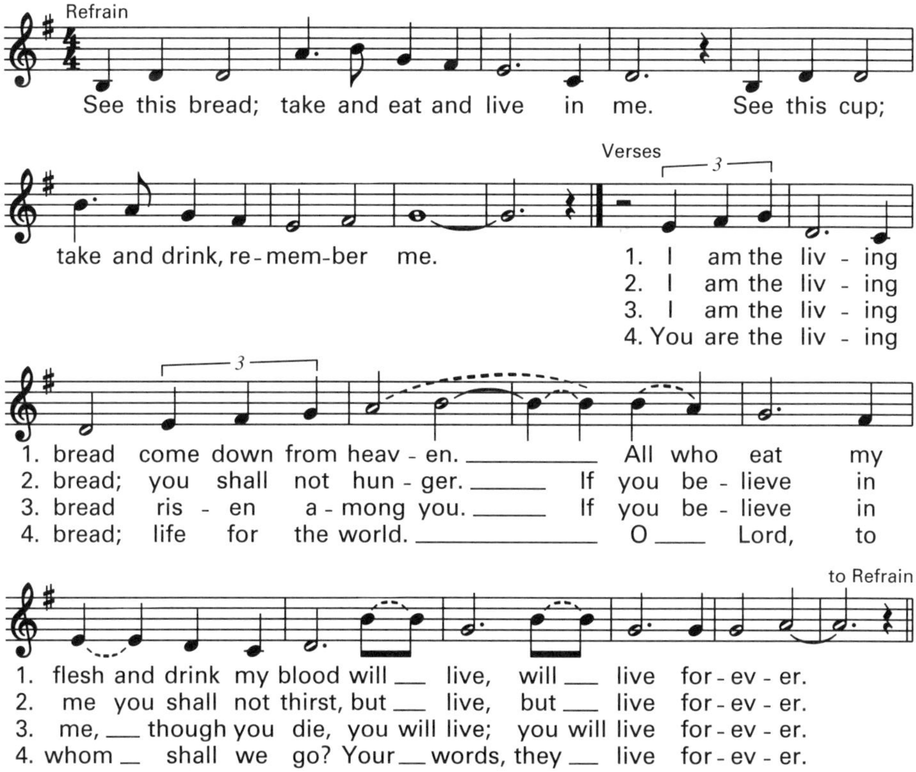

Refrain

See this bread; take and eat and live in me. See this cup; take and drink, re-mem-ber me.

Verses

1. I am the liv - ing bread come down from heav - en. All who eat my flesh and drink my blood will live, will live for - ev - er.
2. I am the liv - ing bread; you shall not hun - ger. If you be - lieve in me you shall not thirst, but live, but live for - ev - er.
3. I am the liv - ing bread ris - en a - mong you. If you be - lieve in me, though you die, you will live; you will live for - ev - er.
4. You are the liv - ing bread; life for the world. O Lord, to whom shall we go? Your words, they live for - ev - er.

to Refrain

Text: Based on John 6; David Haas, b. 1957.
Music: David Haas.

496 Spirit and Grace

Verses
1. Spir - it and grace, here in this meal;
2. Spir - it and grace, here in this meal;
3. Spir - it and grace, here in this place;
4. Spir - it of God, send - ing us forth;
1. you are the wind that breathes through the field.
2. you are the life that flows through the vine.
3. you are the light that shines in this space.
4. we spread your wis-dom through-out all the earth.
1. Gath - er the wheat and form us in Christ.
2. Gath - er this drink and form us in Christ.
3. Gath - er your peo - ple and form us in Christ.
4. Gath - er the na - tions and form us in Christ.
1. Come, be our source and breath of life.
2. Come, be our source and blood of life.
3. Come, be the heart - beat of our lives.
4. Come, be the pres - ence in our lives.
Refrain
In the bread, blessed, bro-ken and shared, Christ is our
life, whose pres-ence we bear. Come, O Spir - it, make your
grace re - vealed in this ho - ly meal.
3

MIRACLE OF GRACE 497

(Bread of Life)

Verses
1. Mir - a - cle of grace, mys-ter - y of faith,
2. Un - wor - thy though we are, you feed the hun - gry heart
3. Your faith-ful - ness re-vealed in this cov - e - nant you've sealed
1. call - ing us to ven - ture to the deep.
2. with bread come down from heav - en a - bove. And
3. with your ver - y bod - y and your blood. Come,
1. Though our sens - es fail, your grac - es still pre - vail, and
2. like a grain of wheat, we fall down at your feet,
3. claim your bride a - gain with love that can - not end, for
1. we be - come the love that we re - ceive.
2. dy - ing here with you. Oh, let us rise!
3. what God joins no one can di - vide.
Refrain
Bread of life, bread of life. Those who eat this bread shall live
and nev - er die. Bread of life, bread of life.
Your true pres - ence in this ho - ly sac - ri - fice.
1, 2
to Verse 2, 3
Bread of life.
Final
Bread of life, bread of life.

Text and music: Curtis Stephan, b. 1973, © 2008, Curtis Stephan.
Published by Spirit & Song®, a division of OCP. All rights reserved.

498 ONE BREAD, ONE BODY

Refrain

One bread, one bod-y, one Lord of all,
one cup of bless-ing which we bless. And we, though
man-y, through-out the earth, we are one bod-y in this
one Lord.

Verses

1. Gen-tile or Jew, ser-vant or free, wom-an or man, no more.
2. Man-y the gifts, man-y the works, one in the Lord of all.
3. Grain for the fields, scat-tered and grown, gath-ered to one, for all.

to Refrain

Text: Based on 1 Corinthians 10:16–17; 12:4, 12–13, 20; Galatians 3:28; Ephesians 4:4–6; The Didache 9; John Foley, S.J., b. 1939.
Music: John Foley, S.J.

499 O SACRAMENT MOST HOLY

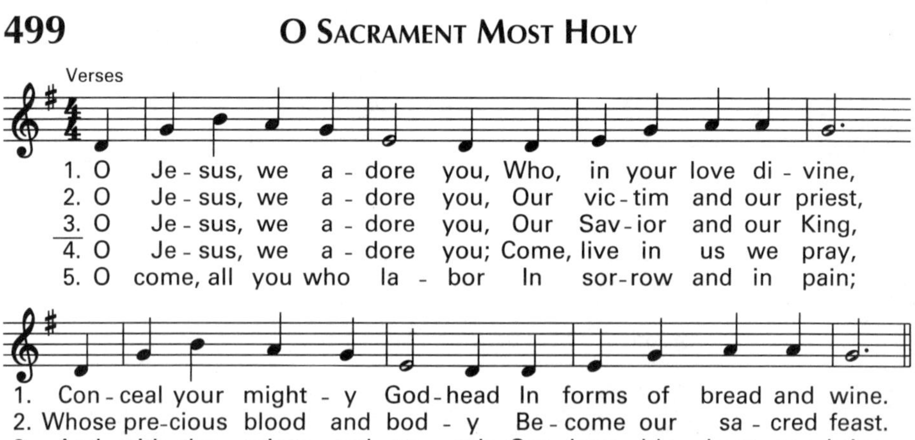
Verses
1. O Je-sus, we a-dore you, Who, in your love di-vine,
2. O Je-sus, we a-dore you, Our vic-tim and our priest,
3. O Je-sus, we a-dore you, Our Sav-ior and our King,
4. O Je-sus, we a-dore you; Come, live in us we pray,
5. O come, all you who la-bor In sor-row and in pain;
1. Con-ceal your might-y God-head In forms of bread and wine.
2. Whose pre-cious blood and bod-y Be-come our sa-cred feast.
3. And with the saints and an-gels Our hum-ble hom-age bring.
4. That all our thoughts and ac-tions Be yours a-lone to-day.
5. Come, eat this bread from heav-en; Your peace and strength re-gain.

Refrain
O sac - ra-ment most ho - ly, O sac - ra-ment di - vine,
All praise and all thanks-giv - ing Be ev - 'ry mo-ment thine!

Text: 76 76 with refrain; refrain fr. the *Raccolta*, Rome, 19th cent.; tr. unknown;
verses by Irvin Udulutsch, OFM, Cap., 1920–2010,
Music: FULDA; *Gebet- und Gesangbuch*, Fulda, 1891.

Our Blessing Cup 500

Refrain

Our bless-ing cup is a com-mun-ion with the blood of Christ;
and the bread we break, it is a shar - ing in the bod - y of the
Lord.

Repeat first time only (or ostinato as desired) *Fine*

Verses

1. How can we make a re - turn
2. Pre-cious in - deed in your sight,
3. Gra-cious and mer - ci - ful God,
4. For you have heard my __ voice,

1. for all the good - ness God has shown? We will take the
2. the life and death of those you love. We __ are your
3. we give you thanks and bless your name: with __ all your
4. for you have heard my plead - ing. Though __ death sur-

1. cup of life, and __ call up - on God's name.
2. ser - vants, for __ you have set us free.
3. peo - ple, praise and glo - ry to your name.
4. round-ed me, you __ heard and an-swered me.

to Refrain (or Verse if ostinato is sung)

Text: 1 Corinthians 10:16; Psalm 116:1, 3, 5, 12–13, 15–16, 17–18; Bob Hurd, b. 1950.
Music: Bob Hurd.

501 PAN DE VIDA

Refrain
Pan de Vi - da, cuer-po del Se - ñor,
cup of bless - ing, blood of Christ the Lord.
At this ta - ble the last shall be first.
Po - der es ser - vir, por-que Dios es a - mor.
1-3
to Verses
4
Po -
Final
3
Verses
1. We are the dwell-ing of God, fra-gile and wound-ed and weak. We are the bod - y of Christ, called to
2. You call me Teach - er and Lord; I, who have washed your feet. So you must do as I do, so the
3. There is no Jew or Greek; there is no slave or free; there is no wom-an or man; on - ly
1. So-mos el tem-plo de Dios, frá - gi - les se - res hu - ma - nos. So-mos el cuer-po de Cris - to, lla -
2. Us - te - des me lla - man "Se - ñor". Me in-cli-no a la - var - les los pies. Ha-gan lo mis-mo, hu - mil - des, sir -
3. No hay es - cla - vos ni li - bres, no hay mu - je - res ni hom - bres, só - lo a - que-llos que he-re - dan el

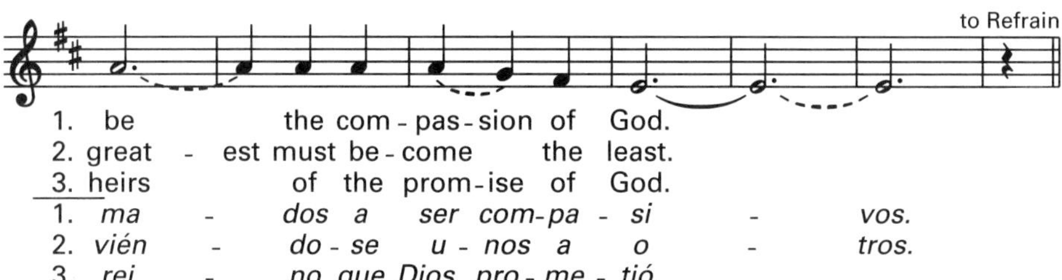
to Refrain
1. be the com - pas - sion of God.
2. great - est must be - come the least.
3. heirs of the prom - ise of God.
1. *ma - dos a ser com - pa - si - vos.*
2. *vién - do - se u - nos a o - tros.*
3. *rei - no que Dios pro - me - tió.*

*Bread of Life, body of the Lord,
**Power is for service, because God is love.

Text: Based on John 13:1–15; Galatians 3:28–29; Bob Hurd, b. 1950, and Pia Moriarty, b. 1948; Spanish adapt. by Jaime Cortez, b. 1963, Magali Jerez, Elena García and Gustavo Castillo.
Music: Bob Hurd.

SEED, SCATTERED AND SOWN **502**

Refrain

Seed, scat - tered and sown, wheat, gath - ered and grown,
bread, bro - ken and shared as one, the liv - ing bread of God.
Vine, fruit of the land, wine, work of our hands, one cup that is
shared by all; the liv - ing cup, the liv - ing bread of God.

Verses

1. Is not the bread we break a shar - ing in our Lord?
2. The seed which falls on rock will with - er and will die.
3. As wheat up - on the hills was gath - ered and was grown,

to Refrain

1. Is not the cup we bless the blood of Christ out - poured?
2. The seed with - in good ground will flow - er and have life.
3. so may the church of God be gath - ered in - to one.

Text: 66 66 with refrain; based on Didache 9; 1 Corinthians 10:16–17; Mark 4:3–6; Dan Feiten. b. 1953.
Music: SEED, SCATTERED AND SOWN; Dan Feiten.

503 That There May Be Bread

Refrain
That there may be bread, that there may be joy for all hu-
man-i-ty to share with grat-i-tude: let this be our prayer, and
may each child of earth long for a free-dom that will
flour-ish in all lands.
Verses
1. Sim-ple is the truth that our
2. Still, the long night falls and yet for
3. Lord, what should I do to
4. Lord, who is my neigh-bor? The
5. Grate-ful for our life, can we be
6. At this ta-ble of thanks-
7. Sign of God's deep love is this
1. love can-not be real un-less we choose to bless each
2. some, deep hun-ger cries as their tears be-come their
3. have e-ter-nal life? Love the God who lives with-
4. one whose strug-gle and whose needs you o-ver-
5. free to thirst and work for the plant-ing and the
6. giv-ing we are fed with the life of Je-sus
7. ban-quet of new life: know the pres-ence of the
1. oth-er, as bless-ing we have known.
2. bread: their hope too soon may die.
3. in you and your neigh-bor as your-self.
4. look, while your own com-fort you se-cure.
5. har-vest of King-dom's life in all?
6. Ri-sen, in whom our hope is born.
7. Ho-ly, in spir-it and in truth.
to Refrain

Text and music: Weston Priory, Gregory Norbet, OSB, b. 1940,

TASTE AND SEE 504

Refrain
Taste and see the good-ness of the Lord. Oh,
taste and see the good-ness of the Lord.
Verse 1
1. I will bless the LORD at all times; his praise ev-er in my
1. mouth, let my soul glo-ry in the LORD.
to Refrain
Verse 2
2. Let the low-ly hear and be glad, let us glo-ri-fy his
2. name. To-geth-er let us praise God's name.
to Refrain
Verse 3
3. Glo-ri-fy the LORD with me, to-geth-er let us praise his
3. name; from my fears God set me free.
to Refrain
Verse 4
4. Look to the LORD and shine in the light, let your fac-es not
4. be a-shamed. The LORD hears the cry of the
4. poor. Bless-ed be the LORD.
7
to Refrain

Text: Based on Psalm 34:2–4, 6, 9, 16. Refrain
Verse 1 and first half of verse 2
Remaining text, Tom Kendzia, b. 1954,
Music: Tom Kendzia,

505 EAT THIS BREAD

Refrain: All

Eat this bread, drink this cup, come to me and nev-er be hun - gry.

Eat this bread, drink this cup, trust in me and you will not thirst.

Verse 1: Cantor

1. I am the bread of life, the true bread sent from the Fa-ther.

to Refrain

Verse 2: Cantor

2. Your an-ces-tors ate man-na in the des - ert, but this is the

2. bread come down from heav - en.

to Refrain

Verse 3: Cantor

3. Eat my flesh and

3. drink my blood, and I will raise you up on the last day.

to Refrain

Verse 4: Cantor
to Refrain
4. An - y - one who eats this bread, will live for ev - er.

Verse 5: Cantor
to Refrain
*
5. If you be-lieve and eat this bread, you will have e - ter-nal life.

*Choose either part.

Text: John 6; adapt. by Robert J. Batastini, b. 1942.
Music: Jacques Berthier, 1923–1994.

We, the Body of Christ 506

Verse 1
1. Be-hold the Lamb of God who takes a-way our sins.
1. Hap-py are we to be called to dine at the ban-quet of the Lord.
to Refrain
Refrain
We, the Bod-y of Christ, taste and see your good-ness.
Fill our hearts with the depth of your love; bind us to-geth-er as one through your Son.
1 to Vs 2
2 to Vs 3
3 to Vs 4
Final
Son. Son. Son.
Verse 2
2. Lord, we are not wor-thy to re-ceive you in-to our heart,
2. but on-ly say the word and we shall be healed of our sin.
to Refrain
Verse 3
3. We have been re-newed by the pres-ence of the Lord.
3. God has come to dwell in us, to re-veal him-self to the world.
to Refrain
Verse 4
4. Pre-pare our hearts to re-ceive you, cleanse our minds of sin.
4. O-pen our hands to em-brace you, Lord, to be sat-is-fied with you.
to Refrain

507 TASTE AND SEE

Refrain

Taste and see, O taste and see, taste and see the goodness of God.

Verses 1, 2

1. Glo - ry, glo - ry to God most high,
2. Who has fash-ioned the earth and sky,

1. glo - ry, bless-ing and praise. With one voice, O peo-ple, re-
2. who cre - a - ted the deep, who ex - alts the low - ly and

to Refrain

1. joice in our God, who hears _ the cry of all ___ in need. O
2. sets cap-tives free, who o-pens the door to all those who seek. O

Verse 3

3. Oh, the love of God! Be-come flesh of our flesh,

to Refrain

3. so that we might live in glo - ry. O

Text: Based on Psalm 34:9, 2–4; 136:5–6; Luke 1:52; Bob Hurd, b. 1950.
Music: Bob Hurd.

508 ONE LOVE RELEASED

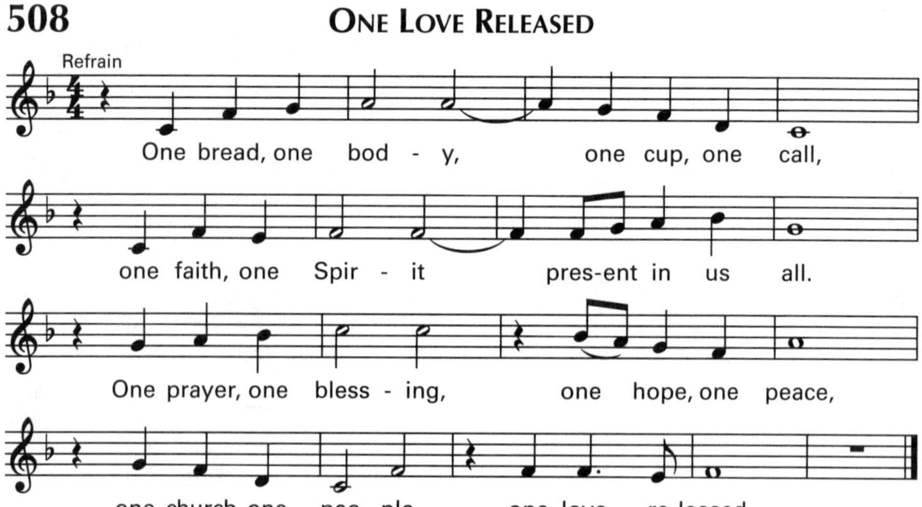
Refrain
One bread, one bod - y, one cup, one call,
one faith, one Spir - it pres-ent in us all.
One prayer, one bless - ing, one hope, one peace,
one church, one peo - ple, one love re-leased.

Verses
1. Is not this bread we share, the bod - y of our Lord?
2. I am the bread of life, eat and you shall live.
3. I am the liv - ing bread, as man - na from the sky.
4. No one will come to me, un - less our God has led.
to Refrain
1. Is not this wine we drink, the blood of Christ out-poured?
2. To those who share this meal, my strength I'll al - ways give.
3. This bread I give to you, that you may nev - er die.
4. And I shall raise them up, ___ raise them from the dead!
Verses
1. As grains of wheat are gath-ered in we've come to - geth - er;
2. Each grain must fall and give it - self: it first is bro - ken;
3. From man - y fields the har-vest comes to feed the hun - gry;
4. Your har - vest, Lord, is gath-ered in; We stand be - fore you
1. from lives a - part we bring our hearts to make one whole.
2. then, joined with oth-ers, makes one bod - y and one bread.
3. the world cries out to taste the good-ness of the Lord.
4. to be your bread, to be your bod - y in the world.
Refrain
For man - y are we, and bro - ken we've come, but
we shall be - come one.
1-3
to Verses
3
4
one.
Repeat Refrain
Final
one.
We shall be one.

Text: Bob Frenzel, b. 1953, and Kevin Keil (ASCAP), b. 1956.
Music: Based on O WALY WALY; Bob Frenzel and Kevin Keil.

As Grains of Wheat 509

510 UBI CARITAS

Refrain: All
*U - bi ca - ri - tas est ve - ra, est ve - ra: De - us i - bi
est, De - us i - bi est.
Verses: Cantor/Choir
1. The love of Christ joins us to - gether. Let us re - joice in him, and in our love and care for all now love God in re - turn.
2. In true com - mu - nion let us gath - er. May all di - vi - sions cease and in their place be Christ the Lord, our ris - en Prince of Peace.
3. May we who gath - er at this ta - ble to share the bread of life be - come a sac - ra - ment of love, your heal - ing touch, O Christ.
4. For those in need make us your mer - cy, for those op - pressed, your might. Make us, your Church, a ho - ly sign of jus - tice and new life.
5. May we one day be - hold your glo - ry and see you face to face, re - joic - ing with the saints of God to sing e - ter - nal praise.
to Refrain
Spanish Verses: Cantor/Choir
1. U - ni - dos co - mo un so - lo cuer - po, en la co - mu - nión de - mos - tre - mos
2. Reu - ni - dos y a - li - men - ta - dos, ya li - bres del ren - cor, vi - va - mos nues - tra
3. Que el pan de vi - da que nos u - ne nos cam - bie el co - ra - zón pa - ra dar al
4. Y pa - ra los ne - ce - si - ta - dos de a - mor y de bon - dad se - a - mos la es - pe -
5. Con - cé - de - nos ya ver tu glo - ria y en tu pre - sen - cia es - tar; y u - ni - dos a los

*Where there is true charity, God is present.
Donde hay caridad verdadera, allí está Dios.

to Refrain
1. nues- tro a - mor a quien pri - me- ro a - mó.
2. co - mu - nión en Cris - to, Sal - va - dor.
3. pró - ji - mo a - mor y sa - na - ción.
4. ran - za, jus - ti - cia y paz.
5. san - tos, can - tar - te sin ce - sar.

Text: Verses 1, 2, 5 based on *Ubi Caritas*, 9th cent.; verses 3, 4, Bob Hurd, b. 1950; Spanish by Pedro Rubalcava, b. 1958.
Music: Bob Hurd.

Taste and See 511

Refrain: 1st time: Cantor, All repeat; thereafter: All

Taste and see, taste and see the good-ness of the Lord. O
taste and see, taste and see the good-ness of the Lord, of the Lord.

Verses: Cantor

1. I will bless the Lord at all times. His praise shall al-ways be on my lips; my soul shall glo-ry in the Lord for he has been so good to me.
2. Glo - ri - fy the Lord with me. To - geth-er let us all praise his name. I called the Lord and he an-swered me; from all my trou-bles he set me free.
3. Wor-ship the Lord, all you peo-ple. You'll want for noth-ing if you ask. Taste and see that God is good; in him we need put all our trust.

to Refrain

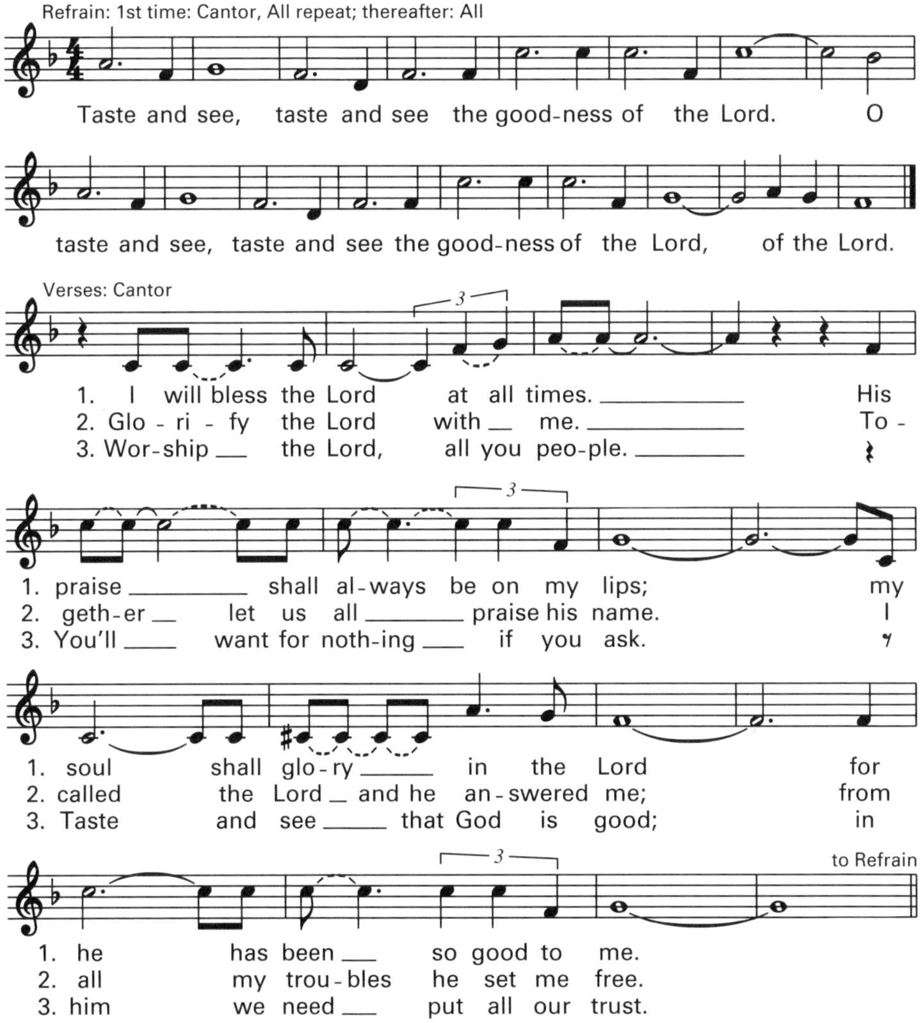

Text: Based on Psalm 34:9a, 2–3, 4–5, 10; James E. Moore, Jr.
Music: James E. Moore, Jr.

512 BREAD, BLESSED AND BROKEN

Verses

1. Je-sus, you're the one I love; you're the one I know.
2. From the clouds of yes - ter-day, through the night of pain,
3. May the bread we break to-day, may the cup we share
4. Pass-ing on to each of us a mea-sure of your love,
5. Je-sus, you're the one I love; you're the one I know.

(Fine)

1. You're the one who makes me strong, Spir-it in my soul. (to Vs. 2)
2. teach me, Lord, to know your way, know it once a - gain. (to Ref.)
3. lift the bur-dens of our hearts, lift them ev - 'ry-where. (to Vs. 4)
4. love to make us whole a - gain, as we share your Word. (to Ref.)
5. You're the one who makes me strong, Spir-it in my soul. *(Fine)*

Refrain

Bread, blessed and bro-ken for us all, sym-bol of your love from the grain so tall. Bread, blessed and bro-ken for us all, bread of life you give to us, bread of life for all.

to Verses

Text and music: Michael B. Lynch, © 1978, 1979 Raven Music.

513 THE SUPPER OF THE LORD

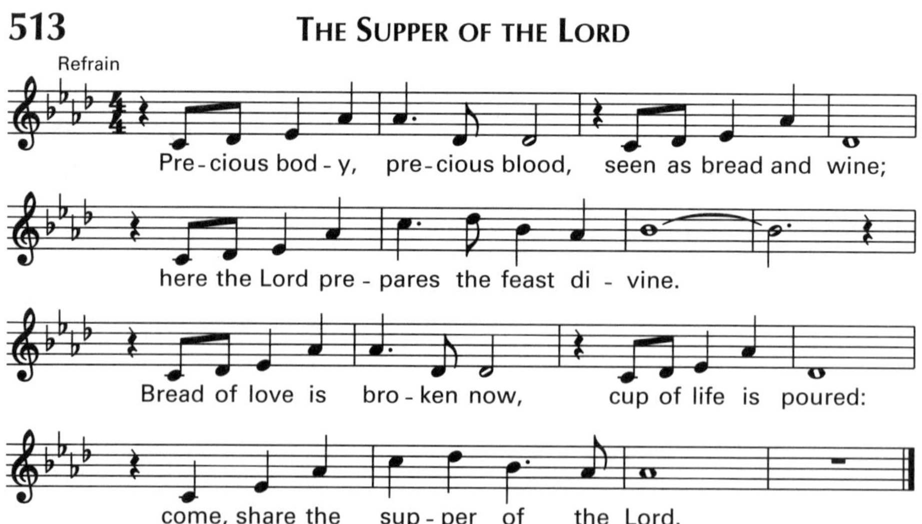
Refrain
Pre-cious bod - y, pre-cious blood, seen as bread and wine;
here the Lord pre - pares the feast di - vine.
Bread of love is bro - ken now, cup of life is poured:
come, share the sup - per of the Lord.

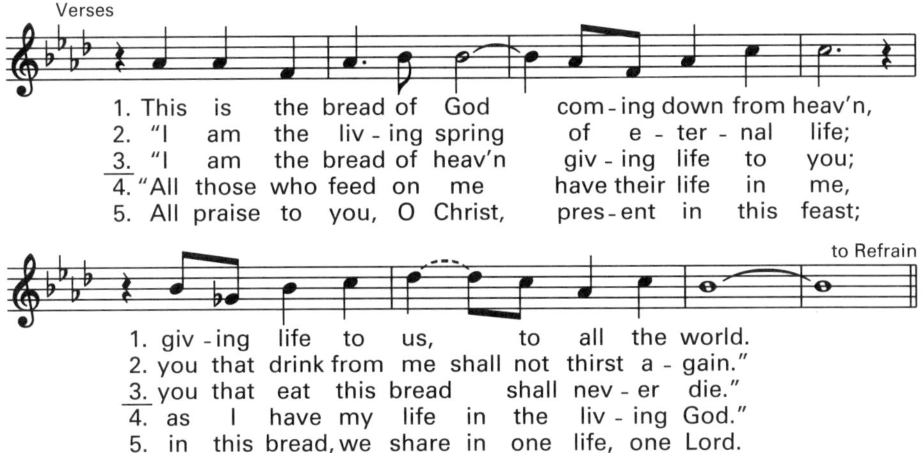
Verses
1. This is the bread of God com-ing down from heav'n,
2. "I am the liv-ing spring of e-ter-nal life;
3. "I am the bread of heav'n giv-ing life to you;
4. "All those who feed on me have their life in me,
5. All praise to you, O Christ, pres-ent in this feast;
to Refrain
1. giv-ing life to us, to all the world.
2. you that drink from me shall not thirst a-gain."
3. you that eat this bread shall nev-er die."
4. as I have my life in the liv-ing God."
5. in this bread, we share in one life, one Lord.

Text: Verses 1–4 based on John 4, 6; Laurence Rosania, b. 1957.
Music: Laurence Rosania.

VINE AND BRANCHES 514

Refrain

I am the vine and you the branch-es. Re-main in  me as I re-main in you; you will bear great fruit in me.

Verses

1. A new com-mand-ment I give you: e-ven as I have loved you, now love one an-oth-er.
2. No great-er love is there than this: than to lay down your life, your life for your friends.
3. I am the liv-ing bread from heav-en; if you eat this bread, you will live for-ev-er.
4. All those who eat my flesh and drink my blood re-main in me and I re-main in them.
5. The words that I have spo-ken are spir-it and life, they are spir-it and life.
6. And now as I have washed your feet, so you must do just as I have done.

to Refrain

Text: Based on John 6:35–63; 13:14–15; 15:1–13; Trevor Thomson, b. 1971.
Music: Trevor Thomson.

515 JESUS, THE BREAD OF LIFE

Refrain

Je - sus, the Bread of life, Je - sus, the

Bread of life. All who eat and drink of him will nev -

- er die, will nev - er die.

Verses: Cantor

1. I am the Bread that came down from
2. All who come to me will not
3. All who love and keep my com-

1. heav - en. I will be ___ your food. ___
2. hun - ger nor will they ev - er thirst. ___
3. mand-ments will be loved by my Fa -

1. ___ All who put their trust in
2. ___ If you turn to me in
3. ther. And we shall both com - fort

to Refrain

1. me will nev - er die.
2. faith I'll nev - er turn a - way.
3. them and make our home in them.

Text: Based on John 6:51, 14:23; Grayson Warren Brown, b. 1948.
Music: Grayson Warren Brown.

516 UNLESS A GRAIN OF WHEAT

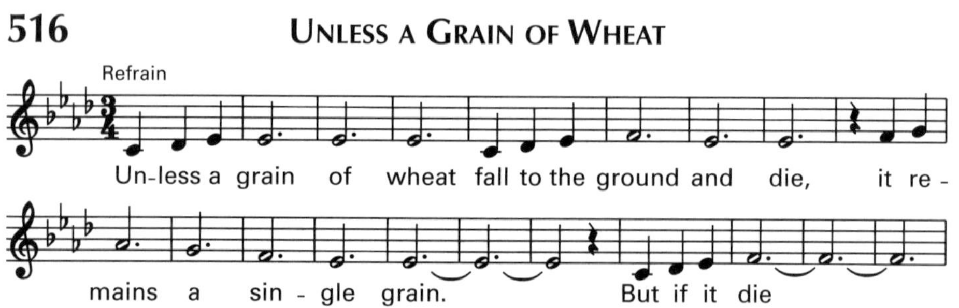
Refrain
Un-less a grain of wheat fall to the ground and die, it re -
mains a sin - gle grain. But if it die

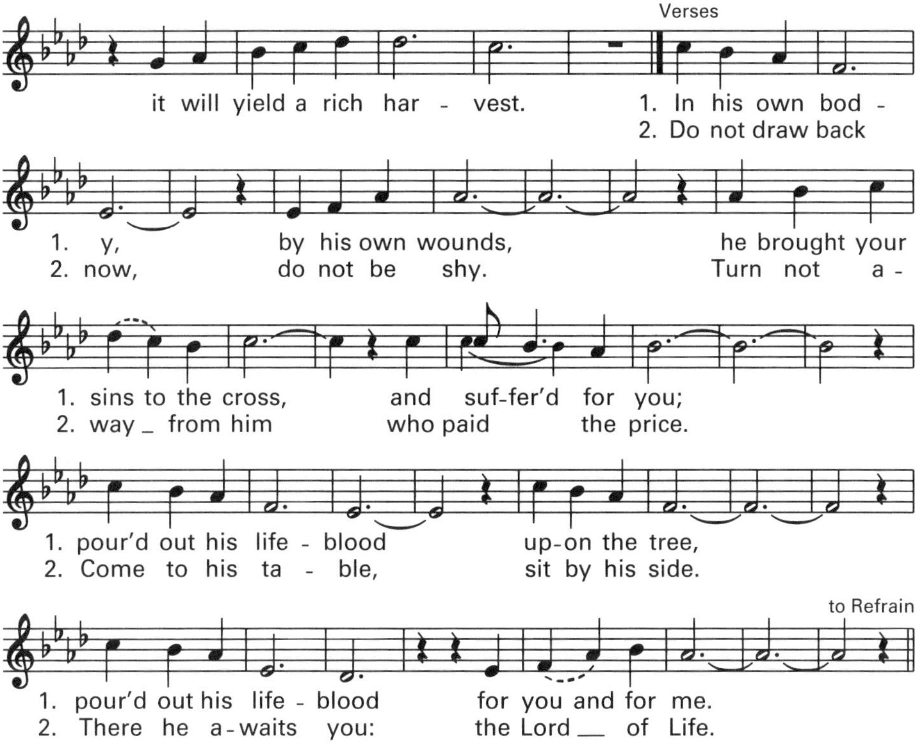

it will yield a rich har - vest.

Verses

1. In his own bod - y, by his own wounds, he brought your sins to the cross, and suf-fer'd for you; pour'd out his life - blood up-on the tree, pour'd out his life - blood for you and for me.

2. Do not draw back now, do not be shy. Turn not a - way _ from him who paid the price. Come to his ta - ble, sit by his side. There he a-waits you: the Lord __ of Life.

to Refrain

Text: Based on John 12:24 and George Herbert's *Love Bade Me Welcome*; adapt. by Bob Hurd, b. 1950.
Music: Bob Hurd.

517 FOR THE HEALING OF THE NATIONS

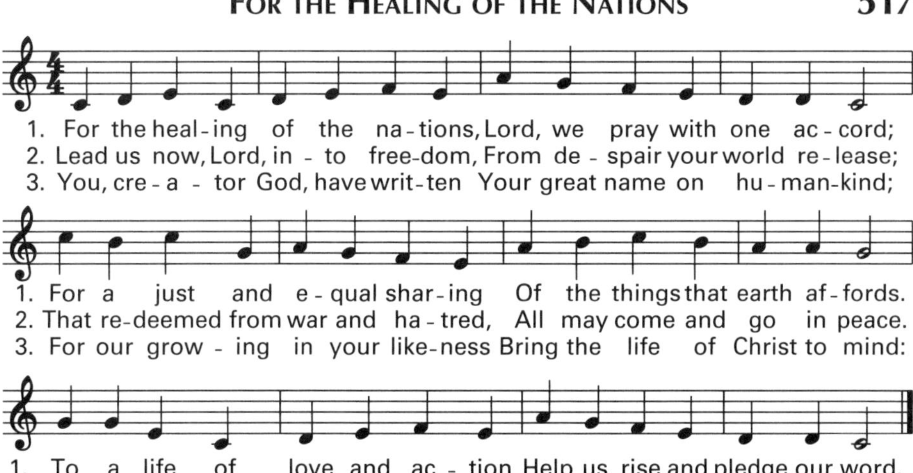
1. For the heal-ing of the na-tions, Lord, we pray with one ac-cord;
2. Lead us now, Lord, in - to free-dom, From de - spair your world re-lease;
3. You, cre - a - tor God, have writ-ten Your great name on hu-man-kind;
1. For a just and e-qual shar-ing Of the things that earth af-fords.
2. That re-deemed from war and ha-tred, All may come and go in peace.
3. For our grow - ing in your like-ness Bring the life of Christ to mind:
1. To a life of love and ac - tion Help us rise and pledge our word.
2. Show us how through care and good-ness Fear will die and hope in-crease.
3. That by our re - sponse and ser - vice Earth its des - ti - ny may find.

Text: 87 87 87; based on Revelation 21:1–27; 22:1–5; Fred Kaan, b. 1929, © 1968, Hope Publishing Co.

Music: ST. THOMAS (TANTUM ERGO); John F. Wade, 1711–1786.

518 GOD OF THE HUNGRY

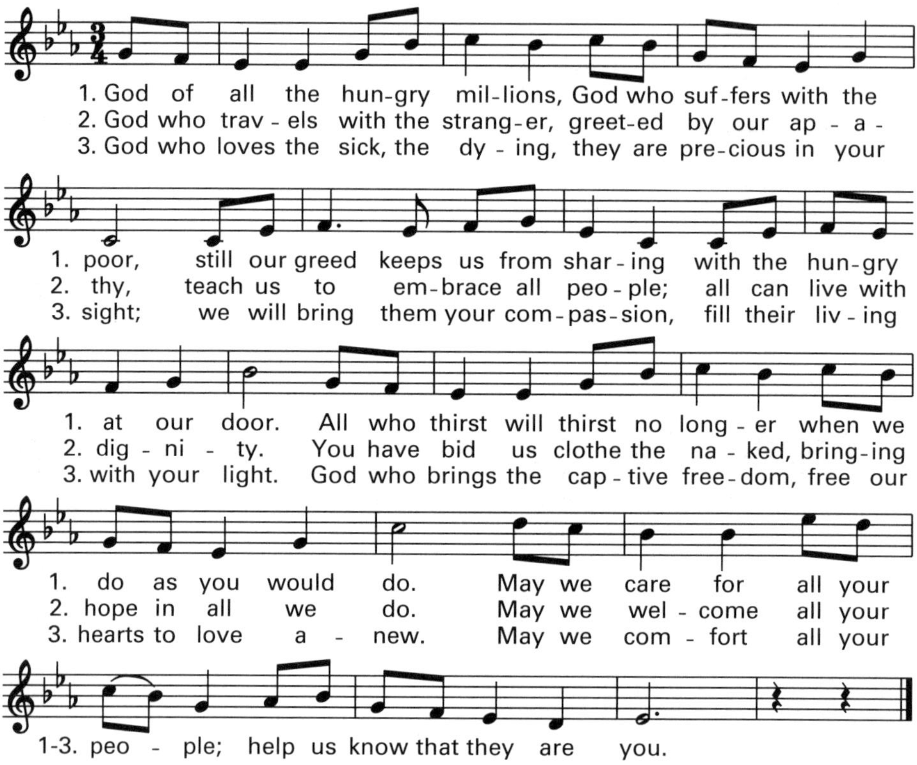

1. God of all the hun-gry mil-lions, God who suf-fers with the
2. God who trav - els with the strang-er, greet-ed by our ap - a -
3. God who loves the sick, the dy - ing, they are pre-cious in your

1. poor, still our greed keeps us from shar - ing with the hun-gry
2. thy, teach us to em-brace all peo - ple; all can live with
3. sight; we will bring them your com-pas-sion, fill their liv - ing

1. at our door. All who thirst will thirst no long - er when we
2. dig - ni - ty. You have bid us clothe the na - ked, bring-ing
3. with your light. God who brings the cap - tive free-dom, free our

1. do as you would do. May we care for all your
2. hope in all we do. May we wel - come all your
3. hearts to love a - new. May we com - fort all your

1-3. peo - ple; help us know that they are you.

Text: Based on Matthew 25:35–40; Scott Soper, b. 1961.
Music: Scott Soper.

519 WHATSOEVER YOU DO

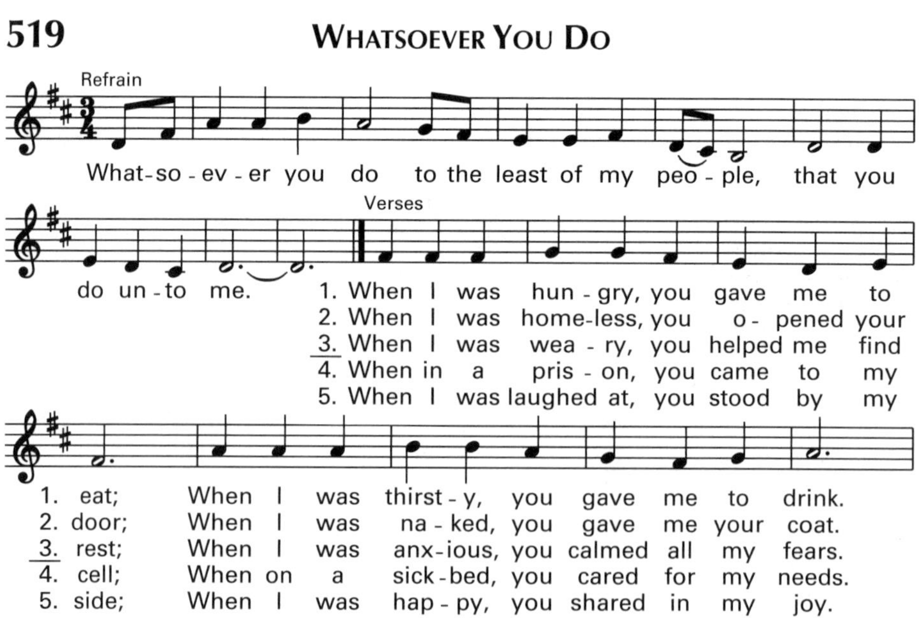
Refrain
What-so - ev - er you do to the least of my peo - ple, that you
do un - to me.
Verses
1. When I was hun - gry, you gave me to
2. When I was home-less, you o - pened your
3. When I was wea - ry, you helped me find
4. When in a pris - on, you came to my
5. When I was laughed at, you stood by my
1. eat; When I was thirst - y, you gave me to drink.
2. door; When I was na - ked, you gave me your coat.
3. rest; When I was anx-ious, you calmed all my fears.
4. cell; When on a sick-bed, you cared for my needs.
5. side; When I was hap - py, you shared in my joy.

to Refrain
1-5. Now en - ter in - to the home of my Fa - ther.

Text and music: Willard F. Jabusch, b. 1930,

ACT JUSTLY

520

Refrain

Act justly; love tenderly.
Walk, walk humbly with your God.

Verses

1. How shall we come before you? With what gifts to adore you? Will our sacrifices please you? What should we bring today?
2. This is what the Lord asks you: only this will remain true, what is good has been explained to you: Listen again today.
3. People, lift up your voices; by your actions make choices. In this time, the only time we have, show us the way to live.
4. On this planet of plenty, lives and futures lie empty. In this world, the only world we have, show us the way to live.
5. Gather, sisters and brothers; gather, fathers and mothers. In this place, the only place we grow, show us the way to live.
6. Bread of life will be broken; word of hope will be spoken. In this sacrament of endless care show us the way to live.

to Refrain

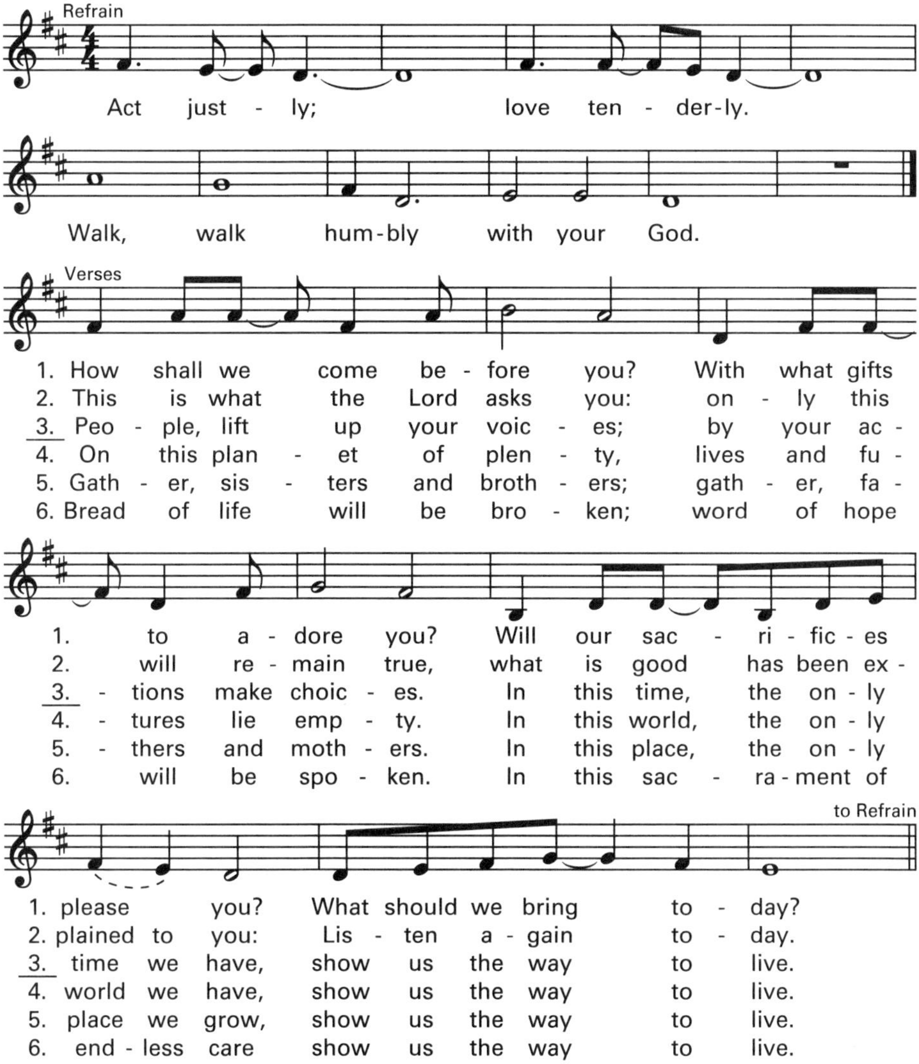

Text: Based on Micah 6:8; Bernadette Farrell, b. 1957.
Music: Bernadette Farrell.

521 Make Your Home in Me

Verses

1. Ev - ery fox, a den; ev - ery bird, a nest; but the
2. Lord, you come to me in your home - less - ness; burn-ing

1. Son of Man has no place to rest. Ev - ery heart, a man; ev - ery
2. in your eyes, such a great dis-tress. Who will heal your wounds? Who will

1. king, a throne; but the Word Made Flesh, no earth - ly home.
2. make your bed? I will com - fort you, I will share my bread.

Refrain

Your bur-den's light and your yoke is eas - y. Your name is
love and your grace is free. My heart was locked but
you had the key. Make your home in me,
make your home in me.

Bridge

Where there is love, there is no fear.
So, make your home and residence here.
I'm so alive when you are near,
so, make your home in me.

Text: Based on Matthew 8:20; 11:30; Luke 9:58; Ben Walther, b. 1977.
Music: Ben Walther.

522 People of Peace

Refrain
To be peo - ple of faith in times of doubt;
to be peo - ple of hope in times of de - spair;

to be peo - ple of peace, peo - ple of peace,
O Lord, your in - stru - ments of peace.
Verse 1
1. Where we en - count - er ha - tred, let us bring your love,
1. where hurt has been op - pres - sive, your heal - ing care;
1. wher - ev - er there are peo - ple who are need - ing to be
1. free; make your church an in - stru - ment of peace.
to Refrain
Verses 2, 3
2. To heal the bro - ken - heart - ed, to com - fort those who mourn;
3. In giv - ing to the hun - gry, in sat - is - fy - ing thirst,
2. to go to those im - pris - oned, bring free - dom to the bound;
3. in wel - com - ing the strang - er, in com - fort - ing the ill;
2. to be a light for all who strug - gle to be free;
3. in be - ing those who hun - ger for jus - tice and for truth:
2. make your church an in - stru - ment of peace.
3. make us all your in - stru - ments of peace.
to Refrain

Text: Based on Isaiah 6 and on the prayer traditionally ascr. to St. Francis of Assisi, 1182–1226; Carey Landry, b. 1944.
Music: Carey Landry.

523 Lord, Whose Love in Humble Service

1. Lord, whose love in hum - ble ser - vice Bore the
2. Still your chil - dren wan - der home - less; Still the
3. As we wor - ship, grant us vi - sion, Till your
4. Called from wor - ship in - to ser - vice Forth in
1. weight of hu - man need, Who up - on the cross, for -
2. hun - gry cry for bread; Still the cap - tives long for
3. love's re - veal - ing light, Till the height and depth and
4. your great name we go, To the child, the youth, the
1. sak - en, Of - fered mer - cy's per - fect deed; We, your
2. free - dom; Still in grief we mourn our dead. As, O
3. great - ness Dawns up - on our hu - man sight: Mak - ing
4. a - ged, Love in liv - ing deeds to show; Hope and
1. ser - vants, bring the wor - ship Not of voice a -
2. Lord, your deep com - pas - sion Healed the sick and
3. known the needs and bur - dens Your com - pas - sion
4. health, good - will and com - fort, Coun - sel, aid, and
1. lone, but heart: Con - se - crat - ing to your
2. freed the soul, Use the love your Spir - it
3. bids us bear, Stir - ring us to tire - less
4. peace we give, That your chil - dren, Lord, in
1. pur - pose Ev - 'ry gift which you im - part.
2. kin - dles Still to save and make us whole.
3. striv - ing, Your a - bun - dant life to share.
4. free - dom, May your mer - cy know, and live.

Text: 87 87 D; 'Lord, whose love in humble service' by Albert F. Bayly, 1901–1984, alt., © 1988, Oxford University Press.
Music: BEACH SPRING; *The Sacred Harp*, 1844.

We Are Called

524

Verses
1. Come! Live in the light!
2. Come! O - pen your heart!
3. Sing! Sing a new song!
1. Shine with the joy and the love of the Lord! We are
2. Show your __ mer - cy to all those in fear! We are
3. Sing of that great day when all will be one! God will
1. called to be light for the king - dom, to
2. called to be hope for the hope - less, so all
3. reign, and we'll walk with each oth - er as
1. live in the free-dom __ of the cit - y __ of God!
2. ha - tred and blind-ness ______ will be ______ no more!
3. sis - ters and broth - ers ______ u - nit-ed __ in love!
Refrain
We are called to act with jus - tice, we are
called to love ten - der - ly, we are called to
serve one an - oth-er; to walk hum - bly with
God.
3

Text: Based on Micah 6:8; David Haas, b. 1957.
Music: David Haas.

525 Alleluia! Raise the Gospel

Refrain

Al - le - lu - ia! Al - le - lu - ia! Raise the Gos - pel
o - ver the earth! Al - le - lu - ia! Al - le -
lu - ia! Peace and jus - tice bring-ing to birth!

*Verses

1. Bless - ed those whose hearts are gen - tle. Bless - ed
2. Bless - ed those who work for jus - tice. Bless - ed
3. Trem - ble, you who build up rich - es. Trem - ble,
4. Trem - ble, you who thirst for pow - er. Trem - ble
5. Glo - ry like the stars of heav - en— Glo - ry
6. Glo - ry to the Word of Jus - tice. Glo - ry

1. those whose spir - its are strong. Bless - ed those who
2. those who an - swer the call. Bless - ed those who
3. you with op - u - lent lives. Trem - ble, when you
4. you who live for ac - claim. Trem - ble, when you
5. like the sun in the sky— Glo - ry shines up -
6. to the Spir - it of Peace. Glo - ry to the

to Refrain

1. choose to bring forth right where there is wrong.
2. dare to dream of last - ing peace for all.
3. meet the poor and see Christ in their eyes.
4. find no com - fort in your wealth and fame.
5. on all peo - ple, e - qual in God's eyes.
6. God of Love whose bless - ings nev - er cease.

*Alternate verses available in the accompaniment books.

Text: Owen Alstott, b. 1947,
Music: Bernadette Farrell, b. 1957,

526 The Cry of the Poor

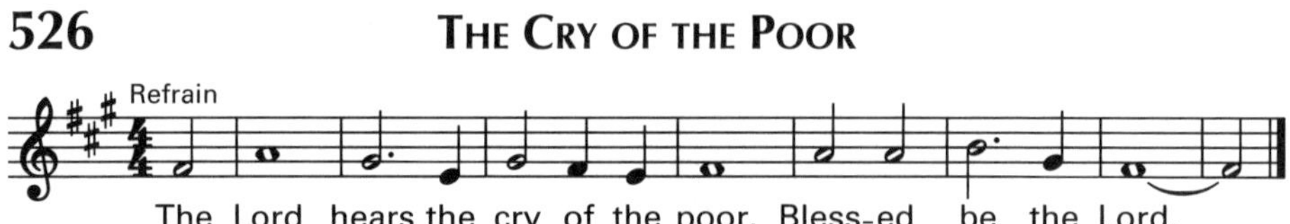
Refrain
The Lord hears the cry of the poor. Bless-ed be the Lord.

Verses: Slightly faster
1. I will bless the Lord at all times, with praise
2. Let the low - ly hear and be glad: the Lord
3. Ev - 'ry spir - it crushed, God will save; will be
4. We pro - claim your great - ness, O God, your praise
1. ev - er in my mouth. Let my soul glo - ry in the
2. lis - tens to their pleas; and to hearts bro - ken, God is
3. ran - som for their lives; will be safe shel - ter for their
4. ev - er in our mouth; ev - 'ry face bright - ened in your
to Refrain
1. Lord, who will hear the cry of the poor.
2. near, who will hear the cry of the poor.
3. fears, and will hear the cry of the poor.
4. light, for you hear the cry of the poor.

Text: Based on Psalm 34:2–3, 18–19a, 19b–20, 4; John Foley, S.J., b. 1939.
Music: John Foley, S.J.

We Shall Overcome 527

1. We shall o - ver - come, we shall o - ver - come,
2. We'll walk hand in hand, we'll walk hand in hand,
3. We shall all be free, we shall all be free,
4. We are not a - fraid, we are not a - fraid,
5. We shall live in peace, we shall live in peace,

1. we shall o - ver - come some - day; Oh, deep in my heart
2. we'll walk hand in hand some - day; Oh, deep in my heart
3. we shall all be free some - day; Oh, deep in my heart
4. we are not a - fraid to - day; Oh, deep in my heart
5. we shall live in peace some - day; Oh, deep in my heart

1. I do be - lieve, we shall o - ver - come some - day.
2. I do be - lieve, we'll walk hand in hand some - day.
3. I do be - lieve, we shall all be free some - day.
4. I do be - lieve, we are not a - fraid to - day.
5. I do be - lieve, we shall live in peace some - day.

Text and music: Traditional.

528 LIGHT OF CHRIST

Refrain
Be the light of Christ in the world. Bring the nations God's own love. Set a blaze in the night, make the earth shine bright. Be the light of Christ to the world.
1, 2
2 to Verses
Final
Bring the light of Christ to the world.
Verse 1
1. No more tears, no more pain, no more hun-ger; we'll laugh a-gain. God of glo-ry will guide our ways. God of mer-cy will light our days.
to Refrain
Verse 2
2. As the stars that shine in the heav-ens, so our light will shine on the earth. Ris-en Je-sus has con-quered the night and freed us from death with this light.
to Refrain

THE SUMMONS

1. Will you come and fol - low me If I but
2. Will you leave your - self be - hind If I but
3. Will you let the blind - ed see If I but
4. Will you love the 'you' you hide If I but
5. Lord, your sum - mons ech - oes true When you but
1. call your name? Will you go where you don't
2. call your name? Will you care for cruel and
3. call your name? Will you set the pris - 'ners
4. call your name? Will you quell the fear in -
5. call my name. Let me turn and fol - low
1. know And nev - er be the same? Will you
2. kind And nev - er be the same? Will you
3. free And nev - er be the same? Will you
4. side And nev - er be the same? Will you
5. you And nev - er be the same. In your
1. let my love be shown, Will you let my
2. risk the hos - tile stare Should your life at -
3. kiss the lep - er clean, And do such as
4. use the faith you've found To re - shape the
5. com - pa - ny I'll go Where your love and
1. name be known, Will you let my life be
2. tract or scare? Will you let me an - swer
3. this un - seen, And ad - mit to what I
4. world a - round, Through my sight and touch and
5. foot - steps show. Thus I'll move and live and
1. grown In you and you in me?
2. pray'r In you and you in me?
3. mean In you and you in me?
4. sound In you and you in me?
5. grow In you and you in me.

Text: 76 76 77 76; John L. Bell, b. 1949,
Music: KELVINGROVE; trad. Scottish melody.

530 Celtic Alleluia: Sending Forth

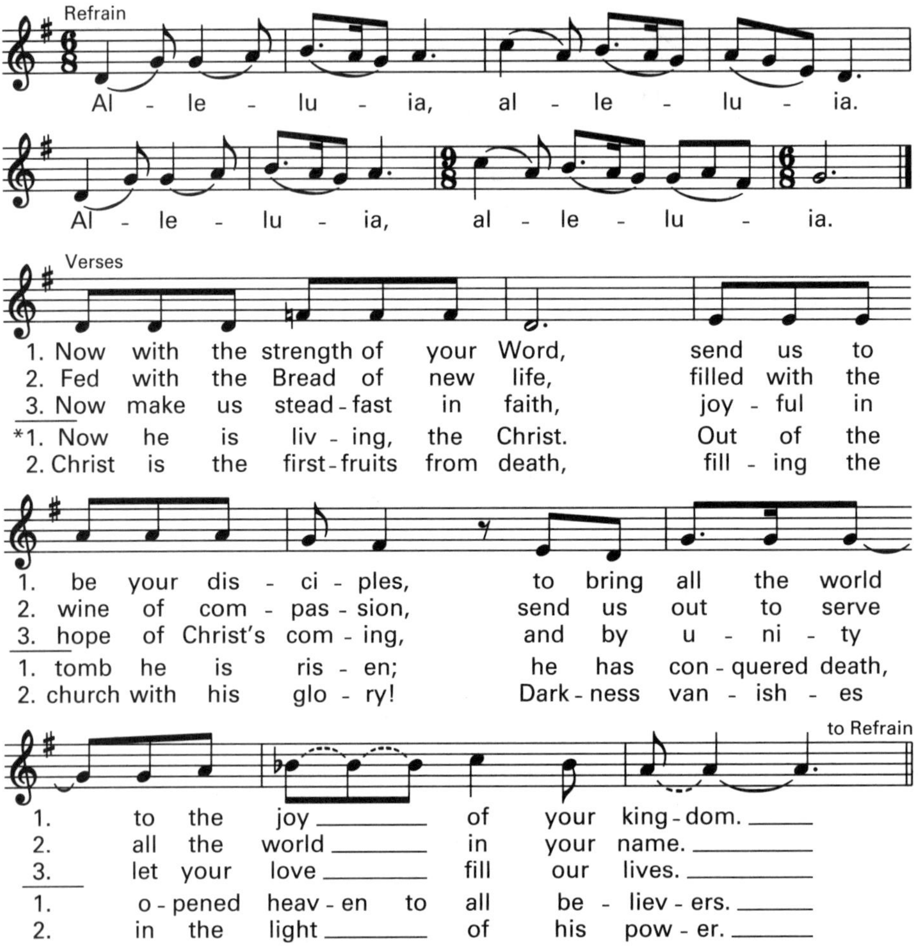

Refrain

Al - le - lu - ia, al - le - lu - ia.

Al - le - lu - ia, al - le - lu - ia.

Verses

1. Now with the strength of your Word, send us to be your dis - ci - ples, to bring all the world to the joy ___ of your king - dom. ___
2. Fed with the Bread of new life, filled with the wine of com - pas - sion, send us out to serve all the world ___ in your name. ___
3. Now make us stead - fast in faith, joy - ful in hope of Christ's com - ing, and by u - ni - ty let your love ___ fill our lives. ___

*1. Now he is liv - ing, the Christ. Out of the tomb he is ris - en; he has con - quered death, o - pened heav - en to all be - liev - ers. ___
2. Christ is the first - fruits from death, fill - ing the church with his glo - ry! Dark - ness van - ish - es in the light ___ of his pow - er. ___

to Refrain

*Verses for the Easter Season

Text and music: *Celtic Mass*; Fintan O'Carroll, 1922–1981, and Christopher Walker, b. 1947,

531 I Send You Out

Verse 1

1. I baptize you in the name of the Father.
I baptize you in the name of the Son.
I baptize you with the Holy Spirit.
Go out and spread Good News!

Refrain: All
I send you out on a mis-sion of love. I send you out
on a mis-sion of love. I send you out

on a mis-sion of love, and know that I am with
you al - ways un-til the end of the world.

Verse 2

2. Well, it's time for us
to become people with spirit.
It's time for us to become people of love.
It's time for us
to know that Jesus Christ is risen,
forgives our sins, and brings us new life!

Text and music: John Angotti,

SENT FORTH BY GOD'S BLESSING 532

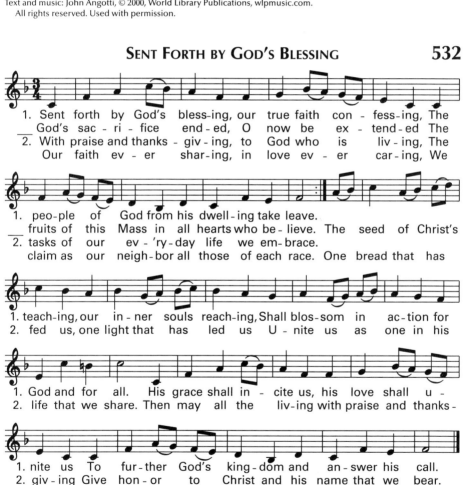

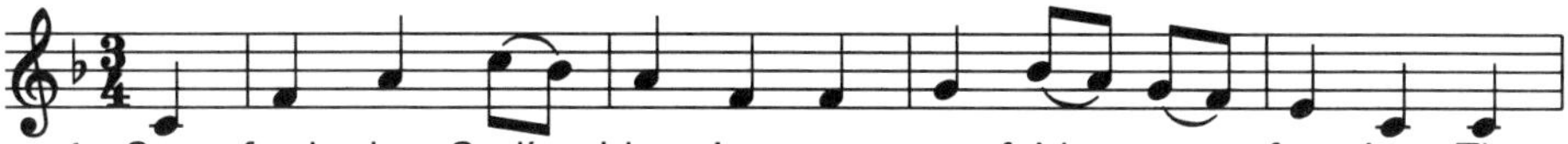

1. Sent forth by God's bless-ing, our true faith con - fess-ing, The
God's sac - ri - fice end - ed, O now be ex - tend - ed The
2. With praise and thanks - giv - ing, to God who is liv - ing, The
Our faith ev - er shar-ing, in love ev - er car-ing, We

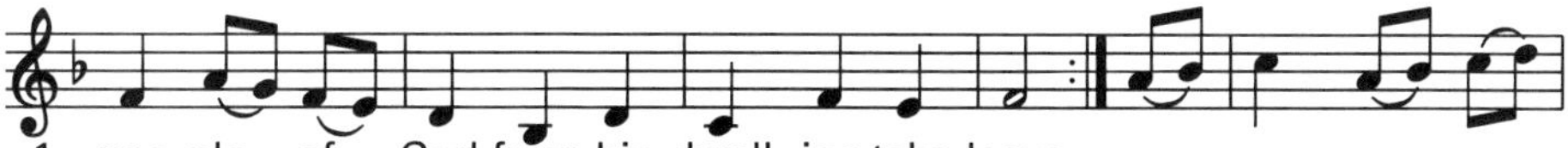

1. peo-ple of God from his dwell - ing take leave.
fruits of this Mass in all hearts who be - lieve. The seed of Christ's
2. tasks of our ev - 'ry-day life we em-brace.
claim as our neigh-bor all those of each race. One bread that has

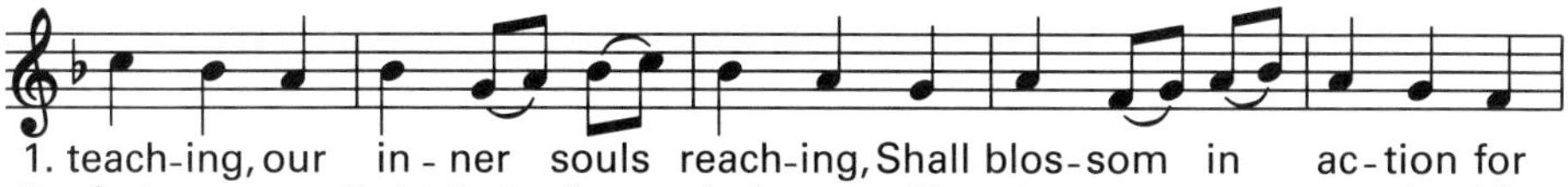

1. teach-ing, our in - ner souls reach-ing, Shall blos-som in ac-tion for
2. fed us, one light that has led us U - nite us as one in his

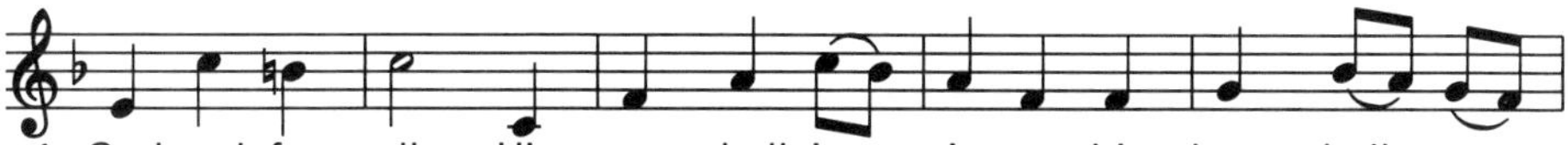

1. God and for all. His grace shall in - cite us, his love shall u -
2. life that we share. Then may all the liv-ing with praise and thanks -

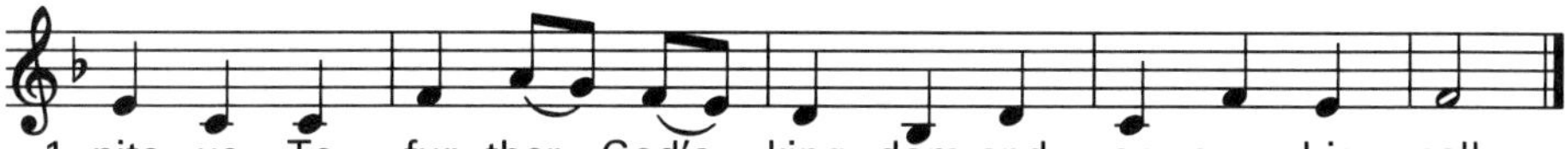

1. nite us To fur-ther God's king - dom and an - swer his call.
2. giv - ing Give hon - or to Christ and his name that we bear.

Text: 12 11 12 11 D; Omer Westendorf, 1916–1997, alt.,
Music: ASH GROVE; trad. Welsh melody.

533 WITHOUT YOU

Refrain
With - out you, O God, there is no peace, there is no
hope, there is no love. With - out you, O God,
there is no mer - cy; we long to be your peace.
Verses 1, 2
1. To be love where ha - tred is com-mon, to for-
2. To be light when dark-ness sur-rounds us, to be
1. give ev - ery man - ner of wrong; be your
2. truth when jus - tice has failed. In the
1. love and your care, in the face of de - spair,
2. dark - ness of night, you a - lone are our light.
to Refrain
1. be your peace a - live in the world.
2. You a - lone, O God, are peace.
Verse 3
3. To be bread for those who hun-ger for truth, to be wine for
3. all thirst-ing for you. In your Spir - it a - live, we are
to Refrain
3. sight to the blind. We are love when love can't be found.

Text: Based on a prayer of St. Francis, 1182–1226; Tom Kendzia, b. 1954.
Music: Tom Kendzia.

YOU HAVE ANOINTED ME 534

Verse 1
1. To bring glad tid - ings to the low - ly, to heal the
1. bro - ken heart, you have a - noint - ed me.
1. To pro - claim lib - er - ty to cap - tives, re - lease to pris -
1. - on - ers, you have a - noint - ed me.
Refrain
Your Spir - it, O God, is u - pon me,
you have a - noint - ed me.
Verse 2
2. To an - nounce a year of fa - vor, to
2. com - fort those who mourn, you have a - noint - ed
2. me. To give to them the oil of glad - ness, and
2. share a man - tle of joy, you have a - noint - ed me.
3
to Refrain

Text: Based on Isaiah 61:1–3; Mike Balhoff, b. 1946, Gary Daigle, b. 1957, and Darryl Ducote, b. 1945.
Music: Mike Balhoff, Gary Daigle, and Darryl Ducote.

535 With One Voice

Verses
1. Take the Word and go out to ev - 'ry land:
2. Take the Word to our neigh - bor-hoods and streets:
3. Take the Word to the peo - ple in de - spair:
4. Take the Word to the na - tions ev - 'ry-where:
1-4. shine the light of Christ for all to see!
1. May the lives of those we touch sing
2. May we all set out to live in
3. May our ac - tions and our deeds bring
4. May the wit - ness of our lives trans -
1. praise to God a - bove. Let us sing, we'll sing:
2. peace and har - mo - ny. They will see and sing:
3. com - fort to their needs. And they'll know and sing:
4. form the world a - new. And we'll shine, we'll shine:
Refrain
With one voice we'll pass the Word a-long; with one
voice, bring jus-tice to the world. And with all the an-
- gels we'll spread the good-ness of God. With all
pow-er and glo - ry the Word of God shall reign.
3

Text and music: Ricky Manalo, CSP, b. 1965,

Go Out, Go Out 536

Refrain
Go out, go out to all the world and tell the
Good News, tell the Good, Good News! Go out, go
out to all the world and tell the Good News,
1, 4
tell the Good, Good News!
2, 3
to Verses
tell the Good, Good News.
Final
tell the Good News, tell the Good, Good News.
Verse 1
1. Praise the LORD, praise the LORD, all you na - tions;
to Refrain
1. Glo - ri - fy him, glo - ri - fy him, you peo - ples!
Verse 2
2. Stead-fast, stead - fast is his kind - ness toward us,
to Refrain
2. and the faith - ful - ness of the LORD en - dures!

537 THE SERVANT SONG

1, 6. Will you let me be your ser - vant, Let me be as
2. We are pil - grims on a jour - ney, We are trav - 'lers
3. I will hold the Christ-light for you In the night - time
4. I will weep when you are weep-ing; When you laugh I'll
5. When we sing to God in heav - en We shall find such

1, 6. Christ to you; Pray that I may have the grace to
2. on the road; We are here to help each oth - er
3. of your fear; I will hold my hand out to you,
4. laugh with you. I will share your joy and sor - row
5. har - mo - ny, Born of all we've known to - geth - er

1, 6. Let you be my ser - vant, too.
2. Walk the mile and bear the load.
3. Speak the peace you long to hear.
4. 'Til we've seen this jour - ney through.
5. Of Christ's love and ag - o - ny.

Text: 87 87; Richard Gillard, b. 1953.
Music: SERVANT SONG; Richard Gillard.

538 CITY OF GOD

Verses 1, 2
1. A-wake from your slum-ber! A - rise from your
2. We are sons of the morn-ing; we are daugh-ters of
1. sleep! A new day is dawn-ing for all those who weep.
2. day. The One who has loved us has bright-ened our way.
1. The peo - ple in dark-ness have seen a great light. The
2. The Lord of all kind-ness has called us to be a
to Refrain
1. Lord of our long-ing has con-quered the night.
2. light for his peo - ple to set their hearts free.

Refrain
Let us build the cit-y of God. May our tears be turned in-to danc-ing! For the Lord, our light and our love, has turned the night in-to day!
3
Verse 3
3. God is light; in him there is no dark-ness.
3. Let us walk in his light, his chil-dren,
3. one and all. O com-fort my
3. peo-ple; make gen-tle your words. Pro-claim to my
3. cit-y the day of her birth.
to Refrain
Verse 4
4. O cit-y of glad-ness, now lift up your voice!
4. Pro-claim the good tid-ings that all may re-joice!
to Refrain

Text: Based on Isaiah 9; 40:1–9; 1 John 1; Dan Schutte, b. 1947.
Music: Dan Schutte.

539 Here I Am, Lord

Verses

1. I, the Lord of sea and sky, I have heard my peo - ple cry.
2. I, the Lord of snow and rain, I have borne my peo-ple's pain.
3. I, the Lord of wind and flame, I will tend the poor and lame.

1. All who dwell in dark and sin My hand will save. I, who
2. I have wept for love of them. They turn a - way. I will
3. I will set a feast for them. My hand will save. Fin-est

1. made the stars of night, I will make their dark-ness bright.
2. break their hearts of stone, Give them hearts for love a - lone.
3. bread I will pro - vide Till their hearts be sat - is - fied.

1. Who will bear my light to them? Whom shall I send?
2. I will speak my word to them. Whom shall I send?
3. I will give my life to them. Whom shall I send?

Refrain

Here I am, Lord. Is it I, Lord? I have heard you

call-ing in the night. I will go, Lord, if you lead me.

I will hold your peo-ple in my heart.

Text: Based on Isaiah 6; Dan Schutte, b. 1947.
Music: Dan Schutte.

540 I Am the Vine

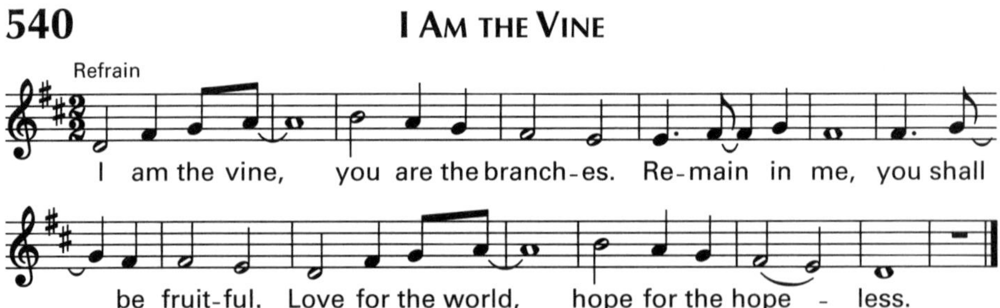
Refrain
I am the vine, you are the branch-es. Re-main in me, you shall
be fruit-ful. Love for the world, hope for the hope - less.

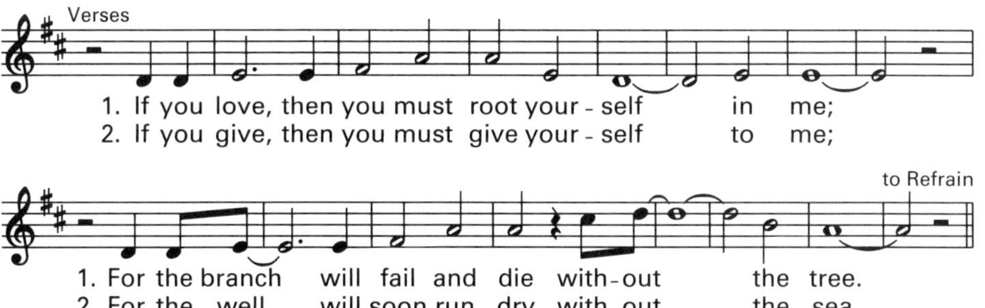
Verses
1. If you love, then you must root your - self in me;
2. If you give, then you must give your - self to me;
to Refrain
1. For the branch will fail and die with - out the tree.
2. For the well will soon run dry with - out the sea.

Text: Based on John 15:1–10; Bob Hurd, b. 1950.
Music: Bob Hurd.

Servant Song 541

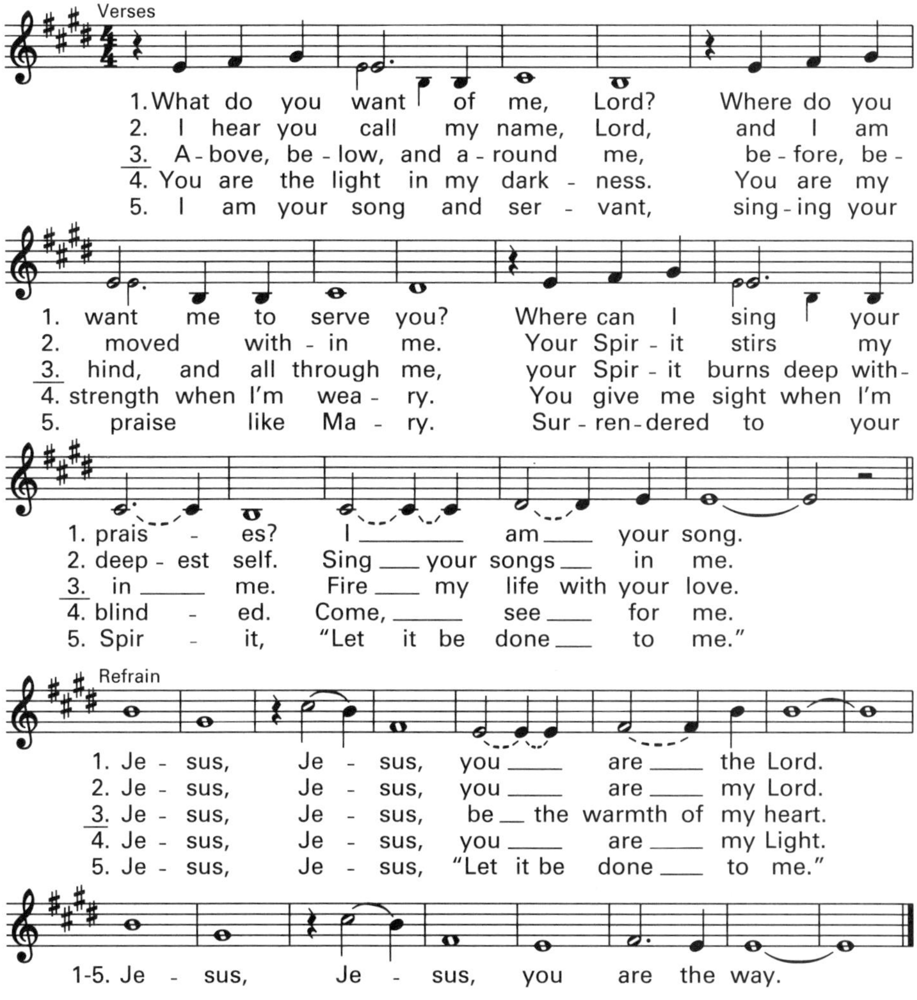

Verses

1. What do you want of me, Lord? Where do you want me to serve you? Where can I sing your prais - es? I am your song.
2. I hear you call my name, Lord, and I am moved with - in me. Your Spir - it stirs my deep - est self. Sing your songs in me.
3. A - bove, be - low, and a - round me, be - fore, be - hind, and all through me, your Spir - it burns deep with - in me. Fire my life with your love.
4. You are the light in my dark - ness. You are my strength when I'm wea - ry. You give me sight when I'm blind - ed. Come, see for me.
5. I am your song and ser - vant, sing - ing your praise like Ma - ry. Sur - ren - dered to your Spir - it, "Let it be done to me."

Refrain

1. Je - sus, Je - sus, you are the Lord.
2. Je - sus, Je - sus, you are my Lord.
3. Je - sus, Je - sus, be the warmth of my heart.
4. Je - sus, Je - sus, you are my Light.
5. Je - sus, Je - sus, "Let it be done to me."

1-5. Je - sus, Je - sus, you are the way.

542 God Has Chosen Me

Verses
1. God has cho-sen me, God has cho-sen me to bring good news to the poor. God has cho-sen me, God has cho-sen me to bring __ new sight to those search-ing for light: God has cho - sen me, cho - sen me:
2. God has cho-sen me, God has cho-sen me to set a - light a new fire. God has cho-sen me, God has cho-sen me to bring __ to birth a new king-dom on earth: God has cho - sen me, cho - sen me:
3. God is call-ing me, God is call-ing me in all whose cry is un-heard. God is call-ing me, God is call-ing me to raise up the voice with no pow - er or choice: God is call - ing me, call - ing me:
Refrain
And to tell the world that God's king-dom is near, to re - move op-pres - sion and break down fear, yes, God's time is near, God's time is near, God's time is near, God's time is near.

543 Take the Word of God with You

Verses

1. Take the word of God with you as you go.
2. Take the peace of God with you as you go.
3. Take the joy of God with you as you go.
4. Take the *love of God with you as you go.

*Add other words if needed, such as "faith," "hope," etc.

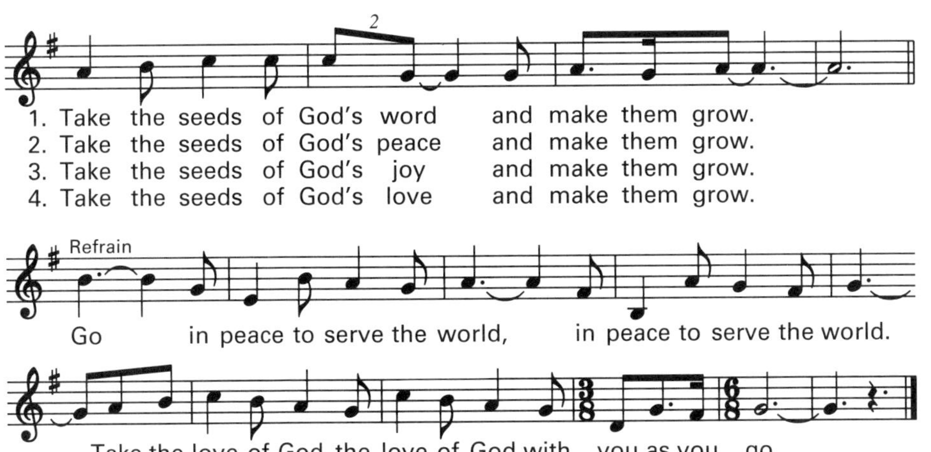
2
1. Take the seeds of God's word and make them grow.
2. Take the seeds of God's peace and make them grow.
3. Take the seeds of God's joy and make them grow.
4. Take the seeds of God's love and make them grow.
Refrain
Go in peace to serve the world, in peace to serve the world.

Take the love of God, the love of God with you as you go.

Text: James Harrison, b. 1979, © 1991, James Harrison. Published by OCP. All rights reserved.
Music: Christopher Walker, b. 1947, © 1991, Christopher Walker. Published by OCP. All rights reserved.

THEY'LL KNOW WE ARE CHRISTIANS 544

Verses

1. We are one in the Spir - it, we are one in the Lord,
2. We will walk with each oth - er, we will walk hand in hand,
3. We will work with each oth - er, we will work side by side,
4. All ___ praise to the Fa - ther, from ___ whom all things come,

1. We are one in the Spir - it, we are one in the Lord,
2. We will walk with each oth - er, we will walk hand in hand,
3. We will work with each oth - er, we will work side by side,
4. And all praise to Christ Je - sus, his ___ on - ly ___ Son,

1. And we pray that all u - ni - ty may one day be re - stored.
2. And to - geth - er we'll spread the news that God is in our land.
3. And we'll guard each one's dig - ni - ty and save _ each one's pride.
4. And all praise to the Spir - it, who ___ makes _ us ___ one.

Refrain

And they'll know we are Chris-tians by our love, by our love, Yes they'll know we are Chris-tians by our love.

Text: 13 13 14 with refrain; Peter Scholtes, 1938–2009.
Music: ST. BRENDAN'S; Peter Scholtes.

545 COMPANIONS ON THE JOURNEY

Refrain
We are com-pan-ions on the jour - ney, break-ing bread and
shar-ing life; and in the love we bear is the hope we share for we be-
lieve in the love of our God, we be-lieve in the love of our God.
Verse 1
1. No long-er strang-ers to each oth - er; no long-er
1. strang-ers in God's house; we are fed and we are nour-ished by the
to Refrain
1. strength of those who care, by the strength of those who care.
Verse 2
2. We have been gift-ed with each oth - er, and we are called by the
2. Word of the Lord: to act with jus-tice, to love ten-der - ly, and to walk
to Refrain
2. hum-bly with our God, to walk hum-bly with our God.
Verse 3
3. We will seek and we shall find; we will knock and the door will be
3. o-pened; we will ask and it shall be giv-en, for we be-lieve in the
to Refrain
3. love of our God, we be-lieve in the love of our God.

Verse 4
4. We are made for the glo-ry of our God, for ser-vice in the name of
4. Je-sus; to walk side by side with hope in our hearts, for we be-
to Refrain
4. lieve in the love of our God, we be-lieve in the love of our God.

Text: Based on Micah 6:8; Matthew 7:7; Carey Landry, b. 1944.
Music: Carey Landry.

Many and Great 546

Verses

1. Man-y and great are bear-ers of the Word: the Christ speaks; the heart seeks. Gath-ered as one, we lis-ten to the Word and share the meal of new birth.
2. Man-y and great are seeds up-on the field: the hand sows; the seeds grow. Take now and eat the cov-e-nant ful-filled, the bread of prom-ise and life.
3. Man-y and great are voic-es of de-spair: the rain falls; the voice calls. Take now and drink the wine of hope and care; our cup of bless-ing we share.
4. Man-y and great are peb-bles in the sand: the sun glows; the wind blows. Take now and spread the Word to ev-'ry land, the Word of good-ness and hope.

Refrain

The wheat grows from spring-time to fall; the wine flows; in Christ we re-call the shar-ing of our lives with one and all.

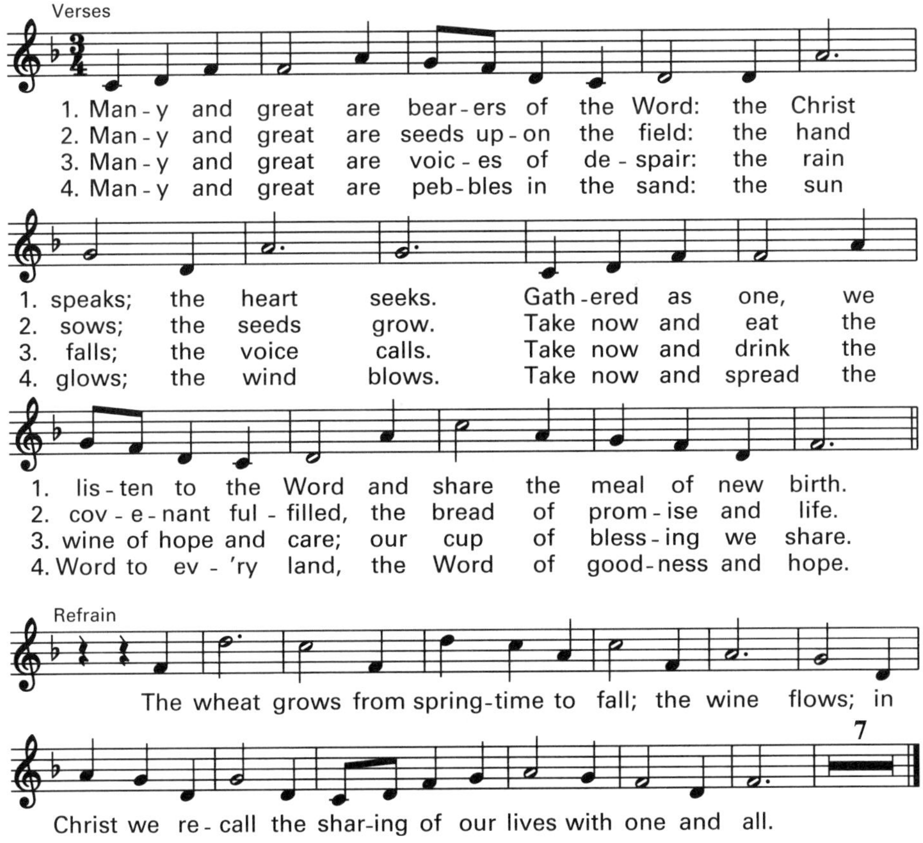

Text and music: Ricky Manalo, CSP, b. 1965,

547 Somos el Cuerpo de Cristo/ We Are the Body of Christ

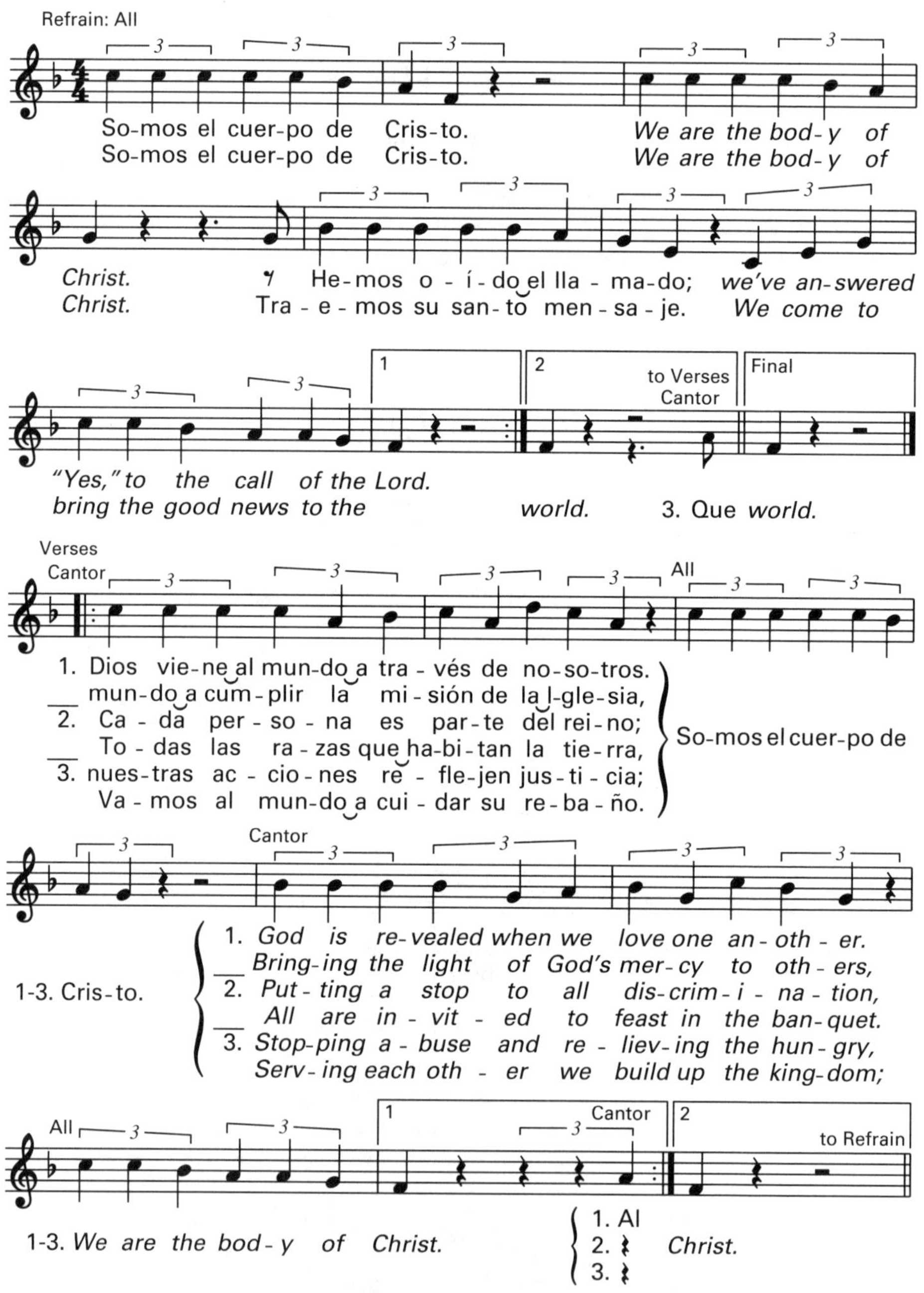
Refrain: All
So-mos el cuer-po de Cris-to. We are the bod-y of
So-mos el cuer-po de Cris-to. We are the bod-y of
Christ. He-mos o - í - do el lla - ma-do; we've an-swered
Christ. Tra - e - mos su san-to men - sa - je. We come to
"Yes," to the call of the Lord.
bring the good news to the world. 3. Que world.
1
2
to Verses
Cantor
Final
Verses
Cantor
All
1. Dios vie-ne al mun-do a tra - vés de no-so-tros.
mun-do a cum-plir la mi-sión de la I-gle-sia,
2. Ca - da per - so - na es par-te del rei-no;
To - das las ra-zas que ha-bi-tan la tie-rra,
3. nues-tras ac - cio-nes re - fle-jen jus-ti - cia;
Va - mos al mun-do a cui - dar su re-ba-ño.
So-mos el cuer-po de
1-3. Cris-to.
Cantor
1. God is re-vealed when we love one an-oth - er.
Bring-ing the light of God's mer-cy to oth - ers,
2. Put - ting a stop to all dis-crim - i - na - tion,
All are in - vit - ed to feast in the ban-quet.
3. Stop-ping a - buse and re - liev-ing the hun-gry,
Serv-ing each oth - er we build up the king-dom;
All
1-3. We are the bod-y of Christ.
1
Cantor
2
to Refrain
1. Al
2.
3.
Christ.

Text: Jaime Cortez, b. 1963, and Bob Hurd, b. 1950.
Music: Jaime Cortez.

In Christ There Is No East or West 548

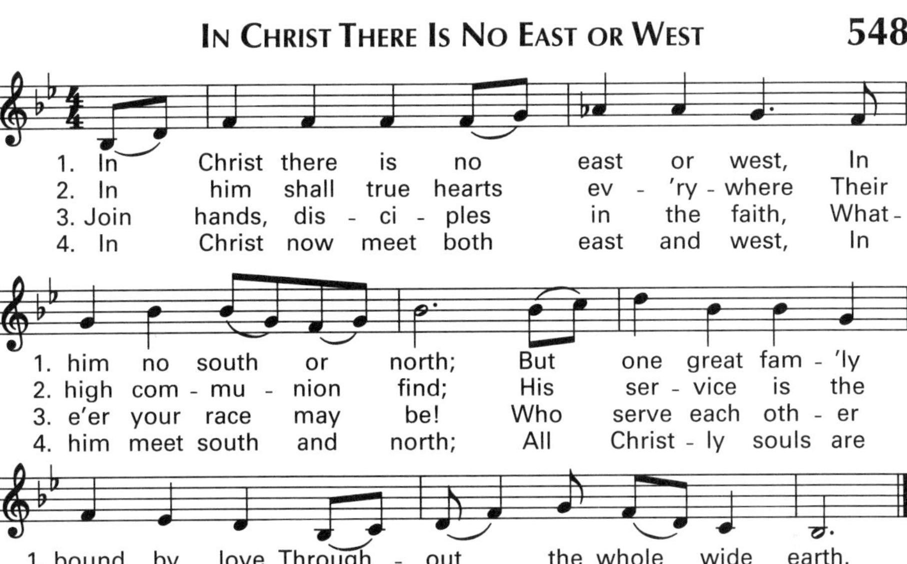
1. In Christ there is no east or west, In him no south or north; But one great fam - 'ly bound by love Through - out the whole wide earth.
2. In him shall true hearts ev - 'ry - where Their high com - mu - nion find; His ser - vice is the gold - en cord Close - bind - ing hu - man - kind.
3. Join hands, dis - ci - ples in the faith, What - e'er your race may be! Who serve each oth - er in Christ's love Are sure - ly kin to me.
4. In Christ now meet both east and west, In him meet south and north; All Christ - ly souls are one in him, Through - out the whole wide earth.

Text: CM; Based on Galatians 3:28; John Oxenham, 1852–1941, alt.
Music: McKEE; Spiritual; adapt. by Harry T. Burleigh, 1866–1949.

As We Celebrate 549

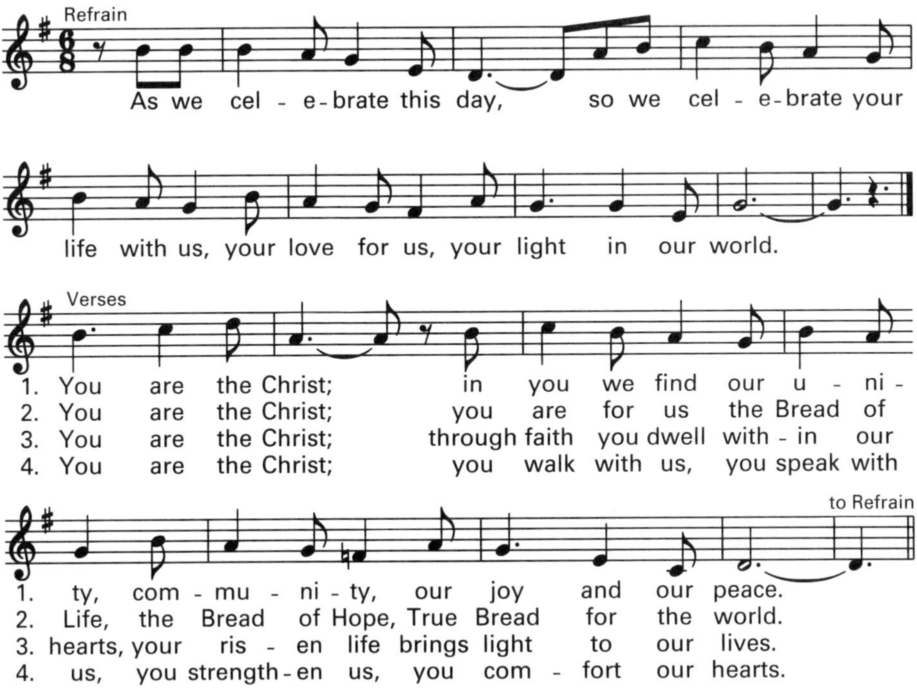

Refrain

As we cel - e - brate this day, so we cel - e - brate your life with us, your love for us, your light in our world.

Verses

1. You are the Christ; in you we find our u - ni - ty, com - mu - ni - ty, our joy and our peace.
2. You are the Christ; you are for us the Bread of Life, the Bread of Hope, True Bread for the world.
3. You are the Christ; through faith you dwell with - in our hearts, your ris - en life brings light to our lives.
4. You are the Christ; you walk with us, you speak with us, you strength - en us, you com - fort our hearts.

to Refrain

Text and music: Carey Landry, b. 1944,

550 We Are Many Parts

Refrain

We are man-y parts, we are all one bod-y, and the gifts we have we are giv-en to share. May the Spir-it of love make us one in-deed; one, the love that we share, one, our hope in de-spair, one, the cross that we bear.

Verses

1. God of all, we look to you, we would be your servants true, let us be your love to all the world. to Refrain
2. So my pain is pain for you, in your joy is my joy, too; all is brought to-geth-er in the Lord.
3. All you seek-ers great and small, seek the great-est gift of all; if you love, then you will know the Lord.

Text: Based on 1 Corinthians 12, 13; Marty Haugen, b. 1950.
Music: Marty Haugen.

551 Many and One

Refrain
We are man - y, yet we are one. We are sep - 'rate, yet bound in his love. And to-geth - er we are all his hands and his feet, bring-ing mer - cy and peace to this world. We are man - y and one.
3

Verses
1. We are fall - en but we are for - giv - en;
2. We are dif - f'rent as morn-ing and eve - ning,
3. We are broth - ers and sis - ters in spir - it,
1. bro - ken and scat - tered, yet be - ing made whole
2. each of us liv - ing as we have been called,
3. found in all na - tions yet near to the Lord,
1. by our re-deem - er, one Lord and one sav - ior,
2. all of us seek - ing, each of us reach-ing to
3. each one be-long - ing, to - geth - er now long-ing for
to Refrain
1-3. the shep-herd who gath-ers us all, gath-ers us all.

Text and music: Steve Angrisano, b. 1965, Sarah Hart, b. 1968, and Dwight Liles, b. 1957,

TAKE UP YOUR CROSS 552

1. Take up your cross, the Sav - ior said, If
2. Take up your cross, be not a - shamed! Let
3. Take up your cross, which gives you strength, Which
4. Take up your cross, and fol - low Christ, Nor
1. you would my dis - ci - ple be; De - ny your - self, the
2. not dis-grace your spir - it fill! For God him - self en -
3. makes your trem-bling spir - it brave: 'Twill guide you to a
4. think till death to lay it down; For on - ly they who
1. world for - sake, And hum - bly fol - low af - ter me.
2. dured to die Up - on a cross, on Cal - vary's hill.
3. bet - ter home And lead to vic - t'ry o'er the grave.
4. bear the cross May hope to wear the glo - rious crown.

Text: LM; Charles W. Everest, 1814–1877, alt.
Music: ERHALT UNS, HERR; J. Klug's *Geistliche Lieder*, Wittenberg, 1543; adapt. by Johann Sebastian Bach, 1685–1750, alt.

553 ALL THAT IS HIDDEN

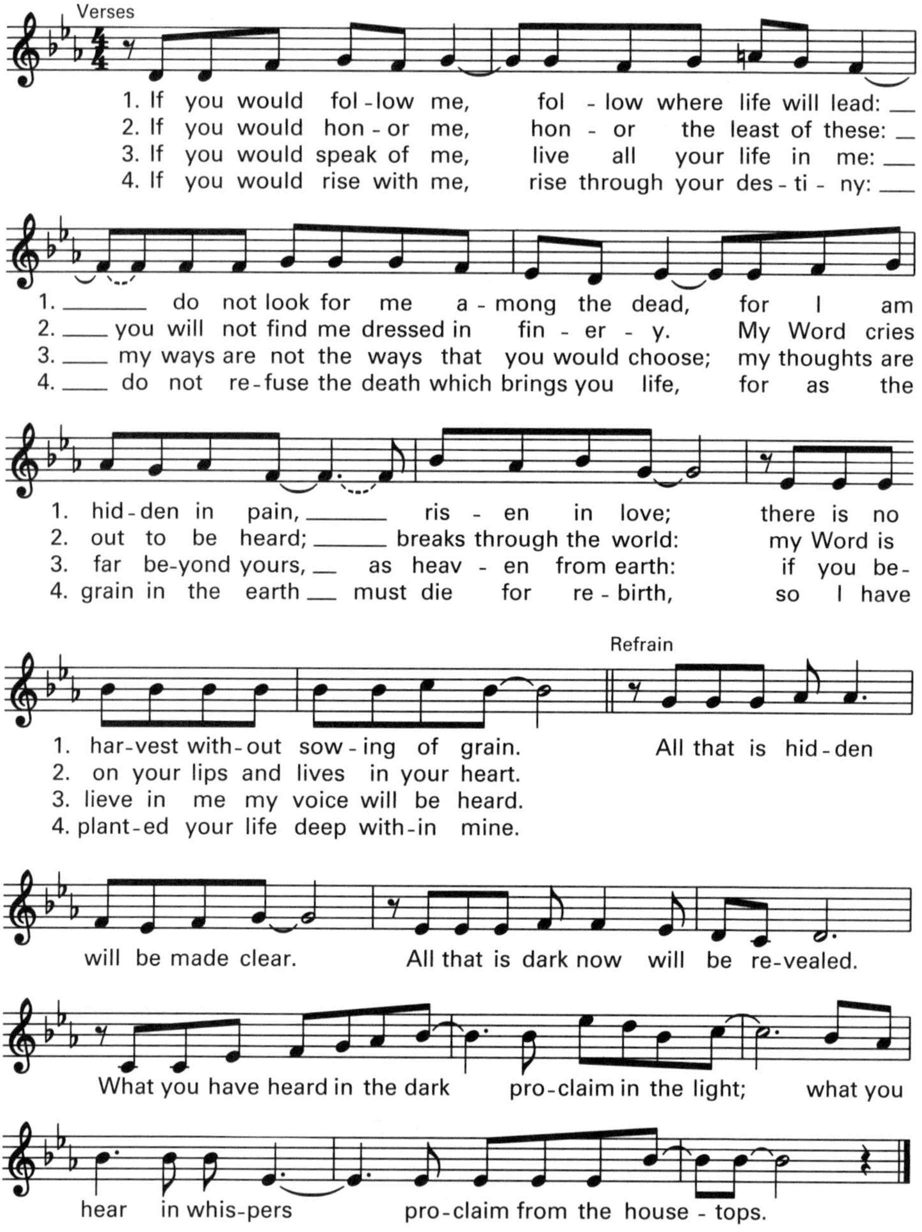

Verses

1. If you would fol - low me, fol - low where life will lead: ___ ___ do not look for me a - mong the dead, for I am hid - den in pain, ___ ris - en in love; there is no har - vest with - out sow - ing of grain.

2. If you would hon - or me, hon - or the least of these: ___ ___ you will not find me dressed in fin - er - y. My Word cries out to be heard; ___ breaks through the world: my Word is on your lips and lives in your heart.

3. If you would speak of me, live all your life in me: ___ ___ my ways are not the ways that you would choose; my thoughts are far be - yond yours, ___ as heav - en from earth: if you be - lieve in me my voice will be heard.

4. If you would rise with me, rise through your des - ti - ny: ___ ___ do not re - fuse the death which brings you life, for as the grain in the earth ___ must die for re - birth, so I have plant - ed your life deep with - in mine.

Refrain

All that is hid - den will be made clear. All that is dark now will be re - vealed. What you have heard in the dark pro - claim in the light; what you hear in whis - pers pro - claim from the house - tops.

Text: Refrain based on Luke 12:2–3; Bernadette Farrell, b. 1957.
Music: Bernadette Farrell.

Go Make a Difference 554

Refrain
Go make a dif - f'rence. We can make a dif - f'rence. Go make a dif - f'rence in the world.
Go make a dif - f'rence. We can make a dif - f'rence. Go make a dif - f'rence in the world.
Verses
1. We are the salt of the earth, called to let the peo - ple see the love of God in you and me. We are the light of the world, not to be hid - den but be seen. Go make a dif - f'rence in the world.
2. We are the hands of Christ reach - ing out to those in need, the face of God for all to see. We are the spir - it of hope; we are the voice of peace. Go make a dif - f'rence in the world.
3. So let your love shine on, let it shine for all to see. Go make a dif - f'rence in the world. And the spir - it of Christ will be with us as we go. Go make a dif - f'rence in the world.
to Refrain

Text: Based on Matthew 5:13–16; Steve Angrisano, b. 1965, and Tom Tomaszek, b. 1950.
Music: Steve Angrisano and Tom Tomaszek.

555 Pescador de Hombres/Lord, You Have Come

Verses
1. Tú has ve - ni - do a la o - ri - lla, no has bus - ca - do
2. Tú sa - bes bien lo que ten - go; en mi bar - ca
3. Tú ne - ce - si - tas mis ma - nos, mi can - san - cio
4. Tú, pes - ca - dor de o - tros la - gos, an - sia e - ter - na
1. Lord, you have come to the sea-shore, nei - ther search-ing for
2. Lord, see my goods, my pos - ses - sions; in my boat you find
3. Lord, take my hands and di - rect them. Help me spend my - self
4. Lord, as I drift on the wa - ters, be the rest - ing place
1. ni a sa - bios ni a ri - cos; tan só - lo quie - res
2. no hay o - ro ni es - pa - das, tan só - lo re - des
3. que a o - tros des - can - se, a - mor que quie - ra
4. de al - mas que es - pe - ran, a - mi - go bue - no,
1. the rich nor the wise, de - sir - ing on - ly
2. no pow - er, no wealth. Will you ac - cept, then,
3. in seek - ing the lost, re - turn - ing love for
4. of my rest - less heart, my life's com - pan - ion,
1. que yo te si - ga.
2. y mi tra - ba - jo.
3. se - guir a - man - do.
4. que a - sí me lla - mas.
1. that I should fol - low.
2. my nets and la - bor?
3. the love you gave me.
4. my friend and ref - uge.
Refrain
Se - ñor, me has mi - ra - do a los o - jos, son - ri - en - do has di - cho mi nom - bre, en la a - re - na he de - ja - do mi bar - ca, jun - to a ti bus - ca - ré o - tro mar.
O Lord, with your eyes set up - on me, gent - ly smil - ing, you have spo - ken my name; all I longed for I have found by the wa - ter, at your side, I will seek oth - er shores.

Text: Spanish, Cesáreo Gabaráin, 1936–1991; English, OCP.
Music: Cesáreo Gabaráin.

ANTHEM

556

Refrain
We are called, we are cho-sen. We are Christ for one an-oth-er. We are
prom-ised to to-mor-row, while we are for him to-day. We are
sign, we are won-der. We are sow-er, we are seed. We are
har-vest, we are hun-ger. We are ques-tion, we are creed.
Verses
1. Then where can we stand jus-ti-fied? In what can we be-lieve? In no one
2. Then how are we to stand at all, this world of bend-ed knee? In noth-ing
3. Then shall we not stand emp-ty at the al-tar of our dreams: When he
1. else but he who suf-fered, noth-ing more than he who rose.
2. more than bar-ren shad-ows. No one else but he could save us.
3. prom-ised us our-selves. Who mark time a-gainst to-mor-row.
1, 2. Who was jus-tice for the poor. Who was rage a-gainst the night.
3. Who are jus-tice for the poor. Who are rage a-gainst the night.
to Refrain
1, 2. Who was hope for peace-ful peo-ple. Who was light.
3. Who are hope for peace-ful peo-ple. Who are light.

557 YOUR SONG OF LOVE

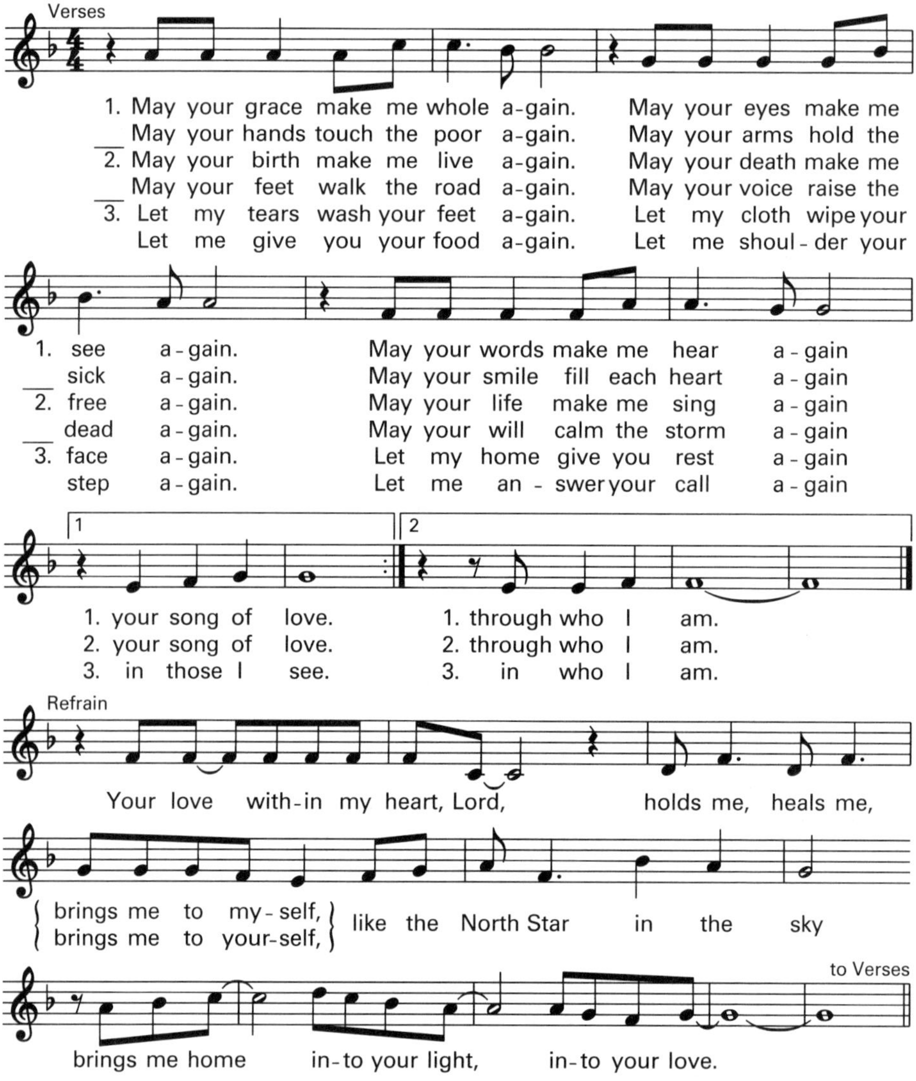

Verses

1. May your grace make me whole a-gain. May your eyes make me see a-gain. May your words make me hear a-gain your song of love.
May your hands touch the poor a-gain. May your arms hold the sick a-gain. May your smile fill each heart a-gain through who I am.

2. May your birth make me live a-gain. May your death make me free a-gain. May your life make me sing a-gain your song of love.
May your feet walk the road a-gain. May your voice raise the dead a-gain. May your will calm the storm a-gain through who I am.

3. Let my tears wash your feet a-gain. Let my cloth wipe your face a-gain. Let my home give you rest a-gain in those I see.
Let me give you your food a-gain. Let me shoul-der your step a-gain. Let me an-swer your call a-gain in who I am.

Refrain

Your love with-in my heart, Lord, holds me, heals me,
{ brings me to my-self, / brings me to your-self, } like the North Star in the sky
brings me home in-to your light, in-to your love.

to Verses

558 COME, FOLLOW ME

Refrain
Come, fol - low me and live; do not be a - fraid. Be -
lieve and trust in me; your faith will give you strength. Leave

all your fears be - hind you; let your heart be free, for
I will be your guide. Oh, come and fol - low me.
Verses
1. Come, fol - low in these foot - steps; I'll lead you gent - ly home.
2. Come, walk a - cross the wa - ter; place all your faith in me.
3. If you re - main with - in me, my words re - main in you.
to Refrain
1. No shel - ter, food nor mon - ey will you need up - on this road.
2. Cast all your doubts be - hind you to the wind and rag - ing sea.
3. What - ev - er you may ask of me, that is what I will do.

Text and music: Gael Berberick (ASCAP), b. 1957, and Barney Walker (ASCAP), b. 1946,

Earthen Vessels 559

Refrain

We hold a trea - sure, not made of gold, in earth - en ves - sels, wealth un - told; one trea - sure on - ly: the Lord, the Christ, in earth - en ves - sels.

Verses

1. Light has shone in our dark - ness: God has shone in our heart
2. God has cho - sen the low - ly who are small in this world;

to Refrain

1. with the light of the glo - ry of Je - sus, the Lord.
2. in this weak - ness is glo - ry in Je - sus, the Lord.

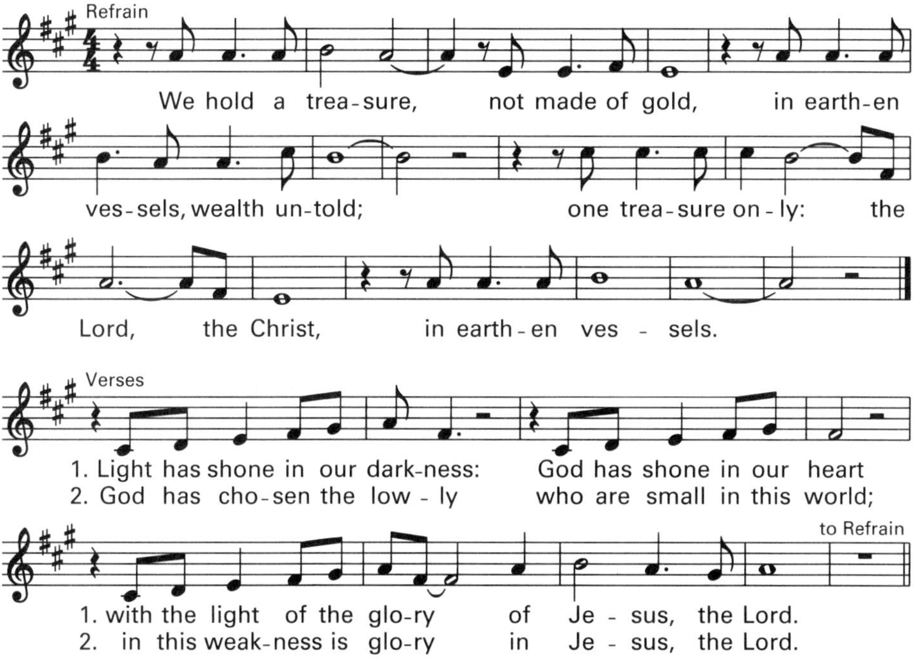

Text: Based on 2 Corinthians 4:6–7; 1 Corinthians 1:27–29; John Foley, S.J., b. 1939.
Music: John Foley, S.J.

560 OUT OF DARKNESS

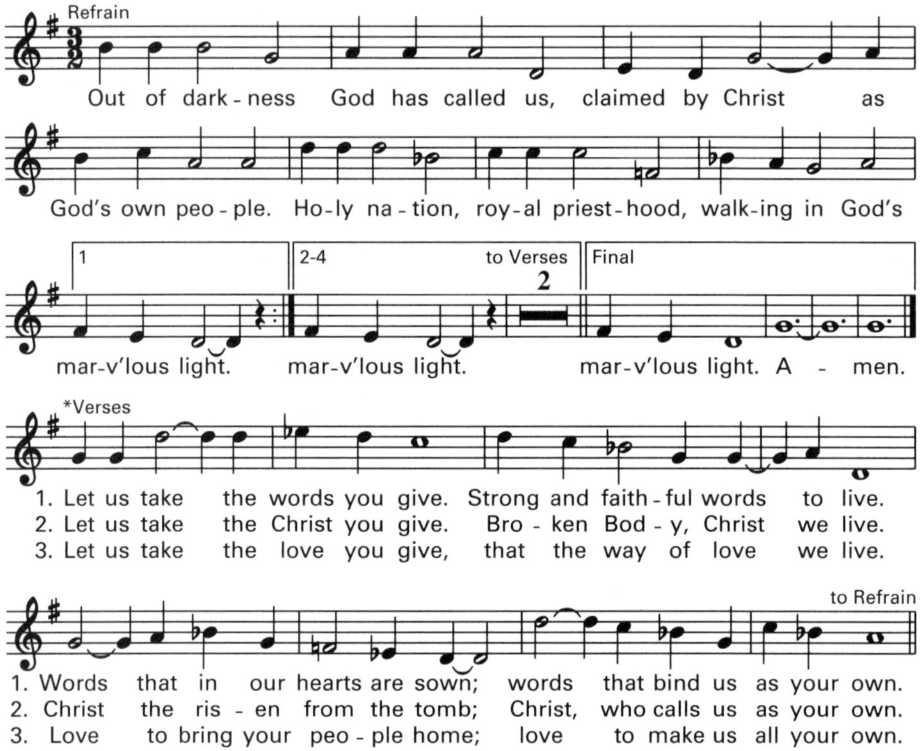

Refrain

Out of dark-ness God has called us, claimed by Christ as God's own peo-ple. Ho-ly na-tion, roy-al priest-hood, walk-ing in God's

1 mar-v'lous light. 2-4 mar-v'lous light. to Verses 2 Final mar-v'lous light. A - men.

*Verses

1. Let us take the words you give. Strong and faith-ful words to live.
2. Let us take the Christ you give. Bro-ken Bod-y, Christ we live.
3. Let us take the love you give, that the way of love we live.

1. Words that in our hearts are sown; words that bind us as your own.
2. Christ the ris-en from the tomb; Christ, who calls us as your own.
3. Love to bring your peo-ple home; love to make us all your own.

to Refrain

*Octavo 9232 provides supplemental verses for Easter, Ordinations, and Chrism Mass.

561 TAKE, LORD, RECEIVE

Verse 1
1. Take, Lord, re-ceive all my lib-er-ty, my
1. mem-o-ry, un-der-stand-ing, my en-tire will.
Refrain
Give me on-ly your love and your grace: that's e-
nough for me. Your love and your grace

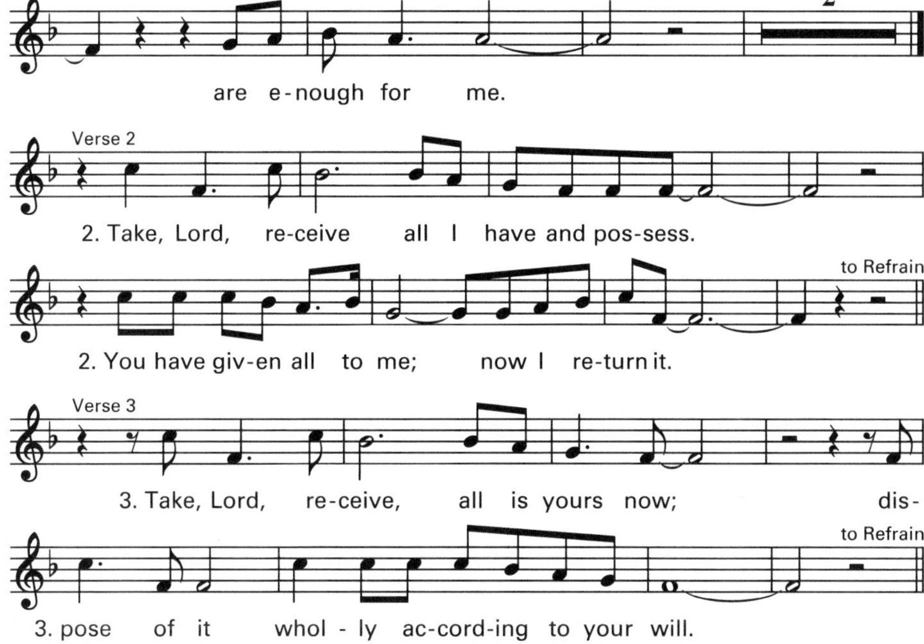
are e-nough for me.
Verse 2
2. Take, Lord, re-ceive all I have and pos-sess.
2. You have giv-en all to me; now I re-turn it.
to Refrain
Verse 3
3. Take, Lord, re-ceive, all is yours now; dis-
3. pose of it whol - ly ac-cord-ing to your will.
to Refrain

Text: Based on *Spiritual Exercises*; St. Ignatius of Loyola, 1491–1556; John Foley, SJ, b. 1939.
Music: John Foley, SJ.

Only This I Want 562

Refrain
On - ly this I want: but to know the Lord,
and to bear his cross, so to wear the crown he wore.
Verses
1. All but this is loss, worth-less ref-use to me,
2. I will run the race; I will fight the good fight,
3. Let your heart be glad, al - ways glad in the Lord,
1. for to gain the Lord is to gain ___ all I need.
2. so to win the prize of the king-dom of my Lord.
3. so to shine like stars in the dark-ness of the night.
to Refrain

Text: Based on Philippians 3:7–16; 2:15, 18; Dan Schutte, b. 1947.
Music: Dan Schutte.

563 UNLESS A GRAIN OF WHEAT

Refrain

Unless a grain of wheat shall fall upon the ground and die,
it remains but a single grain with no life.

Verses

1. If we have died with him, then we shall live with him;
if we hold firm, we shall reign with him.

2. If anyone serves me, then they must follow me;
wherever I am, my servants will be.

3. Make your home in me as I make mine in you;
those who remain in me bear much fruit.

4. If you remain in me and my word lives in you,
then you will be my disciples.

5. Those who love me are loved by my Father;
we shall be with them and dwell in them.

6. Peace I leave with you, my peace I give to you;
peace which the world cannot give is my gift.

to Refrain

Text: Based on John 12:24–26; 14:23, 27; 15:4–5, 7–8; 2 Timothy 2:11–12; Bernadette Farrell, b. 1957.
Music: Bernadette Farrell.

564 WE HAVE BEEN TOLD

Refrain
We have been told, we've seen his face and heard his voice a -
live in our hearts; "Live in my love with all your heart, as the
Fa - ther has loved me, so I have loved you."
2

Verses
1. "I am the vine, you are the branch-es, and
2. "You are my friends, if you keep my com - mands,
3. "No great-er love is there than this: to
to Refrain
1. all who live in me will bear great fruit."
2. no long - er slaves, I call you friends."
3. lay down one's life for a friend."

Text and music: David Haas, b. 1957,

Before the Sun Burned Bright 565

Refrain

Be - fore the sun burned bright and riv-ers flowed,
I called you each by name to share My home.
No long-er be a - fraid; I am your God.
My love will nev - er end, Al - le - lu - ia.

Verses

1. Though you have sent me, Lord, to ev - ery land,
2. The Lord reached out his hand and touched my tongue.
3. My hand will bring you words, so speak them loud.

to Refrain

1. I can't find words to speak Your ways of love.
2. I give My words to you to speak My love.
3. I am your Lord and God; the Faith - ful One.

Text: Based on Jeremiah 1:4–10; Dan Schutte, b. 1947.
Music: Dan Schutte.

566 CHRIST HAS NO BODY NOW BUT YOURS

Refrain

Christ has no bod - y now but yours, no hands but yours. Here on this earth yours is the work, to serve with the joy of com - pas - sion.

Verses

1. No hands but yours to heal the wound - ed world, no hands but yours to soothe all its suf - f'ring, no touch but yours to bind the bro - ken hope of the peo - ple of God.
2. No eyes but yours to see as Christ would see, to find the lost, to gaze with com - pas - sion; no eyes but yours to glimpse the ho - ly joy of the cit - y of God.
3. No feet but yours to jour - ney with the poor, to walk this world with mer - cy and jus - tice. Yours are the steps to build a last - ing peace for the chil - dren of God.
4. Through ev - ery gift, give back to those in need: As Christ has blessed, so now be his bless - ing, with ev - ery gift a ben - e - dic - tion be to the peo - ple of God.

to Refrain

Text: St. Teresa of Ávila, 1515–1582; adapt. by Steven C. Warner, b. 1954.
Music: Steven C. Warner.

567 JESU, JOY OF OUR DESIRING

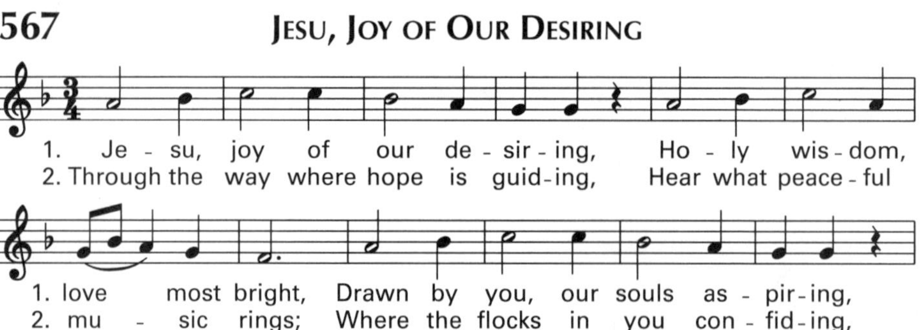
1. Je - su, joy of our de - sir - ing, Ho - ly wis - dom,
2. Through the way where hope is guid - ing, Hear what peace - ful
1. love most bright, Drawn by you, our souls as - pir - ing,
2. mu - sic rings; Where the flocks in you con - fid - ing,

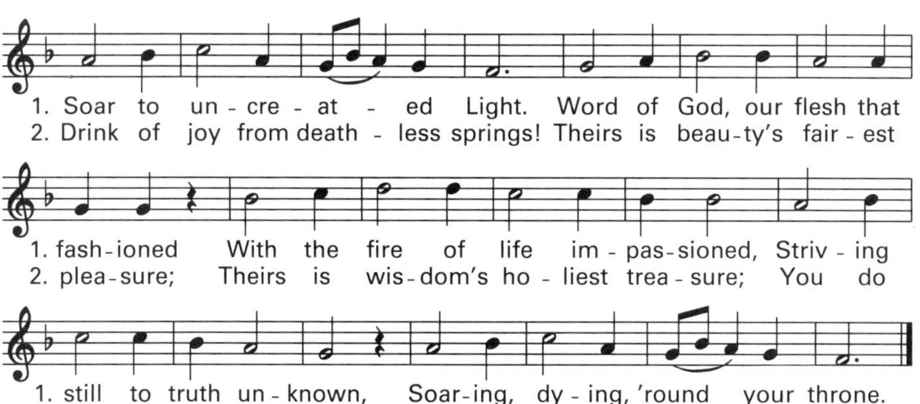
1. Soar to un-cre-at-ed Light. Word of God, our flesh that
2. Drink of joy from death-less springs! Theirs is beau-ty's fair-est
1. fash-ioned With the fire of life im-pas-sioned, Striv-ing
2. plea-sure; Theirs is wis-dom's ho-liest trea-sure; You do
1. still to truth un-known, Soar-ing, dy-ing, 'round your throne.
2. ev-er lead your own, In the love of joys un-known.

Text: 87 87 88 77; *Christlich Herzens Andacht*, 1665; Martin Jahn, ca. 1620–1682; tr. by Robert S. Bridges, 1844–1930, rev.
Music: WERDE MUNTER; *Himmlische Lieder*, Vol. 3, Lüneberg, 1642; Johann P. Schop, ca. 1590–1664.

ONE SPIRIT, ONE CHURCH 568

Refrain

We are a pil-grim peo-ple, we are the Church of God. A fam-'ly of be-liev-ers, dis-ci-ples of the Lord. U-nit-ed in one spir-it, ig-nit-ed by the fire. Still burn-ing through the a-ges, still pres-ent in our lives. lives. A-men!

1, 2 to Vss | Final | Verses

1. Come, Ho-ly Ghost, Cre-a-tor blest, and in our hearts take up thy rest; come with thy grace and heav'n-ly aid to fill the hearts which thou hast made.

2. O Com-fort-er, to thee we cry, thou gift of God sent from on high. Thou font of life and fire of love, the soul's a-noint-ing from a-bove.

to Refrain

Text: Refrain, Maryanne Quinlivan, OSU, © 1990, Ursuline Academy of Cleveland. Published by OCP. All rights reserved. Verses fr. *Veni, Creator Spiritus*; attr. to Rabanus Maurus, 776–856; tr. by Edward Caswall, 1814–1878, alt.
Music: Refrain, Kevin Keil, ASCAP, © 1990, Kevin Keil. Published by OCP. All rights reserved.
Verses based on LAMBILLOTTE.

569 Sing a New Church

Verses
1. Sum-moned by the God who made us Rich in
2. Ra - diant ris - en from the wa - ter, Robed in
3. Trust the good - ness of cre - a - tion; Trust the
4. Bring the hopes of ev - 'ry na - tion; Bring the
5. Draw to - geth - er at one ta - ble All the
1. our di - ver - si - ty, Gath-ered in the name of
2. ho - li - ness and light, Male and fe - male in God's
3. Spir - it strong with - in. Dare to dream the vi - sion
4. art of ev - 'ry race. Weave a song of peace and
5. hu - man fam - i - ly; Shape a cir - cle ev - er
1. Je - sus, Rich - er still in u - ni - ty:
2. im - age, Male and fe - male, God's de - light:
3. prom - ised, Sprung from seed of what has been.
4. jus - tice; Let it sound through time and space.
5. wid - er And a peo - ple ev - er free.
Refrain
Let us bring the gifts that dif - fer And, in
splen - did, var - ied ways, Sing a new church in - to
be - ing, One in faith and love and praise.

Text: 87 87 with refrain; Delores Dufner, OSB, b. 1939,
Music: NETTLETON; J. Wyeth's *Repository of Sacred Music, Pt. II*, 1813.

ALL ARE WELCOME 570

1. Let us build a house where love can dwell And
2. Let us build a house where proph - ets speak, And
3. Let us build a house where love is found In
4. Let us build a house where hands will reach Be -
5. Let us build a house where all are named, Their

1. all can safe - ly live, A place where saints and
2. words are strong and true, Where all God's chil - dren
3. wa - ter, wine and wheat: A ban - quet hall on
4. yond the wood and stone To heal and strength - en,
5. songs and vi - sions heard And loved and trea - sured,

1. chil - dren tell How hearts learn to for - give. Built of
2. dare to seek To dream God's reign a - new. Here the
3. ho - ly ground, Where peace and jus - tice meet. Here the
4. serve and teach, And live the Word they've known. Here the
5. taught and claimed As words with - in the Word. Built of

1. hopes and dreams and vi - sions, Rock of faith and vault of
2. cross shall stand as wit - ness And as sym - bol of God's
3. love of God, through Je - sus, Is re - vealed in time and
4. out - cast and the strang - er Bear the im - age of God's
5. tears and cries and laugh - ter, Prayers of faith and songs of

1. grace; Here the love of Christ shall end di - vi - sions:
2. grace; Here as one we claim the faith of Je - sus:
3. space; As we share in Christ the feast that frees us:
4. face; Let us bring an end to fear and dan - ger:
5. grace, Let this house pro - claim from floor to raf - ter:

1-5. All are wel - come, all are wel - come, all are wel - come

1-5. in this place.

Text: 96 86 87 10 with refrain; Marty Haugen, b. 1950.
Music: TWO OAKS; Marty Haugen.

571 THE CHURCH'S ONE FOUNDATION

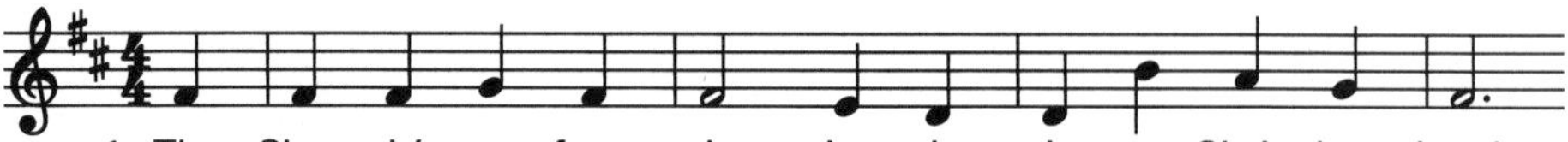

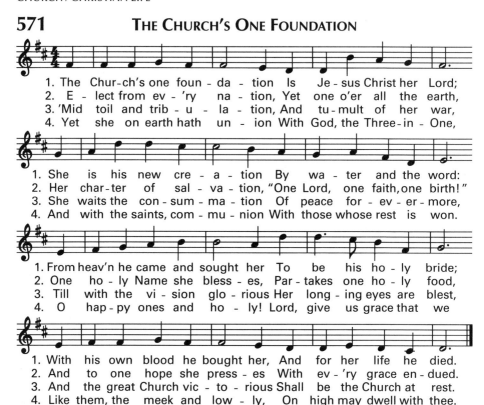

1. The Church's one foundation Is Jesus Christ her Lord;
She is his new creation By water and the word:
From heav'n he came and sought her To be his holy bride;
With his own blood he bought her, And for her life he died.

2. Elect from ev'ry nation, Yet one o'er all the earth,
Her charter of salvation, "One Lord, one faith, one birth!"
One holy Name she blesses, Partakes one holy food,
And to one hope she presses With ev'ry grace endued.

3. 'Mid toil and tribulation, And tumult of her war,
She waits the consummation Of peace forevermore,
Till with the vision glorious Her longing eyes are blest,
And the great Church victorious Shall be the Church at rest.

4. Yet she on earth hath union With God, the Three-in-One,
And with the saints, communion With those whose rest is won.
O happy ones and holy! Lord, give us grace that we
Like them, the meek and lowly, On high may dwell with thee.

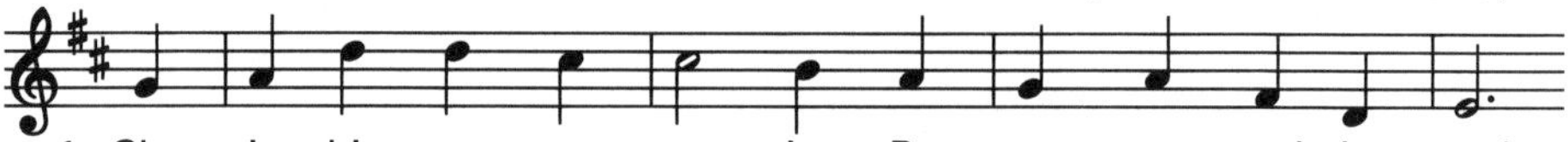

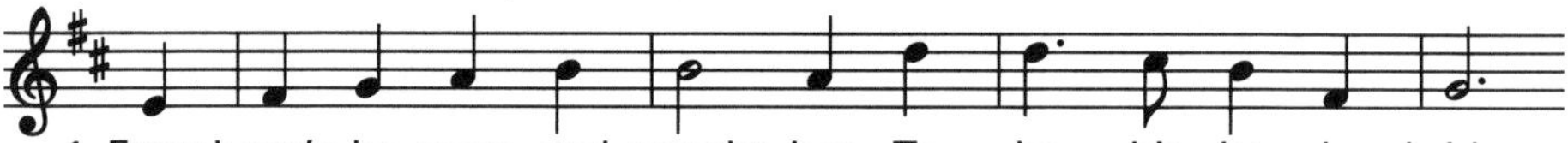

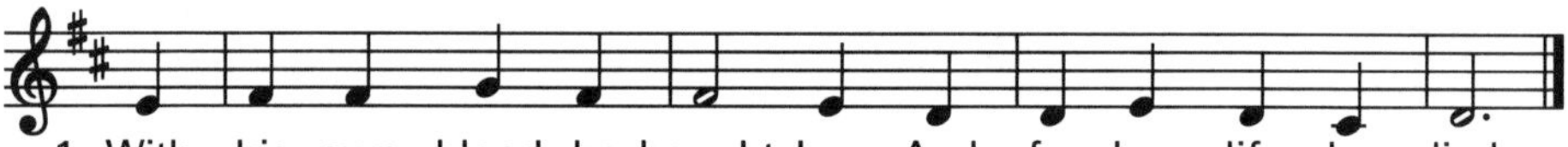

Text: 76 76 D; Samuel J. Stone, 1839–1900, alt.
Music: AURELIA; Samuel S. Wesley, 1810–1876.

572 FATHER OF PEACE

1. Fa-ther of peace, Fa-ther of love,
2. Fa-ther, we pray, day af-ter day,
1. come see our joy now prais-ing your Word.
2. help us to see you; show us your way.
1. Fa-ther of life, Fa-ther of all,
2. Fa-ther of care, guid-ing us all,
1. Fa-ther of ev-'ry-thing that's good. We come to your call.
2. Fill us with ev-'ry-thing that's good. We come to your call.

Christ in Me Arise

573

Refrain
Christ in me a - rise and dis - pel all the dark - ness.
Christ in me a - rise with your pow - er and your strength.
Christ in me pour out your bless - ing and heal - ing.
Christ in me a - rise and I shall rise with you.
Verses
1. Be now my vi - sion; o - pen these eyes, show - ing me
2. Be now my foot - steps, lead - ing the way, tak - ing me
1. all that I must see.
2. where I must go.
On - ward to the king - dom,
1, 2. you are the way. A - rise in me and I shall rise with you.
to Refrain
Bridge
You know my heart and you know my ways, you who
formed me in my moth - er's womb. I live and move in you,
my whole be - ing thrives in you.
2 to Refrain

Text and music: Trevor Thomson, b. 1971, © 2008, Trevor Thomson.

574 I WILL CHOOSE CHRIST

Refrain

I will choose Christ, I will choose love, I choose to serve.
I give my heart, I give my life, I give my all
1-3 to Verses
to you.
Final
to you. I give my all to you.

Verse 1

1. How man-y times must he call my name and show to
1. me that he is God? And as a ser-vant he
1. calls to me, "You must serve too."
to Refrain

Verse 2

2. Christ, my teach - er and heal - er, teach my
2. heart and heal my soul. And as I walk this
2. road with you, teach me to love.
to Refrain

Verse 3

3. As I look up-on your cross, so too
3. must I die with you. And with the death of my

to Refrain
3. own de - sires, I'll rise with you.

Text and music: Tom Booth, b. 1961,

FOR THE SAKE OF CHRIST 575

Refrain

For the sake of Christ, I will-ing-ly ac-cept my weak-ness and my trials,

for when I am pow-er-less, then I am strong.

1, 2, Final — to Verses 1, 2 | 3 — to Verse 3 strong.

Verses 1, 2

1. Al-though in God's love my life was blest, my faith was giv-en to the test. For mer-cy did I pray, and then I heard God say, "My grace is e-nough for you. My grace is e-nough for you."

2. And so when I am weak, then I am free. The pow-er of Christ will rest in me. Through all that I en-dure, the love of God is sure. His grace is e-nough for me. His grace is e-nough for me.

to Refrain

Verse 3

3. He died for all, that those who live might live no long-er for them-selves. Oh, live for Christ who gave his life, and now is raised on high.

to Refrain

Text: Based on 2 Corinthians 5:15; 12:7–10; Ken Canedo, b. 1953.
Music: Ken Canedo.

576 Voice of Christ

Verses 1, 2, 4

1. O ___ Lord, ___ you ___ bless us each day with
2. The ___ spar-row nei-ther sows nor ___ reaps, has
4. We a-wait ___ you with watch-ful ___ eyes, our

1. gifts from your hand. Now ___ as ___ our ___
2. store-house nor barn. And ___ flow-ers nei-ther
4. lamps burn-ing bright. Though we know ___ not when

1. cup o-ver-flows, may we too bring ___ forth.
2. spin nor ___ weave, yet they wear roy-al robes.
4. you will re-turn, we stand wake-ful through the night.

Refrain

We the hands, we the eyes, we the voice of Christ.
O faith-ful God, we en-trust our trea-sure to your heart.

Verse 3

3. The Lord hears the cry of the poor; the
3. lives of the weak he shall save. Bless-ed those who care for the
3. poor; hap-pi-ness is their re-ward.

to Refrain

Text: Based on Luke 12:22–40; Psalm 41:2–3; Psalm 72:12–13; Timothy R. Smith, b. 1960.
Music: Timothy R. Smith.

Women of the Church

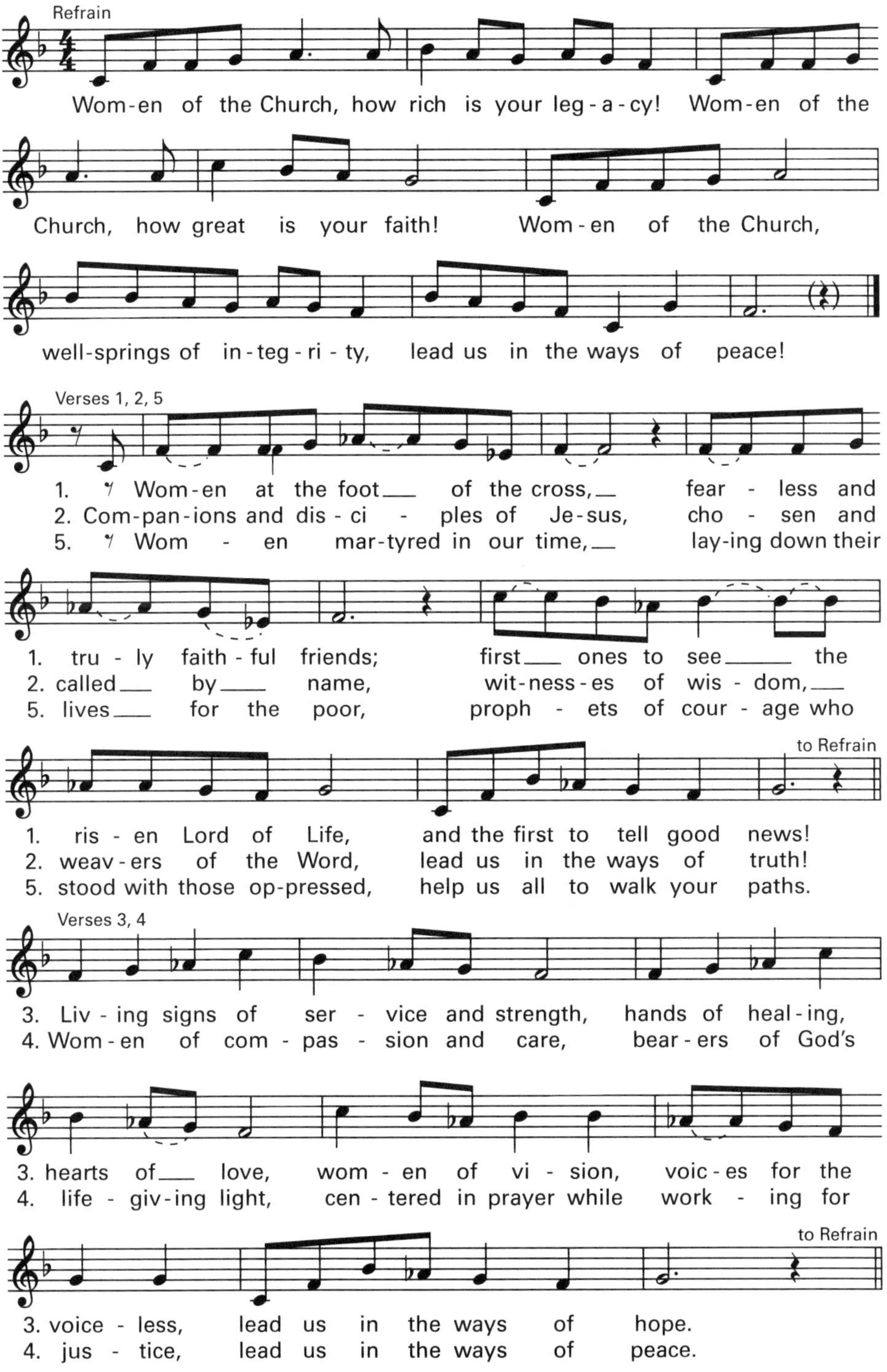

Refrain

Wom-en of the Church, how rich is your leg-a-cy! Wom-en of the Church, how great is your faith! Wom-en of the Church, well-springs of in-teg-ri-ty, lead us in the ways of peace!

Verses 1, 2, 5

1. Wom-en at the foot of the cross, fear-less and tru-ly faith-ful friends; first ones to see the ris-en Lord of Life, and the first to tell good news!
2. Com-pan-ions and dis-ci-ples of Je-sus, cho-sen and called by name, wit-ness-es of wis-dom, weav-ers of the Word, lead us in the ways of truth!
5. Wom-en mar-tyred in our time, lay-ing down their lives for the poor, proph-ets of cour-age who stood with those op-pressed, help us all to walk your paths.

to Refrain

Verses 3, 4

3. Liv-ing signs of ser-vice and strength, hands of heal-ing, hearts of love, wom-en of vi-sion, voic-es for the voice-less, lead us in the ways of hope.
4. Wom-en of com-pas-sion and care, bear-ers of God's life-giv-ing light, cen-tered in prayer while work-ing for jus-tice, lead us in the ways of peace.

to Refrain

578 Now Is the Time

Refrain

Come to us, you who say, "I will not for-get you." Be with us, you who say, "Do not be a-fraid." Take hold of us, our hearts, our minds, our whole be - ing. Make us your own,* now is the time.

Verses

Cantor: 1. Spir-it of love, All: crush the pain of ha-tred.
Cantor: 2. Spir-it of peace, All: si-lence tongues of an-ger.
Cantor: 3. Spir-it of faith, All: rise a-bove our doubt-ing.

Cantor: 1. Spir-it of hope, All: stand be-fore our eyes. Cantor: Spir-it of light,
Cantor: 2. Spir-it of life, All: break the chains of death. Cantor: Spir-it of joy,
Cantor: 3. Spir-it of truth, All: save us from our lies. Cantor: Spir-it of God,

All: 1. dance with-in our dark-ness. Make us your own, now is the time.
All: 2. o-ver-come our sad-ness. Make us your own, now is the time.
All: 3. walk a-mong your peo-ple. Make us your own, now is the time.

to Refrain

*Last time, repeat final phrase twice.

Text and music: Tom Kendzia, b. 1954,

579 Come, Lord Jesus

Refrain
Come, Lord Je - sus, come. Come and fill my heart
with your life. Hold me close, Lord, hold me tight,
and come, Lord Je - sus, come.

Verses
1. Where there's de-spair in life, Lord, let me be your voice of hope. Where there's in-ju-ry, Lord, let me be your voice of peace.
2. Where there is sad-ness let me be your com-fort and your joy. When there's fear in our hearts let me be a sign of faith.
to Refrain

Text: Verses based on a prayer ascribed to St. Francis of Assisi, ca. 1182–1226;
Steve Angrisano, b. 1965, and Tom Tomaszek, b. 1950.
Music: Steve Angrisano and Tom Tomaszek.

COME UNTO ME 580

Refrain

Come, come un-to me; I will make you a jew-el. Pre-cious and rare the glo-ry you'll bear in the crown of God.

Verses

1. There are deeds you a-lone must do; there are words on-ly you can say. Trust in me, and do not trem-ble, for I go with you to show you the way.
2. From the dawn of cre-a-tion, from the tree on Cal-va-ry, I chose you and gave my life to be my own, to be my de-light.

to Refrain

Text: Based on Isaiah 62 and Matthew 11:28–30; Bob Hurd, b. 1950.
Music: Bob Hurd.

581 JESUS IN THE MORNING

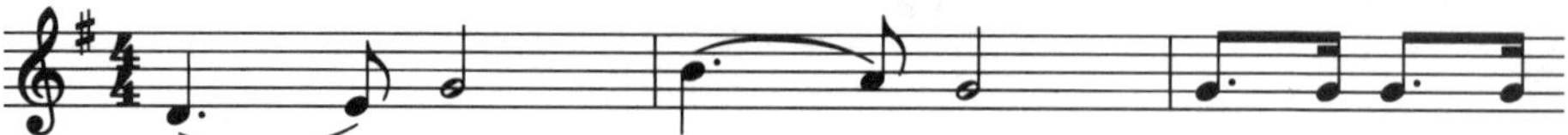

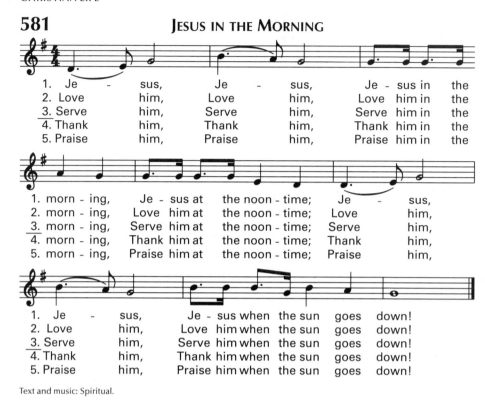

1. Je - sus, Je - sus, Je - sus in the
2. Love him, Love him, Love him in the
3. Serve him, Serve him, Serve him in the
4. Thank him, Thank him, Thank him in the
5. Praise him, Praise him, Praise him in the

1. morn - ing, Je - sus at the noon - time; Je - sus,
2. morn - ing, Love him at the noon - time; Love him,
3. morn - ing, Serve him at the noon - time; Serve him,
4. morn - ing, Thank him at the noon - time; Thank him,
5. morn - ing, Praise him at the noon - time; Praise him,

1. Je - sus, Je - sus when the sun goes down!
2. Love him, Love him when the sun goes down!
3. Serve him, Serve him when the sun goes down!
4. Thank him, Thank him when the sun goes down!
5. Praise him, Praise him when the sun goes down!

Text and music: Spiritual.

582 O BEAUTY, EVER ANCIENT

Verses

1. Oh, late have I loved you, oh, late
2. My un - love - li - ness I ran from, turned to seek you
3. This cre - at - ed world is glo - rious, yet I could not
4. I had wan - dered far, per - ceiv - ing that I walked my
5. In your love - li - ness you made me, in your god - ly

1. have I turned; turned from seek - ing you in crea - tures, flee - ing
2. in all things, things you fash-ioned as a path - way; yet I
3. see with - in, see your love - li - ness be - hind all, find the
4. road a - lone. Yet you called, you shone, you sum-moned, and you
5. im - age true; by your grace you have re - newed me; let me

1. grief and pain with - in.
2. lost my - self in them.
3. Giv - er in the gift.
4. drew my spir - it home.
5. live my life in you!

Refrain

O Beau - ty, ev - er an - cient, O

Beau - ty, ev - er new: you, the mir - ror of my life re -
newed, let me find my life in you!
2

Text: Based on a prayer from St. Augustine of Hippo's *Confessions*, ca. 400; Roc O'Connor, SJ, b. 1949.
Music: Roc O'Connor, SJ.

'Tis the Gift to Be Simple 583

Verses

1. 'Tis the gift to be sim-ple, 'tis the gift to be free, 'Tis the gift to
2. 'Tis the gift to be gen-tle, 'tis the gift to be fair, 'Tis the gift to
3. 'Tis the gift to be lov-ing, 'tis the gift best of all, Like a qui - et

1. come down where you ought to be, And when we find our-selves in the
2. wake and breathe the morn-ing air; And ev - 'ry day to walk in the
3. rain, it bless - es where it falls; And if we have the gift, we will

1. place just ___ right ___ 'Twill be in the val - ley of love and de-light.
2. path we ___choose, 'Tis the gift that we pray we may ne'er come to lose.
3. tru - ly be-lieve ___ 'Tis bet - ter to give than it is to re-ceive.

Refrain

When true sim - plic - i - ty is gained, To bow and to bend we

shan't be a-shamed; To turn, turn will be our de-light, Till by

turn - ing, turn - ing we come 'round right.

Text: Irregular with refrain; Shaker song, 18th cent. Verses 2–3, Joyce Merman, © 1975 (renewed), Shawnee Press, Inc. All rights reserved. Used with permission.
Music: SIMPLE GIFTS; Shaker melody, 18th cent.

584 In Christ Alone

1. In Christ a - lone my hope is found, he is my light, my
2. In Christ a - lone, who took on flesh, full-ness of God in
3. There in the ground his bod - y lay, light of the world, by
4. No guilt in life, no fear in death, this is the pow'r of
1. strength, my song; this cor - ner-stone, this sol - id ground,
2. help - less babe! This gift of love and righ-teous - ness,
3. dark - ness slain; then, burst - ing forth in glo - rious day,
4. Christ in me; from life's first cry to fi - nal breath,
1. firm through the fierc - est drought and storm. What heights of
2. scorned by the ones he came to save. Till on that
3. up from the grave he rose a - gain! And as he
4. Je - sus com-mands my des - ti - ny. No pow'r of
1. love, what depths of peace, when fears are stilled, when striv-ings
2. cross as Je - sus died, the wrath of God was sat - is -
3. stands in vic - to - ry, sin's curse has lost its grip on
4. hell, no scheme of man, can ev - er pluck me from his
1. cease. My com - fort - er, my all in all, here in the
2. fied. For ev - ery sin on him was laid; here in the
3. me; for I am his and he is mine, bought with the
4. hand; till he re-turns or calls me home, here in the
1. love of Christ I stand.
2. death of Christ I live.
3. pre - cious blood of Christ.
4. pow'r of Christ I'll stand!

585 The Eyes and Hands of Christ

Refrain
Where two or three are gath-ered in my name,
love will be found, life will a-bound.
By name we are called, from wa-ter we are sent:
to be-come the eyes and hands of Christ.
3
Verses 1, 2
1. One we be-come, no long-er strang-ers. No long-er
2. One in the Spir-it, one in the Lord. One in the
1. emp-ty ___ or frail. Filled with the Spir-it, ev-'ry
2. break-ing of the bread. Life-giv-ing wit-ness of our
to Refrain
1. hun-ger sat-is-fied. Christ is the cen-ter of our lives.
2. dy-ing and new life. Held by the prom-ise in our hands.
Verse 3
3. Not what we are, but what we be-come. Not what we
3. say, but what we do. Liv-ing the chal-lenge as
to Refrain
3. bear-ers of light. We are the eyes and hands of Christ.

Text and music: Tom Kendzia, b. 1954,

586 CHRIST BEFORE US

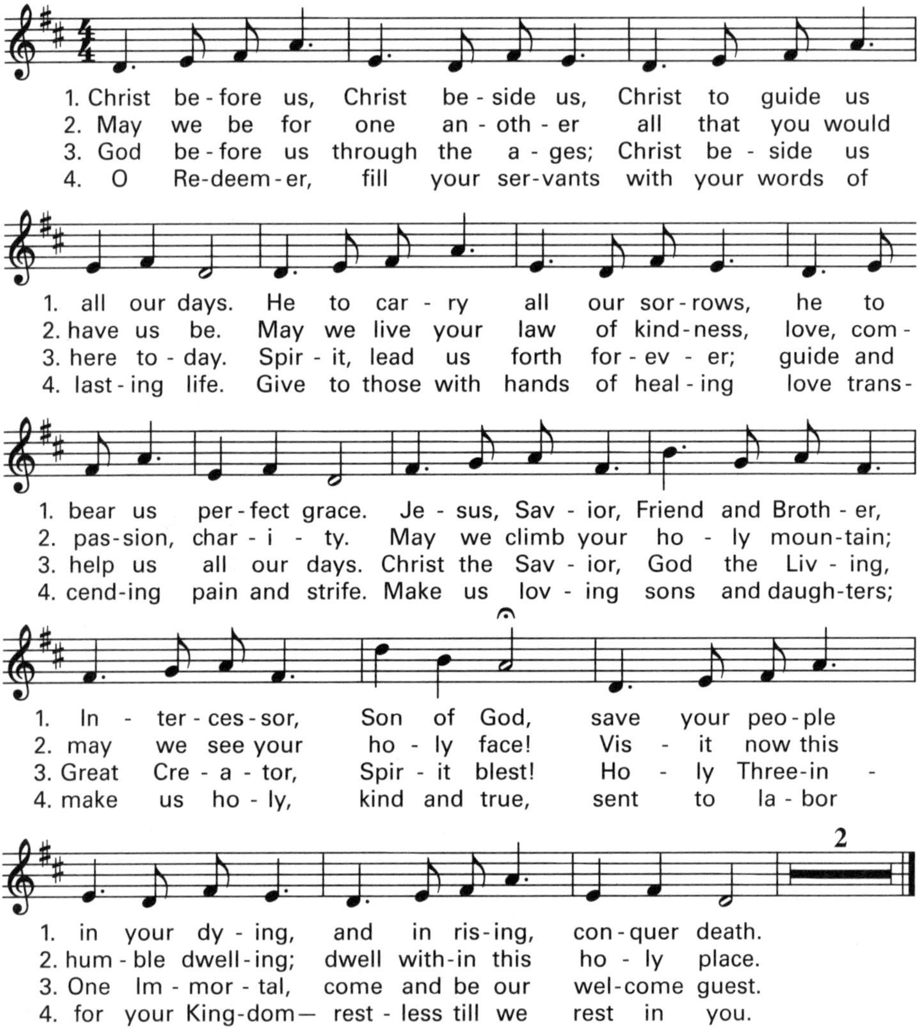

1. Christ be - fore us, Christ be - side us, Christ to guide us
2. May we be for one an - oth - er all that you would
3. God be - fore us through the a - ges; Christ be - side us
4. O Re-deem - er, fill your ser-vants with your words of

1. all our days. He to car - ry all our sor - rows, he to
2. have us be. May we live your law of kind - ness, love, com -
3. here to - day. Spir - it, lead us forth for - ev - er; guide and
4. last - ing life. Give to those with hands of heal - ing love trans-

1. bear us per - fect grace. Je - sus, Sav - ior, Friend and Broth - er,
2. pas - sion, char - i - ty. May we climb your ho - ly moun - tain;
3. help us all our days. Christ the Sav - ior, God the Liv - ing,
4. cend-ing pain and strife. Make us lov - ing sons and daugh-ters;

1. In - ter - ces - sor, Son of God, save your peo - ple
2. may we see your ho - ly face! Vis - it now this
3. Great Cre - a - tor, Spir - it blest! Ho - ly Three-in -
4. make us ho - ly, kind and true, sent to la - bor

1. in your dy - ing, and in ris - ing, con - quer death.
2. hum - ble dwell - ing; dwell with - in this ho - ly place.
3. One Im - mor - tal, come and be our wel - come guest.
4. for your King - dom— rest - less till we rest in you.

Text: 87 87 D; Janèt Sullivan Whitaker, b. 1958,
Music: SUO GÂN; trad. Welsh melody.

587 JESUS, LORD

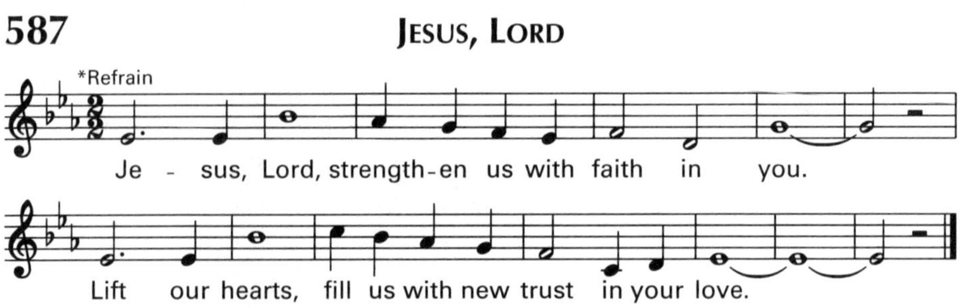
*Refrain
Je - sus, Lord, strength - en us with faith in you.
Lift our hearts, fill us with new trust in your love.

*Opening Refrain is sung twice before proceeding to Verse 1.

Verses
1. God so loved the world he gave his on - ly Son,
2. God ___ sent his Son in - to a bro - ken world,
3. Je - sus is the light by which we see the truth;
to Refrain
1. With our faith in him we shall have e - ter - nal life.
2. Not ___ to con - demn, ___ but that we might be saved.
3. If we fol - low him we are blest in all we do.

Text: Based on John 3:16–21; Randall DeBruyn, b. 1947,
Music: Randall DeBruyn,

We Remember 588

Refrain

We re-mem-ber how you loved us to your death, and still we cel-e-brate, for you are with us here; And we be-lieve that we will see you when you come in your glo-ry, Lord. We re-mem-ber, we cel-e-brate, we be-lieve.

Verses

1. Here, a mil-lion wound-ed souls are yearn-ing just to touch you and be healed. Gath - er all your peo - ple, and hold them to your heart.
2. Now we re - cre - ate your love, we bring the bread and wine to share a meal. Sign of grace and mer - cy, the pres-ence of the Lord.
3. Christ, the Fa-ther's great "A - men" to all the hopes and dreams of ev - 'ry heart, Peace be - yond all tell - ing, and free-dom from all fear.
4. See the face of Christ re - vealed in ev - 'ry per - son stand-ing by your side, Gift to one an - oth - er, and tem - ples of your love.

to Refrain

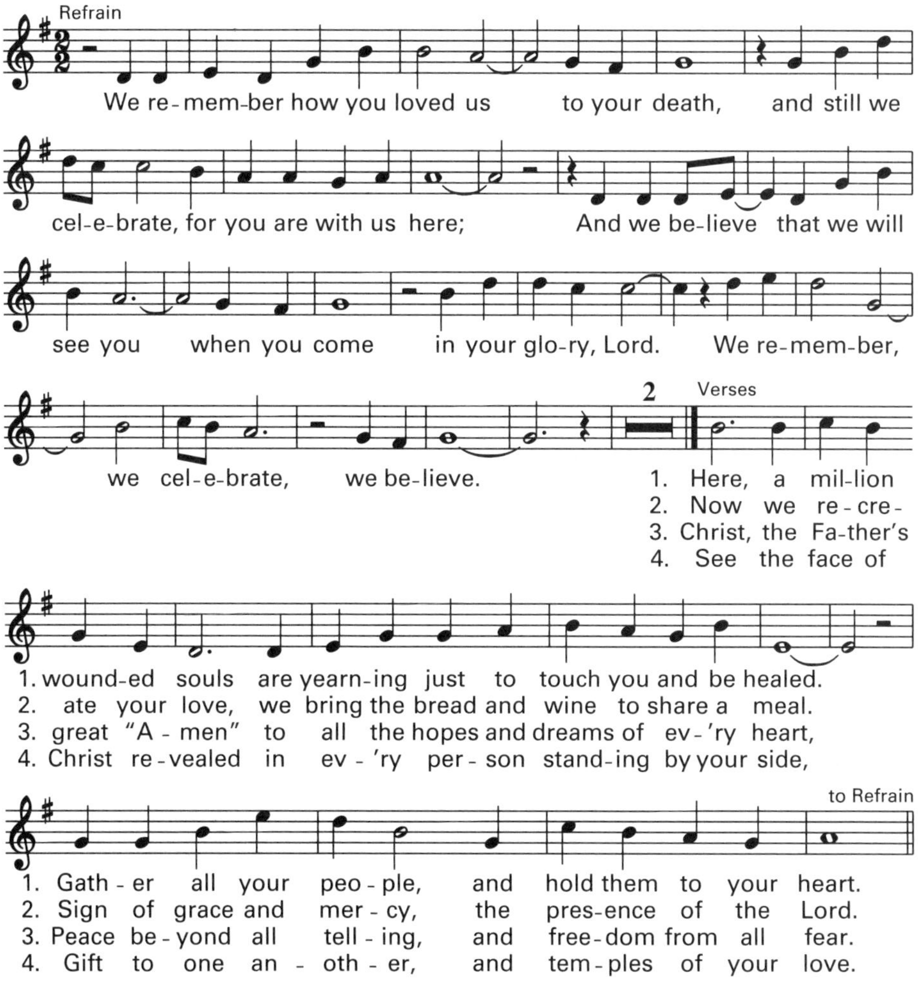

Text and music: Marty Haugen, b. 1950,

589 Do Not Fear to Hope

Refrain

Do not fear to hope though the wick-ed rage and

rise, our God sees not as we see, suc -

cess is not the prize. Do not fear to hope

for though the night be long, the race shall not be

1-4 — to Verses 1-4

to the swift, the fight not to the strong.

5 — to Verse 5

to the swift, the fight not to the strong.

Final

to the swift, the fight not to the strong.

Verses

1. Look to God when you are sure your sin is
2. Look to God when vic - to - ry seems out of
3. Look to God when cyn - ics say our plan-et's
4. Look to God when rea - son fails and ter - ror

1. great - er than grace. Look to God
2. jus - tice' sight. Look to God
3. doom is sealed. Look to God
4. reigns in the night. Look up - on

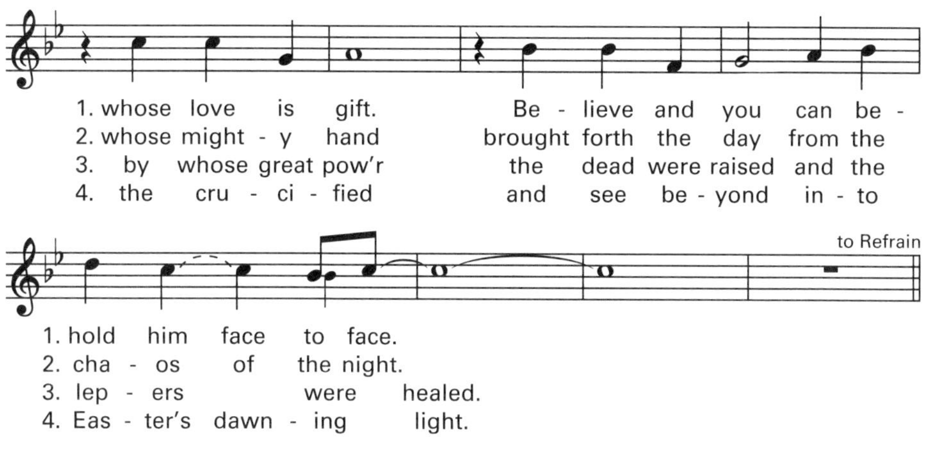
1. whose love is gift. Be - lieve and you can be -
2. whose might - y hand brought forth the day from the
3. by whose great pow'r the dead were raised and the
4. the cru - ci - fied and see be - yond in - to
to Refrain
1. hold him face to face.
2. cha - os of the night.
3. lep - ers were healed.
4. Eas - ter's dawn - ing light.

Verse 5: Cantor

5. Hope is for a pilgrim people looking for a promised land;
hope is like a rose in winter, or an open hand.
It celebrates the light of morning, while working in the dark and cold.
It gathers us together, to share what we've been told:

Text and music: Rory Cooney, b. 1952,

As the Deer Longs 590

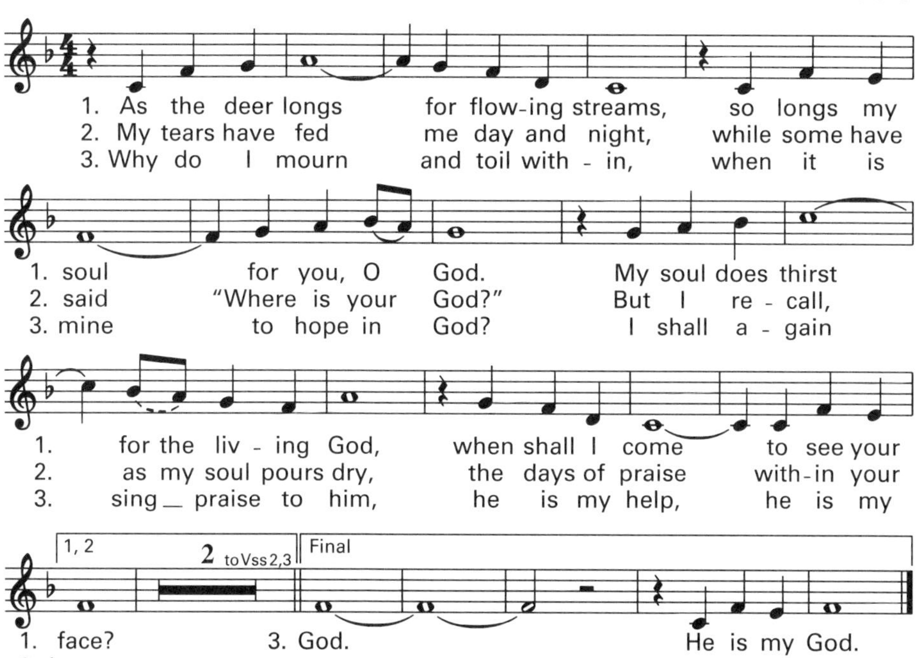
1. As the deer longs for flow-ing streams, so longs my
2. My tears have fed me day and night, while some have
3. Why do I mourn and toil with - in, when it is
1. soul for you, O God. My soul does thirst
2. said "Where is your God?" But I re - call,
3. mine to hope in God? I shall a - gain
1. for the liv - ing God, when shall I come to see your
2. as my soul pours dry, the days of praise with-in your
3. sing _ praise to him, he is my help, he is my
1, 2
2 to Vss 2,3
Final
1. face?
2. house.
3. God.
He is my God.

Text: Irregular; based on Psalm 42; Danna Harkin,
Music: O WALY WALY, alt.; trad. English melody.

591 CENTER OF MY LIFE

Refrain: Repeat 1st time
O Lord, you are the cen-ter of my life: I will al-ways praise you,
I will al-ways serve you, I will al-ways keep you in my sight.
1-5 (to Verses)
Final
1. sight.
2.
3. And
Verses 1-3
1. Keep me safe, O God, I take ref-uge in you. I say to the
2. I will bless the Lord who gives me coun-sel, who e-ven at
3. so my heart re-joic-es, my soul is glad; e-ven in
1. Lord, "You are my God. My hap-pi-ness lies in you a-
2. night di-rects my heart. I keep the Lord ev-er in my
3. safe-ty shall my bod-y rest. For you will not leave my soul a-mong the
to Refrain
1. lone; my hap-pi-ness lies in you a-lone."
2. sight: since he is at my right hand, I shall stand firm.
3. dead, nor let your be-lov-ed know de-cay.
Verse 4
4. You will show me the path of life, the full-ness of
4. joy in your pres-ence, at your right hand,
to Refrain
4. at your right hand hap-pi-ness for-ev-er.

Text: Psalm 16:1–2, 7–11. Refrain, Paul Inwood, b. 1947,
Verses, alt.,
Music: Paul Inwood,

I Believe in the Sun

Refrain
I be-lieve in the sun e-ven when it is-n't shin - ing;
I be-lieve in love e-ven when there's no one there.
And I be-lieve in God, I be-lieve in God,
e - ven when he is si - lent.
1, 2
to Verses
Final
lent, e-ven when he is si - lent.
Verses
1. I be-lieve in mir-a-cles. I be-lieve in light.
2. I be-lieve in the Son of God. I be-lieve his way.
1. I be-lieve there can al-ways be a way. I be-
2. I be-lieve he can lead us to the light. I be-
1. lieve that noth-ing is im - pos-si-ble, I be-lieve that noth-ing is im-
2. lieve that he is call-ing us, I be-lieve that he is
1. pos - si-ble; that all things are pos-si - ble with God.
2. call-ing us and he will lead us on our way.
to Refrain

Text and music: Carey Landry, b. 1944,

593 FAITH OF OUR FATHERS

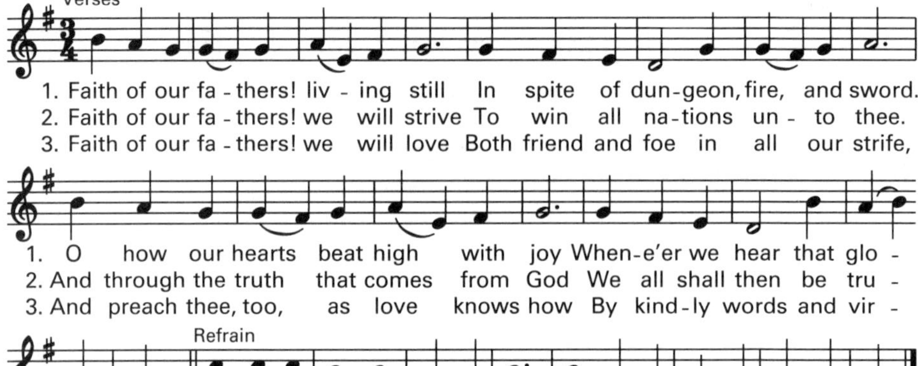
Verses
1. Faith of our fa - thers! liv - ing still In spite of dun-geon, fire, and sword.
2. Faith of our fa - thers! we will strive To win all na-tions un - to thee.
3. Faith of our fa - thers! we will love Both friend and foe in all our strife,
1. O how our hearts beat high with joy When-e'er we hear that glo -
2. And through the truth that comes from God We all shall then be tru -
3. And preach thee, too, as love knows how By kind-ly words and vir -
Refrain
1. rious word! Faith of our fa-thers, ho - ly faith! We will be true to thee till death.
2. ly free:
3. tuous life:

Text: 88 88 88; Frederick W. Faber, 1814–1863, alt.
Music: ST. CATHERINE; Henri F. Hemy, 1818–1888; adapt. by James G. Walton, 1821–1905.

594 WE WALK BY FAITH

1, 5. We walk by faith, and not by sight: No
2. We may not touch his hands and side, Nor
3. Help then, O Lord, our un - be - lief, And
4. That when our life of faith is done In
1, 5. gra - cious words we hear Of him who spoke as
2. fol - low where he trod; Yet in his prom - ise
3. may our faith a - bound; To call on you when
4. realms of clear - er light We may be - hold you
1, 5. none e'er spoke, But we be - lieve him near.
2. we re - joice And cry "My Lord and God!"
3. you are near, And seek where you are found:
4. as you are In full and end - less sight.

Text: CM; based on John 20:24–29; Henry Alford, 1810–1871, alt.
Music: SHANTI; Marty Haugen, b. 1950, © 1984, GIA Publications, Inc.

595 HOLD ME IN LIFE

Refrain
Hold me in life for you are my safe - ty, al-ways my eyes are

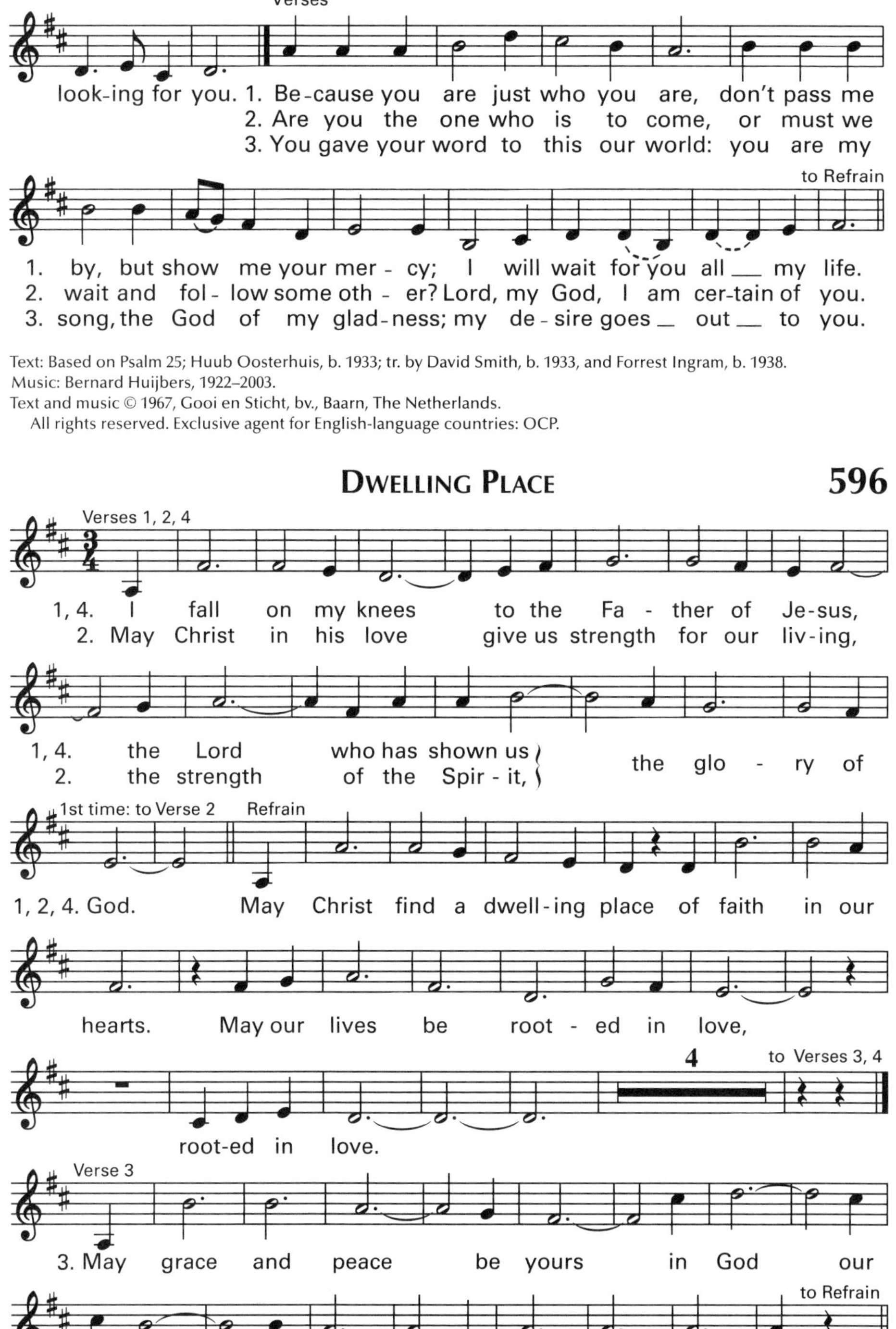
Verses
look-ing for you. 1. Be-cause you are just who you are, don't pass me
2. Are you the one who is to come, or must we
3. You gave your word to this our world: you are my
to Refrain
1. by, but show me your mer - cy; I will wait for you all ___ my life.
2. wait and fol - low some oth - er? Lord, my God, I am cer-tain of you.
3. song, the God of my glad-ness; my de - sire goes ___ out ___ to you.
Verses 1, 2, 4
1, 4. I fall on my knees to the Fa - ther of Je-sus,
2. May Christ in his love give us strength for our liv-ing,
1, 4. the Lord who has shown us
2. the strength of the Spir - it,
the glo - ry of
1st time: to Verse 2
Refrain
1, 2, 4. God. May Christ find a dwell-ing place of faith in our
hearts. May our lives be root - ed in love,
4
to Verses 3, 4
root-ed in love.
Verse 3
3. May grace and peace be yours in God our
to Refrain
3. Fa-ther, and in the Son.

Text: Based on Psalm 25; Huub Oosterhuis, b. 1933; tr. by David Smith, b. 1933, and Forrest Ingram, b. 1938.
Music: Bernard Huijbers, 1922–2003.

Dwelling Place 596

Text: Based on Ephesians 3; John Foley, S.J., b. 1939.
Music: John Foley, S.J.

597 THOSE WHO SEE LIGHT

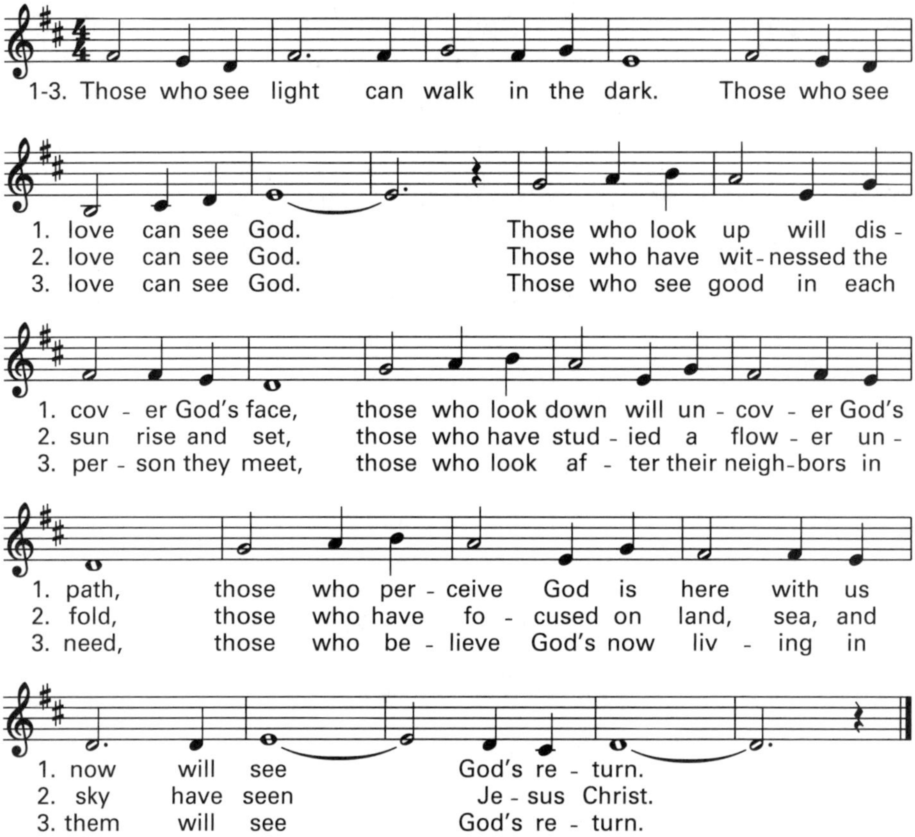

1-3. Those who see light can walk in the dark. Those who see

1. love can see God. Those who look up will dis -
2. love can see God. Those who have wit - nessed the
3. love can see God. Those who see good in each

1. cov - er God's face, those who look down will un - cov - er God's
2. sun rise and set, those who have stud - ied a flow - er un -
3. per - son they meet, those who look af - ter their neigh - bors in

1. path, those who per - ceive God is here with us
2. fold, those who have fo - cused on land, sea, and
3. need, those who be - lieve God's now liv - ing in

1. now will see God's re - turn.
2. sky have seen Je - sus Christ.
3. them will see God's re - turn.

Text: E. Donald Osuna, b. 1936.
Music: Nancy Elze.

598 AGE TO AGE

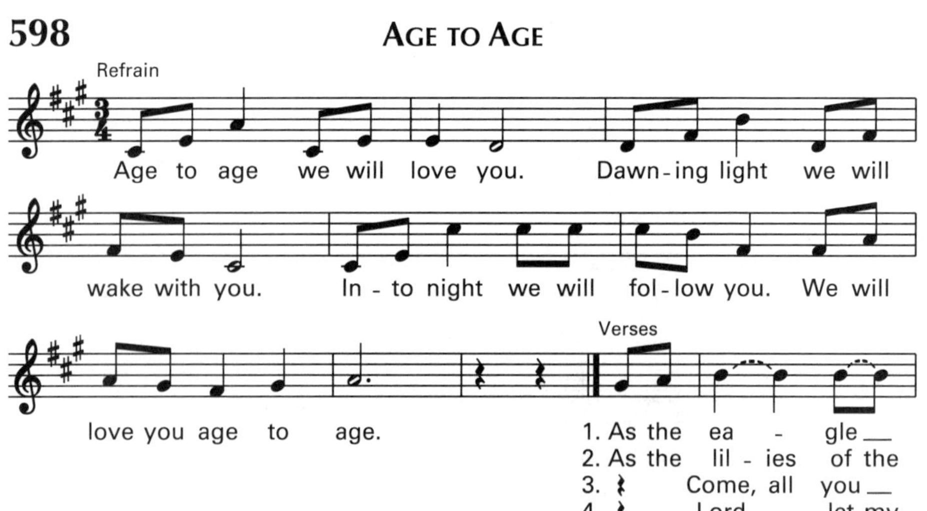
Refrain
Age to age we will love you. Dawn - ing light we will
wake with you. In - to night we will fol - low you. We will
love you age to age.
Verses
1. As the ea - gle
2. As the lil - ies of the
3. Come, all you
4. Lord, let my

1. flies to the heav'ns a - bove, on wings of
2. field nei-ther toil nor spin, what splen - dor we
3. wea - ry, for you are blessed. God will light - en your
4. faith in you be re - vealed. On-ly say the
2 to Refrain
1. faith God will bear you up.
2. find in the love God gives.
3. bur - den and give you rest.
4. word and I shall be healed.

Text: Based on Isaiah 40:31; Matthew 6:28; 11:28–30; Janet Vogt, b. 1953.
Music: Janet Vogt.

The Jesus Song 599

A

Lord Je-sus Christ, Son of God, have mer-cy on me,
have mer-cy on me. Lord Je-sus Christ, Son of God, have
mer-cy on me, have mer-cy on me. A-men.

B

Je - sus, I trust in you. Je - sus, I trust in
you. You are the Son of the Liv - ing God. Je - sus,
I trust in you. Je - sus, I trust in you.

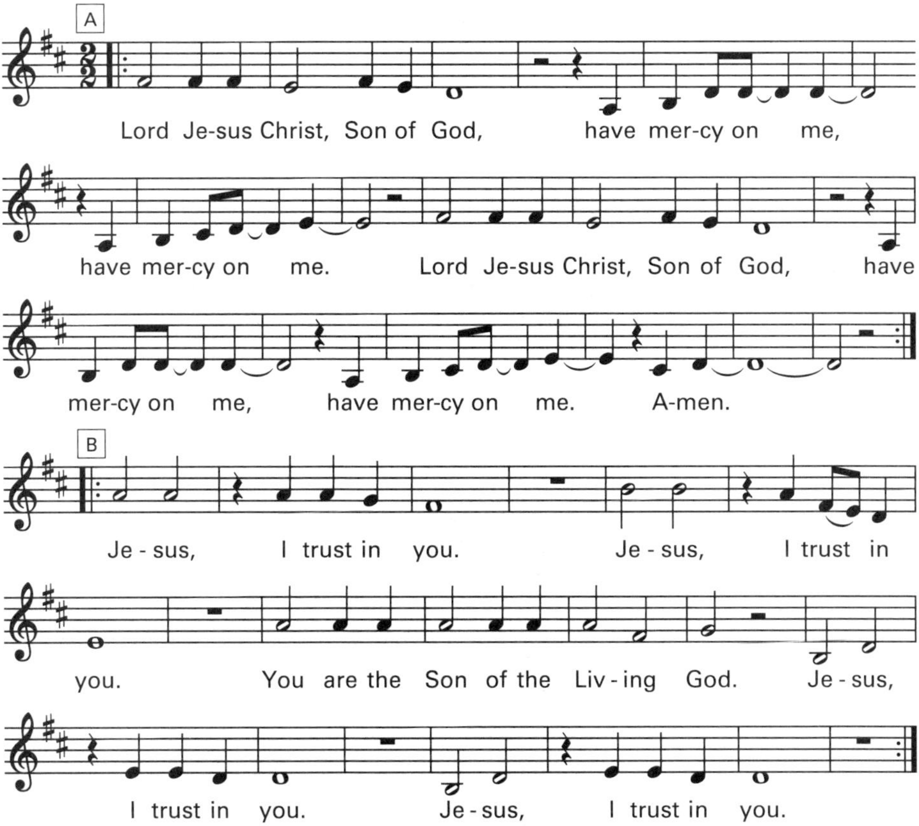

Text: Based on the *Jesus Prayer* and the *Chaplet of Divine Mercy*; Tom Booth, b. 1961.
Music: Tom Booth.

600 Be Not Afraid

Verse 1
1. You shall cross the bar-ren des-ert, but you shall not die of
1. thirst. You shall wan-der far in safe-ty though you do not know the
1. way. You shall speak your words in for-eign lands and all will un-der-
1. stand. You shall see the face of God and live.
to Refrain
Refrain
Be not a-fraid. I go be-fore you al-ways. Come fol-low
me, and I will give you rest.
1, 2
to Vss 2, 3
Final
2
Verse 2
2. If you pass through rag-ing wa-ters in the sea, you shall not
2. drown. If you walk a-mid the burn-ing flames, you shall not be
2. harmed. If you stand be-fore the pow'r of hell and death is at your
2. side, know that I am with you through it all.
to Refrain
Verse 3
3. Bless-ed are your poor, for the king-dom shall be theirs. Blest are you that

3. weep and mourn, for one day you shall laugh. And if wick-ed tongues in-sult and

to Refrain
3. hate you all be-cause of me, bless-ed, bless-ed are you!

Text: Based on Isaiah 43:2–3; Luke 6:20ff; Bob Dufford, SJ, b. 1943.
Music: Bob Dufford, SJ.

FOR YOU ARE MY GOD — 601

Refrain

For you are my God; you a - lone are my joy. De-
fend me, O Lord.

Verses

1. You give mar - vel - ous com-rades to me: the faith - ful who dwell in your land. Those who choose a - li - en gods have cho - sen an a - li - en band.
2. You are my por - tion and cup; it is you that I claim for my prize. Your her - i - tage is my de-light, the lot you have giv - en to me.
3. Glad are my heart and my soul; se - cure - ly my bod - y shall rest. For you will not leave me for dead, nor lead your be - lov - ed a - stray.
4. You show me the path for my life; in your pres-ence the full - ness of joy. To be at your right hand for - ev - er for me would be hap-pi - ness al - ways.

to Refrain

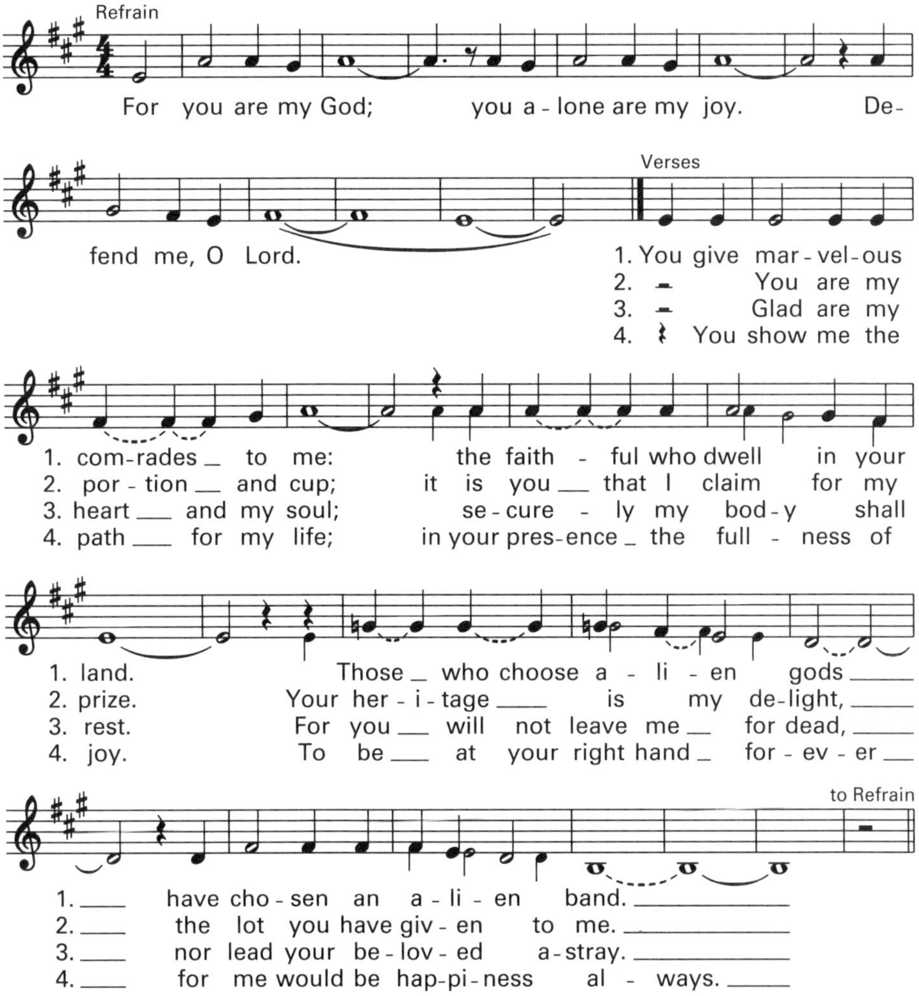

Text: Based on Psalm 16; John Foley, S.J., b. 1939.
Music: John Foley, S.J.

602 ENTRE TUS MANOS

Estribillo
En-tre tus ma-nos es-tá mi vi-da, Se-ñor. En-tre tus
ma-nos pon-go mi e-xis - tir. Hay que mo-rir pa-ra vi-
vir. En-tre tus ma-nos con-fí-o mi ser.
Estrofas
1. Si el gra - no de tri - go no mue - re,
2. Es mi an - he - lo, mi an-he - lo cre - cien - te,
3. Cuan-do die - re por fru - to u - na es - pi - ga,
1. si no mue - re, so - lo que - da - rá;
2. en el sur - co, con - ti - go mo - rir;
3. a los ra - yos de ar - dien - te ca - lor,
1. pe - ro si mue - re, en a - bun - dan - cia da - rá
2. y fe - cun - da se - rá la si - mien - te, Se - ñor,
3. tu rei - na - do ten - drá nue - va vi - da de a - mor,
al Estribillo
1. un fru - to e - ter - no que no mo - ri - rá.
2. re - ves - ti - da de e - ter - no vi - vir.
3. en u - na Hos - tia de e - ter - no es - plen - dor.

Text: Refrain, Ray Repp, b. 1942,
Verses, anon. Verse 1 based on John 12:24.
Music: Ray Repp,

INTO YOUR HANDS 603

Refrain
In - to your hands we com-mend our spir-it, O Lord;
In - to your hands we com-mend our hearts,
For we must die to our-selves in lov-ing you;
In - to your hands we com-mend our love.
Verses
1. O God, my God, why have you gone from me,
2. Our el - ders trust-ed, and you de - liv - ered them;
3. You've been my guide since I was ver - y young;
4. My days are wea - ry with peo - ple hat - ing me,
1. Far from my prayers, far from my cry?
2. To you they cried, and they es - caped;
3. You showed the way when I need - ed some-one's hand.
4. Each place I go, each place I stay;
1. To you I call, and you nev - er an - swer me;
2. In you they trust - ed when dark-ness came their way,
3. And now I'm lone - ly, no - bod - y's by my side;
4. My heart is tired, my bod - y ach - ing.
to Refrain
1. You send no com - fort, and I don't know why.
2. And in your good - ness you made them free.
3. Stay near, my Lord, and be my friend.
4. Give me the cour - age to face each day.

Text and music: Ray Repp, b. 1942,

604 Here I Am

Refrain
Here I am, stand-ing right be-side you. Here I am;
do not be a - fraid. Here I am, wait-ing like a lov - er.
1-3 to Vss.
Final
I am here; here I am. am. I am here; here I am.
Verse 1
1. Do not fear when the tempt - er calls you. Do not
1. fear e - ven though you fall. Do not fear, I have con-quered
to Refrain
1. e - vil. Do not fear, nev-er be a - fraid.
Verse 2
2. I am here in the face of ev - 'ry child.
2. I am here in ev-'ry warm em-brace. I am here with
to Refrain
2. ten-der-ness and mer-cy. Here I am, I am here.
Verse 3
3. I am here in the midst of ev - 'ry tri-al. I am
3. here in the face of de-spair. I am here when

to Refrain
3. par-don-ing your broth-er. Here I am, I am here.

Text and music: Tom Booth, b. 1961,

BLEST BE THE LORD 605

Refrain

Blest be the Lord; blest be the Lord, the God of mer-cy, the God who saves. I shall not fear the dark of night, nor the ar-row that flies by day.

Verses

1. He will re-lease me from the nets of all my foes.
2. I need not shrink be-fore the ter-rors of the night,
3. Al-though a thou-sand strong have fall-en at my side,

1. He will pro-tect me from their wick-ed hands.
2. nor stand a-lone be-fore the light of day.
3. I'll not be shak-en with the Lord at hand.

1. Be-neath the shad-ow of his wings I
2. No harm shall come to me, no ar-row
3. His faith-ful love is all the ar-mor

1. will re-joice to find a dwell-ing place se-cure.
2. strike me down, no e-vil set-tle in my soul.
3. that I need to wage my bat-tle with the foe.

to Refrain

Text: Based on Psalm 91; Dan Schutte, b. 1947.
Music: Dan Schutte.

606 ON EAGLE'S WINGS

Verse 1

1. You who dwell in the shel-ter of the Lord, who a - bide in his

1. shad-ow for life, say to the Lord: "My ref-uge, my rock in whom I trust!"

to Refrain

Refrain

And he will raise you up on ea - gle's wings, bear you on the

breath of dawn, make you to shine like the

sun, and hold you in the palm of his hand.

to Verses (last time to Coda)

Coda

And hold you, hold you in the palm of his hand.

Verse 2

2. The snare of the fowl-er will nev-er cap-ture you, and fam-ine will bring

2. you no fear: un-der his wings your ref-uge, his faith-ful-ness your shield.

to Refrain

Verse 3

3. You need not fear the ter-ror of the night, nor the ar-row that flies by

3. day; though thou-sands fall a - bout you, near you it shall not come.

to Refrain

Verse 4

4. For to his an-gels he's giv-en a com-mand to

4. guard you in all of your ways; up - on their hands they will
to Refrain
4. bear you up, lest you dash your foot a - gainst a stone.

Text: Based on Psalm 91; Michael Joncas, b. 1951.
Music: Michael Joncas.

How Can I Keep from Singing 607

Verses

1. My life flows on in end - less song; A -
2. Through all the tu - mult and the strife, I
3. What though the tem - pest 'round me roar, I
4. When ty - rants trem - ble, sick with fear, And
5. The peace of Christ makes fresh my heart, A

1. bove earth's lam - en - ta - tion. I hear the real though
2. hear that mu - sic ring - ing; It sounds and ech - oes
3. hear the truth it liv - eth. What though the dark - ness
4. hear their death knells ring - ing; When friends re - joice both
5. foun - tain ev - er spring-ing. All things are mine since

1. far - off hymn That hails a new cre - a - tion.
2. in my soul; How can I keep from sing-ing?
3. 'round me close, Songs in the night it giv - eth.
4. far and near, How can I keep from sing-ing?
5. I am his; How can I keep from sing-ing?

Refrain

No storm can shake my in-most calm, While to that rock I'm cling-ing. Since Love is Lord of heav-en and earth, How can I keep from sing-ing?

Text: 87 87 with refrain; attr. to Robert Lowry, 1826–1899, alt.; verse 3, Doris Plenn.
Music: ENDLESS SONG; Quaker Hymn; attr. to Robert Lowry.

608 THE LORD IS NEAR/MAY THE ANGELS

Refrain/Alternate Refrain: All

O the Lord is near to all who call on him; he is close to all who seek his face, slow to anger and full of compassion and abounding in merciful love.

*Alt. *May the angels lead you into paradise; may the martyrs come to welcome you, and take you to the holy city, the new and eternal Jerusalem.*

1-3 to Verses | Final: love. / *rusalem.* A - men.

Verse 1: Cantor

1. The Lord is my light and my salvation, there is nothing at all I fear;
1. the Lord is the refuge of my life; of whom should I be afraid? to Refrain

Verses 2, 3: Cantor

2. One thing I ask of the Lord; there is only one thing I seek: to dwell in the house of the Lord all the days of my life. to Refrain
3. For God will hide me in his house and conceal me in the shelter of his tent. Even now my head is held high over those who would see me fall.

*Alternate refrain for funerals.

Text: Based on Psalm 27; alt. refrain based on *In Paradisum*; Michael Joncas, b. 1951.
Music: Michael Joncas.

WE WILL RISE AGAIN

609

Verse 1
1. Like a shep-herd I will feed you; I will gath - er you with
1. care. I will lead you and hold you close to my heart.
to Refrain
Refrain
We will run and not grow wea - ry, for our God will be our
strength, and we will fly like the ea - gle, we will rise a - gain.
Verse 2
2. I am strength to the wea - ry; to the weak I am new life. Though the
2. young may grow wea - ry, I will be their hope.
to Refrain
Verse 3
3. Lift up your eyes, and see who made the stars. I
3. lead you, and I know you, I call you each by name.
to Refrain
Verse 4
4. Fear not, I am with you; I am your God. I will
4. strength-en you and help you; up - hold you with my hand.
to Refrain

Text: Based on Isaiah 40:11, 26, 29–30; 41:10; David Haas, b. 1957.
Music: David Haas.

You Are Near

Refrain

O Lord, I know you are near, standing always at my side. You guard me from the foe, and you lead me in ways everlasting.

Verses

1. Lord, you have searched my heart, and you know when I sit and when I stand. Your hand is upon me, protecting me from death, keeping me from harm.
2. Where can I run from your love? If I climb to the heavens you are there; if I fly to the sunrise or sail beyond the sea, still I'd find you there.
3. You know my heart and its ways, you who formed me before I was born, in the secret of darkness before I saw the sun, in my mother's womb.
4. Marvelous to me are your works; how profound are your thoughts, my Lord. Even if I could count them, they number as the stars, you would still be there.

to Refrain

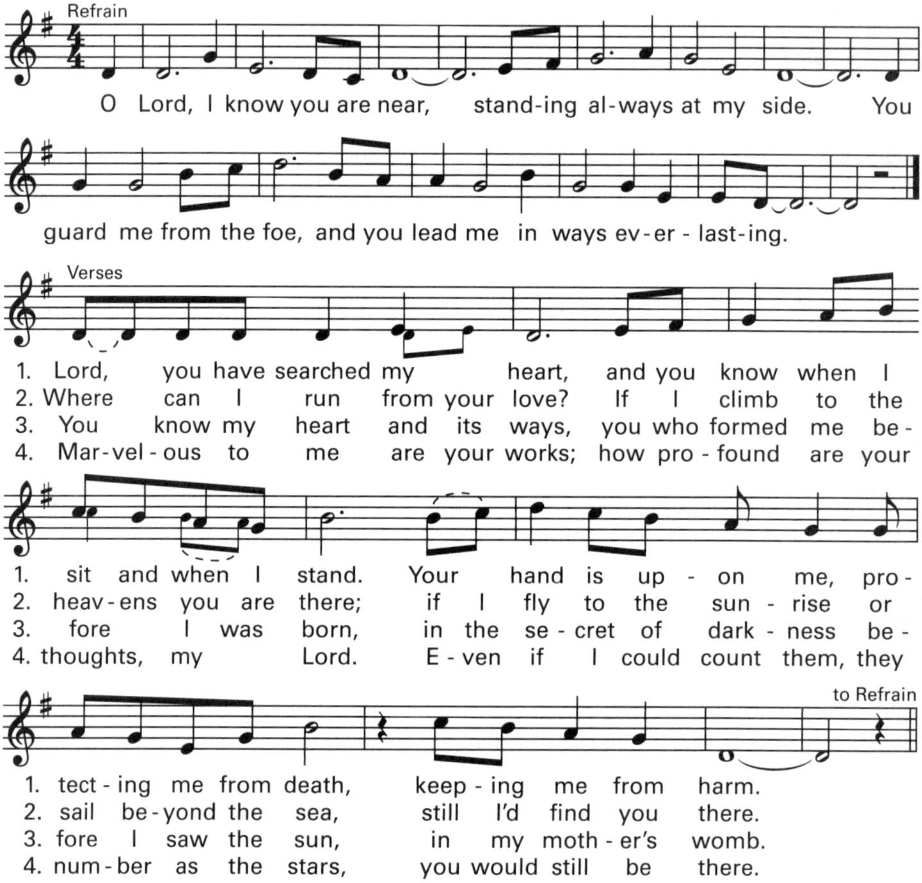

Text: Based on Psalm 139; Dan Schutte, b. 1947.
Music: Dan Schutte.

611
Only in God
Refrain
On - ly in God will my soul be at rest. From
him (God) comes my hope, my sal - va - tion.
He (You) a - lone is (are) my rock of safe - ty, my

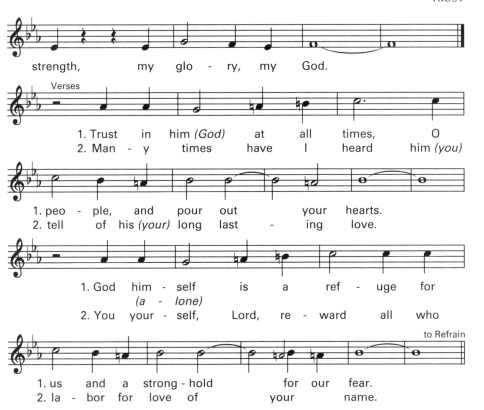

strength, my glo - ry, my God.

Verses

1. Trust in him *(God)* at all times, O
2. Man - y times have I heard him *(you)*

1. peo - ple, and pour out your hearts.
2. tell of his *(your)* long last - ing love.

1. God him - self is a ref - uge for
(a - lone)
2. You your - self, Lord, re - ward all who

to Refrain

1. us and a strong - hold for our fear.
2. la - bor for love of your name.

Text: Based on Psalm 62; John Foley, SJ, b. 1939.
Music: John Foley, SJ.

O God, Our Help in Ages Past 612

1. O God, our Help in a - ges past, Our Hope for years to come,
2. Be - fore the hills in or - der stood, Or earth re-ceived her frame,
3. A thou-sand a - ges in thy sight Are like an eve - ning gone;
4. Time, like an ev - er - roll - ing stream, Soon bears us all a - way;
5. O God, our Help in a - ges past, Our Hope for years to come,
1. Our Shel-ter from the storm-y blast, And our e - ter - nal Home.
2. From ev - er - last - ing thou art God, To end-less years the same.
3. Short as the watch that ends the night Be - fore the ris - ing sun.
4. We fly for - got - ten, as a dream Dies at the o-p'ning day.
5. Be thou our Guard while life shall last, And our e - ter - nal Home.

Text: CM; based on Psalm 90:1–5; Isaac Watts, 1674–1748, alt.
Music: ST. ANNE; William Croft, 1678–1727.

613 SEEK YE FIRST

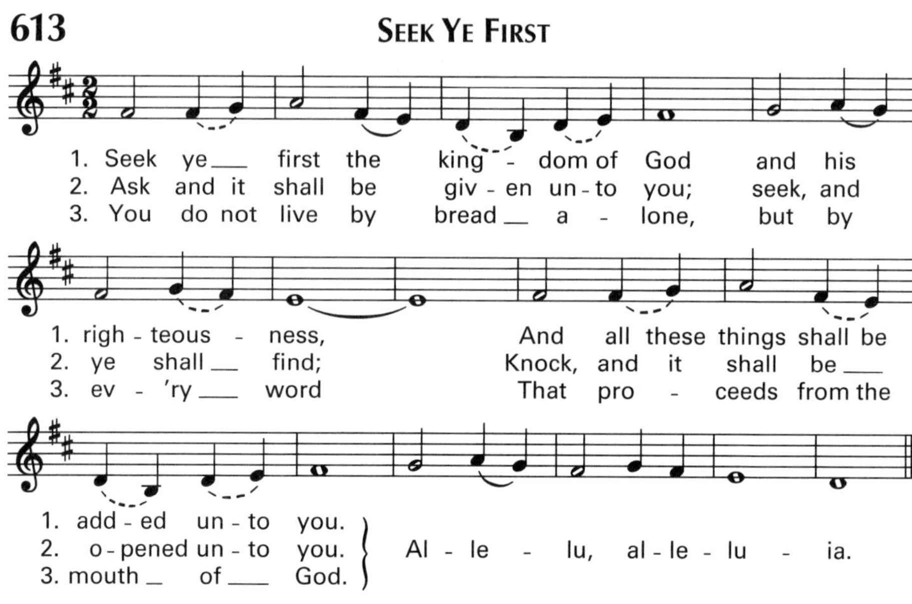
1. Seek ye first the king - dom of God and his
2. Ask and it shall be giv - en un - to you; seek, and
3. You do not live by bread a - lone, but by
1. righ - teous - ness, And all these things shall be
2. ye shall find; Knock, and it shall be
3. ev - 'ry word That pro - ceeds from the
1. add - ed un - to you.
2. o - pened un - to you.
3. mouth of God.
Al - le - lu, al - le - lu - ia.

Text: Based on Matthew 6:33; Karen Lafferty, b. 1948.
Music: Karen Lafferty.

614 AMAZING GRACE

1. A - maz - ing grace! How sweet the sound That saved a
2. 'Twas grace that taught my heart to fear, And grace my
3. The Lord has prom - ised good to me, His word my
4. Through man - y dan - gers, toils, and snares, I have al -
5. When we've been there ten thou - sand years, Bright shin - ing

1. wretch like me! I once was lost, but
2. fears re - lieved; How pre - cious did that
3. hope se - cures; He will my shield and
4. read - y come; 'Tis grace has brought me
5. as the sun, We've no less days to

1. now am found, Was blind but now I see.
2. grace ap - pear The hour I first be - lieved!
3. por - tion be As long as life en - dures.
4. safe thus far, And grace will lead me home.
5. sing God's praise Than when we'd first be - gun.

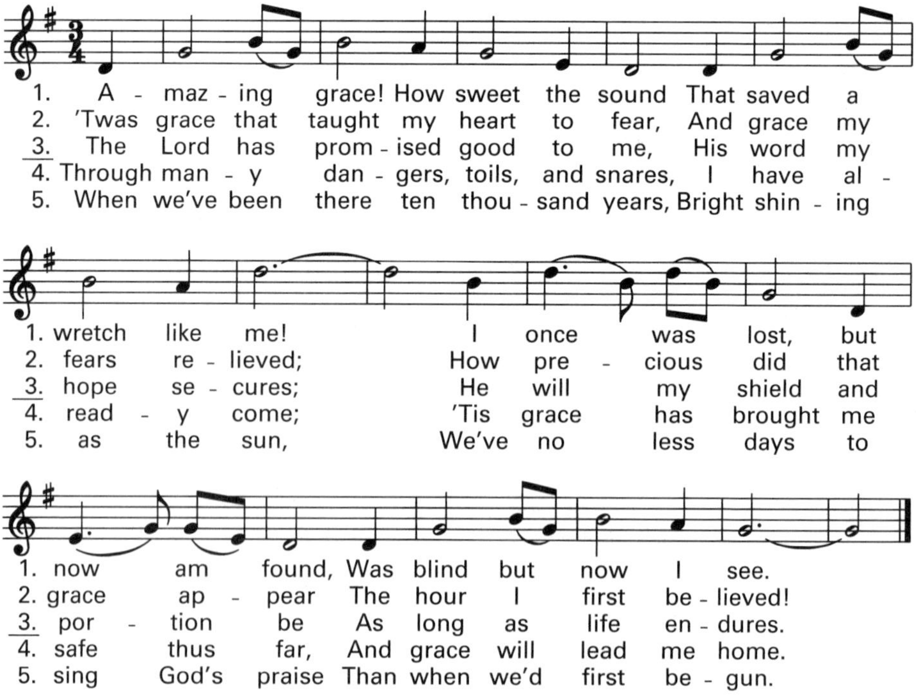

Text: CM; verses 1–4, John Newton, 1725–1807; verse 5, anon., fr. *A Collection of Sacred Ballads*, 1790.
Music: NEW BRITAIN; *Columbian Harmony*, 1829.

Only a Shadow 615

Verses
1. The love we have for you, O Lord, is
2. The bread we take and eat, O Lord, is
3. Our own be - lief in you, O Lord, is
4. The dreams we share to - day, O Lord, are
5. The joy we share to - day, O Lord, is
1. on - ly a shad-ow of your love for us;
2. your bod - y bro - ken and shared with us;
3. on - ly a shad-ow of your faith in us;
4. on - ly a shad-ow of your dreams for us;
5. on - ly a shad-ow of your joys for us;
1. on - ly a shad-ow of your love for us; your
2. your bod - y bro - ken and shared with us; the
3. on - ly a shad-ow of your faith in us; your
4. on - ly a shad-ow of your dreams for us; if
5. on - ly a shad-ow of your joys for us; when
1. deep a - bid - ing love. (to Verse 2)
2. gift of your great love. (to Refrain)
3. deep and last - ing faith. (to Verse 4)
4. we but fol - low you. (to Refrain)
5. we meet face to face. (to Refrain)
Refrain
Our lives are in your hands, our lives
are in your hands. Our love for you will
grow, O Lord; your light in us will shine.

616 A MIGHTY FORTRESS

1. A might - y for - tress is our God, A bul - wark nev - er
2. Did we in our own strength con - fide, Our striv - ing would be
1. fail - ing; Our help - er he a - mid the flood
2. los - ing, Were not the Sav - ior on our side,
1. Of mor - tal ills pre - vail - ing: For
2. The man of God's own choos - ing: Dost
1. still our an - cient foe Doth seek to work us
2. ask who that may be? Christ Je - sus, it is
1. woe; His craft and pow'r are great, And armed with
2. he; Lord Sab - a - oth, his name, From age to
1. cru - el hate, On earth is not his e - qual.
2. age the same, And he must win the bat - tle.

Text: 87 87 66 66 7; based on Psalm 46; Martin Luther, 1483–1546; tr. by Frederick H. Hedge, 1805–1890.
Music: EIN' FESTE BURG; Martin Luther; adapt. by Johann Sebastian Bach, 1685–1750, alt.

YOU ARE ALL THAT I NEED

617

Refrain

You are all that I need. You are all that I want and I need. You are all that I need, my Lord. You are all that I want and I need.

Verses 1, 3

1, 3. When I doubt, when I am a - fraid, when the waves
1, 3. come crash-ing in, when you take my hand and
1, 3. look in - to my eyes tell-ing me that all will be well.

1 to Refrain

2

3. For all is well and ev - er shall be.

to Refrain

Verse 2

2. I trust you Lord, though I do not un - der-stand.
2. You have led me here to - day.
2. Speak to me, show me the way, for
2. all is well and ev - er shall be.

to Refrain

Text and music: Tom Booth, b. 1961, © 2013, Tom Booth.

618 ONLY IN GOD

Verses
1. On - ly in God is my soul at_ rest, in ___ him comes my sal-
2. On - ly in God is found safe - ty when my en - e - my pur-
1. va - tion. He, ___ on - ly, ___ is my_ rock, my strength_ and
2. sues me. On - ly in God is found glo - ry when I am found
1. my ___ sal - va - tion.
2. meek and found low - ly.
Refrain
My strong-hold, my Sav - ior,
I shall not be a - fraid at all. My strong-hold, my
1
to Vs 2
Final
Sav - ior, I shall not be moved. moved. On - ly in
God is my soul at rest, in him comes my sal - va - tion.

Text: Based on Psalm 62; John Michael Talbot, b. 1954.
Music: John Michael Talbot.

THOUGH THE MOUNTAINS MAY FALL 619

Refrain
Though the moun - tains may fall and the hills turn to dust,
yet the love of the Lord will stand
as a shel - ter for all who will call on his name.
Sing the praise and the glo - ry of God.
Verses
1. Could the Lord ev - er leave you? Could the Lord for -
2. Should you turn and for - sake him, he will gent - ly
3. Go to him when you're wea - ry; he will give you
4. As he swore to your fa - thers, when the flood de -
1. get his love? Though a moth - er for -
2. call your name. Should you wan - der a -
3. ea - gle's wings. You will run, nev - er
4. stroyed the land, he will nev - er for -
to Refrain
1. sake her child, he will not a - ban - don you.
2. way from him, he will al - ways take you back.
3. tire, for your God will be your strength.
4. sake you; he will swear to you a - gain.

Text: Based on Isaiah 54:6–10; 49:15; 40:31–32; Dan Schutte, b. 1947.
Music: Dan Schutte.

620 O God, You Search Me

1. O God, you search me and you know me.
2. You know my rest - ing and my ris - ing.
3. Be - fore a word is on my tongue, Lord,
4. Al - though your Spir - it is up - on me,
5. For you cre - at - ed me and shaped me,

1. All my thoughts lie o - pen to your gaze.
2. You dis - cern my pur - pose from a - far,
3. You have known its mean - ing through and through.
4. Still I search for shel - ter from your light.
5. Gave me life with - in my moth - er's womb.

1. When I walk or lie down you are be - fore me:
2. And with love ev - er - last - ing you be - siege me:
3. You are with me be - yond my un - der - stand - ing:
4. There is no - where on earth I can es - cape you:
5. For the won - der of who I am, I praise you:

1. Ev - er the mak - er and keep - er of my days.
2. In ev - 'ry mo - ment of life or death, you are.
3. God of my pres - ent, my past and fu - ture, too.
4. E - ven the dark - ness is ra - diant in your sight.
5. Safe in your hands, all cre - a - tion is made new.

Text: Based on Psalm 139; Bernadette Farrell, b. 1957.
Music: Bernadette Farrell.

621 Lead Me, Guide Me

Refrain
Lead me, guide me, a - long the way, for if you
lead me, I can - not stray. Lord, let me walk each
day with thee. Lead me, oh Lord, lead me.

Verses

1. I am weak and I need thy strength and
2. Help me tread in the paths of righ - teous -
3. I am lost if you take your hand from

1. pow'r to help me o - ver my weak - est
2. ness, be my aid when Sa - tan and sin op -
3. me, I am blind with - out thy Light to

1. hour. Help me through the dark - ness thy face to
2. press. I am put - ting all my trust in
3. see, Lord, just al - ways let me thy ser - vant

to Refrain

1. see, lead me, oh Lord, lead me.
2. thee. Lead me, oh Lord, lead me.
3. be. Lead me, oh Lord, lead me.

Jesus, Come to Us 622

Refrain
Je - sus, come to us, lead us to your light. Je - sus, be with us,
for we need you.
Verses
1. Lord, we come be - fore you, lis - ten
2. Lord, we come to praise you for your faith - ful -
3. Lord, you give us won - ders, your glo -
to Refrain
1. to our prayer. Fill us all with hope and your love.
2. ness through night. You will be with us, this we know.
3. ry to all. We be - lieve in you, come to us.

623 LORD OF ALL HOPEFULNESS

1. Lord of all hope-ful-ness, Lord of all joy, Whose
2. Lord of all ea - ger-ness, Lord of all faith, Whose
3. Lord of all kind - li - ness, Lord of all grace, Your
4. Lord of all gen - tle-ness, Lord of all calm, Whose

1. trust, ev - er child-like, no cares can de - stroy, Be
2. strong hands were skilled at the plane and the lathe, Be
3. hands swift to wel-come, your arms to em - brace, Be
4. voice is con - tent-ment, whose pres-ence is balm, Be

1. there at our wak-ing, and give us, we pray, Your
2. there at our la - bors, and give us, we pray, Your
3. there at our hom-ing, and give us, we pray, Your
4. there at our sleep-ing, and give us, we pray, Your

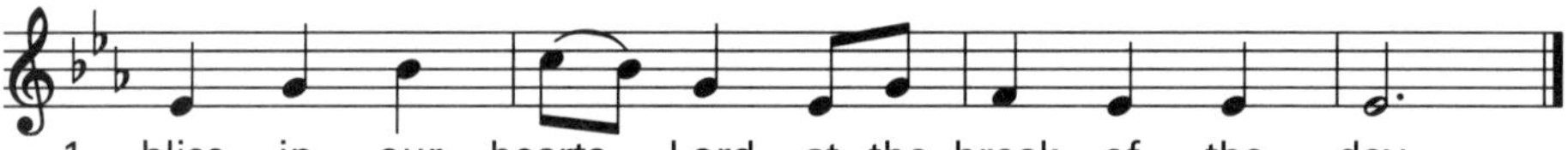

1. bliss in our hearts, Lord, at the break of the day.
2. strength in our hearts, Lord, at the noon of the day.
3. love in our hearts, Lord, at the eve of the day.
4. peace in our hearts, Lord, at the end of the day.

Text: 10 11 11 12; 'Lord of all hopefulness', words by Jan Struther, 1901–1953; fr. *Enlarged Songs of Praise*, 1931.

Music: SLANE; trad. Irish melody; adapt. fr. *The Church Hymnary*, 1927.

624 YOU ARE THE HEALING

Cantor

1. Je-sus, you are the heal-ing, you came to make us whole a - gain.
2. Je-sus, you are the free-dom, you break the chains that bind __ us.
3. Je-sus, you are the pow - er, you tri-umph o - ver sin and death.
4. Je-sus, the res-ur-rec-tion, you raise us to e - ter-nal life.

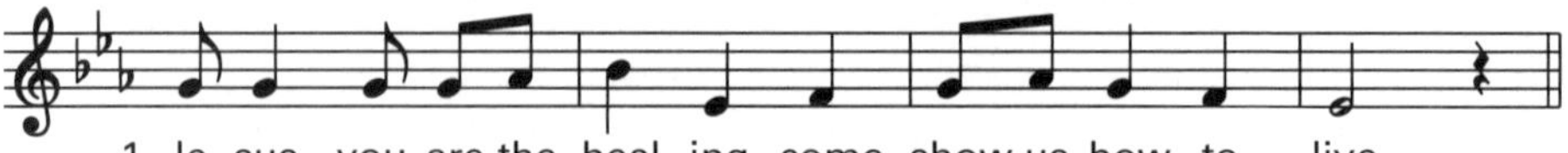

1. Je-sus, you are the heal-ing, come show us how to live.
2. Je-sus, you are the free-dom, come show us how to live.
3. Je-sus, you are the pow - er, come show us how to live.
4. Je-sus, the res-ur - rec - tion, come show us how to live.

All
1. Je-sus, you are the heal-ing, Je-sus, you are the heal - ing,
2. Je-sus, you are the free-dom, Je-sus, you are the free - dom,
3. Je-sus, you are the pow-er, Je-sus, you are the pow - er,
4. Je-sus, the res-ur-rec-tion, Je-sus, the res-ur-rec - tion,
1. Je-sus, you are the heal-ing, come show us how to live.
2. Je-sus, you are the free-dom, come show us how to live.
3. Je-sus, you are the pow-er, come show us how to live.
4. Je-sus, the res-ur-rec-tion, come show us how to live.

Text and music: Scott Soper, b. 1961,

CHRIST BE BESIDE ME 625

1. Christ be be - side me, Christ be be - fore me, Christ be be -
2. Christ on my right hand, Christ on my left hand, Christ all a -
3. Christ be in all hearts think-ing a - bout me; Christ be on
1. hind me, King of my heart. Christ be with - in me,
2. round me, shield in the strife. Christ in my sleep - ing,
3. all tongues tell - ing of me. Christ be the vi - sion
1. Christ be be - low me, Christ be a - bove me, nev - er to part.
2. Christ in my sit - ting, Christ in my ris - ing, light of my life.
3. in eyes that see me; In ears that hear me, Christ ev - er be.

Text: 55 54 D; *New Hymns for All Seasons*; St. Patrick's Breastplate, para.; tr. by James Quinn, SJ, 1919–2010,
Music: ST. ROSE; Laura Wasson, b. 1952,

O GOD, HEAR US 626

O God, hear us; hear our prayer.

Note: Verses available in accompaniment books.

Text and music: Bob Hurd, b. 1950,

627 God, Our Source and Life, Unite Us

Refrain

God, our source and life, u - nite us. Come and take a - way the dark that blinds us. Fill us with your light and peace; trans - form us with your love, trans - form us with your love.

Verses

1. When our pain dis - torts our vi - sion, trans - form us with your love.
2. When our hurt grows deep with an - ger, trans - form us with your love.
3. When our fear re - plac - es free-dom, trans - form us with your love.

1. When our pain con-sumes our joy with hurt, trans-form us with your love.
2. When our hurt con-sumes our trust with fear, trans-form us with your love.
3. When our fear con-sumes our hope-ful-ness, trans-form us with your love.

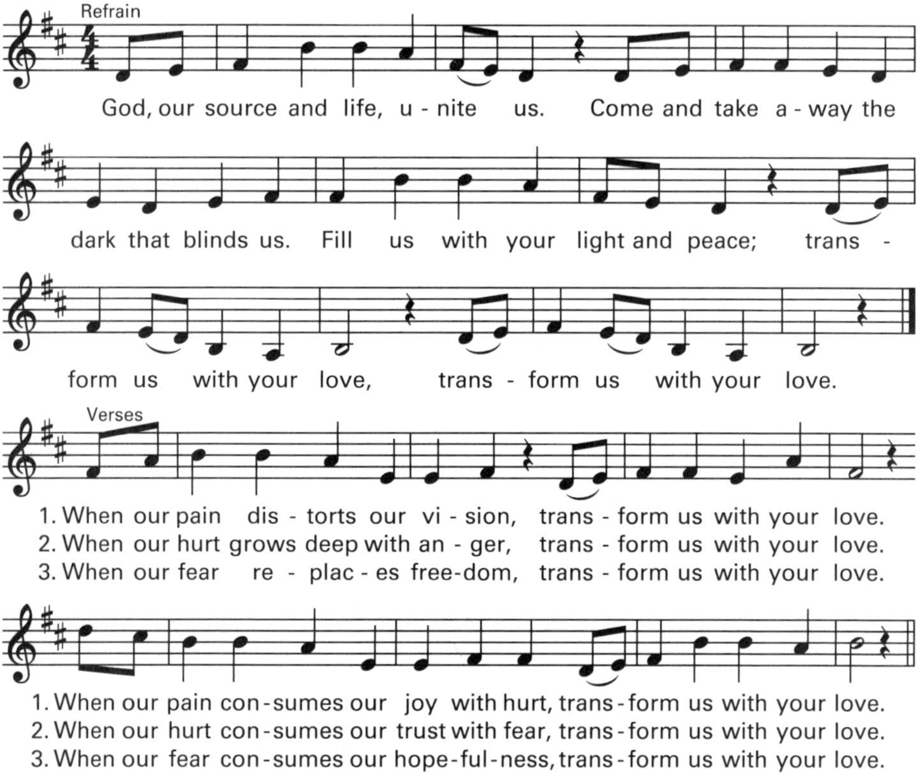

Text and music: Trevor Thomson, b. 1971,

628 God Be in My Head

1. God be in my head, God be in my heart,
2. God be in my work, God be in my play,
1. God be in my mind, God be in my soul,
2. God be in my home, God be in my prayer,
1. God be in my eyes, so that I may see your face;
2. God be in my song, so that I may sing your praise;

1. God be on my lips, God be in my life.
2. God be in my night, God be in my day.

Stand by Me 629

Verses

1. When the storms of life are rag-ing, Lord, stand by me.
2. In the midst of per - se - cu-tion, Lord, stand by me.

1. When the cur - rent pulls me un - der, Lord, stand by me.
2. When my en - e - mies sur-round me, Lord, stand by me.

1. When the ris - ing wa - ters toss me like a ship up - on the sea,
2. When the ty - rant wields his ter - ror and the ar - mies wage their might,

1. You who rule the wind and wa - ter, Lord, stand by me.
2. When the dark - ness o - ver-whelms me, Lord, stand by me.

Refrain

Stand by me, stand by me. Lift me up from the rest - less sea.

When I am lost, when love can't be found, when no one cares, Lord,

1 stand by me. to Verse 2 ‖ Final stand by me. Repeat twice

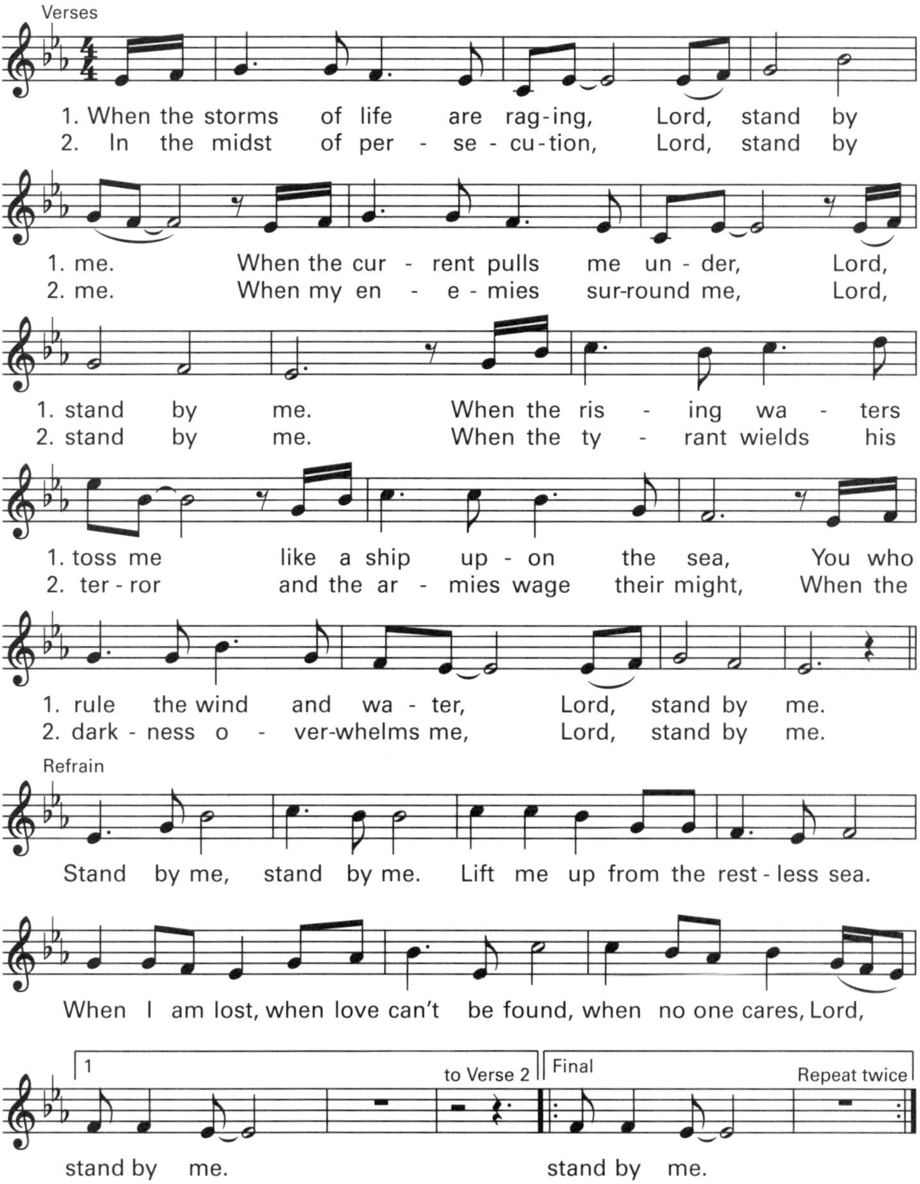

Text: Inspired by "Stand by Me" by Charles A. Tindley, 1851–1933; Tom Kendzia, b. 1954.
Music: Tom Kendzia.

630 To You, O God, I Lift Up My Soul

Refrain: 1st time: Cantor, All repeat; thereafter: All

To you, O God, I lift up my soul; lift up my spir-it to my Lord. To you I lift up my soul.

1 | 2-4 to Vss. | Final

To you I lift up my soul. To you I lift up my soul.

Verses: Cantor

1. Make me to know your ways, O God; teach me your paths, guide me. You are my Sav - ior.
2. Good and up-right our gra - cious God, show-ing the way, guid-ing the hum-ble to jus - tice.
3. Stead-fast and kind your ways, O God; all who re-vere your cov - e - nant know your friend-ship.

to Refrain

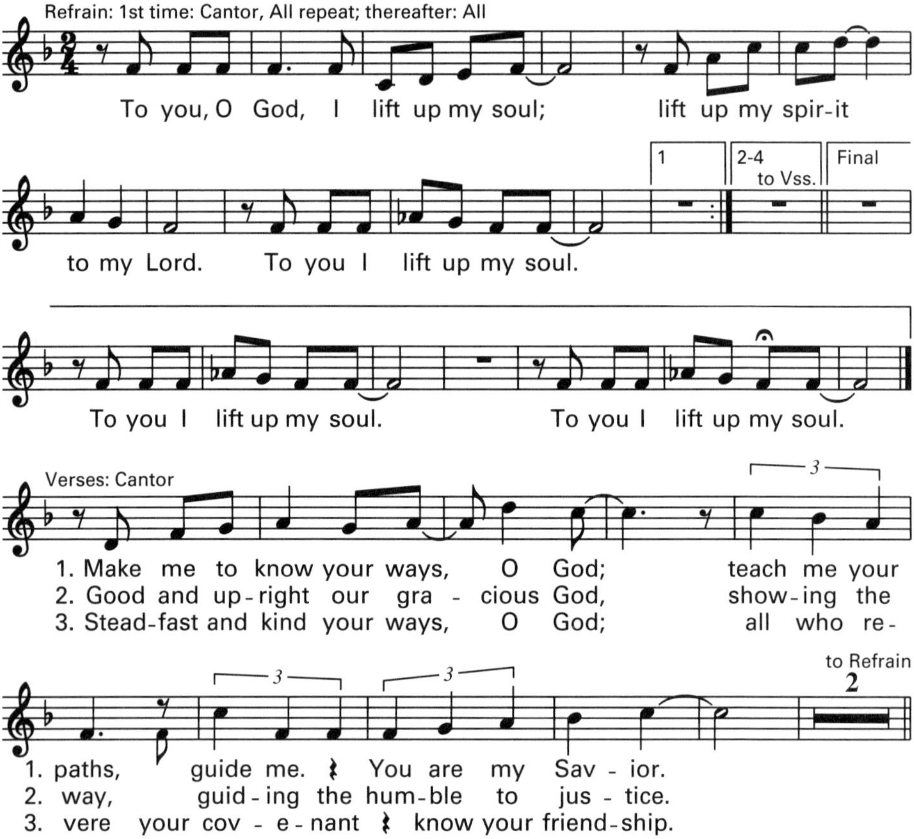

Text: Based on Psalm 25:1, 4–5, 8–9, 10, 14; Bob Hurd, b. 1950.
Music: Bob Hurd.

631 This Alone

Refrain
One thing I ask, this a-lone I seek, to
dwell in the house of the Lord all my days. For one
day with-in your tem-ple heals ev - 'ry day a - lone. O
Lord, bring me to your dwell - ing.

Verses 1, 3
1. Hear, O Lord, the sound of my call - ing.
3. Wait on the Lord, and hope in his mer - cy.
to Refrain
1. Hear, O Lord, and show me your way.
3. Wait on the Lord, and live in his love.
Verse 2
2. The Lord is my light and hope of sal - va - tion. The
to Refrain
2. Lord is my ref - uge; whom should I fear?

Text: Based on Psalm 27; Tim Manion, b. 1951.
Music: Tim Manion.

THESE ALONE ARE ENOUGH 632

1. Take my heart, O Lord, take my hopes and
2. Take my thoughts, O Lord, and my mem - o -
3. I sur - ren - der, Lord, all I have and
4. When the dark - ness falls on my fi - nal

1. dreams. Take my mind with all its plans and
2. ry. Take my tears, my joys, my lib - er -
3. hold. I re - turn to you your gifts un -
4. days, take the ver - y breath that sang your

1. schemes.
2. ty.
3. told.
4. praise.
Give me noth - ing more than your love and

1-4. grace. These a-lone, O God, are e-nough for me.

Text: Based on "Suscipe" Prayer of St. Ignatius of Loyola; Dan Schutte, b. 1947.
Music: Dan Schutte.

633 Be Thou My Vision

1. Be Thou my vi - sion, O Lord of my heart;
2. Be Thou my wis - dom, and Thou my true word;
3. Rich - es I heed not, or man's emp - ty praise,
4. High King of heav - en, my vic - to - ry won,

1. Naught be all else to me, save that Thou art:
2. I ev - er with Thee and Thou with me, Lord:
3. Thou mine in - her - i - tance, now and al - ways:
4. May I reach heav - en's joys, O bright heav'n's Sun!

1. Thou my best thought, by day or by night,
2. Thou my great Fa - ther, I Thy true son,
3. Thou and Thou on - ly, first in my heart,
4. Heart of my own heart, what - ev - er be - fall,

1. Wak - ing or sleep - ing, Thy pres - ence my light.
2. Thou in me dwell - ing, and I with Thee one.
3. High King of heav - en, my trea - sure Thou art.
4. Still be my vi - sion, O Rul - er of all.

Text: 10 10 10 10; ancient Irish; tr. by Mary E. Byrne, 1905; fr. Eleanor Hull's *Poem Book of the Gael*, 1912, alt.
Music: SLANE; trad. Irish melody; adapt. fr. *The Church Hymnary*, 1927.

634 There Is a Longing

Refrain
There is a long-ing in our hearts, O Lord, for you to re - veal your - self to us. There is a long-ing in our hearts for love we on - ly find in you, our God.
Verses
1. For jus - tice,
2. For wis - dom,
3. For heal - ing,
4. Lord save us,

1. for free - dom, for mer - cy: hear our prayer. In
2. for cour - age, for com-fort: hear our prayer. In
3. for whole-ness, for new life: hear our prayer. In
4. take pit - y, light in our dark - ness. We
to Refrain
1. sor - row, in grief:
2. weak-ness, in fear:
3. sick - ness, in death:
4. call you, we wait:
be near, hear our prayer, O God.

SACRED SILENCE 635

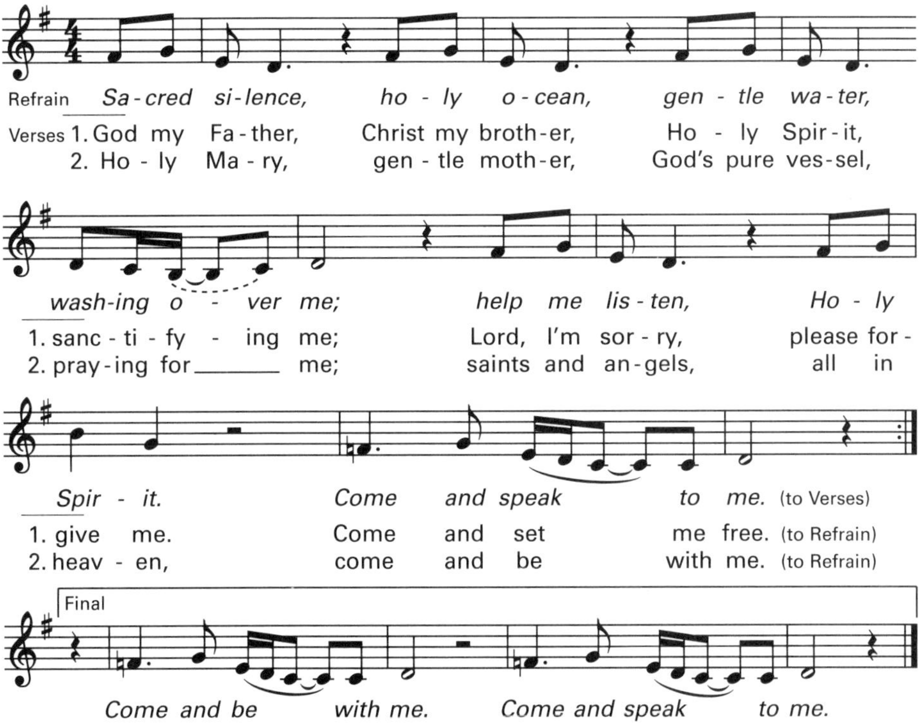

Refrain *Sa - cred si - lence, ho - ly o - cean, gen - tle wa - ter,*
Verses 1. God my Fa - ther, Christ my broth - er, Ho - ly Spir - it,
2. Ho - ly Ma - ry, gen - tle moth - er, God's pure ves - sel,

wash - ing o - ver me; help me lis - ten, Ho - ly
1. sanc - ti - fy - ing me; Lord, I'm sor - ry, please for -
2. pray - ing for ___ me; saints and an - gels, all in

Spir - it. Come and speak to me. (to Verses)
1. give me. Come and set me free. (to Refrain)
2. heav - en, come and be with me. (to Refrain)

Final
Come and be with me. Come and speak to me.

636 Open My Eyes/Abre Mis Ojos

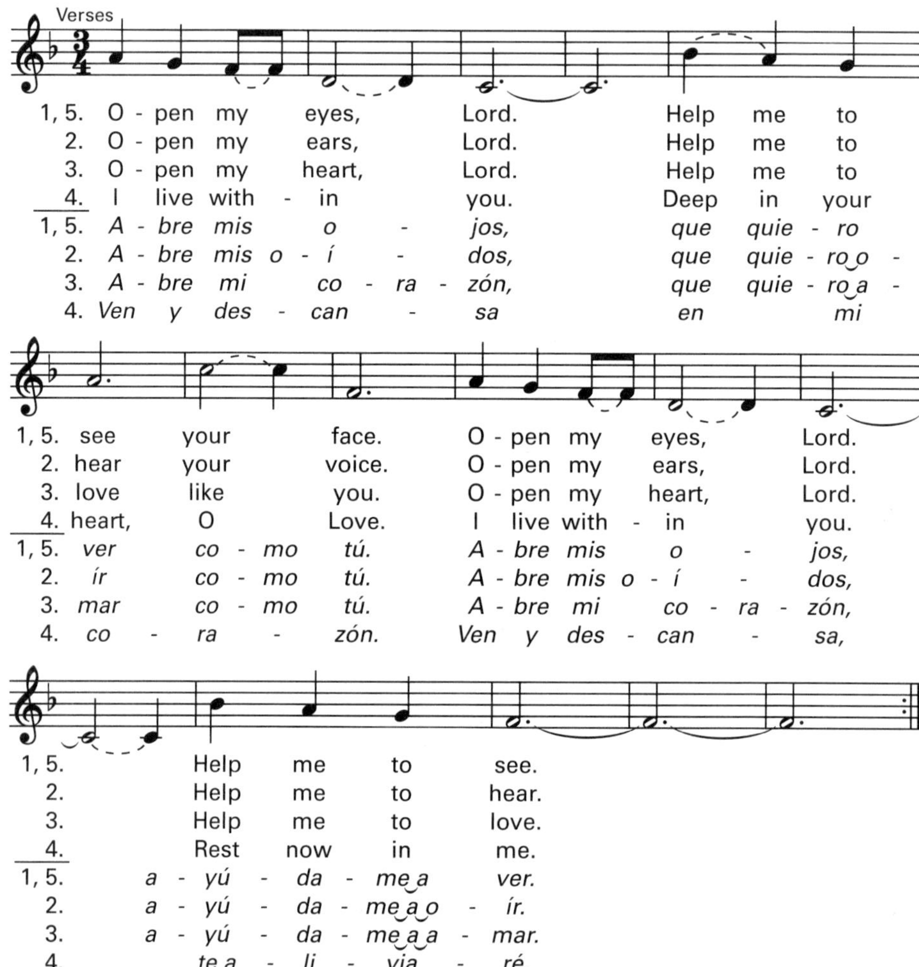
Verses
1, 5. O - pen my eyes, Lord. Help me to
2. O - pen my ears, Lord. Help me to
3. O - pen my heart, Lord. Help me to
4. I live with - in you. Deep in your
1, 5. A - bre mis o - jos, que quie - ro
2. A - bre mis o - í - dos, que quie - ro o -
3. A - bre mi co - ra - zón, que quie - ro a -
4. Ven y des - can - sa en mi
1, 5. see your face. O - pen my eyes, Lord.
2. hear your voice. O - pen my ears, Lord.
3. love like you. O - pen my heart, Lord.
4. heart, O Love. I live with - in you.
1, 5. ver co - mo tú. A - bre mis o - jos,
2. ír co - mo tú. A - bre mis o - í - dos,
3. mar co - mo tú. A - bre mi co - ra - zón,
4. co - ra - zón. Ven y des - can - sa,
1, 5. Help me to see.
2. Help me to hear.
3. Help me to love.
4. Rest now in me.
1, 5. a - yú - da - me a ver.
2. a - yú - da - me a o - ír.
3. a - yú - da - me a a - mar.
4. te a - li - via - ré.

Bridge

And the first shall be last,
and our eyes are opened
and we'll hear like never before.
And we'll speak in new ways,
and we'll see God's face
in places we've never known.

Dame la alegría de tu salvación,
crea en mí un corazón puro.
No me arrojes lejos de tu rostro, Señor,
no me quites tu santo espíritu.

IRISH BLESSING 

637

(Blessing Prayer)

Refrain
May the road rise up to meet you. May the wind be al-ways with you.

May the sun-shine warm you al-ways 'til we meet a-gain.

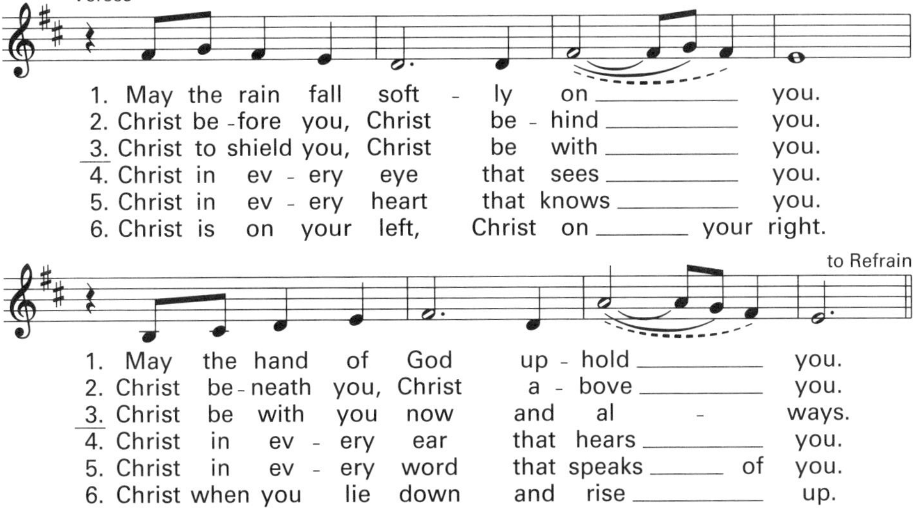
Verses
1. May the rain fall soft - ly on ___ you.
2. Christ be-fore you, Christ be-hind ___ you.
3. Christ to shield you, Christ be with ___ you.
4. Christ in ev-ery eye that sees ___ you.
5. Christ in ev-ery heart that knows ___ you.
6. Christ is on your left, Christ on ___ your right.
to Refrain
1. May the hand of God up-hold ___ you.
2. Christ be-neath you, Christ a-bove ___ you.
3. Christ be with you now and al - ways.
4. Christ in ev-ery ear that hears ___ you.
5. Christ in ev-ery word that speaks ___ of you.
6. Christ when you lie down and rise ___ up.

Text: Refrain based on trad. Irish blessing; verses based on St. Patrick's Breastplate; Bob Fabing, SJ, b. 1942.
Music: Bob Fabing, SJ.

MAY GOD BLESS AND KEEP YOU

638

1st time: Cantor; thereafter: All
May God bless and keep you. May God's face shine on you.
May God be kind to you and give you peace.

Text: Based on Numbers 6:22–27; Christopher Walker, b. 1947.
Music: Christopher Walker.

639 May the Road Rise Up

(An Irish Blessing)

May the road rise up to meet you, may the wind be al-ways at your back. May the sun shine warm up - on your face, the rain fall soft up-on your fields.

And un - til we meet a - gain, un - til we meet a - gain, may God hold you in the palm of his hand. Un - til we meet a - gain, un - til we meet a - gain, may God hold you, may God hold you, may God hold you in the palm of his hand.

Text: Traditional Irish.
Music: Tom Kendzia, b. 1954, © 2015, Tom Kendzia. Published by OCP.

640 Like a Child Rests

Refrain: 1st time: Cantor, All repeat; thereafter: All
1
Like a child rests in its moth-er's arms, so will I rest in you. Like a
2
so will I rest in you.

Verses
to Refrain
1. My God, I am not proud. I do not look for things too great.
2. My God, I trust in you. You care for me, you give me peace.
3. O Is - rael, trust in God, ___ now and al - ways trust in God.

Text: Based on Psalm 131; Christopher Walker, b. 1947.
Music: Christopher Walker.

BECAUSE THE LORD IS MY SHEPHERD 641

Verses

1. Be - cause ___ the Lord is my shep - herd, I have
2. And when ___ the road leads to dark - ness, I shall
3. In love ___ you make me a ban - quet for my
4. Your good - ness ___ al - ways is with me and your

1. ev - 'ry thing ___ I need. He lets me rest in the
2. walk there ___ un - a - fraid. E - ven when death is close ___
3. en - e - mies ___ to see. You make me wel - come, ___
4. mer - cy ___ I know. Your lov - ing kind - ness ___

1. mead - ow and leads me to the qui - et streams. He re -
2. ___ I have cour - age, for your help is there. You are
3. pour - ing down hon - or from your might - y hand, and this
4. strength - ens me al - ways as I go through life. I shall

1. stores ___ my soul and he leads me in the paths that are right:
2. close ___ be - side me with com - fort, you are guid - ing my way:
3. joy ___ fills me with glad - ness; it is too much to bear:
4. dwell in your pres - ence for - ev - er, giv - ing praise to your name:

Refrain

Lord, you are my shep - herd, you are my friend.
I want to fol - low you al - ways, just to fol - low my friend.

Text: Based on Psalm 23; Christopher Walker, b. 1947.
Music: Christopher Walker.

642 Shepherd Me, O God

Refrain
Shep-herd me, O God, be - yond my wants, be -
yond my fears, from death in - to life.
1-3, 5
to Vss 1-3, 5
4
to Verse 4
life.
Final
life.
Verses 1-3
1. God is my shep-herd, so noth-ing shall I want, I
2. Gen - tly you raise me and heal my wea - ry soul, you
3. Though I should wan-der the val - ley of death, I
1. rest in the mead-ows of faith - ful - ness and love, I
2. lead me by path-ways of righ-teous-ness and truth, my
3. fear no e - vil, for you are at my side, your
to Refrain
1. walk by the qui - et wa - ters of peace.
2. spir - it shall sing the mu - sic of your Name.
3. rod and your staff, my com-fort and my hope.
Verse 4
4. You have set me a ban-quet of love in the face of
to Refrain
4. ha-tred, crown-ing me with love be-yond my pow'r to hold.
Verse 5
5. Sure-ly your kind-ness and mer-cy fol-low me all the days of my

to Refrain
5. life; I will dwell in the house of my God for-ev-er-more.

Text: Based on Psalm 23; Marty Haugen, b. 1950.
Music: Marty Haugen.

All Is Well with My Soul 643

Verses

1. When peace, like a riv - er, at - tend - eth my
2. My soul is at rest in the Lord God a -
3. My God is my safe - ty, my glo - ry, my
4. O God, I will bless you as long as I

1. way; When sor - rows like sea bil - lows roll; What -
2. lone; From God comes sal - va - tion and hope. With
3. strength; My ref - uge when life takes its toll. I
4. live; For your grace a - lone makes me whole. With

1. ev - er my lot, you have taught me to
2. God as my rock, I shall not be dis -
3. trust in my God, as I pour out my
4. glad - ness and joy I will sing of your

1. say, "It is well, it is well with my soul."
2. turbed: All is well, all is well with my soul.
3. heart: All is well, all is well with my soul.
4. name: All is well, all is well with my soul!

Refrain

1. It is well with my soul;
2-4. All is well with my soul;

1. It is well, it is well with my soul.
2-4. All is well, all is well with my soul.

Text: 11 8 11 9 with refrain. Verse 1, traditional; fr. *It Is Well with My Soul*; Horatio Gates Spafford, 1827–1888.
Verses 2–4 based on Psalm 62:2–3, 6–9; 63:5; Carey Landry, b. 1944, © 2008, 2010, Carey Landry.

Music: VILLE DU HAVRE; Philip P. Bliss, 1838–1876.

644 Come to Me

Refrain
Come to me, all who la - bor and are heav-y bur - dened, and
I shall give you rest. Take up my yoke and learn from
me, for I am meek and hum - ble of heart,
and you'll find rest for your souls. Yes, my
yoke is eas - y and my bur - den is
light.
Verses
1. You, God, are my shep-herd.
2. Be - side peace-ful wa - ters
3. Should I be sur-round-ed
4. Be - fore my deep hun - ger
5. Pur - sue me, O God,
1. I shall nev - er be in need. Fresh and green are the
2. you re - store my true self; There you lead me to
3. by the shad - ows of death, I will not fear, for
4. you spread out your feast. My skin you a -
5. with your fath - om - less love. In your tent let me
to Refrain
1. mead-ows where you give me rest.
2. walk in the path of new life.
3. you are stead-fast in your love.
4. noint with the rich - est of oil.
5. dwell all the days of my life.

Text: Based on Matthew 11:28–30; Psalm 23; original text, Weston Priory, Gregory Norbet, OSB, b. 1940.
Music: Weston Priory, Gregory Norbet, OSB.

EYE HAS NOT SEEN

Refrain
Eye has not seen, ear has not heard what God has read-y for
those who love him; Spir-it of love, come, give us the mind of
Je-sus, teach us the wis-dom of God.
Verses 1-3
1. When pain and sor-row weigh us down, be near to us, O
2. Our lives are but a sin-gle breath, we flow-er and we
3. To those who see with eyes of faith, the Lord is ev-er
1. Lord, for-give the weak-ness of our faith, and bear us up with-
2. fade, yet all our days are in your hands, so we re-turn in
3. near, re-flect-ed in the fac-es of all the poor and
to Refrain
1. in your peace-ful word.
2. love what love has made.
3. low-ly of the world.
Verse 4
4. We sing a mys-t'ry from the past, in halls where saints have
4. trod, yet ev-er new the mu-sic rings to Je-sus, Liv-ing
to Refrain
4. Song of God.

Text: Based on 1 Corinthians 2:9–10; Marty Haugen, b. 1950.
Music: Marty Haugen.

646 I Heard the Voice of Jesus

1. I heard the voice of Jesus say, "Come unto me and rest;
Lay down, thou weary one, lay down Thy head upon my breast."
I came to Jesus as I was, So weary, worn and sad;
I found in him a resting place, And he has made me glad.

2. I heard the voice of Jesus say, "Behold, I freely give
The living water; thirsty one, Stoop down, and drink, and live."
I came to Jesus, and I drank Of that life-giving stream;
My thirst was quenched, my soul revived, And now I live in him.

3. I heard the voice of Jesus say, "I am this dark world's light;
Look unto me, thy morn shall rise, And all thy day be bright."
I looked to Jesus, and I found In him my star, my sun;
And in that light of life I'll walk Till trav'ling days are done.

Text: CMD; Horatius Bonar, 1808–1889, alt.
Music: KINGSFOLD; trad. English melody; *English Country Songs*, 1893; adapt. by Ralph Vaughan Williams, 1872–1958.

647 Fly like a Bird

Refrain
Fly like a bird to the Lord, my soul. I want to soar like an eagle.
Though I may journey far away from home, I know I'll never be alone.
Verses
1. O God, you know who I am.
2. Where can I run from your love?
3. When I am down and afraid,

1. You know my hopes and my dreams. In my
2. Where can I hide from my God? From the
3. when I am fall - ing a - way, you ex -
1. pon - der - ing and fears, in my joy and in my tears,
2. dawn of morn - ing's light to the dark - ness of the night,
3. tend a gen - tle hand, and I know you un - der - stand.
to Refrain
1-3. O God, your pres - ence is real.

Text: Based on Psalm 139:1–4, 7–12, 23–24; Ken Canedo, b. 1953.
Music: Ken Canedo.

The King of Love My Shepherd Is 648

1. The King of love my shep - herd is, Whose
2. Where streams of liv - ing wa - ter flow With
3. Per - verse and fool - ish I have strayed, But
4. In death's dark vale I fear no ill With
5. You spread a ta - ble in my sight, Your
6. And so through all the length of days Your

1. good - ness fails me nev - er; I noth - ing lack if
2. gen - tle care he leads me, And where the ver - dant
3. yet in love he sought me, And on his shoul - der
4. you, dear Lord, be - side me; Your rod and staff my
5. sav - ing grace be - stow - ing; And O what joy and
6. good - ness fails me nev - er: Good Shep - herd, may I

1. I am his, And he is mine for - ev - er.
2. pas - tures grow, With heav'n - ly food he feeds me.
3. gent - ly laid, And home, re - joic - ing, brought me.
4. com - fort still, Your cross be - fore to guide me.
5. true de - light From your pure chal - ice flow - ing!
6. sing your praise With - in your house for - ev - er.

Text: 87 87; based on Psalm 23; Matthew 18; John 10; Henry W. Baker, 1821–1877, alt.
Music: ST. COLUMBA; trad. Irish melody.

649 SHELTER ME, O GOD

Refrain
Shel-ter me, O God; hide me in the shad-ow of your wings. You a-lone are my hope.
Verses
1. When my foes sur-round me, set me high a-bove their reach. Hear me when I call your name.
2. As a moth-er gath-ers her young be-neath her care, gath-er me in-to your arms.
3. Though I walk in dark-ness, through the nee-dle's eye of death, you will nev-er leave my side.
to Refrain

Text: Based on Psalm 16; Psalm 61; Luke 13:34; Bob Hurd, b. 1950.
Music: Bob Hurd.

650 PASTURES OF THE LORD

1. Lord, now your ser - vant may go in peace;
2. The day is gone, the work is done;
3. Lord, lay me down in ver-dant fields,
4. Lord, let this trav - 'ler find sweet re - pose.
5. Lord, now your ser - vant may go in peace;

1. your sal - va-tion mine eyes have seen.
2. man-y bat-tles I've lost and won.
3. in green val-leys with gold-en hills,
4. From pain and sor-row your mer-cy leads
5. your sal - va-tion mine eyes have seen.

1. I will walk near run-ning streams
2. I shall rest and find wel-come
3. there to find your face re-vealed
4. to liv-ing wa-ters, where an-gels sing
5. On-ly good-ness shall fol-low me

1-5. in the pas-tures of the Lord.

Text and music: Curtis Stephan, b. 1973,

You Are Mine 651

Verses

1. I will come to you in the si - lence,
2. I am hope for all who are hope - less,
3. I am strength for all the de - spair - ing,
4. am the Word that leads all to free - dom, I

1. I will lift you from ___ all your fear.
2. I am eyes for all who long to see. In the
3. heal - ing for the ones who dwell in shame.
4. am the peace the world ___ can - not give.

1. You will hear my voice, I claim you as my choice, be
2. shad - ows of the night, ___ I will be your light, ___
3. All the blind will see, the lame will all run free, and
4. I will call your name, em - brac - ing all your pain, stand

1. still and know I am here. (to Verse 2)
2. come and rest in me. (to Refrain)
3. all will know my name. (to Refrain)
4. up, now walk, and live! (to Refrain)

Refrain

Do not be a - fraid, I am with you. I have called you each by name. Come and fol - low me, I will bring you home; I love you and you are mine. (4. I)

Text and music: David Haas, b. 1957,

652 PSALM 23

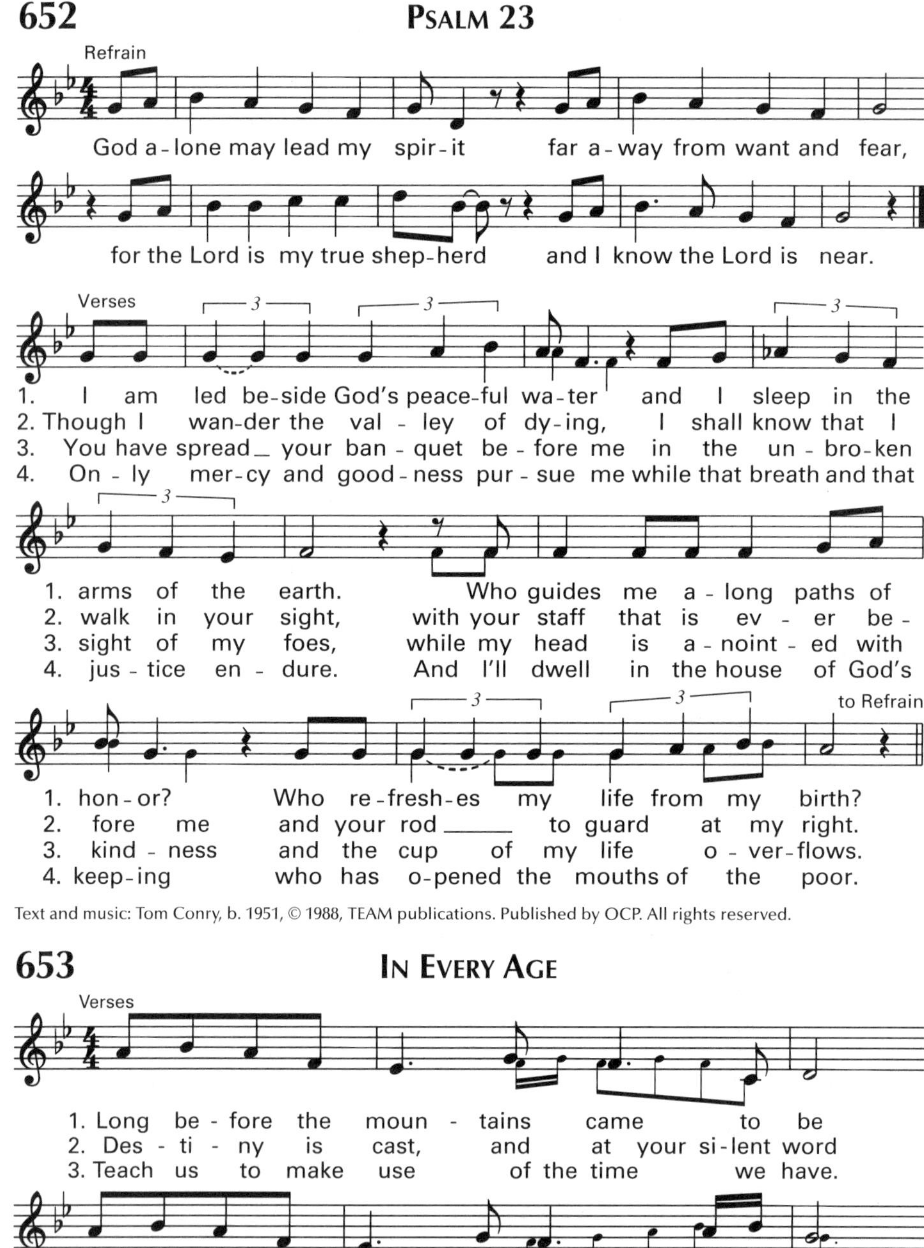
Refrain
God a-lone may lead my spir-it far a-way from want and fear,
for the Lord is my true shep-herd and I know the Lord is near.
Verses
1. I am led be-side God's peace-ful wa-ter and I sleep in the
2. Though I wan-der the val-ley of dy-ing, I shall know that I
3. You have spread_ your ban-quet be-fore me in the un-bro-ken
4. On-ly mer-cy and good-ness pur-sue me while that breath and that
1. arms of the earth. Who guides me a-long paths of
2. walk in your sight, with your staff that is ev-er be-
3. sight of my foes, while my head is a-noint-ed with
4. jus-tice en-dure. And I'll dwell in the house of God's
to Refrain
1. hon-or? Who re-fresh-es my life from my birth?
2. fore me and your rod_____ to guard at my right.
3. kind-ness and the cup of my life o-ver-flows.
4. keep-ing who has o-pened the mouths of the poor.

653 IN EVERY AGE

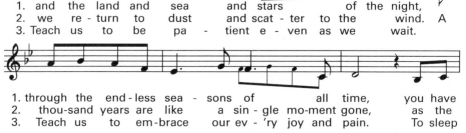

Verses

1. Long be-fore the moun-tains came to be
2. Des-ti-ny is cast, and at your si-lent word
3. Teach us to make use of the time we have.

1. and the land and sea and stars of the night,
2. we re-turn to dust and scat-ter to the wind. A
3. Teach us to be pa-tient e-ven as we wait.

1. through the end-less sea-sons of all time, you have
2. thou-sand years are like a sin-gle mo-ment gone, as the
3. Teach us to em-brace our ev-'ry joy and pain. To sleep

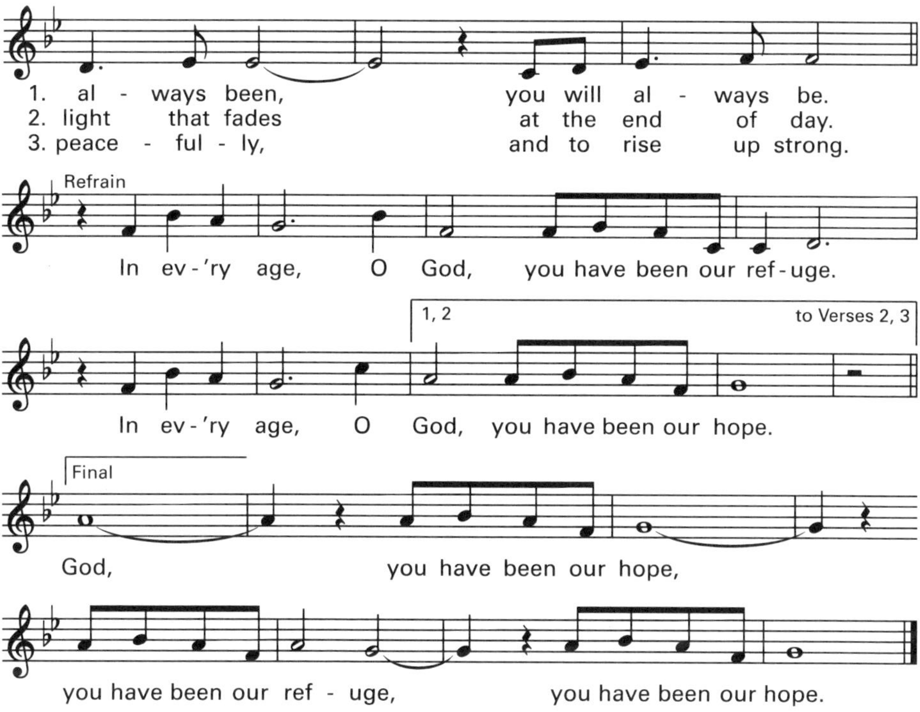

1. al - ways been, you will al - ways be.
2. light that fades at the end of day.
3. peace - ful - ly, and to rise up strong.

Refrain

In ev - 'ry age, O God, you have been our ref - uge.

1, 2 — to Verses 2, 3

In ev - 'ry age, O God, you have been our hope.

Final

God, you have been our hope,

you have been our ref - uge, you have been our hope.

Text: Based on Psalm 90:1–4, 12; Janèt Sullivan Whitaker, b. 1958.
Music: Janèt Sullivan Whitaker.

THERE IS A BALM IN GILEAD 654

Refrain
There is a balm in Gil - e - ad to make the wound - ed whole,
there is a balm in Gil - e - ad to heal the sin - sick soul.
Verses
1. Some - times I feel dis - cour - aged, And _ think my work's in vain,
2. If you can - not preach like Pe - ter, If you can - not pray like Paul,
3. Don't _ ev - er feel dis - cour - aged, For _ Je - sus is your friend;

to Refrain
1. But _ then the Ho - ly Spir - it Re - vives my soul a - gain.
2. You can tell the love of Je - sus, And say, "He died for all."
3. And _ if you lack for knowl - edge, He'll ne'er re - fuse to lend.

Text: 76 76 with refrain; based on Jeremiah 8:22; Spiritual.
Music: BALM IN GILEAD; Spiritual.

655 GOD IS LOVE

Refrain

God is love, and all who live in love a - bide in God, and

1 God a - bides in them. 2 God a - bides in them. to Verses (Fine)

Verses

1. The love of Christ has gath - ered us as one: In
2. There - fore, as now we gath - er in - to one, let
3. Then with the saints let us be - hold your face, a -

1. him let us re - joice; in him let us be glad.
2. dis - cord find no place, nor ha - tred rule our hearts.
3. light with glo - ry, Christ, our broth - er and our God.

1. Let us re - vere and love the liv - ing God. With
2. Let e - vil deeds and bit - ter words now cease, that
3. And may this joy, un - bound - ed and im - mense, ful -

to Refrain

1. heart and mind and soul now let us love sin - cere - ly.
2. Christ stay in our midst and dwell with us for - ev - er.
3. fill our hearts' de - sire through a - ges with - out end - ing.

Text: Based on 1 John 4:16b and *Ubi Caritas*; Michael Joncas, b. 1951.
Music: Michael Joncas.

656 ALL I ASK OF YOU

Refrain
All I ask of you is for-ev-er to re-mem-ber me as lov-ing
1-5
to Verses
you.
Final
you, for - ev - er as lov - ing you.

Verses
1. Deep the joy of be - ing ___ to - geth - er in one heart ___ and for me that's just ___ where it is.
2. As we make our way ___ through all the joys and pain, ___ can we sense our young - er, tru - er selves?
3. Some - one will be call - ing you to be there for a - while. ___ Can you hear their cry from deep with - in?
4. Laugh - ter, joy and pres - ence: ___ the on - ly gifts you are! ___ Have you time? I'd like to be with you.
5. Per - sons come in - to the fi - ber of our lives and then their shad - ows fade and dis - ap - pear. But
to Refrain

Text and music: Weston Priory, Gregory Norbet, OSB, b. 1940, © 1973, The Benedictine Foundation of the State of Vermont, Inc. All rights reserved. Used with permission.

CHRISTIANS, LET US LOVE ONE ANOTHER 657

1. Chris - tians, let us love one an - oth - er, As we share the true liv - ing bread. Je - sus is our God and our broth - er; With his flesh and blood we are fed.
2. We who break this bread are one bod - y, We who share this cup are all one. Chil - dren of our Fa - ther in heav - en, We are heirs with God's on - ly son.
3. We who eat and drink at this ta - ble Die and rise a - gain with our Lord. Draw - ing from our Rock liv - ing wa - ter Giv'n to all who thirst for ac - cord.
4. On the path of life we may fal - ter, Earth - ly food a - lone leaves us weak; Al - ways you in - vite from the al - tar, "Hun - gry souls their food here must seek."
5. Wheat and grape in - car - nate a mys - t'ry: Je - sus is the true liv - ing bread. Let us eat with joy and thanks - giv - ing, Trust - ing in the word he has said.
6. Je - sus is the vine, we the branch - es; We are grains of wheat, Christ the bread. Those who eat this bread live for - ev - er, One with Christ, our Lord and our Head.

1-6. Ev - 'ry - one who loves is born of God. Je - sus is our life. God is love.

Text: 98 98 98; Claudia Foltz, SNJM, and Armand Nigro, SJ, b. 1928, © 1973, Claudia Foltz, SNJM, and Armand Nigro, SJ. Published by OCP. All rights reserved.
Music: PICARDY; French, 17th cent.; *Chansons populaires des Provinces de France*, 1860.

658 ENDLESS IS YOUR LOVE

Refrain

You know my heart. You know my mind. You know my words long be - fore I speak them. There is no place that I can hide. End-less is your love for us. How vast the sum of all your deeds! End-less is your love for us.

Verses

1. Sure - ly there's a place e - ven you don't know. If I climb there, if I fly there, can I hide from you?
2. Can't I hide at night, dark - ness be my light? Can you see the day in dark - ness, can you find me there?
3. Won - der - ful your works, count - less as the sand. Earth and heav - en know your beau - ty, fash - ioned by your hand.

to Refrain

Text: Based on Psalm 139; Tom Kendzia, b. 1954.
Music: Tom Kendzia.

FAITHFUL FAMILY

Refrain
Be like our God, who chose to live and learn our ways and die in deep, un-bound-ed love. For-give each oth-er ten-der-ly, the faith-ful fam-'ly of our God.
Verses
1. Wher-ev-er there is char-i-ty, self-less, giv-ing care, sure-ly our God is there. The love of Christ has gath-ered us to one from is-land ways: let us sing for joy all our days.
2. And let us love the liv-ing God, mer-ci-ful, and kind, bod-y and heart and mind. Let us love each oth-er well, hold the strang-er dear, reach-ing out to all with-out fear.
3. When we are to-geth-er, let us act as one, ways of greed and con-flict done. Let there be no bit-ter-ness, quar-rel-ing, nor strife. In our midst is Christ, our life.
4. One day in the com-pa-ny of the saints in light, may we see your face shine bright. Bright up-on your fam-i-ly, faith-ful, hu-man, flawed. Shine in glo-ry, Christ, our God.
to Refrain

Text: Based on *Ubi Caritas;* Rory Cooney, b. 1952.
Music: Rory Cooney.

660 IN PERFECT CHARITY

1. O most high and glo-rious God, cast your light in - to
2. O most high and glo-rious God, o - pen wide the door
3. Then most high and thank-ful praise I will sing un - to

1. the dark - ness of my heart. Give me right faith, and cer-tain
2. that leads me to your love. Give me your firm, yet gen-tle
3. the glo - ry of your name: To Fa - ther, Son, and Spir - it

1. hope, and ___ per - fect, per-fect char - i - ty. Give me true
2. strength; may I live that per-fect char - i - ty. Lord, may your
3. bright, Liv-ing Pres - ence, Per-fect Char - i - ty. Praise to the

1. in-sight, Lord, and wis-dom, that I may al-ways live with-
2. peace be ev - er in me, that I may al-ways seek to
3. Love that shines in splen-dor, that lights the path-ways of my

1. in your ev - er ho - ly will. Lord, may your light with -
2. serve your chil-dren here on earth; that I may find my
3. heart, and brings me close to you. O Ho - ly One, in -

1. in me burn, shin - ing out in per-fect char - i - ty.
2. home with you, and ___ live in per-fect char - i - ty.
3. vite me in, where you live in per-fect char - i - ty.

Text: Irregular; verse 1 based on a prayer of St. Francis of Assisi, 1182–1226; verses 2–3, Randall DeBruyn, b. 1947.
Music: PERFECT CHARITY; Randall DeBruyn.

661 GOD OF LOVE

Refrain
God is love, and all who dwell in love will live, will
live in God, and God will live in them.

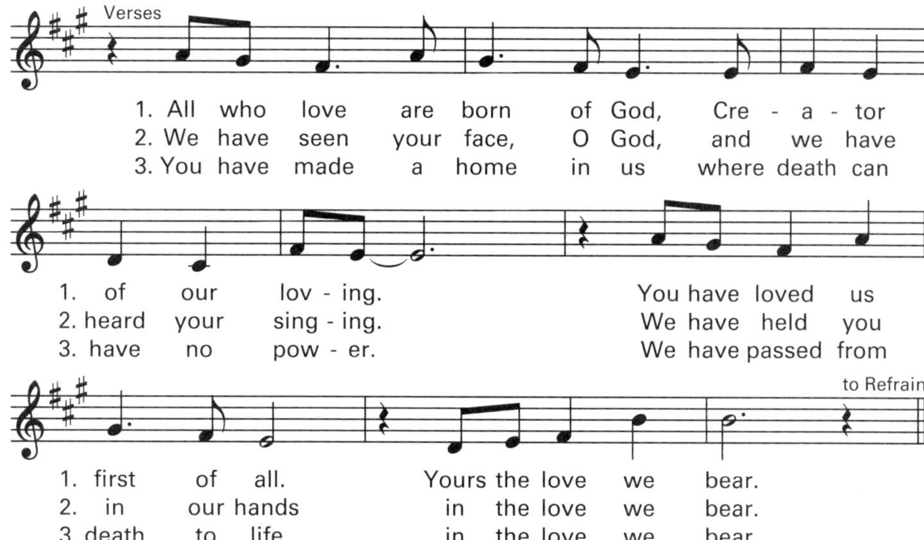
Verses
1. All who love are born of God, Cre - a - tor
2. We have seen your face, O God, and we have
3. You have made a home in us where death can
1. of our lov - ing. You have loved us
2. heard your sing - ing. We have held you
3. have no pow - er. We have passed from
to Refrain
1. first of all. Yours the love we bear.
2. in our hands in the love we bear.
3. death to life in the love we bear.

Love Divine, All Loves Excelling 662

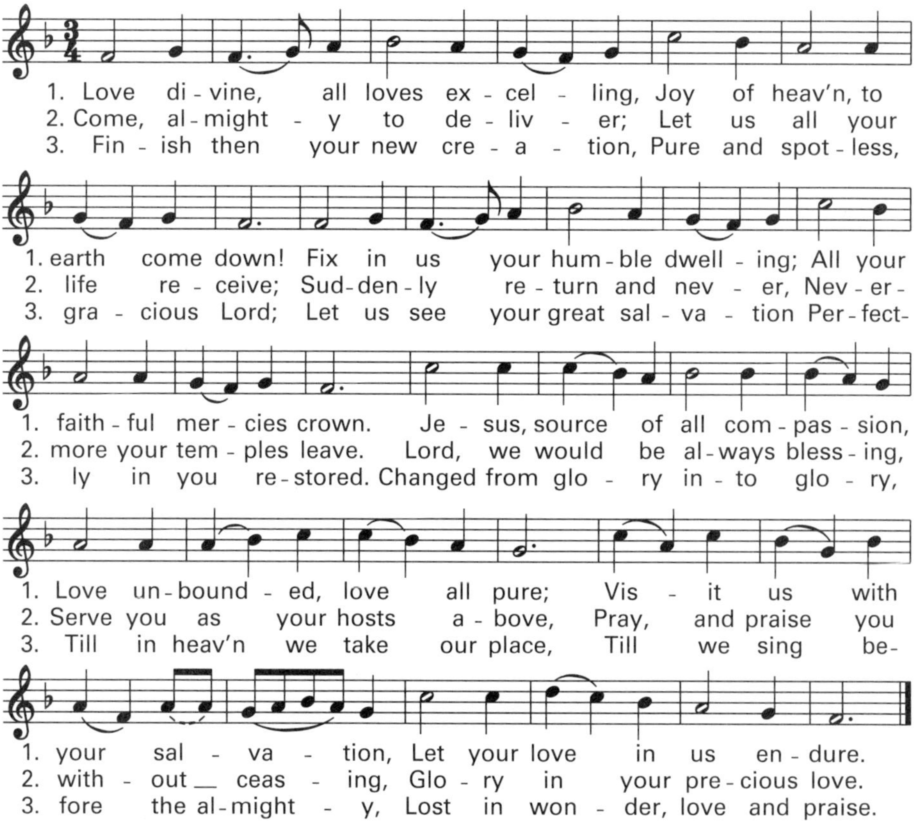

1. Love di - vine, all loves ex - cel - ling, Joy of heav'n, to earth come down! Fix in us your hum - ble dwell - ing; All your faith - ful mer - cies crown. Je - sus, source of all com - pas - sion, Love un - bound - ed, love all pure; Vis - it us with your sal - va - tion, Let your love in us en - dure.

2. Come, al - might - y to de - liv - er; Let us all your life re - ceive; Sud - den - ly re - turn and nev - er, Nev - er - more your tem - ples leave. Lord, we would be al - ways bless - ing, Serve you as your hosts a - bove, Pray, and praise you with - out __ ceas - ing, Glo - ry in your pre - cious love.

3. Fin - ish then your new cre - a - tion, Pure and spot - less, gra - cious Lord; Let us see your great sal - va - tion Per - fect - ly in you re - stored. Changed from glo - ry in - to glo - ry, Till in heav'n we take our place, Till we sing be - fore the al - might - y, Lost in won - der, love and praise.

Text: 87 87 D; Charles Wesley, 1707–1788, alt.
Music: HYFRYDOL; Rowland H. Prichard, 1811–1887.

663 LOVER OF US ALL

Refrain
With all the earth we sing your praise! We come to give you thanks, O lov - er of us all, and giv - er of our lov - ing.
With sun and moon we dance for joy! We are your work of art, the glo - ry of your hand, the chil-dren of your lov - ing.
1
2
Verses 1-3
1. I am mak - er of moun-tains; I am God of the earth.
2. As I know of your la - bor, so I watch while you sleep.
3. If the night would sur-round you and the sun fall from sight,
to Refrain
1. Like a moth - er in la - bor I bring all to birth.
2. Ev - er close at your call-ing so my love will be.
3. yet my hand will pro-tect you; I will be your light.
Verses 4-6
4. Long be - fore there were mead-ows, or wa - ters on the shore,
5. If you trav - el the heav-ens, or sail the far-thest shore,
6. In the womb of my wis - dom, I fash-ioned ev - 'ry star,
to Refrain
4. I laughed and I loved you, so now and ev - er - more!
5. I stand there be-side you, to guide you ev - er - more!
6. I formed you in won - der, and loved you from a - far!

Text: Based on Ephesians 2:7–10; 5:19–20; Dan Schutte, b. 1947.
Music: Dan Schutte.

Ubi Caritas

664

Refrain
U - bi ca - ri - tas et a - mor, De - us i - bi
1
est.
2 to Verses
(Fine)
est.
Verses 1, 3
1. We gath - er to - geth - er in the love of Christ; let each one be glad in him and re - joice.
Our God is a - live, the God of love is near; so love one an - oth - er with a heart sin - cere.
(to Refrain)
3. Then, joined with the bless - ed, filled with hope and grace, dear Lord, in great glo - ry may we see your face.
Our joy none can mea - sure, joy that knows no end, re - sound - ing from end - less age to age. A - men.
(to Refrain)
Verse 2
2. We, the man - y, be - come one bod - y as the Spir - it binds, and we seek to be one in Christ and one in heart and mind.
Let all quar - rels, all di - vi - sion, all our con - flict cease; then will Christ tru - ly dwell a - mong us as our Lord of Peace.
(to Refrain)

Text: Adapt. fr. Holy Thursday Liturgy; Laurence Rosania, b. 1957.
Music: Laurence Rosania.

665 LOVE ONE ANOTHER

Refrain: All
Love one an - oth - er as I have loved you. Care for each
oth - er. I have cared for you. Bear each oth - er's bur - dens.
Bind each oth - er's wounds; and so you will know my re - turn.

*Verses: Cantor

1. My friends, do you know
   what I have done for you?
   I have washed your feet with my hands.
   If I, your Lord, have knelt at your feet,
   you should do at each other's feet
   as I have done for you.

2. When the world will hate you
   and revile you,
   when they laugh at your care
   for the poor,
   when they hold you in darkness
   and imprison your tongues,
   remember how they listened to me.

3. Let not your hearts be troubled.
   Put your trust in God and in me.
   In my Father's home I prepare your
   room, that where I am you may be.

4. This bread which I give is my body.
   This cup holds the blood of my life.
   And all will be broken
   that you may have life,
   that you may learn to forgive.

5. I am the vine, you are the branches.
   Remain in my love and bring
   forth fruit.

6. For love is patient, love is kind,
   love is always there to forgive,
   to endure.
   All the world will crumble,
   but love will remain;
   for Love's own self is God.

7. You will weep in pain
   while the world rejoices,
   but your grief will be changed
   into joy.
   For the world will forget you,
   but have courage, my friends,
   for I have overcome the world.

*It is not intended that all verses be sung on the same occasion. Some common combinations are: Ordinary Time—Verses 1, 2, 4, 6 or 1, 2, 6; Holy Thursday—Verses 1, 2, 4, 6; Social Justice—Verses 2, 7, 6; Wedding—Verses 3, 5, 6.

Text: Based on John 14—16; 1 Corinthians 13; Bob Dufford, SJ, b. 1943.
Music: Bob Dufford, SJ.

666 LOVE GOES ON

1. Love is pa - tient, love is kind, nev - er
2. Love is faith - ful, love is true, ev - er
3. Love a - lone has shaped our soul, and our
4. Love our jour - ney, love our goal. Though our
5. Love, our Sav - ior's one com - mand: "Love the
6. There are three gifts that re - main when all

1. end - ing, nev - er end - ing; slow to an - ger, rich in
2. joy - ful and for - giv - ing; love en - dures when life is
3. hearts are al - ways rest - less un - til love be - comes our
4. faith may move the moun - tains, love a - lone can heal the
5. way that I have loved you," with a tow - el and a
6. oth - er things have per - ished. On - ly faith, hope, love en -

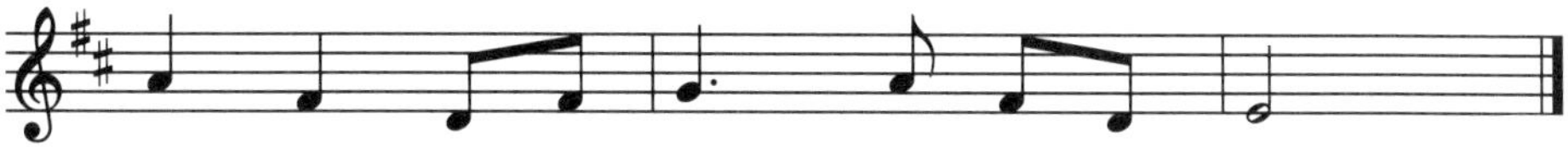

1. mer - cy, love goes on be - yond all time.
2. o - ver, love is old and love is new.
3. pur - pose, new cre - a - tion to un - fold.
4. bro - ken; on - ly love will make us whole.
5. ba - sin, wash - ing feet with ser - vant hands.
6. dur - ing, and the great - est gift is love.

Text: Based on 1 Corinthians 13, John 13; Bernadette Farrell, b. 1957.
Music: Bernadette Farrell.

May Love Be Ours 667

Verses

1. Not for tongues of heav - en's an - gels, not for wis - dom
2. Love is hum - ble, love is gen - tle, love is ten - der,
3. Nev - er jeal - ous, nev - er self - ish, love will not re -
4. In the day this world is fa - ding faith and hope will

1. to dis - cern, not for faith that mas - ters moun - tains,
2. true and kind; love is gra - cious, ev - er pa - tient,
3. joice in wrong; nev - er boast - ful nor re - sent - ful,
4. play their part; but when Christ is seen in glo - ry

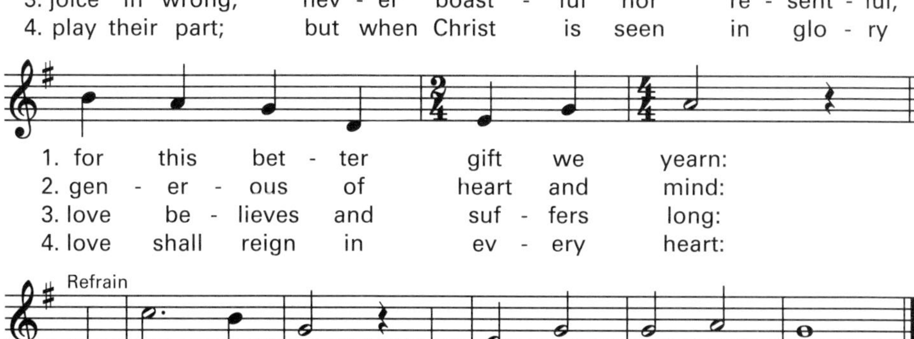
1. for this bet - ter gift we yearn:
2. gen - er - ous of heart and mind:
3. love be - lieves and suf - fers long:
4. love shall reign in ev - ery heart:
Refrain

May love be ours, may love be ours, O Lord.

Text: Based on 1 Corinthians 13; Timothy Dudley-Smith, b. 1926, © 1985, Hope Publishing Company.

Music: Dan Schutte, b. 1947, © 1992, Daniel L. Schutte.

668 WHAT WONDROUS LOVE IS THIS

1. What won-drous love is this, O my soul, O my
2. What won-drous love is this, O my soul, O my
3. To God and to the Lamb I will sing, I will
4. And when from death I'm free, I'll sing on, I'll sing
1. soul? What won-drous love is this, O my soul? What
2. soul? What won-drous love is this, O my soul? What
3. sing; To God and to the Lamb, I will sing; To
4. on; And when from death I'm free, I'll sing on; And
1. won-drous love is this that caused the Lord of
2. won-drous love is this that caused the Lord of
3. God and to the Lamb, who is the great I
4. when from death I'm free, I'll sing and joy - ful
1. bliss To bear the dread-ful curse for my soul, for my
2. bliss To send this pre-cious peace to my soul, to my
3. AM, While mil-lions join the theme, I will sing, I will
4. be, And through e - ter - ni - ty, I'll sing on, I'll sing
1. soul, To bear the dread-ful curse for my soul?
2. soul, To send this pre-cious peace to my soul?
3. sing; While mil-lions join the theme, I will sing.
4. on! And through e - ter - ni - ty, I'll sing on.

Text: 12 9 12 12 9; anon.; first appeared in *A General Selection of the Newest and Most Admired Hymns and Spiritual Songs*, 1811, adapt.
Music: WONDROUS LOVE; William Walker's *The Southern Harmony*, 1835.

LOVE HAS COME

669

Verses
1. With one voice the an - gels sing songs that make cre - a - tion ring. Proph - ets hear and call us to live in spir - it and in truth.
2. God the Fa - ther, El - o - him, voice of thun - der, spir - it, wind: breathe on me your ver - y life; grace will make the dark - ness bright.
3. God of Cov - e - nant, di - vine, lead us to the end of time, be - yond sor - row, be - yond fear, be - yond pride and earth - en tears.
4. Keep - er of the sac - ri - fice man - i - fest in Je - sus Christ, born to die and wake the dead, as we hun - ger keep us fed.
5. Now sal - va - tion has come in the New Je - ru - sa - lem. Danc - ers dance and sing - ers roar; pro - claim - ing Je - sus Christ is Lord!
Refrain
Word of God, en - throned, dwell in us for - ev - er - more.
Love has come to show the way. Hal - le - lu - jah, peace be with us. Love has come to show the way.

Text and music Matt Maher, b. 1974. © 2000, Matt Maher.

670 THERE'S A WIDENESS IN GOD'S MERCY

1. There's a wide-ness in God's mer-cy Like the wide-ness
2. For the love of God is broad-er Than the mea-sures
3. Trou-bled souls, why will you scat-ter Like a crowd of

1. of the sea; There's a kind-ness in his jus-tice
2. of our mind, And the heart of the E-ter-nal
3. fright-ened sheep? Fool-ish hearts, why will you wan-der

1. Which is more than lib-er-ty. There is plen-ti-ful re-
2. Is most won-der-ful-ly kind. If our love were but more
3. From a love so true and deep? There is wel-come for the

1. demp-tion In the blood that has been shed; There is
2. sim-ple We should take him at his word, And our
3. sin-ner And more grac-es for the good; There is

1. joy for all the mem-bers In the sor-rows of the Head.
2. lives would be thanks-giv-ing For the good-ness of our Lord.
3. mer-cy with the Sav-ior, There is heal-ing in his blood.

Text: 87 87 D; Frederick W. Faber, 1814–1863, alt.
Music: IN BABILONE; *Oude en Nieuwe Hollantse Boerenlieties en Contredansen*, ca. 1710.

671 DONA NOBIS PACEM

(Round)

①
Do-na no-bis pa-cem, pa-cem. Do-na no-bis pa-cem.
②
Do-na no-bis pa-cem. Do-na no-bis pa-cem.
③
Do-na no-bis pa-cem. Do-na no-bis pa-cem.

Text and music: Traditional.

LET THERE BE PEACE ON EARTH 672

Let there be peace on earth and let it be - gin with me.
Let there be peace on earth, the peace that was meant to
be. With God as our Fa-ther, broth - ers
(optional text) we are
all are we; Let me walk with my broth - er in
fam - i - ly. Let us walk with each oth - er
per - fect har - mo - ny. Let peace be - gin with me, let
this be the mo-ment now. With ev - 'ry step I take, let
this be my sol - emn vow: To take each mo-ment and live each
mo-ment in peace e - ter - nal - ly. Let there be peace on earth and
1
let it be - gin with me.
Final
let it be - gin with me.

Text and music: Sy Miller, 1908–1971, and Jill Jackson, 1913–1995,

673 DAY OF PEACE

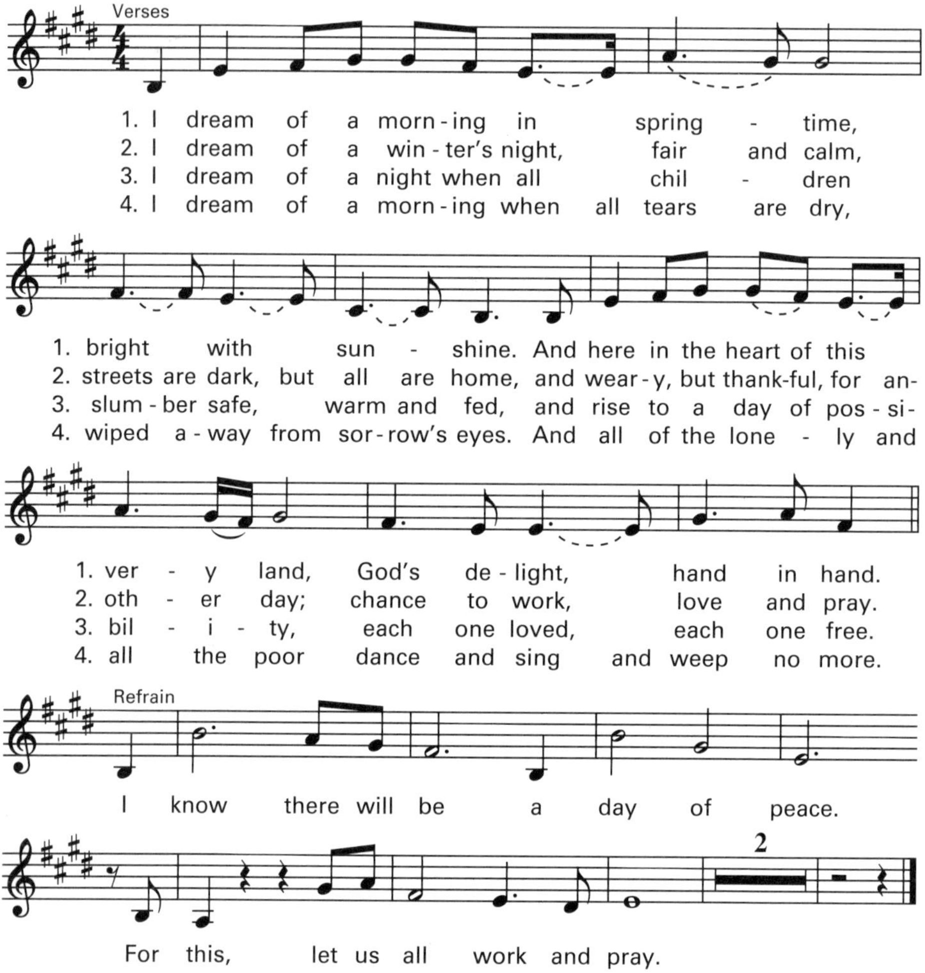

Verses

1. I dream of a morn-ing in spring - time,
2. I dream of a win-ter's night, fair and calm,
3. I dream of a night when all chil - dren
4. I dream of a morn-ing when all tears are dry,

1. bright with sun - shine. And here in the heart of this
2. streets are dark, but all are home, and wear-y, but thank-ful, for an-
3. slum-ber safe, warm and fed, and rise to a day of pos-si-
4. wiped a-way from sor-row's eyes. And all of the lone - ly and

1. ver - y land, God's de-light, hand in hand.
2. oth - er day; chance to work, love and pray.
3. bil - i - ty, each one loved, each one free.
4. all the poor dance and sing and weep no more.

Refrain

I know there will be a day of peace.

For this, let us all work and pray.

Text and music: Janèt Sullivan Whitaker, b. 1958,

674 GIVE US YOUR PEACE

Refrain
Give us your peace, O God; give us your peace,
1
your peace.
2
to Verses
(Fine)
your peace.

Verses
1. When we're a - fraid, run - ning from truth,
2. When we are tired, wea - ry, and worn,
3. Lord, we be - long to you a - lone;
1. gath - er us back to you. Take ev - ery fear
2. take us in - to your arms, where there is no need,
3. show us the way back home in - to your light,
to Refrain
1. and fill our hearts.
2. there is no want.
3. in - to your love.
Give us your peace, O God.

Text and music: Jesse Manibusan, b. 1958, and Sarah Hart, b. 1968, © 2009, Jesse Manibusan and Sarah Hart.
Published by Two by Two Ministries and Spirit & Song®, a division of OCP.

Peace Is Flowing like a River 675

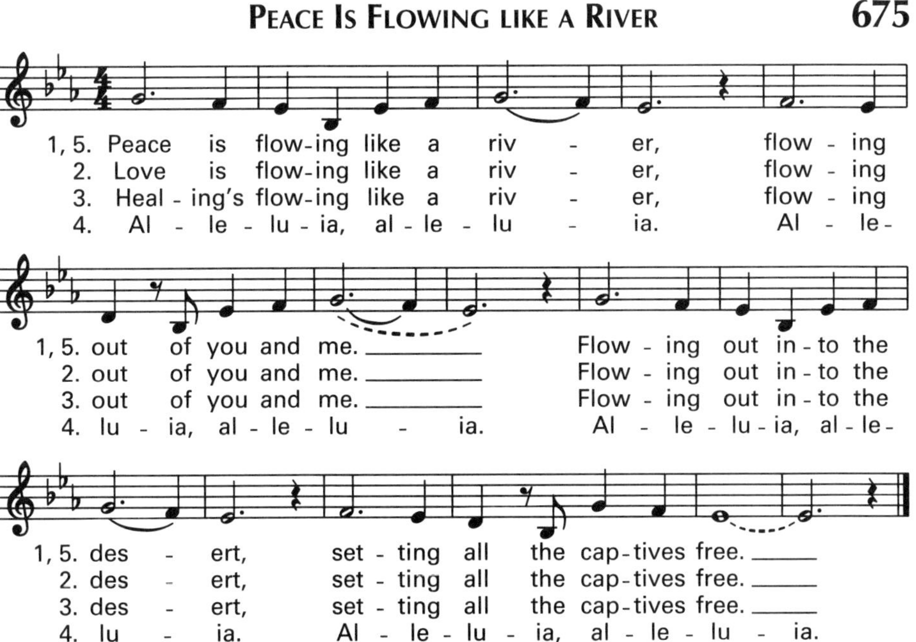
1, 5. Peace is flow-ing like a riv - er, flow - ing
2. Love is flow-ing like a riv - er, flow - ing
3. Heal - ing's flow-ing like a riv - er, flow - ing
4. Al - le - lu - ia, al - le - lu - ia. Al - le-
1, 5. out of you and me. Flow - ing out in - to the
2. out of you and me. Flow - ing out in - to the
3. out of you and me. Flow - ing out in - to the
4. lu - ia, al - le - lu - ia. Al - le - lu - ia, al - le-
1, 5. des - ert, set - ting all the cap-tives free.
2. des - ert, set - ting all the cap-tives free.
3. des - ert, set - ting all the cap-tives free.
4. lu - ia. Al - le - lu - ia, al - le - lu - ia.

Text: Based on Psalm 107; traditional; adapt. by Carey Landry, b. 1944.
Music: Traditional; adapt. by Carey Landry.

676 DONA NOBIS PACEM

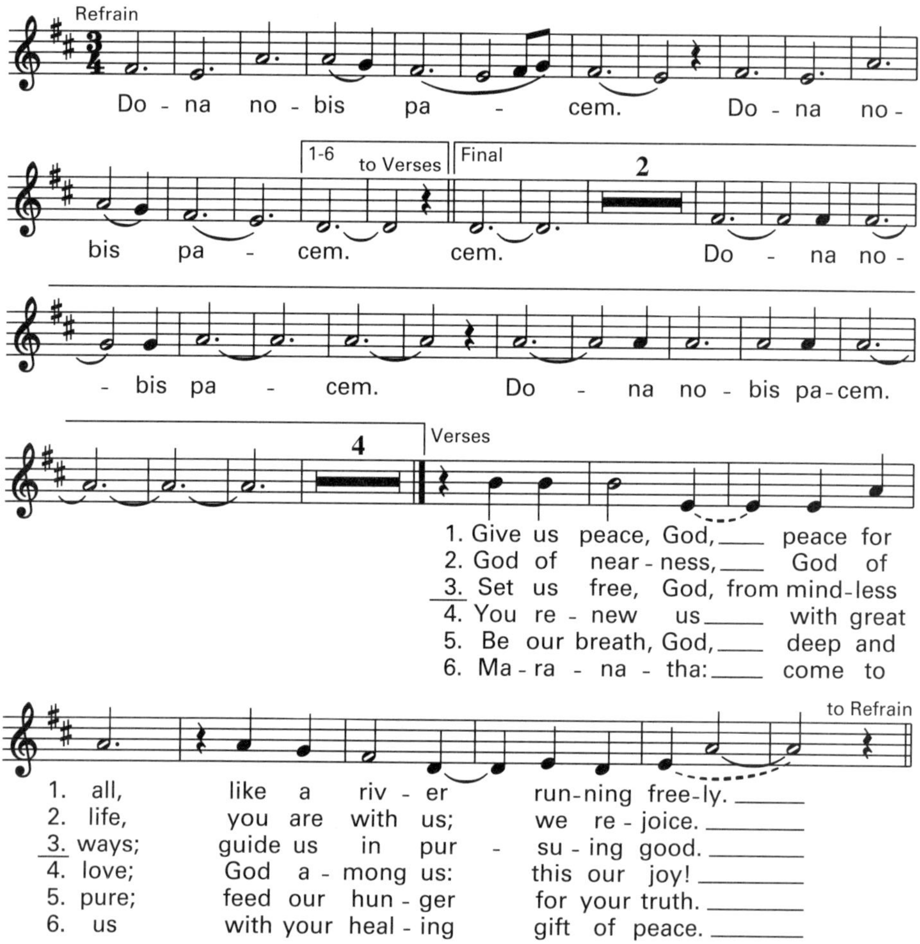

Refrain

Do - na no - bis pa - cem. Do - na no - bis pa - cem.

1-6 to Verses

Final: cem. Do - na no - bis pa - cem. Do - na no - bis pa-cem.

Verses

1. Give us peace, God, peace for all, like a riv - er run-ning free-ly.
2. God of near - ness, God of life, you are with us; we re - joice.
3. Set us free, God, from mind-less ways; guide us in pur - su - ing good.
4. You re - new us with great love; God a - mong us: this our joy!
5. Be our breath, God, deep and pure; feed our hun - ger for your truth.
6. Ma - ra - na - tha: come to us with your heal - ing gift of peace.

to Refrain

677 MAKE OUR LIVES A PRAYER OF PEACE

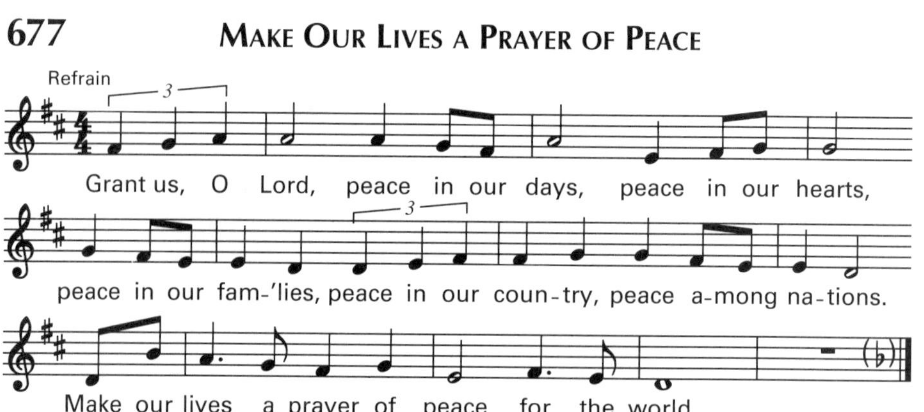
Refrain
Grant us, O Lord, peace in our days, peace in our hearts,
peace in our fam-'lies, peace in our coun-try, peace a-mong na-tions.
Make our lives a prayer of peace for the world.

Verses
1. Help us act in jus-tice and to love ten-der-ly, and to
2. Help us to for-give, and to seek for-give-ness.
3. Help us live more sim-ply by ac-cept-ing what we have.
4. Help us be con-tent and be faith-ful to your word;
to Refrain
1. walk hum-bly with our God.
2. Help us rid our-selves of pride.
3. Give us ev-ery-thing we need.
4. guide our jour-ney with your peace.

Text: Refrain based on a prayer of Pope Pius XII; adapt. by Paul Hillebrand, b. 1959.
Music: Paul Hillebrand.

Grant Us Peace 678

Refrain

Grant us peace, grant us peace.

On-ly love can make us free. Grant us peace.

Verses

1. Ev-er-lov-ing God, hear our prayer. We, your chil-
2. Lead-ers of the world, hear God now. Beat the swords
3. Peo-ple of the world, we are one. May the na-

1. -dren, have a song for you. May the Spir-it shine in
2. in-to a farm-er's plow. Je-sus said, "My peace I
3. -tions train for war no more, for the Lord pro-claims a

to Refrain

1. all we do. May we al-ways fol-low you.
2. give to you." May com-pas-sion see you through.
3. last-ing peace. May he rule from sea to sea.

Text: Based on Micah 4:3; John 14:27; Psalm 85:9; Psalm 72:8; Ken Canedo, b. 1953.
Music: Ken Canedo.

679 Prayer of St. Francis/ Oración de San Francisco

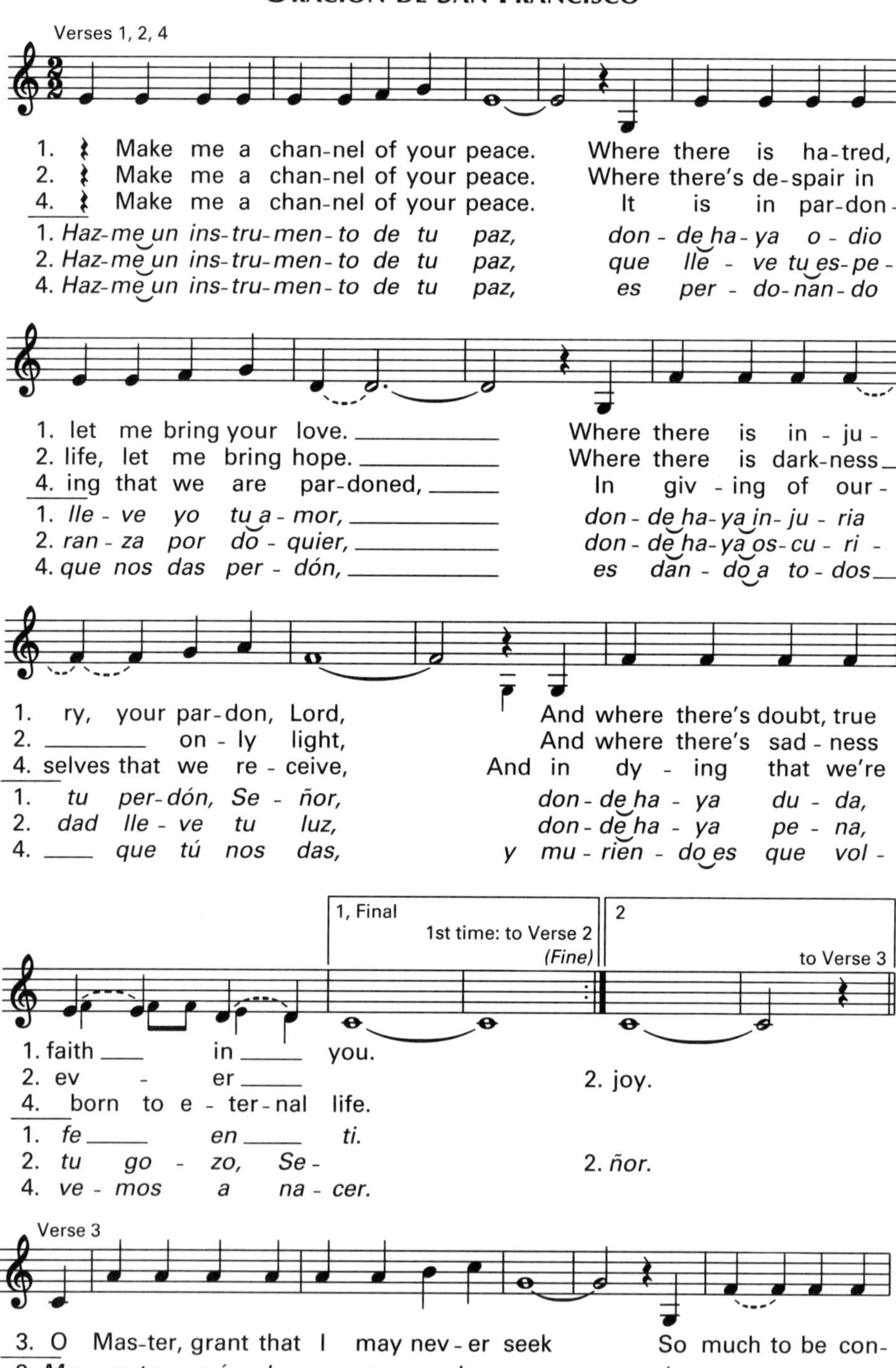
Verses 1, 2, 4
1. Make me a chan-nel of your peace. Where there is ha-tred,
2. Make me a chan-nel of your peace. Where there's de-spair in
4. Make me a chan-nel of your peace. It is in par-don-
1. Haz-me un ins-tru-men-to de tu paz, don-de ha-ya o-dio
2. Haz-me un ins-tru-men-to de tu paz, que lle-ve tu es-pe-
4. Haz-me un ins-tru-men-to de tu paz, es per-do-nan-do
1. let me bring your love. Where there is in-ju-
2. life, let me bring hope. Where there is dark-ness
4. ing that we are par-doned, In giv-ing of our-
1. lle-ve yo tu a-mor, don-de ha-ya in-ju-ria
2. ran-za por do-quier, don-de ha-ya os-cu-ri-
4. que nos das per-dón, es dan-do a to-dos
1. ry, your par-don, Lord, And where there's doubt, true
2. on-ly light, And where there's sad-ness
4. selves that we re-ceive, And in dy-ing that we're
1. tu per-dón, Se-ñor, don-de ha-ya du-da,
2. dad lle-ve tu luz, don-de ha-ya pe-na,
4. que tú nos das, y mu-rien-do es que vol-
1, Final
1st time: to Verse 2
(Fine)
2
to Verse 3
1. faith in you.
2. ev-er 2. joy.
4. born to e-ter-nal life.
1. fe en ti.
2. tu go-zo, Se- 2. ñor.
4. ve-mos a na-cer.
Verse 3
3. O Mas-ter, grant that I may nev-er seek So much to be con-
3. Ma-es-tro a-yú-da-me a nun-ca bus-car ser con-so-

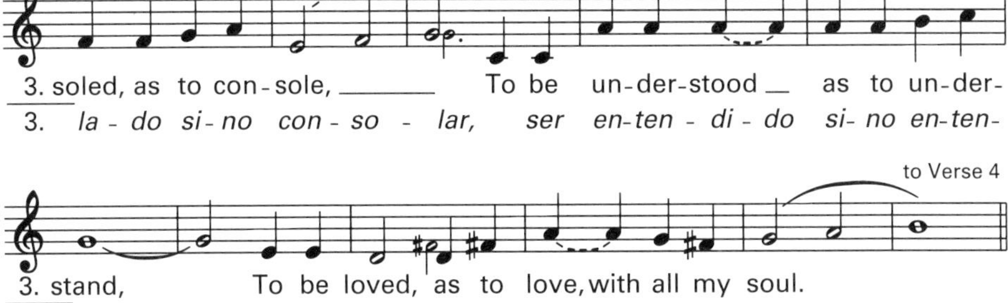
3. soled, as to con-sole, To be un-der-stood as to un-der-
3. la - do si - no con - so - lar, ser en-ten - di - do si- no en-ten-
to Verse 4
3. stand, To be loved, as to love, with all my soul.
3. der, ser a - ma-do si - no a - mar.

Text: Based on the prayer traditionally ascr. to St. Francis of Assisi, ca. 1182–1226; Sebastian Temple, 1928–1997.
Music: Sebastian Temple.
 Dedicated to Mrs. Frances Tracy.

Peace Prayer 680

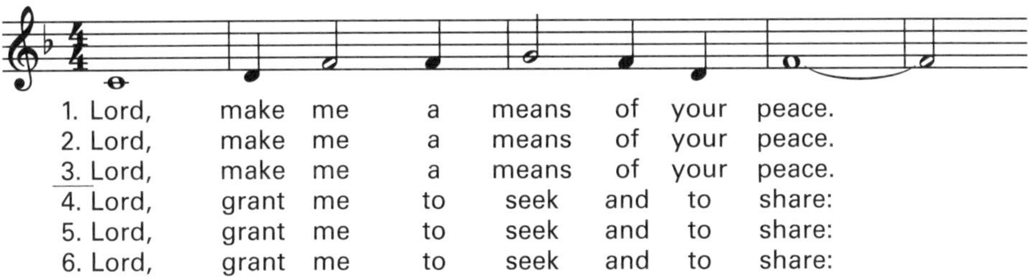

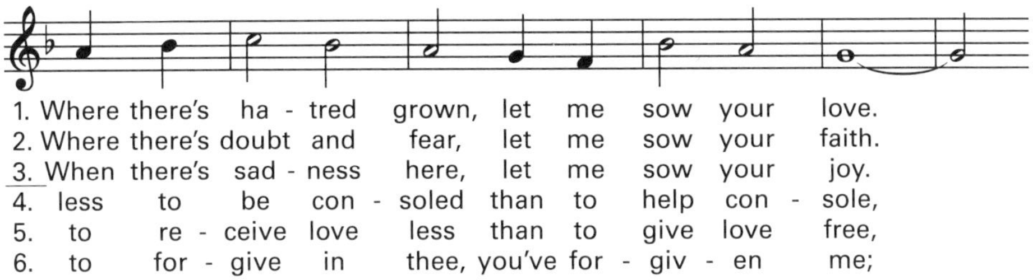

1. Lord, make me a means of your peace.
2. Lord, make me a means of your peace.
3. Lord, make me a means of your peace.
4. Lord, grant me to seek and to share:
5. Lord, grant me to seek and to share:
6. Lord, grant me to seek and to share:

1. Where there's ha - tred grown, let me sow your love.
2. Where there's doubt and fear, let me sow your faith.
3. When there's sad - ness here, let me sow your joy.
4. less to be con - soled than to help con - sole,
5. to re - ceive love less than to give love free,
6. to for - give in thee, you've for - giv - en me;

1. Where there's in - jury, Lord, let for - give-ness be my sword.
2. In this world's de - spair, give me hope in you to share.
3. When the dark-ness nears, may your light dis - pel our fears.
4. less be un - der - stood than to un - der-stand your good.
5. just to give in thee, just re - ceiv - ing from your tree.
6. for to die in thee is e - ter - nal life to me.

1-6. Lord, make me a means of your peace.

Text: Based on a prayer of St. Francis of Assisi, 1182–1226; John Foley, SJ, b. 1939.
Music: John Foley, SJ.

681 Peace

Refrain

Peace I leave with you, my friends, peace the world can-not give.

(Repeat Final time)

Peace I leave with you, my friends, so that your joy be ev-er full.

Verses

1. The Fa-ther's love I came to give,
2. Take __ his gift and be at peace;
3. By __ this love which you should have,
4. Take __ my words of life to heart,
5. All __ I have I give to you;
6. I came so that you may have life,
7. If __ you love me, keep my word,

to Refrain

1. to be the hope for all who live.
2. the Spir-it of our love I bring.
3. all __ will know you are my friends.
4. and you will live with hope and joy.
5. I share with you the Fa-ther's love.
6. and have it to __ the full.
7. and __ our home we'll make with you.

Text: Based on John 14:27ff; Weston Priory, Gregory Norbet, OSB, b. 1940.
Music: Weston Priory, Gregory Norbet, OSB.

682 I Want to Walk as a Child of the Light

Verses
1. I want to walk as a child of the light; I want to
2. I want to see __ the bright-ness of God; I want to
3. I'm look-ing for __ the com-ing of Christ; I want to
1. fol-low Je-sus. God set the stars to give
2. look at Je-sus. Clear Sun of righ-teous-ness,
3. be with Je-sus. When we have run __ with
1. light to the world; the star of my life __ is Je-sus.
2. shine on my path, and show me the way to the Fa-ther.
3. pa-tience the race, we shall know the joy __ of Je-sus.

Refrain
In him there is no dark-ness at all; the night and the
day are both a - like. The Lamb is the light of the
cit - y of God: Shine in my heart, Lord Je - sus.

Text: Irregular; Kathleen Thomerson, b. 1934.
Music: HOUSTON; Kathleen Thomerson.

Christ, Be Our Light 683

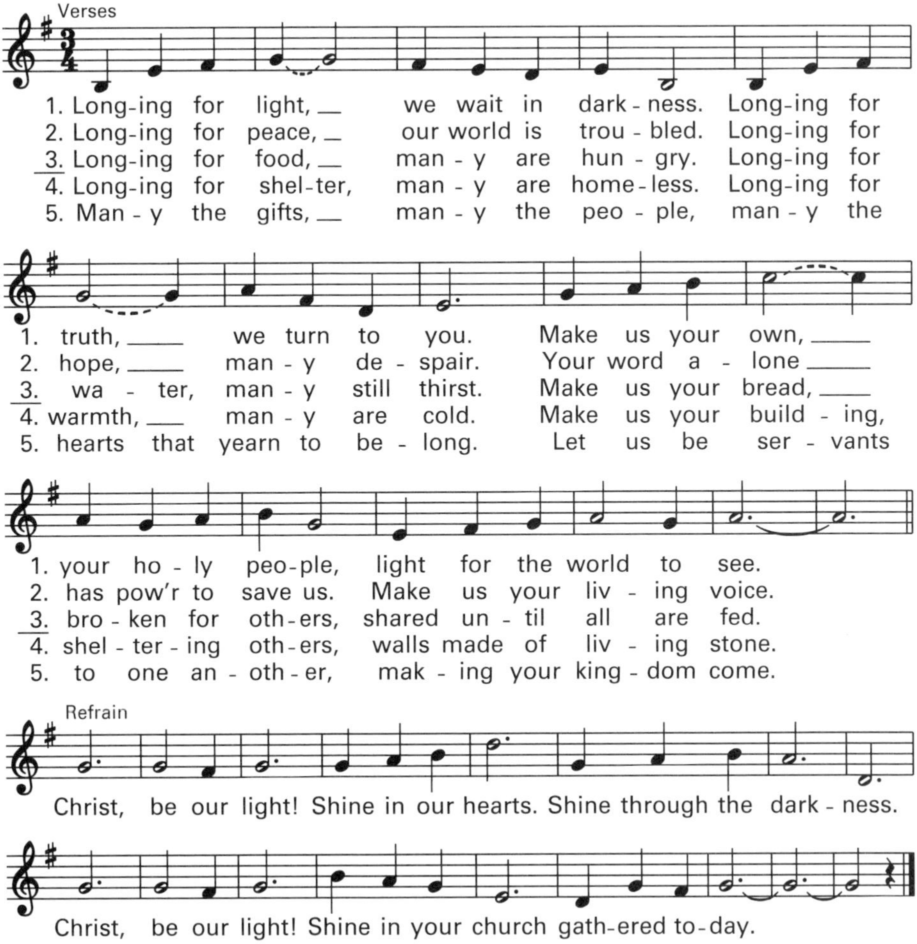

Verses

1. Long-ing for light, we wait in dark-ness. Long-ing for truth, we turn to you. Make us your own, your ho - ly peo-ple, light for the world to see.
2. Long-ing for peace, our world is trou - bled. Long-ing for hope, man - y de - spair. Your word a - lone has pow'r to save us. Make us your liv - ing voice.
3. Long-ing for food, man - y are hun - gry. Long-ing for wa - ter, man - y still thirst. Make us your bread, bro - ken for oth-ers, shared un - til all are fed.
4. Long-ing for shel-ter, man - y are home-less. Long-ing for warmth, man - y are cold. Make us your build - ing, shel - ter - ing oth-ers, walls made of liv - ing stone.
5. Man - y the gifts, man - y the peo - ple, man - y the hearts that yearn to be - long. Let us be ser - vants to one an - oth - er, mak - ing your king - dom come.

Refrain

Christ, be our light! Shine in our hearts. Shine through the dark - ness.
Christ, be our light! Shine in your church gath-ered to-day.

684 I Am the Light of the World

Refrain
"I am the Light of the world," says the Lord,
"They who fol-low me will have the light of life."
Verses 1, 2
1. "A - rise," says the Lord, "Have no fear with - in you; for in my pres - ence there will be no dark - ness. I am the Light of the world."
2. "Walk in the light, there is no cause to stum - ble; I have come to light the path be - fore you. I am the Light of the world."
to Refrain
Verse 3
3. "Lis-ten to my words; they are from the One who sent me: For you, my friends, are called to share God's glo - ry. You are the Light of the world."
to Refrain

Text: Based on John 8:12; Ephesians 5:14; 1 John 2:10; Matthew 5:14; Greg Hayakawa, b. 1953.
Music: Greg Hayakawa.

What You Hear in the Dark 685

Refrain
What you hear in the dark you must speak in the light. You are salt for the earth; you are light for the world.
Verses
1. Let your light be seen; stand a - gainst the night. Let your words of mer - cy tell the glo - ry of the Lord.
2. Earth shall pass a - way; heav - en will be un - done. Nev - er shall the word of God be bro - ken or de - stroyed.
3. God will keep you safe; see the spar - rows that fly. You are worth a world of spar - rows shel - tered by the Lord.
4. Strength - en wea - ry arms; stead - y all trem - bling knees. Say to ev - ery fear - ful heart: have cour - age, trust in God.
to Refrain

Text: Based on Matthew 10, 5; Dan Schutte, b. 1947.
Music: Dan Schutte.

686 CHRIST THE LORD

1. Dark - ness hangs, the world is ach - ing, Yearn - ing for the
2. As we wait with hope for res - cue Love de - scends and
3. Part - ing clouds re - veal his won - der: Might - y King in
4. On us now the Son is shin - ing, Lift - ing us to
1. com - ing light. In his ris - ing, hope a - wak - ing,
2. all is well. Proph - ets tell, "Your God is with us.
3. vic - to - ry. Trem - bling earth and roll - ing thun - der,
4. his em - brace. Shame is cursed, no more con - found - ing;
1. Love has come to steal the night. In our hearts true east we're
2. Heav - en's gift, Em - ma - nu - el." He is here, but hid as
3. Blaz - ing sun and quak - ing sea. Now he comes, our King, in
4. Lift your head and know his face. Love in - car - nate, breath in -
1. fac - ing, Toward the com - ing of our Lord. Morn - ing ris - ing,
2. low - ly In the poor and mys - ter - y. Where the bread and
3. glo - ry; Saints re - joice and dark - ness flees. Ris - ing rays of
4. dwell - ing, Now in truth is truth made known. We are his and
1. gloom now flee - ing; Christ re - turned! His word is true!
2. wine are of - fered He is here: our God and King.
3. light his char - iot, Christ the Lord has made us free.
4. he for - ev - er Is our God and he a - lone.

Text and music: Sarah Hart, b. 1968, and Robert Feduccia, b. 1967,

We Are the Light of the World

Verses

1. Bless - ed are they who are poor in spir - it,
2. Bless - ed are they who are meek and hum - ble,
3. Bless - ed are they who will mourn in sor - row,
4. Bless those who hun - ger and thirst for jus - tice,
5. Bless - ed are they who show oth - ers mer - cy,
6. Bless - ed are hearts that are clean and ho - ly,
7. Bless - ed are they who bring peace a - mong us,
8. Bless those who suf - fer from per - se - cu - tion,

1. Theirs is the king - dom of God. Bless us, O Lord, make us
2. They will in - her - it the earth. Bless us, O Lord, make us
3. They will be com - fort - ed. Bless us, O Lord, when we
4. They will be sat - is - fied. Bless us, O Lord, hear our
5. They will know mer - cy too. Bless us, O Lord, hear our
6. They will be - hold ___ the Lord. Bless us, O Lord, make us
7. They are the chil - dren of God. Bless us, O Lord, may your
8. Theirs is the king - dom of God. Bless us, O Lord, when they

1. poor in spir - it; Bless us, O Lord, our God.
2. meek and hum - ble; Bless us, O Lord, our God.
3. share their sor - row; Bless us, O Lord, our God.
4. cry for jus - tice; Bless us, O Lord, our God.
5. cry for mer - cy; Bless us, O Lord, our God.
6. pure and ho - ly; Bless us, O Lord, our God.
7. peace be with us; Bless us, O Lord, our God.
8. per - se - cute us; Bless us, O Lord, our God.

Refrain
We are the light of the world, may our light shine be - fore all,
That they may see the good that we do, and give glo - ry to God.

Text: 10 6 10 6 with refrain; based on the Beatitudes; adapt. by Jean Anthony Greif, 1898–1981, alt.
Music: GREIF; Jean Anthony Greif.

688 THE LIGHT OF CHRIST

Refrain

The light of Christ has come in-to the world, the light of Christ has come in - to the world.

Verses

1. We must all be born a - gain to ___ see the king-dom of God; ___ the ___ wa - ter and the Spir - it bring new _ life ___ in God's love. ___
2. God gave up his on - ly Son out of love ___ for the world, ___ so that all ___ who be-lieve in him will _ live ___ for - ev - er.
3. The light of God has come to us so that we might have sal - va - tion; from the dark-ness of our sins we walk in-to glo - ry with Christ Je - sus.

to Refrain

Text: John 1:1–9, 3:16, 19; Donald Fishel, b. 1950.
Music: Donald Fishel.

689 LORD, TO WHOM SHALL WE GO

Refrain
Lord, to whom shall we go? For you a - lone have words of e - ter - nal life.
Verses
1. Your words, O Lord, are a feast for my soul:
2. Your words, O Lord, are my light and my hope:
3. Your words, O Lord, are my strength and my shield:
your Word
1-3. is my hope of sal - va - tion.
2
to Refrain

Text: Based on John 6:68; Michael Joncas, b. 1951.
Music: Michael Joncas.

O Word of God 690

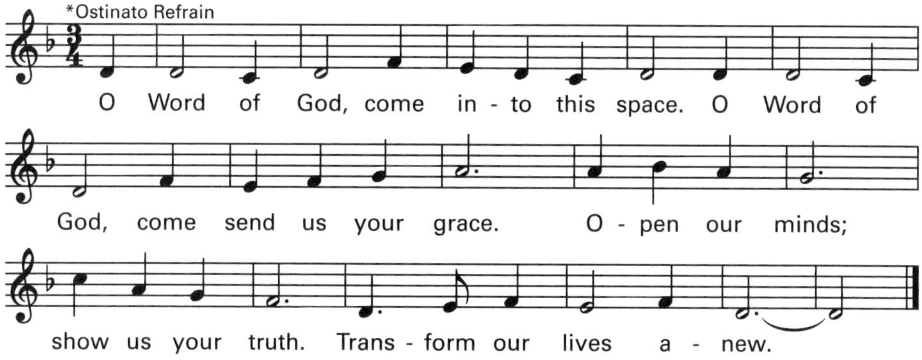

*Ostinato Refrain
O Word of God, come in - to this space. O Word of
God, come send us your grace. O - pen our minds;
show us your truth. Trans - form our lives a - new.

*Verses available in accompaniment books.

Text and music: Ricky Manalo, CSP, b. 1965,

Praise to You, O Christ, Our Savior 691

Refrain

Praise to you, O Christ, our Sav-ior, Word of the Fa-ther, call-ing us to life;
Son of God who leads us to free-dom: glo-ry to you, Lord Je-sus Christ!

Verses

1. You are the Word who calls us out of dark-ness; you are the Word who leads us in - to light; you are the Word who brings us through the des - ert: glo - ry to you, Lord Je-sus Christ!
2. You are the one whom proph-ets hoped and longed for; you are the one who speaks to us to - day; you are the one who leads us to our fu - ture: glo - ry to you, Lord Je-sus Christ!
3. You are the Word who calls us to be ser - vants; you are the Word whose on - ly law is love; you are the Word - made - flesh who lives a-mong us: glo - ry to you, Lord Je-sus Christ!
4. You are the Word who binds us and u - nites us; you are the Word who calls us to be one; you are the Word who teach - es us for-give-ness: glo - ry to you, Lord Je-sus Christ!

to Refrain

Text and music: Bernadette Farrell, b. 1957,

692 Your Words Are Spirit and Life

Refrain
Your words are spir - it and life, O Lord: rich - er than
gold, strong - er than death. Your words are spir - it and
life, O Lord; life ev - er - last - ing.
Verses
1. God's law is per - fect, re - fresh - ing the soul, re -
2. God's pre - cepts keep us; their pur - pose is right. They
3. Liv - ing by God's truth is ho - ly and sure; God's
4. God's word is pre - cious, de - sired more than gold; worth
1. viv - ing the wea - ry spir - it. God's
2. glad - den the hearts of peo - ple. God's com-
3. pres - ence is ev - er - last - ing. God's
4. more than we dare i - mag - ine and,
1. rule can be trust - ed: bring - ing us wis - dom,
2. mand is so clear it brings us new vi - sion;
3. truth is e - ter - nal, bring - ing us jus - tice;
4. sweet - er than hon - ey, this word will feed us,
to Refrain
1. bring - ing God's wis - dom to birth.
2. bring - ing God's light to our eyes.
3. bring - ing God's jus - tice to earth.
4. bring - ing ful - fill - ment and joy.

Text: Based on Psalm 19:8–11; Bernadette Farrell, b. 1957.
Music: Bernadette Farrell.

YOU ARE CHILD

693

Refrain
You are child of the u - ni-verse, you are no
less than the trees and the stars.
You are child of the Lord of Light,
be still and know I am God, you are child.
Verses
1. O Lord, my God, how great, how glo - ri - ous!
2. When I be - hold the works your hands have made;
3. O Lord, my God, it is for you I long;
1. Your name re - sounds in all the earth.
2. the moon and stars which you ar - ranged,
3. my bod - y aches, my spir - it thirsts.
1. Yet you have made us just less than an - gels,
2. Lord, what is man? Lord, what is wom - an?
3. So will I praise you, so will I bless you;
to Refrain
1. and you have fash-ioned us to rule the earth.
2. What is the child of these that you should care?
3. my soul clings fast to you, I shout for joy.

Text and music: Cyprian Consiglio, OSB Cam., b. 1958,

694 How Great Thou Art

Verses
1. O Lord my God! When I in awe-some won-der Con - si - der
2. When through the woods and for - est glades I wan - der, And hear the
3. And when I think that God, his Son not spar - ing, Sent him to
4. When Christ shall come with shout of ac - cla - ma - tion And take me
1. all the *worlds thy hands have made, I see the stars, I
2. birds sing sweet - ly in the trees; When I look down from
3. die, I scarce can take it in, That on the cross, my
4. home, what joy shall fill my heart! Then I shall bow in
1. hear the *roll - ing thun - der, Thy pow'r through - out the
2. lof - ty moun-tain gran - deur And hear the brook, and
3. bur - den glad - ly bear - ing, He bled and died to
4. hum - ble ad - o - ra - tion, And there pro - claim, my
Refrain
1. u - ni - verse dis-played; Then sings my soul, my Sav-ior God to
2. feel the gen - tle breeze;
3. take a - way my sin;
4. God, how great thou art!
thee; How great thou art, how great thou art! Then sings my soul, my
Sav-ior God to thee; How great thou art, how great thou art!

*Author's original words are "works" and "mighty."

Words: Stuart K. Hine.
Music: Traditional Swedish folk tune/adapt. by Stuart K. Hine.

ALL THE EARTH 695

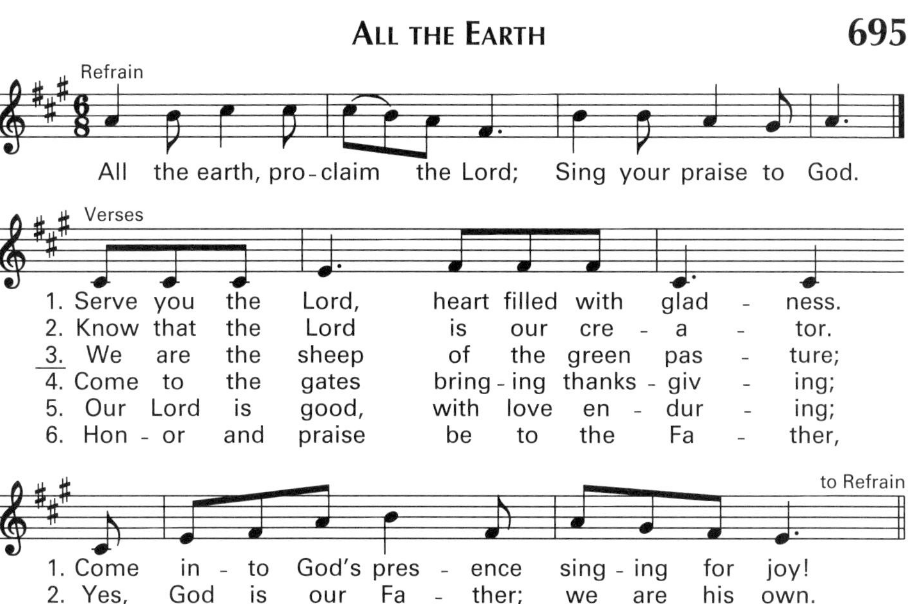
Refrain
All the earth, pro-claim the Lord; Sing your praise to God.
Verses
1. Serve you the Lord, heart filled with glad - ness.
2. Know that the Lord is our cre - a - tor.
3. We are the sheep of the green pas - ture;
4. Come to the gates bring - ing thanks - giv - ing;
5. Our Lord is good, with love en - dur - ing;
6. Hon - or and praise be to the Fa - ther,
to Refrain
1. Come in - to God's pres - ence sing - ing for joy!
2. Yes, God is our Fa - ther; we are his own.
3. For we are God's peo - ple, cho - sen by God.
4. O en - ter the court - yards sing - ing in praise.
5. God's word is a - bid - ing now with us all.
6. The Son, and the Spir - it, world with - out end.

Text: Based on Psalm 100; Lucien Deiss, CSSp, 1921–2007.
Music: Lucien Deiss, CSSp.

BEAUTIFUL SAVIOR 696

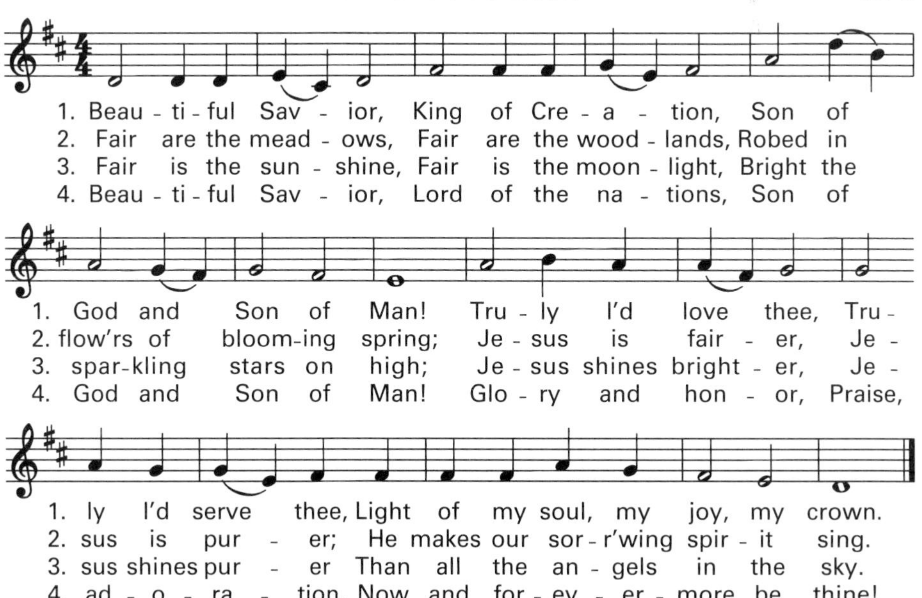
1. Beau - ti - ful Sav - ior, King of Cre - a - tion, Son of
2. Fair are the mead - ows, Fair are the wood - lands, Robed in
3. Fair is the sun - shine, Fair is the moon - light, Bright the
4. Beau - ti - ful Sav - ior, Lord of the na - tions, Son of
1. God and Son of Man! Tru - ly I'd love thee, Tru -
2. flow'rs of bloom-ing spring; Je - sus is fair - er, Je -
3. spar-kling stars on high; Je - sus shines bright - er, Je -
4. God and Son of Man! Glo - ry and hon - or, Praise,
1. ly I'd serve thee, Light of my soul, my joy, my crown.
2. sus is pur - er; He makes our sor - r'wing spir - it sing.
3. sus shines pur - er Than all the an - gels in the sky.
4. ad - o - ra - tion, Now and for - ev - er - more be thine!

Text: 55 7 55 8; Psalm 45:3; *Schönster Herr Jesu*, in *Münster Gesangbuch*, 1677; tr. by Joseph A. Seiss, 1823–1904.
Music: ST. ELIZABETH; trad. Silesian melody; Hoffman and Richter's *Schlesische Volkslieder*, Leipzig, 1842.

697 FOR THE FRUITS OF THIS CREATION

1. For the fruits of this cre - a - tion, Thanks be to God;
2. In the just re - ward of la - bor, God's will be done;
3. For the har-vests of the Spir - it, Thanks be to God;

1. For the gifts of ev - 'ry na - tion, Thanks be to God;
2. In the help we give our neigh-bor, God's will be done;
3. For the good we all in - her - it, Thanks be to God;

1. For the plow - ing, sow-ing, reap-ing, Si - lent growth while we are
2. In the world-wide task of car - ing For the hun - gry and de-
3. For the won - ders that as-tound us, For the truths that will con -

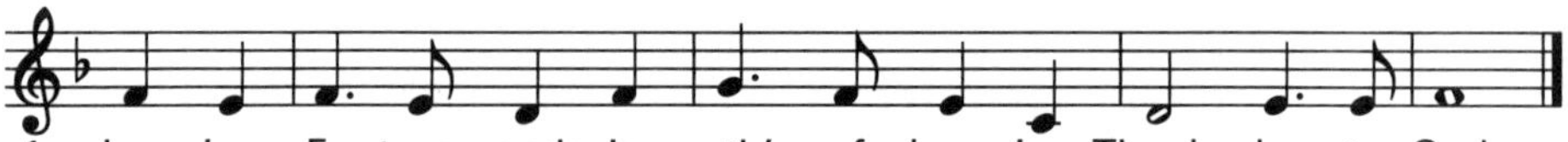

1. sleep-ing, Fu - ture needs in earth's safe-keep-ing, Thanks be to God.
2. spair - ing, In the har-vests we are shar-ing, God's will be done.
3. found us, Most of all, that love has found us, Thanks be to God.

Text: 84 84 88 84; Fred Pratt Green, 1903–2000,
Music: AR HYD Y NOS; trad. Welsh melody.

698 GOD, BEYOND ALL NAMES

Verses

1. God, be - yond our dreams, you have stirred in us a
2. God, be - yond all names, you have made us in your
3. God, be - yond all words, all cre - a - tion tells your
4. God, be - yond all time, you are la - bor - ing with -
5. God of ten - der care, you have cra - dled us in

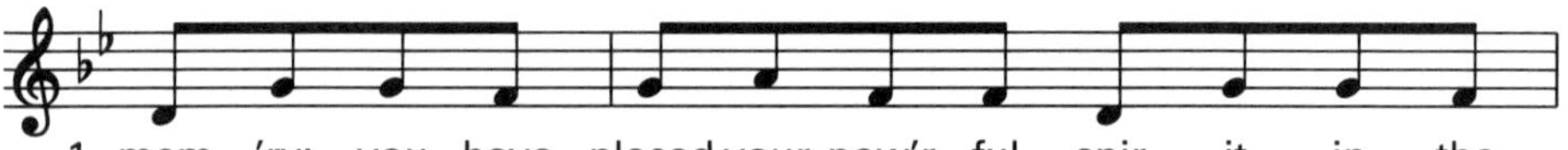

1. mem - 'ry; you have placed your pow'r - ful spir - it in the
2. im - age; we are like you, we re - flect you; we are
3. sto - ry; you have shak - en with our laugh - ter, you have
4. in us; we are mov - ing, we are chang - ing in your
5. good-ness, you have moth-ered us in whole-ness, you have

1. hearts of hu - man - kind.
2. wom - an, we are man.
3. trem - bled with our tears.
4. spir - it ev - er new.
5. loved us in - to birth.

Refrain

All a - round us we have

known you, all cre - a - tion lives to hold you. In our
liv - ing and our dy - ing we are bring-ing you to birth.

I Sing the Mighty Power of God 699

1. I sing the might - y pow'r of God That made the
2. I sing the good-ness of the Lord That filled the
3. There's not a plant or flow'r be - low, But makes thy

1. moun-tains rise, That spread the flow - ing seas a - broad, And
2. earth with food; He formed the crea-tures with his word, And
3. glo - ries known; And clouds a - rise, and tem-pests blow By

1. built the loft - y skies. I sing the wis - dom
2. then pro-nounced them good. Lord, how thy won - ders
3. or - der from thy throne; While all that bor - rows

1. that or - dained The sun to rule the day; The moon shines
2. are dis - played Wher - e'er I turn my eye; If I sur -
3. life from thee Is ev - er in thy care, And ev - 'ry -

1. full at his com-mand, And all the stars o - bey.
2. vey the ground I tread, Or gaze up - on the sky!
3. where that I can be, Thou, God, are pres - ent there.

Text: CMD; Isaac Watts, 1674–1748, alt.
Music: ELLACOMBE; *Gesangbuch der Herzogl, Wirtembergischen Katholischen Hofkapelle*, 1784, alt.; adapt. fr. Würth's *Katholisches Gesangbuch*, 1863.

700 Give Thanks to the Lord

Verses 1 & 2, 4 & 5, 7 & 8, 10
1. Give thanks to the Lord who does won - drous deeds, who
2. Give thanks to the God who has blessed our land, who
4. Give thanks to the God of the sum - mer rains, who
5. Give thanks to the Lord who is mer - ci - ful, whose
7. Give thanks to the Lord for the blaz - ing sun, for
8. Give thanks to the Lord for the crim - son skies, for
10. Give thanks to the God who has set us free, who
1. mas - ters the winds and the rag - ing seas,
2. guards ev - 'ry step with a might - y hand,
4. spreads out the hills and the gold - en plains,
5. kind - ness is wide and love boun - ti - ful,
7. great, roll - ing waves where the dol - phins run,
8. wild, wind - y heights where the ea - gle flies,
10. raised us to life on a bless - ed tree,
whose
love is for ev - er, whose love is for ev - er, whose love is for
1, 4, 7, Final
Fine
2, 5, 8
ev - er more! more!
Verses 3, 6, 9
3. O, bless the Lord for ev - 'ry gift that comes to grace our way. And
6. O, bless the Lord with mu - sic, ev - 'ry crea - ture great and small. And
9. O, bless the Lord all peo - ple, for the mu - sic of the skies. And
3. praise the God of faith - ful - ness, who comes to light our day. (to Vss 4 & 5)
6. sing through all the a - ges of God's fa - vor to us all. (to Vss 7 & 8)
9. tell the won - drous sto - ry of a love that nev - er dies. (to Vs 10)

MEADOWS AND MOUNTAINS 701

Refrain
Mead-ows and moun - tains, ye for - ests and foun - tains, ye heav - ens and hill - sides, give
Prin - ces and pau - pers, ye winds and ye wa - ters, in day - light and dark - ness, give
1 thanks to the Lord!
2 thanks to the Lord!
Verses 1-3
1. Sing, riv - ers and rain - storms! Sing, light - ning and thun - der! Sing, sum - mer and snow, riv - ers that flow, sing to your God!
2. Sing, light of the morn - ing! Sing, shad - ows of night - fall! Sing, plan - ets and moon, splen - dor of noon, sing to your God!
3. Sing, art - ists and dream - ers! Sing, pil - grims and lov - ers! Sing, an - gels of night, chil - dren of light, sing to your God!
to Refrain
Verse 4
4. Sing, crea - tures of heav - en! Sing, chil - dren of earth! Great bless - ings and small come from the Lord: Bless - ed be God!
to Refrain

Text: Based on Daniel 3:51–90; Dan Schutte, b. 1947.
Music: Dan Schutte.

702 COME, YE THANKFUL PEOPLE, COME

1. Come, ye thank - ful peo - ple, come, Raise the song of
2. All the world is God's own field, Fruit un - to his
3. For the Lord our God shall come, And shall take his
4. E - ven so, Lord, quick - ly come To your fi - nal

1. har - vest - home: All is safe - ly gath - ered in, Ere the
2. praise to yield; Wheat and tares to - geth - er sown, Un - to
3. har - vest home; From his field shall in that day All of -
4. har - vest - home; Gath - er all your peo - ple in, Free from

1. win - ter storms be - gin; God, our Mak - er, does pro - vide
2. joy or sor - row grown; First the blade, and then the ear,
3. fens - es purge a - way; Give his an - gels charge at last
4. sor - row, free from sin; There, for ev - er pu - ri - fied,

1. For our wants to be sup - plied; Come to God's own
2. Then the full corn shall ap - pear: Grant, O har - vest
3. In the fire the tares to cast, But the fruit - ful
4. In your pres - ence to a - bide: Come, with all your

1. tem - ple, come, Raise the song of har - vest - home.
2. Lord, that we Whole-some grain and pure may be.
3. ears to store In his gar - ner ev - er - more.
4. an - gels, come, Raise the glo - rious har - vest - home.

Text: 77 77 D; Henry Alford, 1810–1871, alt.
Music: ST. GEORGE'S WINDSOR; George J. Elvey, 1816–1893.

703 ALL GOOD GIFTS

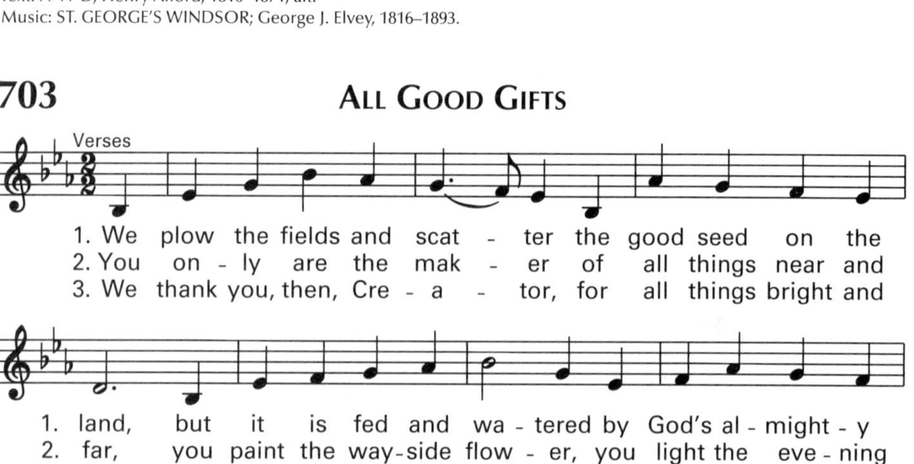
Verses
1. We plow the fields and scat - ter the good seed on the
2. You on - ly are the mak - er of all things near and
3. We thank you, then, Cre - a - tor, for all things bright and
1. land, but it is fed and wa - tered by God's al - might - y
2. far, you paint the way-side flow - er, you light the eve - ning
3. good, the seed-time and the har - vest, our life, our health, our

1. hand. God sends the snow in win - ter, the warmth to swell the
2. star. The winds and waves o - bey you, by you the birds are
3. food. And all that we can of - fer, your bound-less love im-

1. grain, the breez-es and the sun-shine, and soft, re-fresh-ing rain.
2. fed; much more, to us, your chil - dren, you give our dai - ly bread.
3. parts; the gifts to you most pleas - ing are hum-ble, thank-ful hearts.

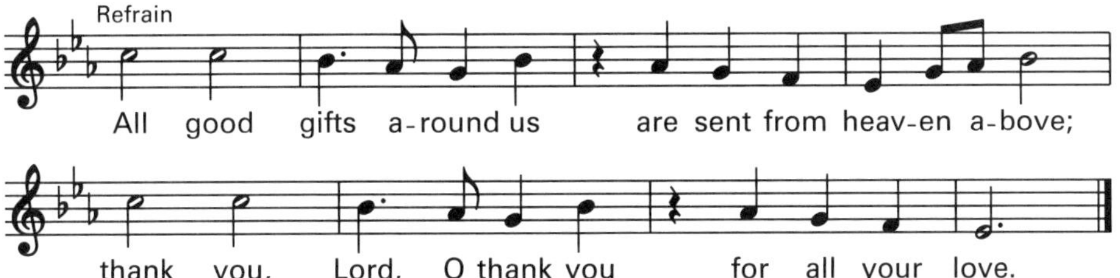
Refrain
All good gifts a-round us are sent from heav-en a-bove;
thank you, Lord, O thank you for all your love.

Text: 76 76 D with refrain; Matthias Claudius, 1740–1815; tr. by Jane M. Campbell, 1817–1878, alt.
Music: HEISLMAN; Kevin Keil (ASCAP), b. 1956,

NOW THANK WE ALL OUR GOD 704

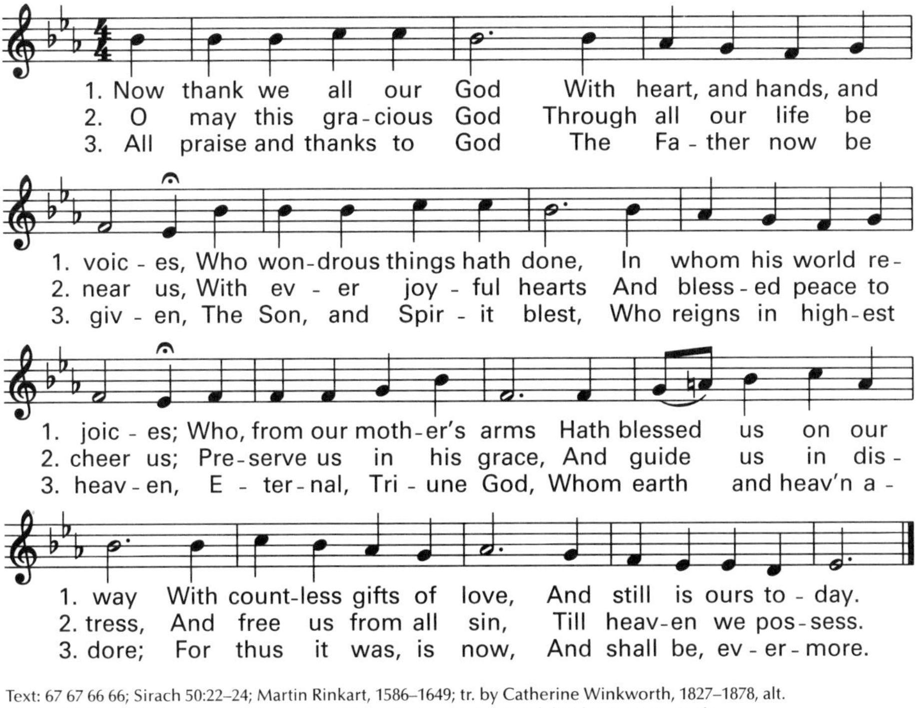

1. Now thank we all our God With heart, and hands, and
2. O may this gra-cious God Through all our life be
3. All praise and thanks to God The Fa - ther now be

1. voic - es, Who won-drous things hath done, In whom his world re-
2. near us, With ev - er joy - ful hearts And bless - ed peace to
3. giv - en, The Son, and Spir - it blest, Who reigns in high-est

1. joic - es; Who, from our moth-er's arms Hath blessed us on our
2. cheer us; Pre-serve us in his grace, And guide us in dis -
3. heav - en, E - ter - nal, Tri - une God, Whom earth and heav'n a -

1. way With count-less gifts of love, And still is ours to - day.
2. tress, And free us from all sin, Till heav-en we pos-sess.
3. dore; For thus it was, is now, And shall be, ev - er - more.

Text: 67 67 66 66; Sirach 50:22–24; Martin Rinkart, 1586–1649; tr. by Catherine Winkworth, 1827–1878, alt.
Music: NUN DANKET; Johann Crüger, 1598–1662; adapt. by Felix Mendelssohn, 1809–1847, alt.

705 FOR THE BEAUTY OF THE EARTH

1. For the beau - ty of the earth, For the beau - ty of the skies, For the love which from our birth O - ver and a - round us lies:
2. For the beau - ty of each hour Of the day and of the night, Hill and vale, and tree and flow'r, Sun and moon, and stars of light:
3. For the joy of ear and eye, For the heart and mind's de - light, For the mys - tic har - mo - ny Link - ing sense to sound and sight:
4. For the joy of hu - man love, Broth - er, sis - ter, par - ent, child, Friends on earth and friends a - bove; For all gen - tle thoughts and mild:
5. For the Church, who ev - er - more Lifts her ho - ly hands a - bove, Of - f'ring up on ev - 'ry shore Her pure sac - ri - fice of love:
6. For each per - fect gift di - vine To our world so free - ly giv'n, Joys be - stowed by love's de - sign, Flow'rs of earth and fruits of heav'n:
Lord of all to
1-6. you we raise This our hymn of grate - ful praise.

Text: 77 77 77; *Lyra Eucharistica*, 1864; Folliot S. Pierpoint, 1835–1917, alt.
Music: DIX; Conrad Kocher, 1786–1872; adapt. by William H. Monk, 1823–1889.

706 LET ALL THINGS NOW LIVING

1. Let all things now liv - ing A song of thanks - giv - ing To God our Cre - a - tor tri - um-phant-ly raise;
Who fash-ioned and made us, Pro - tect - ed and stayed us, By guid-ing us on to the end of our days. God's ban - ners are
2. His law he en - forc - es, The stars in their cours - es, The sun in its or - bit o - be-dient-ly shine,
The hills and the moun-tains, The riv - ers and foun-tains, The depths of the o - cean pro-claim God di - vine. We, too, should be

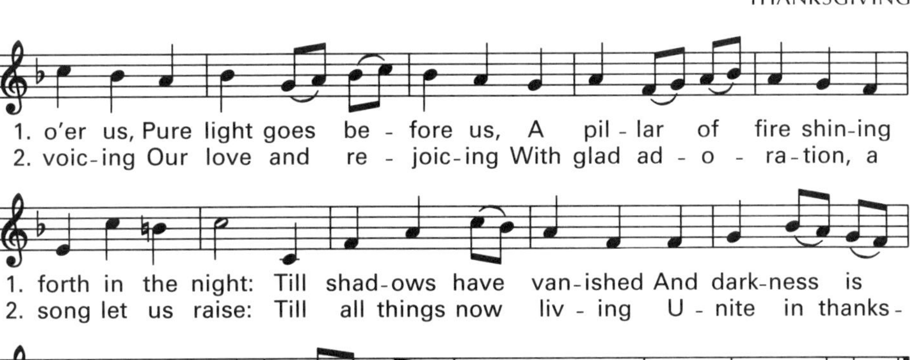
1. o'er us, Pure light goes be - fore us, A pil - lar of fire shin-ing
2. voic-ing Our love and re - joic-ing With glad ad - o - ra-tion, a
1. forth in the night: Till shad-ows have van-ished And dark-ness is
2. song let us raise: Till all things now liv - ing U - nite in thanks -

1. ban-ished, As for-ward we trav - el from light in - to Light.
2. giv - ing, To God in the high - est, ho - san - na and praise.

Text: 66 11 66 11 D; Katherine K. Davis, 1892–1980,
Music: ASH GROVE; trad. Welsh melody.

All My Days **707**

Refrain

Till the end of my days, O Lord, I will bless your name,
sing your praise, give you thanks, all my days.

Verses

1. You have made me lit - tle less than a god, ___
2. You have blessed _ me with good things and plen-ty ___
3. Your sun ___ and your moon give me light, ___
4. How great ___ is your love, O ___ Fa-ther, ___

1. and have lav-ished my heart with your love. With dig-ni-ty and
2. and sur-round-ed my ta - ble with friends. Their love _ and their
3. and your stars show the way through the night. Your riv - ers and
4. that you sent us your Sav - ior Son. His death _ and his

to Refrain

1. hon - or you've clothed me, giv-en me rule o-ver all.
2. laugh - ter en - rich me; to-geth-er we sing your _ praise.
3. streams have re - freshed me. I ___ will sing your _ praise.
4. ris - ing will heal us, and draw us ___ all un-to you.

Text: Based on Psalm 8; J-Glenn Murray, SJ.
Music: Dan Schutte, b. 1947.

708 GRATEFUL

Refrain
Grate - ful for the life you give us, thank - ful
Grate - ful for the Bread of Heav - en, thank - ful
for your Ho - ly Son, joy - ful in your
for your Ho - ly Word, joy - ful in your
Spir - it flow - ing o - ver all, O God of Love.
mer - cy flow - ing,
1
2
to Verses
Final
we will praise you. we will praise you.
Verses
1. You are more than we i - mag - ine, An - cient, Ho - ly, Liv -
2. May our lives pro - claim your jus - tice, may our voic - es sing
1. - ing Lord. E - ven when we doubt your pres -
2. your praise. May our hands work in your ser -
to Refrain
1. - ence you are faith - ful to your word.
2. - vice to the glo - ry of your name.

Like Cedars

709

Refrain
I will play for you on my harp, with my lute and ten-stringed lyre. I will fill the night with your song. I will sing of your ways, O Lord.
3
Verses
1. Good it is that we should sing to honor your great name, to thank you for your love at dawn, your faith-ful-ness through night.
2. Great and wide your kind-ness, Lord, and fath-oms deep your love. The wick-ed heart can-not con-ceive, the fool-ish heart will fail.
3. Up-on my head you pour your oil; you mark me as your own. And filled with glad-ness I shall sing; my horn shall sound your call.
4. The just shall grow as tall as palms; like ce-dars they shall stand. And plant-ed firm-ly on their God they shall not break nor bow.
to Refrain

Text: Based on Psalm 92; Dan Schutte, b. 1947.
Music: Dan Schutte.

710 ALABARÉ/O COME AND SING

Estribillo/Refrain
A - la - ba - ré, a - la - ba - ré, a - la - ba - ré a mi Se - ñor. A - la - ba - ré, (a - la - ba - ré,) a - la - ba - ré, (a - la - ba - ré,) a - la - ba - ré a mi Se - ñor.
O come and sing! O come and sing! Come, sing your prais-es to the Lord. O come and sing! (O come and sing!) O come and sing! (O come and sing!) Come, sing your prais-es to the Lord.
1-3 (1-4)
a las Estrofas/ to Verses
Final
ñor.
Lord.
Estrofas/Verses
1. Juan vio el nú - me - ro de los re - di - mi - dos y to - dos a - la - ba - ban al Se - ñor.
2. To - dos u - ni - dos, a - le - gres can - ta - mos glo - ria y a - la - ban - zas al Se - ñor.
3. So - mos tus hi - jos, Dios Pa - dre e - ter - no, Tú nos has cre - a - do por a - mor.
1. All of the faith - ful were gath - ered 'round the ta - ble, in mind and spir - it one in true ac - cord.
2. All were u - nit - ed in joy - ful cel - e - bra - tion all through the night un - til the morn - ing sun,
3. Filled with the Spir - it, they cried with ex - al - ta - tion: "The love of God is here a - mong us all!
4. We now in - her - it the joy of the dis - ci - ples, we sing and dance and of - fer con - stant praise.

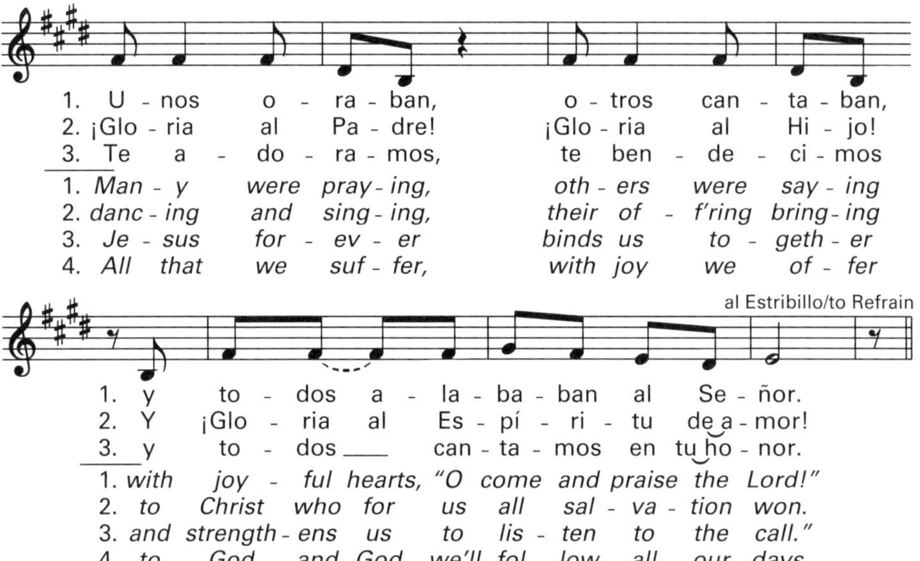
1. U - nos o - ra - ban, o - tros can - ta - ban,
2. ¡Glo - ria al Pa - dre! ¡Glo - ria al Hi - jo!
3. Te a - do - ra - mos, te ben - de - ci - mos
1. Man - y were pray - ing, oth - ers were say - ing
2. danc - ing and sing - ing, their of - f'ring bring - ing
3. Je - sus for - ev - er binds us to - geth - er
4. All that we suf - fer, with joy we of - fer
al Estribillo/to Refrain
1. y to - dos a - la - ba - ban al Se - ñor.
2. Y ¡Glo - ria al Es - pí - ri - tu de a - mor!
3. y to - dos can - ta - mos en tu ho - nor.
1. with joy - ful hearts, "O come and praise the Lord!"
2. to Christ who for us all sal - va - tion won.
3. and strength - ens us to lis - ten to the call."
4. to God, and God we'll fol - low all our days.

Text: Based on Revelation 7:4, 9–12; Manuel José Alonso and José Pagán. English tr. by Owen Alstott, b. 1947.
Music: Manuel José Alonso and José Pagán.

Come, Christians, Join to Sing 711

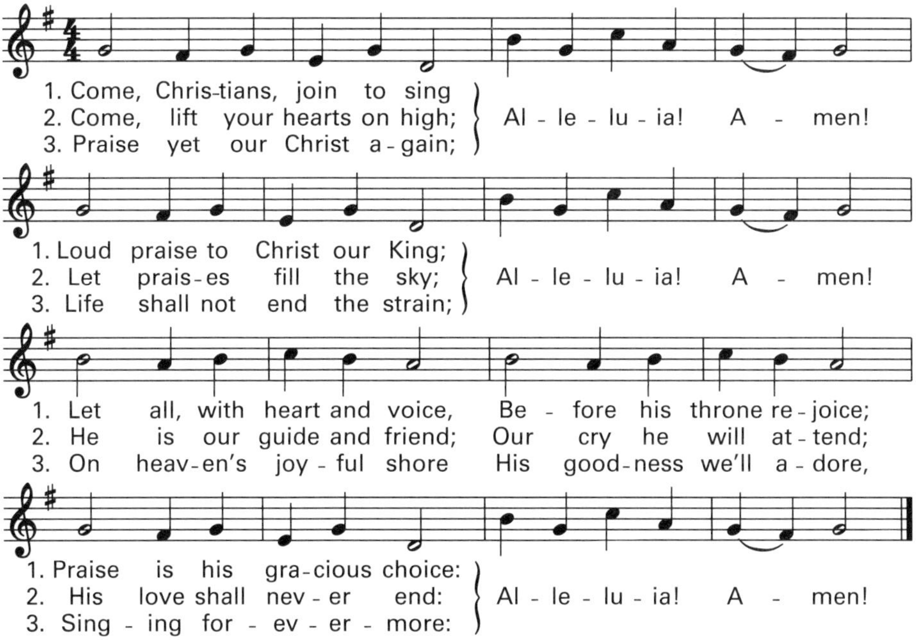

1. Come, Chris-tians, join to sing
2. Come, lift your hearts on high;
3. Praise yet our Christ a - gain;
Al - le - lu - ia! A - men!

1. Loud praise to Christ our King;
2. Let prais - es fill the sky;
3. Life shall not end the strain;
Al - le - lu - ia! A - men!

1. Let all, with heart and voice, Be - fore his throne re - joice;
2. He is our guide and friend; Our cry he will at - tend;
3. On heav - en's joy - ful shore His good - ness we'll a - dore,

1. Praise is his gra - cious choice:
2. His love shall nev - er end:
3. Sing - ing for - ev - er - more:
Al - le - lu - ia! A - men!

Text: 66 66 D; Christian H. Bateman, 1813–1889, alt.
Music: MADRID; anon. melody, Philadelphia, 1826.

712 ALL THE ENDS OF THE EARTH

Refrain
All the ends of the earth, all you crea-tures of the sea, lift up your
eyes to the won - ders of the Lord. For the Lord of the earth, the
mas-ter of the sea, has come with jus-tice for the world.
Verse 1
1. Break in - to song at the deeds of the Lord,
1. the won-ders God has done in ev - 'ry age.
to Refrain
Verse 2
2. Heav - en and earth shall re - joice in his might;
2. ev - 'ry heart ev - 'ry na - tion call him Lord.
to Refrain
Verse 3
3. The Lord has made sal - va - tion known, faith-ful to the prom-
3. - is - es of old. Let the ends of the earth, let the
3. sea and all it holds make mu - sic be - fore our King!
to Refrain

Text: Based on Psalm 98; Bob Dufford, SJ, b. 1943.
Music: Bob Dufford, SJ.

Alle, Alle, Alleluia

713

Refrain Al - le, al - le, al - le - lu - ia,
Verses 1. Fa - ther, Fa - ther, mak - er of the world.
2. Je - sus, Je - sus, Je - sus is the way.
3. Spir - it, Spir - it, come down on us, Lord.

al - le, al - le, al - le - lu - ia.
1. Fa - ther, Fa - ther, cre - a - tor of the earth.
2. Je - sus, Je - sus, Je - sus is the truth.
3. Spir - it, Spir - it, rain down on us, Lord.

Al - le, al - le, al - le - lu - ia.
1. Fa - ther, Fa - ther, speak - er of the word.
2. Je - sus, Je - sus, Je - sus is the life.
3. Spir - it, Spir - it, flood us with your pow'r.

Al - le, al - le, al - le, al - le - lu - ia.
1. Make us, Fa - ther, break us, Fa - ther, mold us in your ways.
2. Je - sus is the way, he is the truth, he is the life.
3. Fill us with the light of God, oh, fill us with your pow'r.

1-6
Al - le, al - le, al - le, al - le - lu - ia. (to Verses)

1. Make us, Fa - ther, break us, Fa - ther, mold us in your ways. (to Refrain)
2. Je - sus is the way, he is the truth, he is the life. (to Refrain)
3. Fill us with the light of God, oh, fill us with your pow'r. (to Refrain)

Final
ia. Al - le, al - le, al - le - lu - ia.
Al - le, al - le, al - le - lu - ia. Al - le!

Text and music: *Caribbean Mass;* Fr. Richard Ho Lung, M.O.P., b. 1939,

714 All Creatures of Our God and King

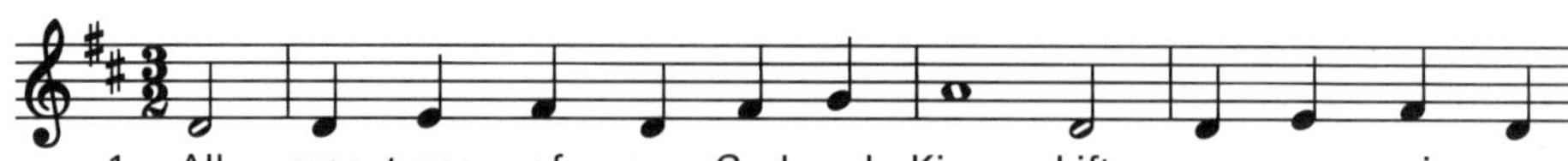

1. All crea-tures of our God and King, Lift up your voic - es,
2. Great rush - ing winds who are so strong, You clouds a - bove that
3. Swift flow - ing wa - ter, pure and clear, Make mu - sic for your
4. Dear moth - er earth, who day by day Un - folds your bless-ings
5. All you with mer - cy in your heart, For - giv - ing oth - ers,
6. And e - ven you, most gen - tle death, Wait - ing to hush our
7. Let all things their Cre - a - tor bless, And wor-ship him in

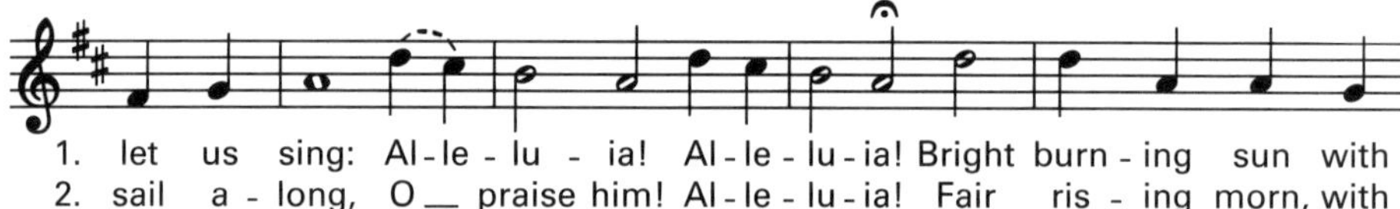

1. let us sing: Al - le - lu - ia! Al - le - lu - ia! Bright burn - ing sun with
2. sail a - long, O _ praise him! Al - le - lu - ia! Fair ris - ing morn, with
3. Lord to hear, Al - le - lu - ia! Al - le - lu - ia! Fire so in - tense and
4. on our way, O _ praise him! Al - le - lu - ia! All flow'rs and fruits that
5. take your part, O _ sing now! Al - le - lu - ia! All you that pain and
6. fi - nal breath, O _ praise him! Al - le - lu - ia! You lead back home the
7. hum - ble - ness, O _ praise him! Al - le - lu - ia! Praise God the Fa - ther,

1. gold - en beams, Soft sil - ver moon that gent - ly gleams, O praise him!
2. praise re - joice, Stars night - ly shin - ing, find a voice, O praise him!
3. fierce - ly bright, Who gives to us both warmth and light, O praise him!
4. in you grow, Let them his glo - ry al - so show: O praise him!
5. sor - row bear, Praise God, and cast on him your care: O praise him!
6. child of God, For Christ our Lord that way has trod: O praise him!
7. praise the Son, And praise the Spir - it, Three in One: O praise him!

1-7. O praise him! Al - le - lu - ia! Al - le - lu - ia! Al - le - lu - ia!

Text: LM with additions; St. Francis of Assisi, 1182–1226; *Laudato sia Dio mio Signore*;
tr. by Rev. William H. Draper, 1855–1933, alt.,
Music: LASST UNS ERFREUEN; *Auserlesene Catholische Geistliche Kirchengesänge*, Cologne, 1623.

Been So Busy

Verses

1. Been so bus - y prais-ing my Je - sus, I ain't got time to
2. Been so bus - y sing-ing God's prais-es, I ain't got time to

1. die. I've been so bus - y prais-ing my Je - sus, I
2. die. I've been so bus - y sing-ing God's prais-es, I

1. ain't got time to die. He woke me up this
2. ain't got time to die. I'll sing them in the

1. morn - ing and start-ed me on my way. Been so bus - y
2. morn - ing and when _ the sun goes down. Been so bus - y

1. prais-ing my Je - sus, I ain't got time to die.
2. sing-ing God's prais - es, I ain't got time to die.

Refrain

I ain't got time to die. I

ain't got time to die. I've been so bus - y

prais-ing my Lord, I ain't got time to die.

Text and music: Grayson Warren Brown, b. 1948,

716 ABBA! FATHER

Refrain *Ab - ba, Ab - ba, Fa -*
Verses 1. Mold us, mold us and fash - ion
2. Fa - ther, may we be one in
3. Glo - ry, glo - ry and praise to

ther. You are the pot - ter;
1. us in - to the im - age of
2. you. May we be one in you as
3. you. Glo - ry and praise to you for-

we are the clay, the work of your
1. Je - sus, your Son, of Je - sus, your
2. he is in you, and you are in
3. ev - er, a - men, for - ev - er, a -

1-6 2 Final 2

hands. (to Verses) *Ab - ba!*
1. Son. (to Refrain)
2. him. (to Refrain)
3. men. (to Refrain)

Text: Refrain based on Jeremiah 18:6; Romans 8:15; verse 1 based on Romans 8:29; verse 2 based on John 17:21; Carey Landry, b. 1944.
Music: Carey Landry.

717 BLESSED BY YOUR SACRIFICE

1. Blessed by your sac - ri - fice, Strong in your love, O Christ,
2. O Splen-dor, Glo - ry bright, Brought forth as Light from Light!
3. Come, raise the an-them high! Let prais-es fill the sky!
1. Our grate-ful voic - es to you we raise. True ad - o - ra - tion
2. O Day, all days en - light-en - ing! An-gels with one ac - cord
3. Sing out a new song un - to the Lord! Let all, with heart and voice,

1. Through-out cre - a - tion Rings out in joy - ful songs of praise.
2. Cry "Ho - ly, Ho - ly Lord!" To you, our ev - er - last - ing King.
3. Be - fore the throne re-joice Of him whom heav'n and earth a - dore.

Text: Irregular; Owen Alstott, b. 1947, and Jeanne Frolick, SFCC,
Music: ST. ELIZABETH; trad. Silesian melody; Hoffman and Richter's *Schlesische Volkslieder*, Leipzig, 1842.

718 From All That Dwell Below the Skies/ Praise God from Whom All Blessings Flow

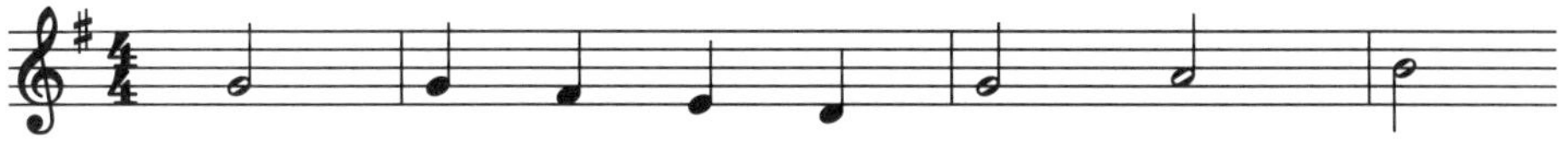

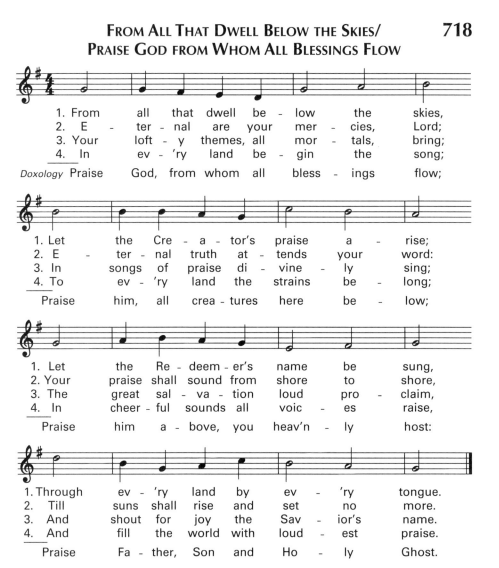

1. From all that dwell be - low the skies,
2. E - ter - nal are your mer - cies, Lord;
3. Your loft - y themes, all mor - tals, bring;
4. In ev - 'ry land be - gin the song;

Doxology Praise God, from whom all bless - ings flow;

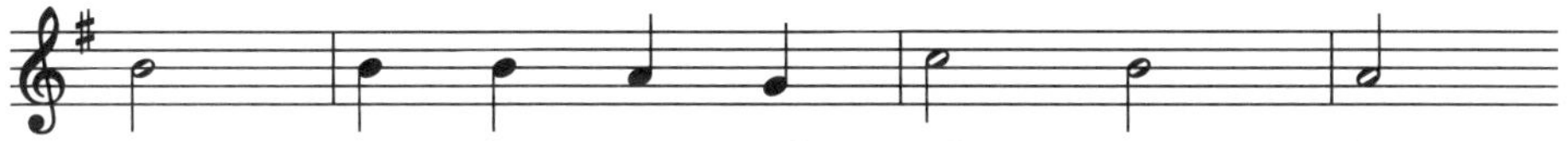

1. Let the Cre - a - tor's praise a - rise;
2. E - ter - nal truth at - tends your word:
3. In songs of praise di - vine - ly sing;
4. To ev - 'ry land the strains be - long;

Praise him, all crea - tures here be - low;

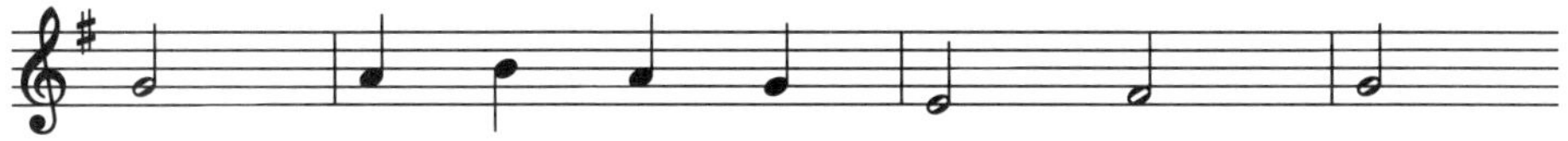

1. Let the Re - deem - er's name be sung,
2. Your praise shall sound from shore to shore,
3. The great sal - va - tion loud pro - claim,
4. In cheer - ful sounds all voic - es raise,

Praise him a - bove, you heav'n - ly host:

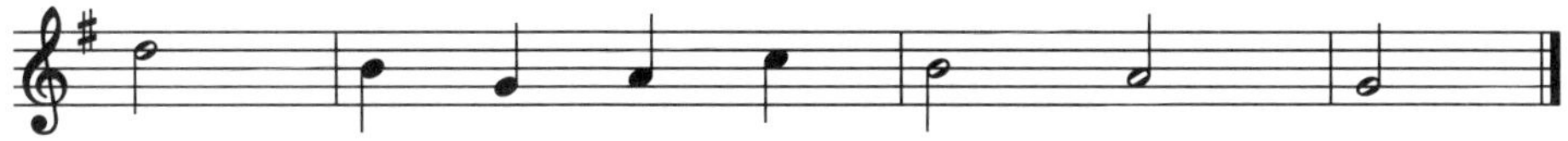

1. Through ev - 'ry land by ev - 'ry tongue.
2. Till suns shall rise and set no more.
3. And shout for joy the Sav - ior's name.
4. And fill the world with loud - est praise.

Praise Fa - ther, Son and Ho - ly Ghost.

Text: LM; based on Psalm 117; verses 1–2, Isaac Watts, 1674–1748, alt; verses 3–4, anon., ca. 1781; Doxology, Thomas Ken, 1637–1711.
Music: OLD HUNDREDTH; *Genevan Psalter*, 1551; attr. to Louis Bourgeois, ca. 1510–1561, alt.

719 God, We Praise You

1. God, we praise you! God, we bless you! God, we
2. True a - pos - tles, faith - ful proph - ets, Saints who
3. Je - sus Christ, the King of glo - ry, Ev - er -
4. Christ, at God's right hand vic - to - rious, You will
1. name you sov-'reign Lord! Might - y King whom an - gels
2. set their world a - blaze, Mar - tyrs, once un - known, un -
3. last - ing Son of God, Hum - ble was your vir - gin
4. judge the world you made; Lord, in mer - cy help your
1. wor - ship, Fa - ther, by your Church a - dored:
2. heed - ed, Join one grow - ing song of praise,
3. moth - er, Hard the lone - ly path you trod:
4. ser - vants For whose free - dom you have paid:
1. All cre - a - tion shows your glo - ry, Heav'n and
2. While your Church on earth con - fess - es One ma -
3. By your cross is sin de - feat - ed, Hell con -
4. Raise us up from dust to glo - ry, Guard us
1. earth draw near your throne, Sing - ing "Ho - ly, ho - ly,
2. jes - tic Trin - i - ty: Fa - ther, Son, and Ho - ly
3. front - ed face to face, Heav - en o - pened to be -
4. from all sin to - day; King en - throned a - bove all
1. ho - ly," Lord of hosts and God a - lone!
2. Spir - it, God, our hope e - ter - nal - ly.
3. liev - ers, Sin - ners jus - ti - fied by grace.
4. prais - es, Save your peo - ple, God, we pray.

Text: 87 87 D; *Te Deum laudamus*; attr. to St. Nicetas, ca. 335–414; tr. by Christopher Idle, b. 1938,

Music: NETTLETON; J. Wyeth's *Repository of Sacred Music, Part II*, 1813.

Hallelujah Is Our Song 720

Verses
1. What hope we have, e - ven in the long - est night, for the light will o - ver - come.
2. What peace we have, e - ven in this wound - ed world where the bat - tle rag - es on.
3. What joy we have, for the stone is rolled a - way and the tomb holds noth - ing now.
4. What hope we have, e - ven in the long - est night, for the light will o - ver - come.
1. We will not fear, for we know the
2. We will not fear, for we know who
3. No sting of death, no pow - er o - ver
4. And we shall live; sin - ners, we will

1st time to Verse 2
1. sun will rise.
2. heals our souls.
3. sin or grave.
4. rise to saints.
Hal - le - lu - jah is our song.

Refrain
Hal - le - lu - jah! Hal - le - lu - jah! He is ris - en o - ver all. Hal - le - lu - jah! Hal - le - lu - jah! Hal - le - lu - jah is our song.

Text and music: Sarah Hart, b. 1968, Sarah Kroger, Josh Blakesley, b. 1976, and Trey Heffinger,

721 Holy God, We Praise Thy Name

1. Ho - ly God, we praise thy name; Lord of all, we
2. Hark! the loud ce - les - tial hymn An - gel choirs a -
3. Lo! the ap - os - tol - ic train Join, the sa - cred
4. Ho - ly Fa - ther, Ho - ly Son, Ho - ly Spir - it,
1. bow be - fore thee! All on earth thy scep - tre claim,
2. bove are rais - ing; Cher - u - bim and Ser - a - phim,
3. Name to hal - low; Proph - ets swell the loud re - frain,
4. Three we name thee; While in es - sence on - ly One,
1. All in heav'n a - bove a - dore thee; In - fi -
2. In un - ceas - ing cho - rus prais - ing; Fill the
3. And the white - robed mar - tyrs fol - low; And from
4. Un - di - vid - ed God we claim thee; And a -
1. nite, thy vast do - main, Ev - er - last - ing
2. heav'ns with sweet ac - cord: "Ho - ly, ho - ly,
3. morn to set of sun, Through the Church the
4. dor - ing, bend the knee, While we own the
1. is thy reign. In - fi - nite, thy vast do -
2. ho - ly Lord!" Fill the heav'ns with sweet ac -
3. song goes on. And from morn to set of
4. mys - ter - y. And a - dor - ing, bend the
1. main, Ev - er - last - ing is thy reign.
2. cord: "Ho - ly, ho - ly, ho - ly Lord!"
3. sun, Through the Church the song goes on.
4. knee, While we own the mys - ter - y.

Text: 78 78 77 with repeat; *Te Deum laudamus*; attr. to St. Nicetas, ca. 335–414; *Grosser Gott, wir loben dich*; tr. ascr. to Ignaz Franz, 1719–1790; tr. by Clarence A. Walworth, 1820–1900.
Music: GROSSER GOTT; *Allgemeines Katholisches Gesangbuch*, Vienna, ca. 1774.

SING TO THE MOUNTAINS 722

Refrain
Sing to the moun-tains, sing to the sea. Raise your voic - es,
lift your hearts. This is the day the Lord has made. Let all the
to Verses
Last time
earth re - joice. Let all the earth re - joice.
Verse 1
1. I will give thanks to you, my Lord. You have
1. an-swered my plea. You have saved my
to Refrain
1. soul from death. You are my strength and my song.
Verse 2
2. Ho - ly, ho - ly, ho - ly Lord. Heav -
to Refrain
2. en and earth are full of your glo - ry.
Verse 3
3. This is the day that the Lord has made. Let us be glad and re-joice.
to Refrain
3. Death has lost and all is life. Sing of the glo-ry of God.

Text: Based on Psalm 118:24; Isaiah 6:3; Bob Dufford, SJ, b. 1943.
Music: Bob Dufford, SJ.

723 GLORY AND PRAISE TO OUR GOD

Refrain

Glo - ry and praise to our God, who a - lone gives light to our days.
Man - y are the bless - ings he bears to those who trust in his ways.

Verses 1-3

1. We, the daugh - ters and sons of him who built the val - leys and plains, praise the won - ders our God has done in ev - 'ry heart that sings.
2. In his wis - dom he strength - ens us, like gold that's test - ed in fire. Though the pow - er of sin pre - vails, our God is there to save.
3. Ev - 'ry mo - ment of ev - 'ry day our God is wait - ing to save, al - ways read - y to seek the lost, to an - swer those who pray.

to Refrain

Verse 4

4. God has wa - tered our bar - ren land and spent his mer - ci - ful rain. Now the riv - ers of life run full for an - y - one to drink.

to Refrain

Text: Based on Psalms 65 and 66; Dan Schutte, b. 1947.
Music: Dan Schutte.

724 I WILL REJOICE

Refrain
I will re - joice, I will be glad. I will praise
God who holds my life in his hands.

Verses
1. I will praise my Fa - ther each and ev - ery day.
2. I will praise the Fa - ther, I will praise the Son.
to Refrain
1. O and I will sing his love songs for - ev - er more.
2. O and I will praise God's Spir - it for - ev - er more.

Text and music: Grayson Warren Brown, b. 1948,

Lift Up Your Hearts 725

Refrain

Lift up your hearts to the Lord, praise God's gra - cious mer - cy!
Sing out your joy to the Lord, whose love is en - dur - ing.

Verses

1. Shout with joy to the Lord, all the earth! Praise the name a - bove all names! Say to God, "How won - drous your works, how glo - rious your name!"
2. Let the earth wor - ship, sing - ing your praise. Praise the glo - ry of your name! Come and see the deeds of the Lord; bless God's ho - ly name!
3. God's right hand made a path through the night, split the wa - ters of the sea. All cre - a - tion, lift up your voice: "Our God set us free!"
4. Lis - ten now, all you ser - vants of God, as I tell of these great works. Bless - ed be the Lord of my life, whose love shall en - dure!

to Refrain

Text: Based on Psalm 66; Roc O'Connor, SJ, b. 1949.
Music: Roc O'Connor, SJ.

726 JOYFUL, JOYFUL, WE ADORE THEE

1. Joy - ful, joy - ful, we a - dore thee, God of glo - ry,
2. All thy works with joy sur - round thee, Earth and heav'n re -
3. Thou art giv - ing and for - giv - ing, Ev - er bless - ing,
4. Mor - tals, join the might - y cho - rus Which the morn - ing

1. Lord of love; Hearts un - fold like flow'rs be - fore thee,
2. flect thy rays, Stars and an - gels sing a - round thee,
3. ev - er blest, Well-spring of the joy of liv - ing,
4. stars be - gan; Love di - vine is reign - ing o'er us,

1. O - p'ning to the sun a - bove. Melt the clouds of
2. Cen - ter of un - bro - ken praise; Field and for - est,
3. O - cean depth of hap - py rest! Thou our Fa - ther,
4. Bind - ing all with - in its span. Ev - er sing - ing,

1. sin and sad - ness; Drive the dark of doubt a - way;
2. vale and moun - tain, Flow - 'ry mead - ow, flash - ing sea,
3. Christ our broth - er, All who live in love are thine;
4. march we on - ward, Vic - tors in the midst of strife;

1. Giv - er of im - mor - tal glad - ness, Fill us with the light of day.
2. Chant - ing bird and flow - ing foun - tain, Call us to re - joice in thee.
3. Teach us how to love each oth - er, Lift us to the joy di - vine.
4. Joy - ful mu - sic leads us sun - ward, In the tri - umph song of life.

Text: 87 87 D; Henry van Dyke, 1852–1933, alt.
Music: HYMN TO JOY; Ludwig van Beethoven, 1770–1827; adapt. by Edward Hodges, 1796–1867.

727 HE IS THE LORD

Refrain
Sing to the Lord with shouts of joy, let all cre -
a - tion re - joice! Come join the song of praise to our
God! He is the Lord! He is the Lord!

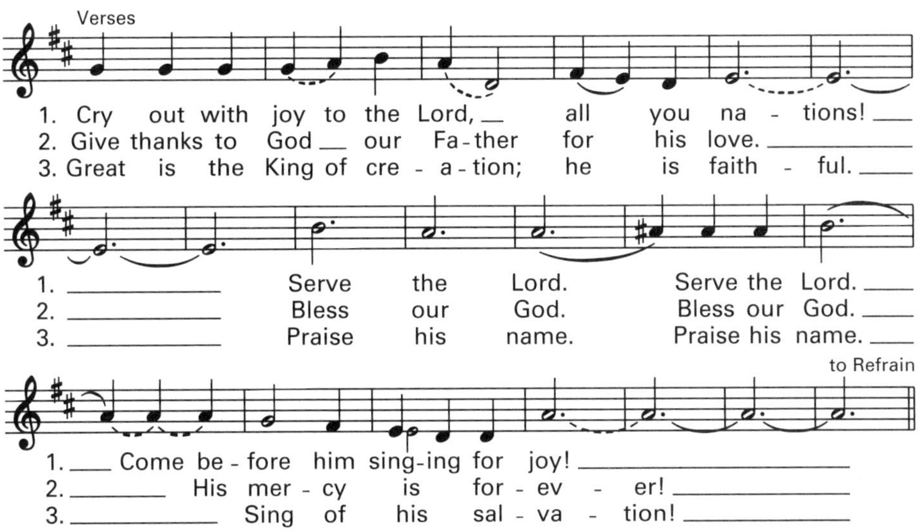
Verses
1. Cry out with joy to the Lord, all you na - tions!
2. Give thanks to God our Fa-ther for his love.
3. Great is the King of cre - a - tion; he is faith - ful.
1. Serve the Lord. Serve the Lord.
2. Bless our God. Bless our God.
3. Praise his name. Praise his name.
to Refrain
1. Come be - fore him sing-ing for joy!
2. His mer - cy is for - ev - er!
3. Sing of his sal - va - tion!

May We Praise You 728

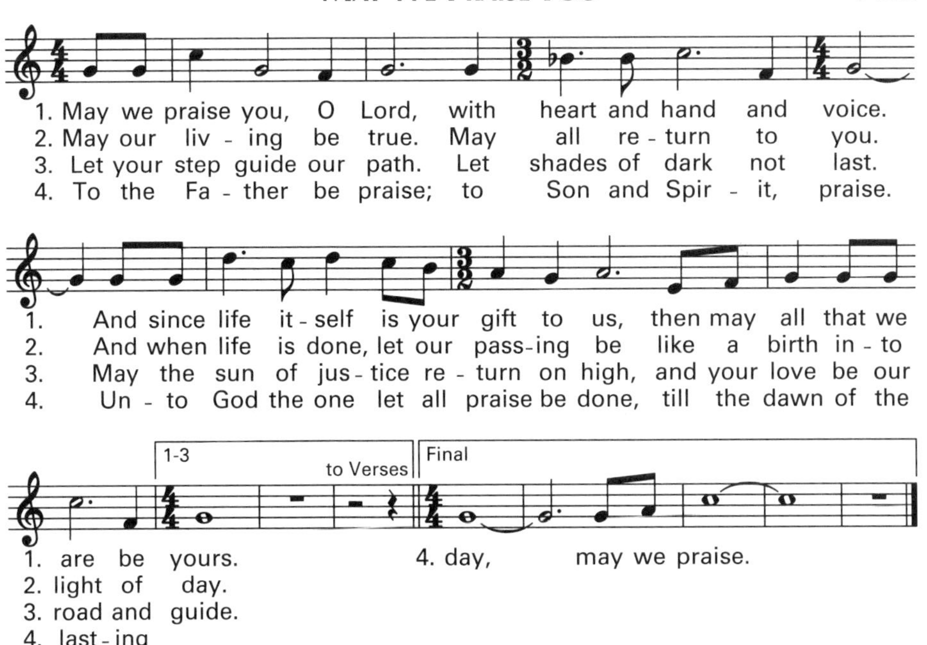
1. May we praise you, O Lord, with heart and hand and voice.
2. May our liv - ing be true. May all re - turn to you.
3. Let your step guide our path. Let shades of dark not last.
4. To the Fa - ther be praise; to Son and Spir - it, praise.
1. And since life it - self is your gift to us, then may all that we
2. And when life is done, let our pass-ing be like a birth in - to
3. May the sun of jus - tice re - turn on high, and your love be our
4. Un - to God the one let all praise be done, till the dawn of the
1-3
to Verses
Final
1. are be yours.
2. light of day.
3. road and guide.
4. last - ing
4. day, may we praise.

729 O Bless the Lord

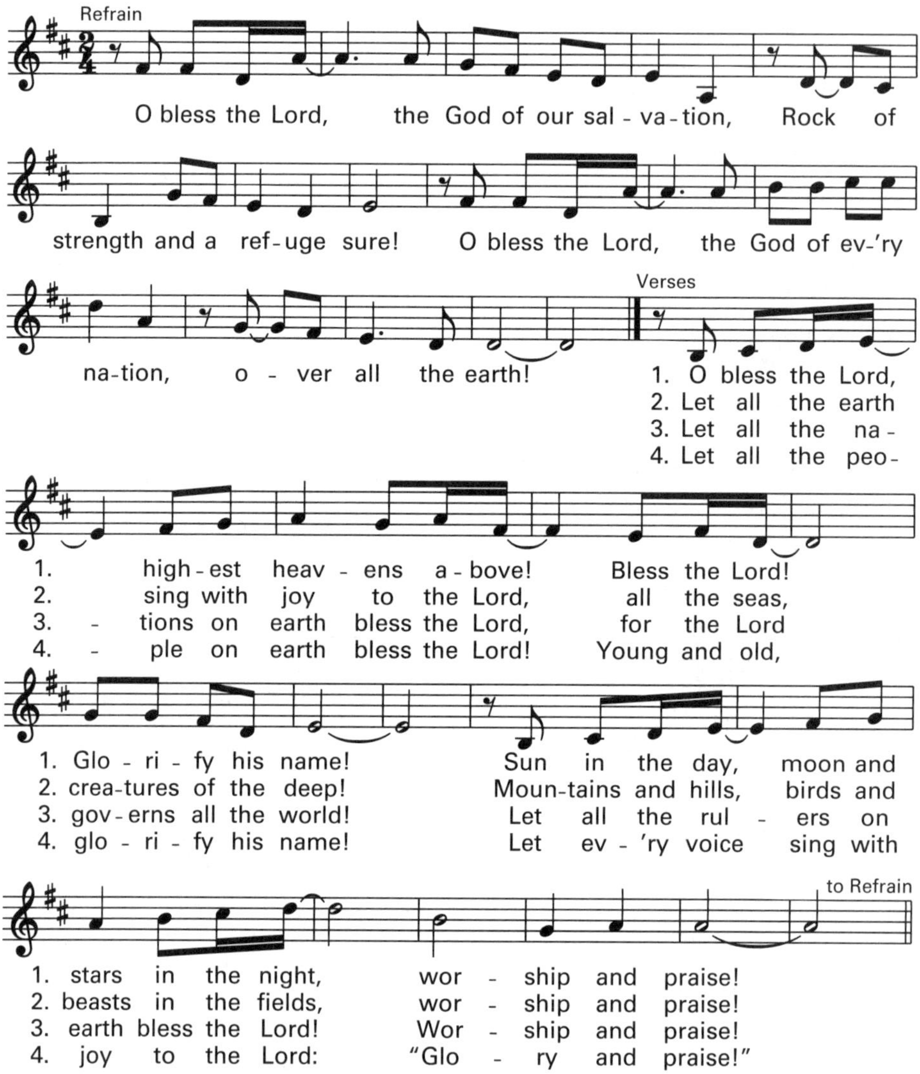

Refrain

O bless the Lord, the God of our sal-va-tion, Rock of strength and a ref-uge sure! O bless the Lord, the God of ev-'ry na-tion, o-ver all the earth!

Verses

1. O bless the Lord, highest heav-ens a-bove! Bless the Lord! Glo-ri-fy his name! Sun in the day, moon and stars in the night, wor-ship and praise!
2. Let all the earth sing with joy to the Lord, all the seas, crea-tures of the deep! Moun-tains and hills, birds and beasts in the fields, wor-ship and praise!
3. Let all the na-tions on earth bless the Lord, for the Lord gov-erns all the world! Let all the rul-ers on earth bless the Lord! Wor-ship and praise!
4. Let all the peo-ple on earth bless the Lord! Young and old, glo-ri-fy his name! Let ev-'ry voice sing with joy to the Lord: "Glo-ry and praise!"

to Refrain

Text: Based on Psalm 148; John Michaels, b. 1947.
Music: John Michaels.

730 Let All Mortal Flesh Keep Silence

1. Let all mor-tal flesh keep si-lence, And with fear and
2. King of kings, yet born of Ma-ry, As of old on
3. Rank on rank the host of heav-en Spreads its van-guard
4. At his feet the six-winged ser-aph; Cher-u-bim with

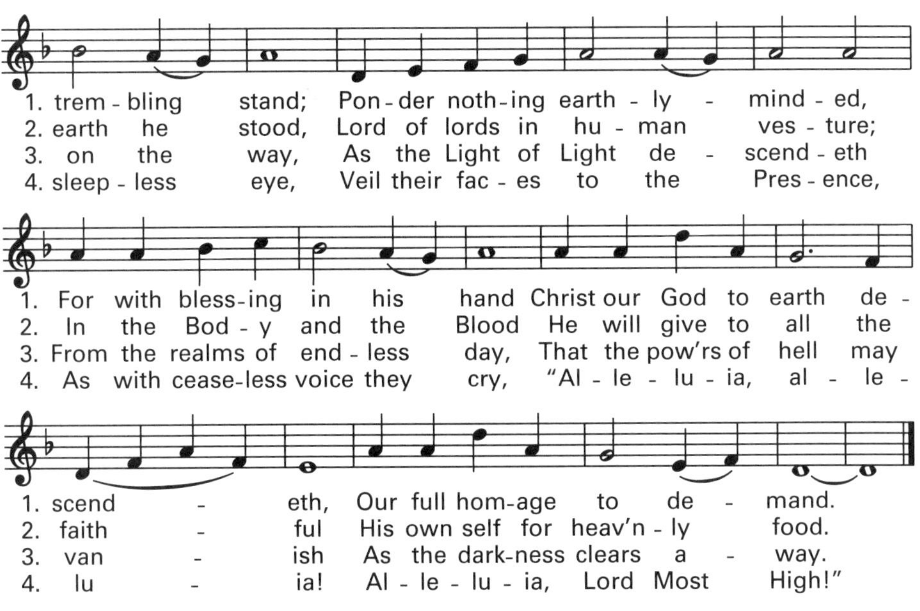
1. trem - bling stand; Pon - der noth - ing earth - ly - mind - ed,
2. earth he stood, Lord of lords in hu - man ves - ture;
3. on the way, As the Light of Light de - scend - eth
4. sleep - less eye, Veil their fac - es to the Pres - ence,
1. For with bless - ing in his hand Christ our God to earth de -
2. In the Bod - y and the Blood He will give to all the
3. From the realms of end - less day, That the pow'rs of hell may
4. As with cease - less voice they cry, "Al - le - lu - ia, al - le -
1. scend - eth, Our full hom - age to de - mand.
2. faith - ful His own self for heav'n - ly food.
3. van - ish As the dark - ness clears a - way.
4. lu - ia! Al - le - lu - ia, Lord Most High!"

Text: 87 87 87; *Liturgy of St. James*, 4th cent.; para. by Gerard Moultrie, 1829–1885, alt.
Music: PICARDY; French, 17th cent.; *Chansons populaires des Provinces de France*, 1860.

Praise the Lord, Ye Heavens 731

1. Praise the Lord! ye heav'ns a - dore him; Praise him an - gels, in the height;
2. Praise the Lord! for he is glo - rious; Nev - er shall his prom - ise fail;
3. Wor - ship, hon - or, glo - ry, bless - ing, Lord, we of - fer un - to thee;

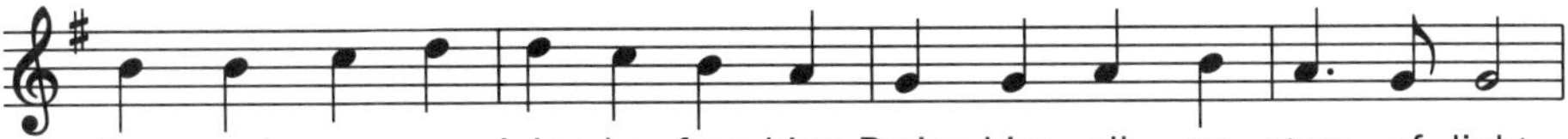

1. Sun and moon, re - joice be - fore him; Praise him, all ye stars of light.
2. God has made his saints vic - to - rious; Sin and death shall not pre - vail.
3. Young and old, thy praise ex - press - ing, In glad hom - age bend the knee.

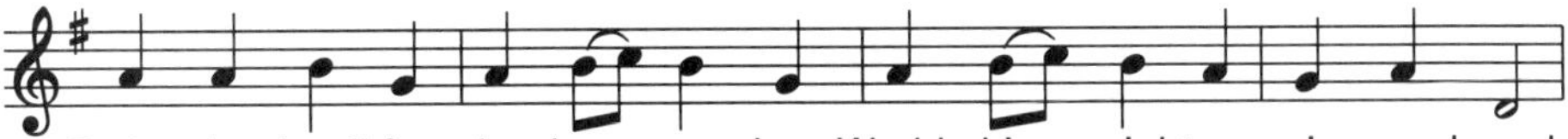

1. Praise the Lord! for he has spo - ken; Worlds his might - y voice o - beyed;
2. Praise the God of our sal - va - tion! Hosts on high his pow'r pro - claim;
3. All the saints in heav'n a - dore thee, We would bow be - fore thy throne;

1. Laws which nev - er shall be bro - ken For their guid - ance he has made.
2. Heav'n, and earth, and all cre - a - tion, Laud and mag - ni - fy his name.
3. As thine an - gels serve be - fore thee, So on earth thy will be done.

Text: 87 87 D; based on Psalm 148; verses 1, 2, *Psalms, Hymns, and Anthems of the Foundling Hospital*, 1796; verse 3, Edward Osler, 1798–1863.
Music: HYMN TO JOY; Ludwig van Beethoven, 1770–1827; adapt. by Edward Hodges, 1796–1867.

732 Praise to the Lord

1. Praise to the Lord, the Al - might - y, the King of cre -
2. Praise to the Lord, a - bove all things so won - drous - ly
3. Praise to the Lord, who will pros - per your work and de -
4. Praise to the Lord! O let all that is in me a -

1. a - tion! O my soul, praise him, for
2. reign - ing, Shel - t'ring you un - der his
3. fend you; Sure - ly his good - ness and
4. dore him! All that has life and breath,

1. he is your health and sal - va - tion!
2. wings, and so gent - ly sus - tain - ing.
3. mer - cy shall dai - ly at - tend you.
4. come now with prais - es be - fore him!

1. Come, all who hear: Now to his al - tar draw
2. Have you not seen All that is need - ful has
3. Pon - der a - new What the Al - might - y can
4. Let the "A - men!" Sound from his peo - ple a -

1. near, Join - ing in glad ad - o - ra - tion!
2. been Sent by his gra - cious or - dain - ing?
3. do As with his love he be - friends you.
4. gain, Glad - ly with praise we a - dore him!

Text: 14 14 47 8; Joachim Neander, 1650–1680; tr. by Catherine Winkworth, 1827–1878, alt.
Music: LOBE DEN HERREN; *Ernewerten Gesangbuch*, Stralsund, 1665.

733 O God beyond All Praising

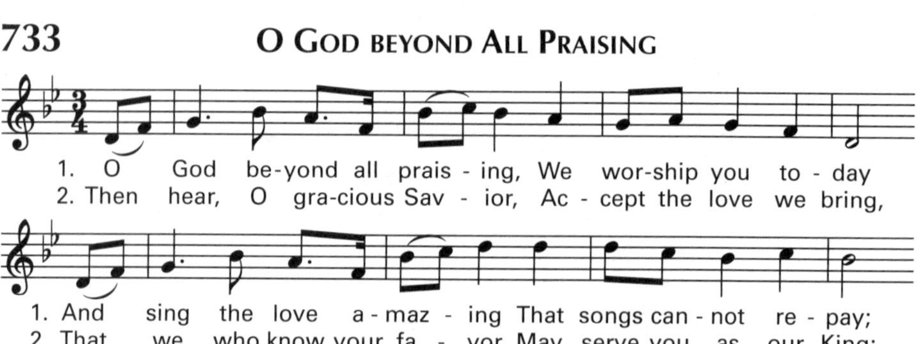
1. O God be-yond all prais - ing, We wor-ship you to - day
2. Then hear, O gra-cious Sav - ior, Ac - cept the love we bring,
1. And sing the love a - maz - ing That songs can - not re - pay;
2. That we who know your fa - vor May serve you as our King;

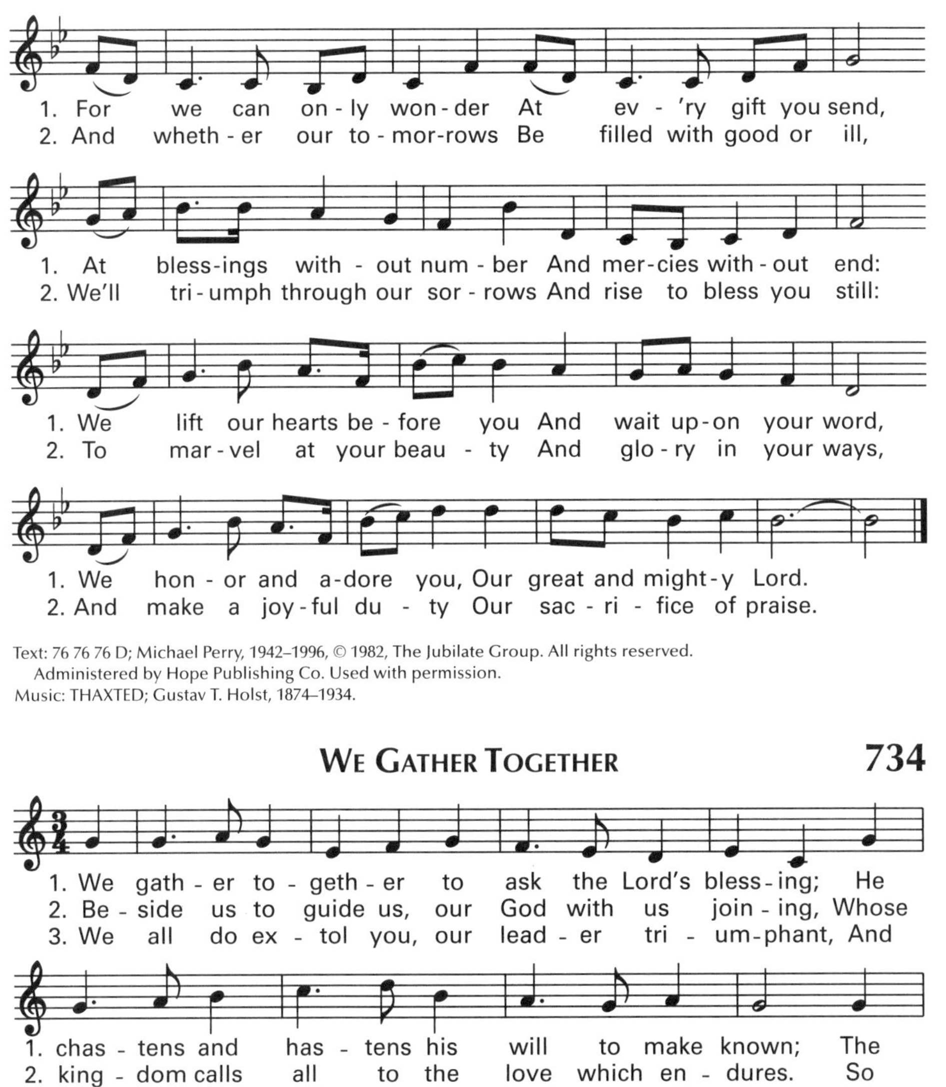
1. For we can on-ly won-der At ev - 'ry gift you send,
2. And wheth - er our to - mor-rows Be filled with good or ill,
1. At bless-ings with - out num - ber And mer-cies with - out end:
2. We'll tri - umph through our sor - rows And rise to bless you still:
1. We lift our hearts be - fore you And wait up-on your word,
2. To mar - vel at your beau - ty And glo - ry in your ways,
1. We hon - or and a-dore you, Our great and might-y Lord.
2. And make a joy - ful du - ty Our sac - ri - fice of praise.

Text: 76 76 76 D; Michael Perry, 1942–1996,
Music: THAXTED; Gustav T. Holst, 1874–1934.

WE GATHER TOGETHER 734

1. We gath - er to - geth - er to ask the Lord's bless - ing; He
2. Be - side us to guide us, our God with us join - ing, Whose
3. We all do ex - tol you, our lead - er tri - um-phant, And

1. chas - tens and has - tens his will to make known; The
2. king - dom calls all to the love which en - dures. So
3. pray that you still our de - fend - er will be. Let

1. wick - ed op - press - ing now cease from dis - tress - ing: Sing
2. from the be - gin - ning the fight we were win - ning: You,
3. your con - gre - ga - tion es - cape trib - u - la - tion: Your

1. prais - es to his name; he for - gets not his own.
2. Lord, were at our side; all ___ glo - ry be yours!
3. name be ev - er praised! O ___ Lord, make us free!

Text: 12 11 12 11; *Wilt heden nu treden*; tr. by Theodore Baker, 1851–1934, alt.
Music: KREMSER; Valerius' *Nederlandtsche Gedenckclanck*, Haarlem, 1626.

735 PRAISE, MY SOUL, THE KING OF HEAVEN

1. Praise, my soul, the King of heav - en;
2. Praise him for his grace and fa - vor
3. Fa - ther - like he tends and spares us;
4. Frail as sum - mer's flow'r we flour - ish,
5. An - gels, help us to a - dore him;
1. To his feet thy trib - ute bring; Ran - somed,
2. To his peo - ple in dis - tress; Praise him
3. Well our fee - ble frame he knows; In his
4. Blows the wind and it is gone; But while
5. You be - hold him face to face; Sun and
1. healed, re - stored, for - giv - en, Ev - er - more his
2. still the same as ev - er, Slow to chide, and
3. hands he gent - ly bears us, Res - cues us from
4. mor - tals rise and per - ish, God en - dures un-
5. moon, bow down be - fore him, All who dwell in
1. prais - es sing:
2. swift to bless:
3. all our foes.
4. chang - ing on:
5. time and space:
Al - le - lu - ia! Al - le -
1-5. lu - ia!
Praise the ev - er - last - ing King.
Glo - rious in his faith - ful - ness.
Wide - ly yet his mer - cy flows.
Praise the high e - ter - nal one!
Praise with us the God of grace.

Text: 87 87 87; based on Psalm 103; Henry F. Lyte, 1793–1847, alt.
Music: LAUDA ANIMA; John Goss, 1800–1880.

We Praise You

736

Refrain

We praise you, O Lord, for all your works are won-der-ful. We praise

you, O Lord, for ev-er is your love.

Verses

1. Your wis-dom made the
2. You have cho-sen
3. You led us out of
4. The na-tions fash-ioned
5. O house of Is-ra-
*6. Hap-py is the
*7. May the Lord give

1. heav-ens and the earth, O Lord; you formed the land, then
2. Ja-cob for your-self, O Lord; so ten-der-ly you
3. E-gypt with a guid-ing hand. You raised your arm to
4. sil-ver i-dols, gol-den gods; but none have hear-ing,
5. el, now come to bless the Lord, O house of Aar-on,
6. home of you that fear the Lord; so fruit-ful shall your
7. you his bless-ings all your days. May you see him

1. set the lights; and like your love the sun will
2. spoke his name; then called a ho-ly na-tion,
3. set us free. And like a ten-der vine you
4. speech or sight. Their mak-ers shall be like their
5. bless his name. O bless the Lord, all you who
6. love be-come. Your chil-dren flour-ish like the
7. fill your land un-til your chil-dren bring their

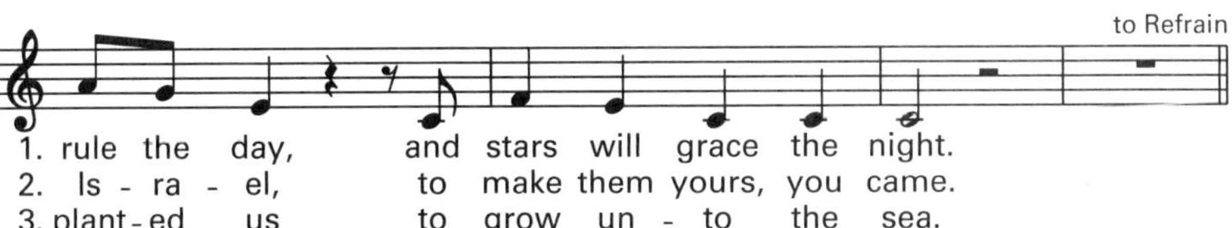
to Refrain

1. rule the day, and stars will grace the night.
2. Is-ra-el, to make them yours, you came.
3. plant-ed us to grow un-to the sea.
4. emp-ty gods, the Lord a-lone brings life.
5. hon-or him, and praise his ho-ly name.
6. ol-ive plants, for ev-er are you one.
7. chil-dren home to show his love a-gain.

*Wedding verses.

Text: Verses 1–5 based on Psalms 80:9–12; 135:15–18; 136:5–9; verses 6, 7 based on Psalm 128:1, 3, 5–6; Mike Balhoff, b. 1946.
Music: Darryl Ducote, b. 1945, and Gary Daigle, b. 1957.

737 Praise God in This Holy Dwelling

Refrain

1 to Vs. 1 | 2-4 to Vss. 2-4

Al - le - lu - ia, al - le - lu - ia, al - le - lu - ia! lu - ia!

Final

lu - ia!

Verses

1. Praise God in this ho - ly dwell - ing; Praise God on the might - y throne; Prais - ing for all won - der - ful deeds; Sing praise to our Sov - 'reign Maj - es - ty.
2. Praise God with the blast of trum - pet; Bring praise now with lyre and harp; Prais - ing with the tim - brel and dance; With the gen - tle sound of string and reed.
3. Praise God with re - sound - ing cym - bals; With cym - bals that crash, give praise; O let ev - 'ry - thing that has breath, Let all liv - ing crea - tures praise the Lord.
4. Praise God, the al - might - y Fa - ther; Praise Christ, his be - lov - ed Son; Give praise to the Spir - it of love; For - ev - er the tri - une God be praised.

to Refrain

Text: Based on Psalm 150:1–6; Omer Westendorf, 1916–1997.
Music: Jan Vermulst, 1925–1994.

738 Praise the Lord, My Soul

1. Praise the Lord, my soul, let fire and rain give praise to him, give praise to him, who is
2. Bless the Lord, my soul, let all I am give praise to him; and not for - get he is
3. Mer - ci - ful and kind, he knows our ways, he knows we're dust; and like the flow - ers that
4. Glo - ry to our God, let all that is give praise to him; give praise to him, all you

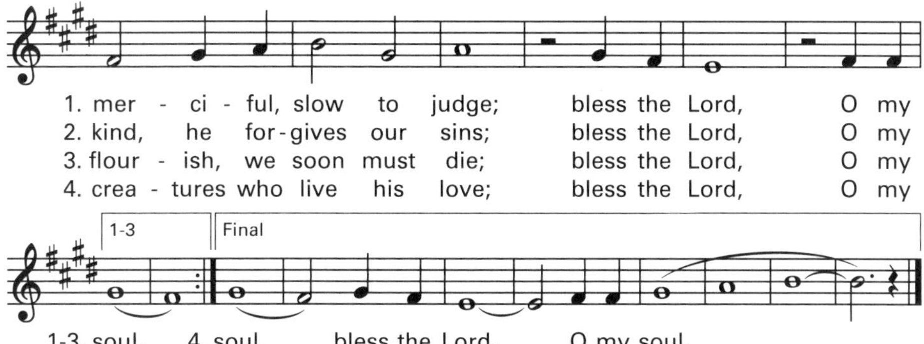
1. mer - ci - ful, slow to judge; bless the Lord, O my
2. kind, he for-gives our sins; bless the Lord, O my
3. flour - ish, we soon must die; bless the Lord, O my
4. crea - tures who live his love; bless the Lord, O my
1-3
Final
1-3. soul. 4. soul, bless the Lord, O my soul.

Text: Based on Psalm 103; John Foley, SJ, b. 1939.
Music: John Foley, SJ.

Sing a New Song 739

Refrain

Sing a new song un-to the Lord; let your song be sung from moun-tains high. Sing a new song un-to the Lord, sing-ing al - le - lu - ia.

Verses

1. Shout with glad-ness! Dance for joy! O come be - fore the Lord. And play for God on glad tam - bou-rines, and let your trum - pet sound.
2. Rise, O chil-dren, from your sleep; your Sav - ior now has come. He has turned your sor - row to joy, and filled your soul with song.
3. Glad my soul for I have seen the glo - ry of the Lord. The trum - pet sounds; the dead shall be raised. I know my Sav - ior lives.

to Refrain

Text: Based on Psalm 98:1, 4–6; Dan Schutte, b. 1947.
Music: Dan Schutte.

740 Sing of the Lord's Goodness

Verses

1. Sing of the Lord's good-ness, Fa-ther of all wis-dom,
2. Pow-er he has wield-ed, hon-or is his gar-ment,
3. Cour-age in our dark-ness, com-fort in our sor-row,
4. Praise him with your sing-ing, praise him with the trum-pet,

1. come to him and bless his name. Mer-cy he has shown us,
2. ris-en from the snares of death. His word he has spo-ken,
3. Spir-it of our God most high; so-lace for the wear-y,
4. praise God with the lute and harp; praise him with the cym-bals,

1. his love is for-ev-er, faith-ful to the end of days.
2. one bread he has bro-ken, new life he now gives to all.
3. par-don for the sin-ner, splen-dor of the liv-ing God.
4. praise him with your danc-ing, praise God till the end of days.

Refrain

Come, then, all you na-tions, sing of your Lord's good-ness, mel-o-dies of praise and thanks to God. Ring out the Lord's glo-ry, praise him with your mu-sic, wor-ship him and bless his name.

741 Sing Alleluia, Sing

Refrain
Sing al-le-lu-ia, sing al-le-lu-ia, sing al-le-lu-ia
to the Lord!
Sing his praise, sing his praise!
Sing al-le-lu-ia to the Lord!

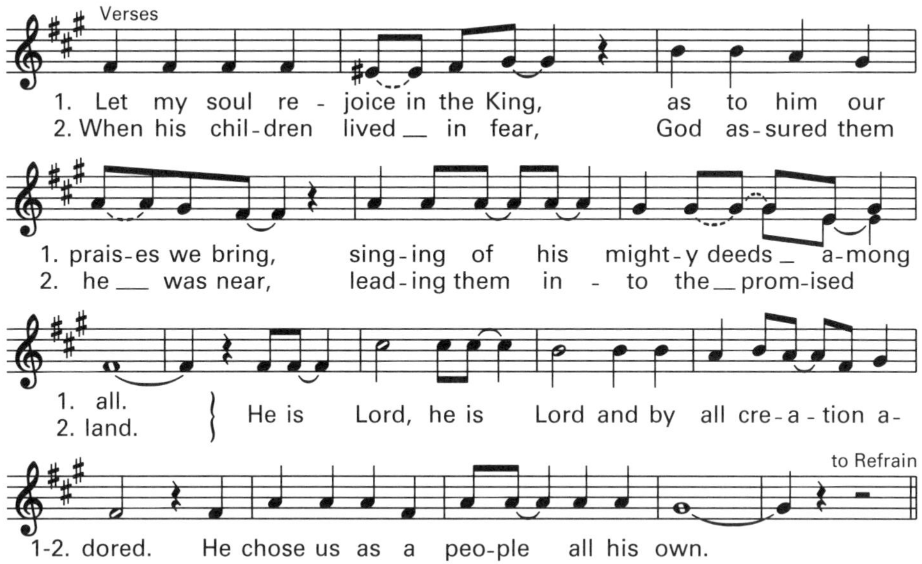
Verses
1. Let my soul re - joice in the King, as to him our
2. When his chil-dren lived __ in fear, God as-sured them
1. prais-es we bring, sing-ing of his might-y deeds _ a-mong
2. he __ was near, lead-ing them in - to the __ prom-ised
1. all.
2. land.
He is Lord, he is Lord and by all cre-a-tion a-
to Refrain
1-2. dored. He chose us as a peo-ple all his own.

Sing a New Song 742

Refrain

Sing a new song to the Lord. Praise him in the as-sem - bly
of his church. Sing a new song to the Lord. Praise him,
all you peo - ple of God.

Verses

1. Be glad, ___ O ___
2. Praise his name with
3. Let God's peo - ple

1. Is - ra - el, be - cause ___ of your cre - a - tor; re - joice, ___
2. danc - ing, play drums and harp __ in praise, ___ for God de-
3. cel - e-brate the tri - umph of ___ their king. ________ Let them

to Refrain

1. O ______ Zi - on, be - cause ___ of ___ your king.
2. lights in his peo - ple, and lifts his chil-dren on high.
3. shout _ and praise his name, while sing - ing all the night long.

743 SING A JOYFUL SONG

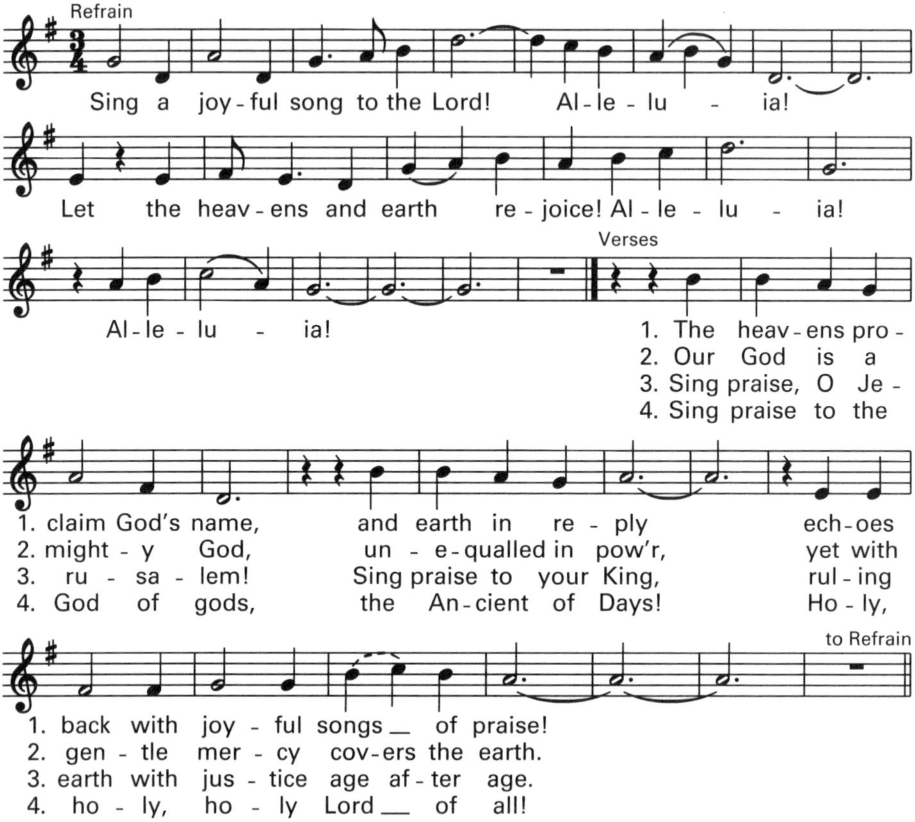

Refrain

Sing a joy-ful song to the Lord! Al-le-lu-ia!
Let the heav-ens and earth re-joice! Al-le-lu-ia!
Al-le-lu-ia!

Verses

1. The heav-ens pro-claim God's name, and earth in re-ply ech-oes back with joy-ful songs of praise!
2. Our God is a might-y God, un-e-qualled in pow'r, yet with gen-tle mer-cy cov-ers the earth.
3. Sing praise, O Je-ru-sa-lem! Sing praise to your King, rul-ing earth with jus-tice age af-ter age.
4. Sing praise to the God of gods, the An-cient of Days! Ho-ly, ho-ly, ho-ly Lord of all!

to Refrain

744 SING, O SING

1. Sing, O sing, like the wind and sea; let mu-sic fill the
2. Night and day we an-nounce your praise, O Lord of ev-'ry
3. Might-y Mas-ter of rag-ing storm, we kneel be-fore your
4. Hear us, Lord of the sun and moon; we bless you night and
5. Make us shine like the stars of night; we bless your ho-ly
1. skies! Lift your voice like the thun-d'ring waves: let songs of
2. land, give you thanks for the sun and stars, all bless-ings
3. pow'r. Lov-ing Lord of the faith-ful rain that makes the
4. day. Guide us, Lord, as we jour-ney home; be with us
5. name! Make our love like a blaz-ing light; O set our

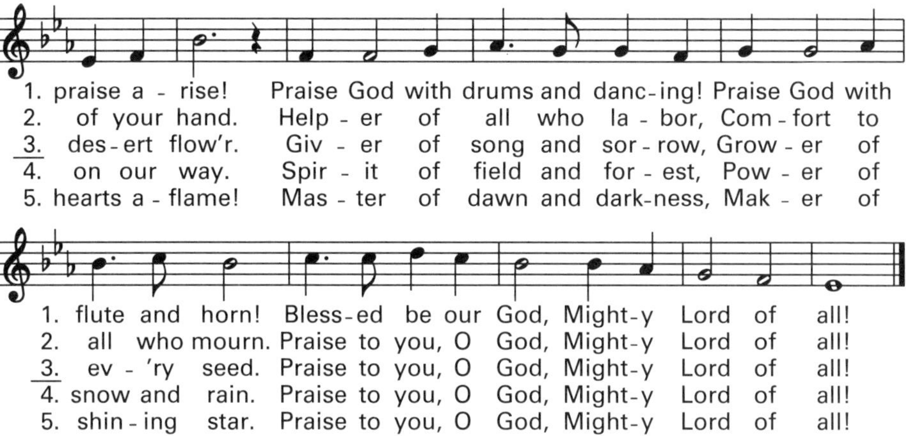
1. praise a - rise! Praise God with drums and danc-ing! Praise God with
2. of your hand. Help - er of all who la - bor, Com - fort to
3. des - ert flow'r. Giv - er of song and sor - row, Grow - er of
4. on our way. Spir - it of field and for - est, Pow - er of
5. hearts a - flame! Mas - ter of dawn and dark-ness, Mak - er of
1. flute and horn! Bless-ed be our God, Might-y Lord of all!
2. all who mourn. Praise to you, O God, Might-y Lord of all!
3. ev - 'ry seed. Praise to you, O God, Might-y Lord of all!
4. snow and rain. Praise to you, O God, Might-y Lord of all!
5. shin - ing star. Praise to you, O God, Might-y Lord of all!

AMERICA 745

1. My coun-try, 'tis of thee, Sweet land of lib - er - ty,
2. My na - tive coun - try, thee, Land of the no - ble free,
3. Let mu - sic swell the breeze, And ring from all the trees
4. Our fa - thers' God, to thee, Au - thor of lib - er - ty,

1. Of thee I sing; Land where my fa - thers died,
2. Thy name I love; I love thy rocks and rills,
3. Sweet free - dom's song; Let mor - tal tongues a - wake;
4. To thee we sing; Long may our land be bright

1. Land of the pil - grims' pride, From ev - 'ry
2. Thy woods and tem - pled hills; My heart with
3. Let all that breathe par - take; Let rocks their
4. With free - dom's ho - ly light; Pro - tect us

1. moun - tain - side Let free - dom ring!
2. rap - ture thrills, Like that a - bove.
3. si - lence break, The sound pro - long.
4. by thy might, Great God, our King.

Text: 66 4 666 4; Samuel F. Smith, 1808–1895.
Music: AMERICA; *Thesaurus Musicus*, 1744.

746 Eternal Father, Strong to Save

1. E - ter - nal Fa - ther, strong to save, Whose arm has bound the
2. O Christ, the Lord of hill and plain O'er which our traf - fic
3. O Spir - it, whom the Fa - ther sent To spread a - broad the
4. O Trin - i - ty of love and pow'r, Your chil - dren shield in

1. rest - less wave, Who bids the might - y o - cean deep Its
2. runs a - main By moun - tain pass or val - ley low; Where-
3. fir - ma - ment; O Wind of heav - en, by your might Save
4. dan - ger's hour; From rock and tem - pest, fire and foe, Pro -

1. own ap - point - ed lim - its keep: O hear us when we
2. ev - er, Lord, your loved ones go, Pro - tect them by your
3. all who dare the ea - gle's flight, And keep them by your
4. tect them where - so - e'er they go; And then shall rise with

1. raise our plea For those in per - il on the sea.
2. guard - ing hand From ev - 'ry per - il on the land.
3. watch - ful care From ev - 'ry per - il in the air.
4. voic - es free Glad praise from air and land and sea.

Text: 88 88 88; verses 1, 4, William Whiting, 1825–1878, alt.; verses 2, 3, Robert N. Spencer, 1877–1961, alt.
Music: MELITA; John B. Dykes, 1823–1876.

747 This Is My Song

1. This is my song, O God of all the na - tions,
2. My coun-try's skies are blu - er than the o - cean,
3. This is my prayer, O Lord of all earth's king-doms:
1. A song of peace for lands a - far and mine.
2. And sun-light beams on clo - ver - leaf and pine;
3. Thy king-dom come; on earth thy will be done.
1. This is my home, the coun-try where my heart is;
2. But oth - er lands have sun-light too, and clo - ver,
3. Let Christ be lift - ed up till all shall serve him,

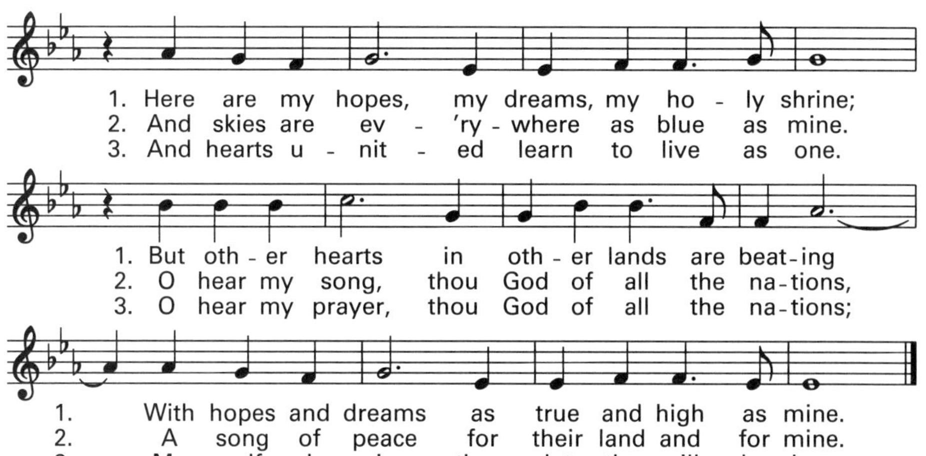
1. Here are my hopes, my dreams, my ho - ly shrine;
2. And skies are ev - 'ry - where as blue as mine.
3. And hearts u - nit - ed learn to live as one.
1. But oth - er hearts in oth - er lands are beat - ing
2. O hear my song, thou God of all the na - tions,
3. O hear my prayer, thou God of all the na - tions;
1. With hopes and dreams as true and high as mine.
2. A song of peace for their land and for mine.
3. My - self I give thee; let thy will be done.

Text: 11 10 11 10 11 10; verses 1, 2, Lloyd Stone; verse 3, Georgia Harkness, © 1964, Lorenz Corporation.

Music: FINLANDIA; Jean Sibelius, 1865–1957.

GOD OF OUR FATHERS 748

1. God of our fa - thers, whose al - might - y hand
2. Thy love di - vine hath led us in the past,
3. From war's a - larms, from dead - ly pes - ti - lence,
4. Re - fresh thy peo - ple on their toil - some way,

1. Leads forth in beau - ty all the star - ry band
2. In this free land by thee our lot is cast;
3. Be thy strong arm our ev - er sure de - fense;
4. Lead us from night to nev - er - end - ing day;

1. Of shin - ing worlds in splen - dor through the skies,
2. Be thou our rul - er, guard - ian, guide, and stay,
3. Thy true re - li - gion in our hearts in - crease,
4. Fill all our lives with love and grace di - vine,

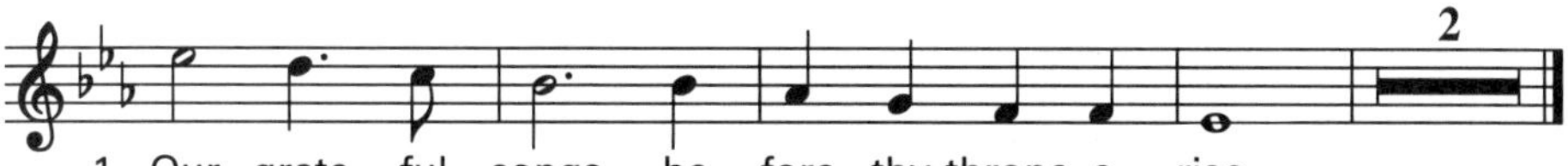

1. Our grate - ful songs be - fore thy throne a - rise.
2. Thy word our law, thy paths our cho - sen way.
3. Thy boun - teous good - ness nour - ish us in peace.
4. And glo - ry, laud, and praise be ev - er thine.

Text: 10 10 10 10; Daniel Crane Roberts, 1841–1907.
Music: NATIONAL HYMN; George William Warren, 1828–1902.

749 America the Beautiful

1. O beau - ti-ful for spa-cious skies, For am - ber waves of grain,
2. O beau - ti-ful for pil - grim feet, Whose stern, im-pas-sioned stress
3. O beau - ti-ful for he - roes proved In lib - er - at - ing strife,
4. O beau - ti-ful for pa - triot dream That sees be-yond the years

1. For pur - ple moun-tain maj - es - ties A - bove the fruit - ed plain!
2. A thor-ough-fare for free-dom beat A - cross the wil - der - ness!
3. Who more than self their coun-try loved, And mer - cy more than life!
4. Thine al - a - bas - ter cit - ies gleam, Un-dimmed by hu - man tears!

1. A - mer - i - ca! A - mer - i - ca! God shed his grace on thee,
2. A - mer - i - ca! A - mer - i - ca! God mend thine ev - 'ry flaw,
3. A - mer - i - ca! A - mer - i - ca! May God thy gold re - fine,
4. A - mer - i - ca! A - mer - i - ca! God shed his grace on thee,

1. And crown thy good with broth - er-hood From sea to shin-ing sea.
2. Con - firm thy soul in self - con-trol, Thy lib - er - ty in law.
3. Till all suc-cess be no - ble-ness, And ev - 'ry gain di - vine.
4. And crown thy good with broth - er-hood From sea to shin-ing sea.

Text: CMD; Katherine L. Bates, 1859–1929.
Music: MATERNA; Samuel A. Ward, 1848–1903.

750 Soon and Very Soon

1. Soon and ver - y soon, We are going to see the King;
2. No more cry - ing there, We are going to see the King;
3. No more dy - ing there, We are going to see the King;
1. Soon and ver - y soon, We are going to see the King;
2. No more cry - ing there, We are going to see the King;
3. No more dy - ing there, We are going to see the King;

1. Soon and ver - y soon, We are going to see the King;
2. No more cry - ing there, We are going to see the King;
3. No more dy - ing there, We are going to see the King;
Hal - le -
1-3. lu - jah! Hal - le - lu - jah! We're going to see the King.

Text: 57 57 57 86; Andraé Crouch, 1945–2015.
Music: SOON AND VERY SOON; Andraé Crouch; adapt. by William F. Smith, b. 1941.

751 Let the Heavens Be Glad

Refrain

Let the heav - ens be glad and the earth re - joice, the
sea and what fills it re - sound. Let the plains and the fields be
filled with joy, for the Lord comes to rule the land.

Verses

1. Then shall the trees, the trees of the for - est ex - ult
2. The Lord shall rule with jus - tice for all of the earth.

1. be - fore the Lord, who comes now to rule the earth.
2. In con - stant love he comes now to rule the earth.

to Refrain

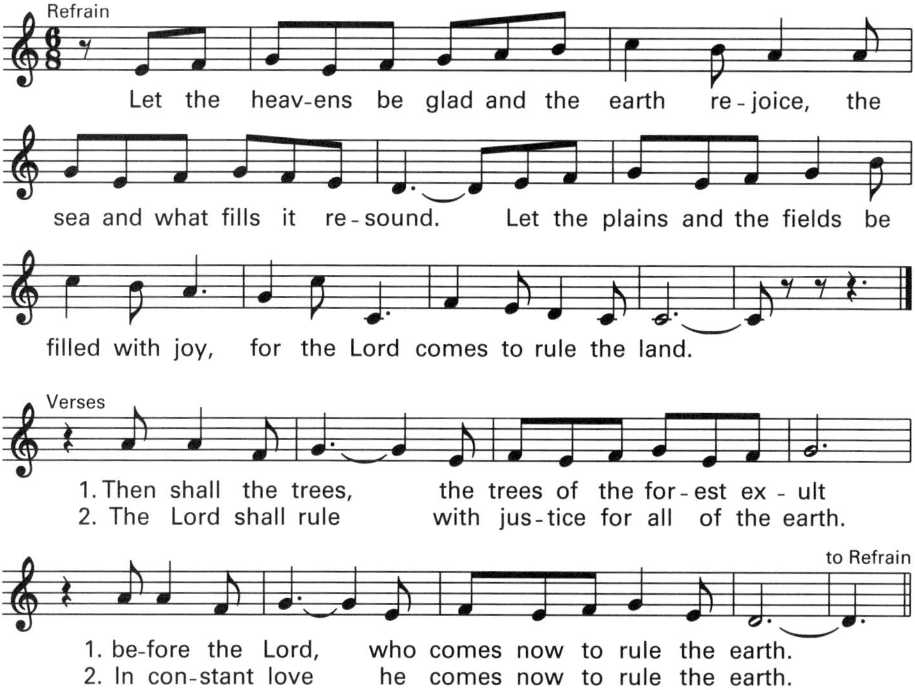

Text: Based on Psalm 96:11–13; Dan Feiten, b. 1953.
Music: Dan Feiten.

752 In the Day of the Lord

Refrain

In the day of the Lord, the sun will shine like the dawn of e-ter - nal day. All cre-a-tion will rise to dance and sing the glo-ry of the Lord!

Verses

1. And on that day will jus - tice tri - umph, on that day will all be free: free from want, free from fear, free to live!
2. Then shall the na-tions throng to-geth - er to the moun-tain of the Lord: they shall walk in the light of the Lord!
3. And they shall beat their swords to plow-shares; there will be an end to war: one in peace, one in love, one in God!
4. For Is - ra - el shall be de - liv - ered, and the des - ert lands will bloom. Say to all, "Do not fear. Here is your God!"
5. And on that day of Christ in glo - ry, God will wipe a - way our tears, and the dead shall rise up from their graves!
6. O give us eyes to see your glo - ry, give us hearts to un - der - stand. Let our ears hear your voice 'til you come!

to Refrain

Text: Based on Isaiah 2, 25, 41; M.D. Ridge.
Music: M.D. Ridge.

753 Jesus Died upon the Cross

Je - sus died up - on the cross, Christ a - rose
from the dead; and just as sure as the sun will
rise, Je-sus Christ, my Lord and Sav-ior, will come a-gain!

WORTHY IS THE LAMB

Refrain
Wor-thy is the Lamb that was slain to re - ceive hon-or and glo - ry. Wor-thy are the ones who be - lieve to re - ceive the good-ness of God.
Verses
1. Wor - thy are you, O Pas - chal Lamb.
2. Wor - thy are you, O Bread of Life. Sal -
3. Wor - thy are you, O Ris - en Christ.
1. Wis - dom and strength be - long now to you. You
2. va - tion and joy be - long now to us. By
3. Won - ders and signs, re - veal - ing your might. Your
1. laid down your life and died up-on the cross: we've be -
2. con - quer - ing death and ris - ing to new life, we've be -
3. pow - er and glo - ry shine up-on our lives: we've be -
2 to Refrain
1. come a peo - ple of hope.
2. come a peo - ple of praise.
3. come your light for the world.

Text: Based on Revelation 5:9–14; Ricky Manalo, CSP, b. 1965.
Music: Ricky Manalo, CSP.

755 Mine Eyes Have Seen the Glory

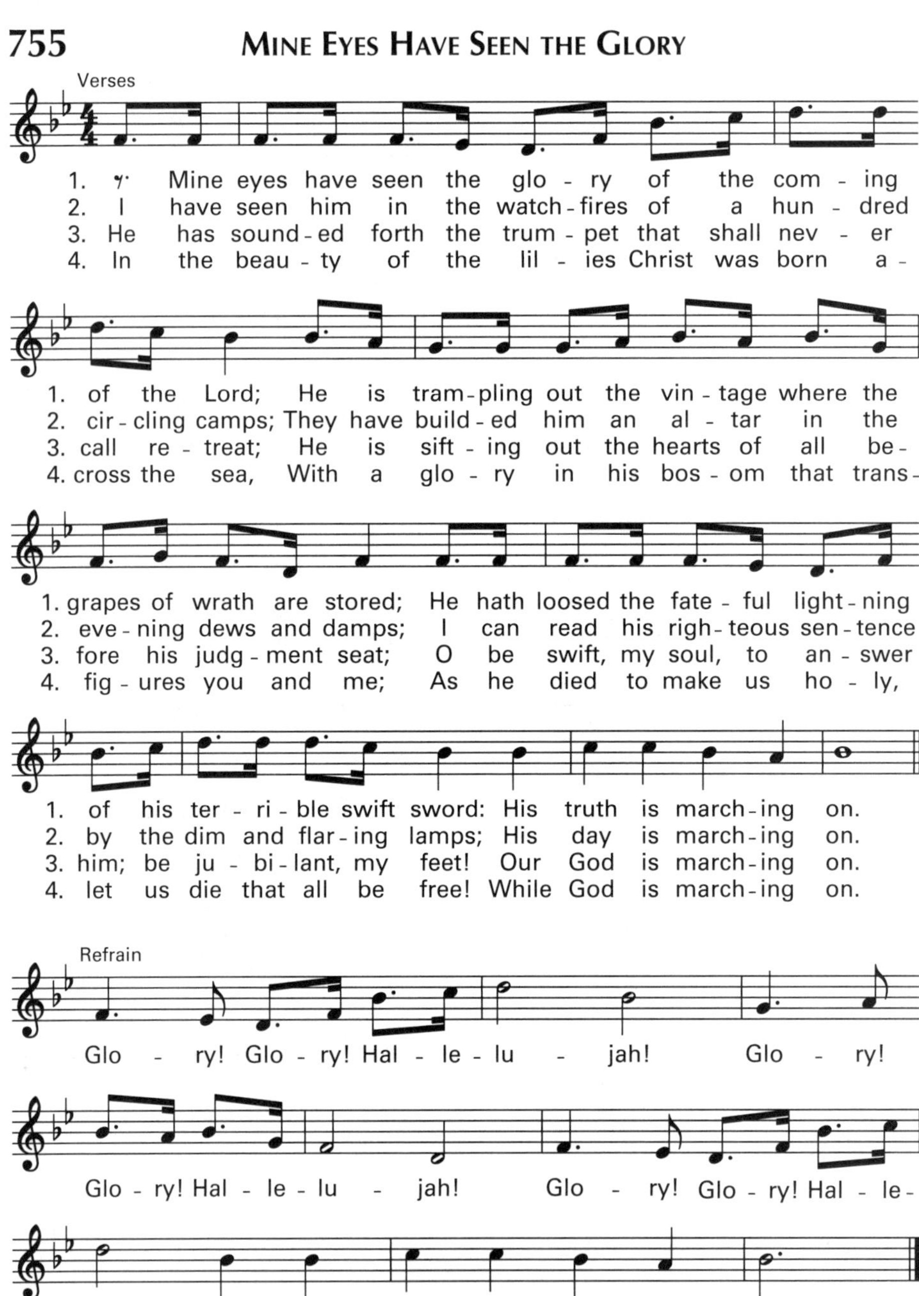
Verses
1. Mine eyes have seen the glo - ry of the com - ing
2. I have seen him in the watch - fires of a hun - dred
3. He has sound - ed forth the trum - pet that shall nev - er
4. In the beau - ty of the lil - ies Christ was born a -
1. of the Lord; He is tram - pling out the vin - tage where the
2. cir - cling camps; They have build - ed him an al - tar in the
3. call re - treat; He is sift - ing out the hearts of all be -
4. cross the sea, With a glo - ry in his bos - om that trans -
1. grapes of wrath are stored; He hath loosed the fate - ful light - ning
2. eve - ning dews and damps; I can read his righ - teous sen - tence
3. fore his judg - ment seat; O be swift, my soul, to an - swer
4. fig - ures you and me; As he died to make us ho - ly,
1. of his ter - ri - ble swift sword: His truth is march - ing on.
2. by the dim and flar - ing lamps; His day is march - ing on.
3. him; be ju - bi - lant, my feet! Our God is march - ing on.
4. let us die that all be free! While God is march - ing on.
Refrain
Glo - ry! Glo - ry! Hal - le - lu - jah! Glo - ry!
Glo - ry! Hal - le - lu - jah! Glo - ry! Glo - ry! Hal - le -
lu - jah! His truth is march - ing on.

Text: 15 15 15 6 with refrain; Julia W. Howe, 1819–1910, alt.
Music: BATTLE HYMN OF THE REPUBLIC; trad. American melody; attr. to William Steffe, ca. 1830–1911.

A Rightful Place

756

Refrain
Let us live our lives so that all might see that our hearts are rest - less till they rest in thee. Let us build your king - dom in truth and grace so that all might know they have a right-ful place.
Verses
1. Beau - ty ev - er an - cient and new,
2. To gath - er in your pres-ence we came
1. break - ing through our deaf - ness so we hear you.
2. to be one in spir - it, in truth and name;
1. Shat - ter - ing the dark-ness of night, a new dawn is ris -
2. strength-ened by the bod - y of Christ, tak - ing up the
to Refrain
1. - ing to bring your light to all the world.
2. call now to share your light with all the world.

Text: Refrain and Verse 1 based on *Confessions*, St. Augustine of Hippo, ca. 400; Steve Angrisano, b. 1965.
Music: Steve Angrisano.

757 Beatitudes

Verses
1. Blest are you, the poor who trust the Fa - ther
2. Blest are you, the low - ly ones, who know your
3. Blest are those whose mer - cy shows the Fa - ther's
4. Blest are you who work for peace a - mong the
1. with your lives,
2. need to share,
3. love to all,
4. Fa - ther's own,
For with - in your heart is born the
1-4. King - dom of the Lord.
1. Blest are you, the sor - row - ing,
2. Blest are you whose search - ing souls
3. Blest are you, the pure in heart,
4. Blest are you who suf - fer hate
1. who know your Fa - ther wise,
2. will draw you to God's care,
3. who live the Fa - ther's call,
4. to pre - pare the day to come,
For with - in your heart
1-4. is born the King - dom of the Lord.
1, 3
2, 4
Refrain
Let your light shine for all the world to see: the bright - ness of
your life with - in, the peace that sets you free. Let your
light shine to fill your nights and days; all will see the deeds

1
to Verse 3
3
Final
you do and give your Fa - ther praise.

I Will Not Die 758

Verses

1. I will not die be-fore I've lived to see that land;
2. I will not rest un-til your dawn is in my eyes;
3. And I will breathe _ in that might-y wind of jus-tice;
4. You will stand up ___ for the poor and the need - y;

1. firm as the earth, your own prom-ise.
2. that frag-ile light, new like morn-ing.
3. I'll know my name and rise up sing-ing.
4. you'll break the chains that bind your peo-ple.

1. I'll not let go un-til I've held it in my hand;
2. I will not sleep be-fore I've wak-ened to that sun-rise;
3. And I will call un-til my words bring on the thun-der;
4. For you are home ___ for the lost ____ and the des-p'rate;

Fine

1. that word of hope, and gen - tle laugh-ter. ___ (to Vs. 2)
2. and all the world knows your glo - ry. ___ (to Refrain)
3. washed in that rain, then I'll know you. ___ (to Vs. 4)
4. your strong right hand goes be - fore us. ___ (to Refrain)

Refrain

For your right hand has de-liv-ered us from death; you have re-gard-ed our tears, you who are good-ness and grace.

1st time: to Vs. 3
2nd time: to Vs. 1 & *Fine*

759 Blest Are They

Verses 1-3
1. Blest are they, the poor in spir - it, theirs is the
2. Blest are they, the low - ly ones, they shall in -
3. Blest are they ___ who show mer - cy, mer - cy
1. king - dom of God. Blest are they, ___
2. her - it the earth. Blest are they who
3. shall be theirs. Blest are they, the
1. full ___ of sor - row, they shall be ___ con - soled.
2. hun - ger and thirst, they shall have ___ their fill.
3. pure ___ of heart, they ___ shall see God!
Refrain
Re - joice and be glad! Bless - ed are you, ho - ly are you! Re-
joice and be glad! Yours is the king - dom of God!
(to Verses 2-5)
Verses 4, 5
4. Blest are they ___ who seek peace; they are the
5. Blest are you who suf - fer hate, all be -
4. chil - dren of God. ___ Blest ___ are they who
5. cause of me. ___ Re - joice and be glad, ___
to Refrain
4. suf - fer in faith, the glo - ry of God is theirs.
5. yours is the king - dom; shine for all to see.

Text: Based on Matthew 5:3–12; David Haas, b. 1957.
Music: David Haas.

LEAD ME, LORD

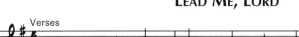

Verses

1. Bless - ed are the poor in spir - it, long - ing for their Lord, for God's com - ing king - dom shall be theirs.
2. Bless - ed are the mer - ci - ful, for mer - cy shall be theirs, and the pure in heart shall see their God.
3. Blest are they who through their life-times sow the seeds of peace, all will call them chil - dren of the Lord.

1. Bless - ed are the sor - row - ing, for they shall be con - soled, and the meek shall come to rule the world.
2. Blest are they whose hun - ger on - ly ho - li - ness can fill, for I say they shall be sat - is - fied.
3. Blest are you, though per - se - cu - ted in your ho - ly life, for in heav - en, great is your re - ward.

Refrain
Lead me, Lord, lead me, Lord, by the light of truth to
seek and to find the nar-row way. Be my way;
be my truth; be my life, my Lord, and lead me, Lord, to -
1-2
to Verses
Final
day. day. And lead me, Lord, to - day.

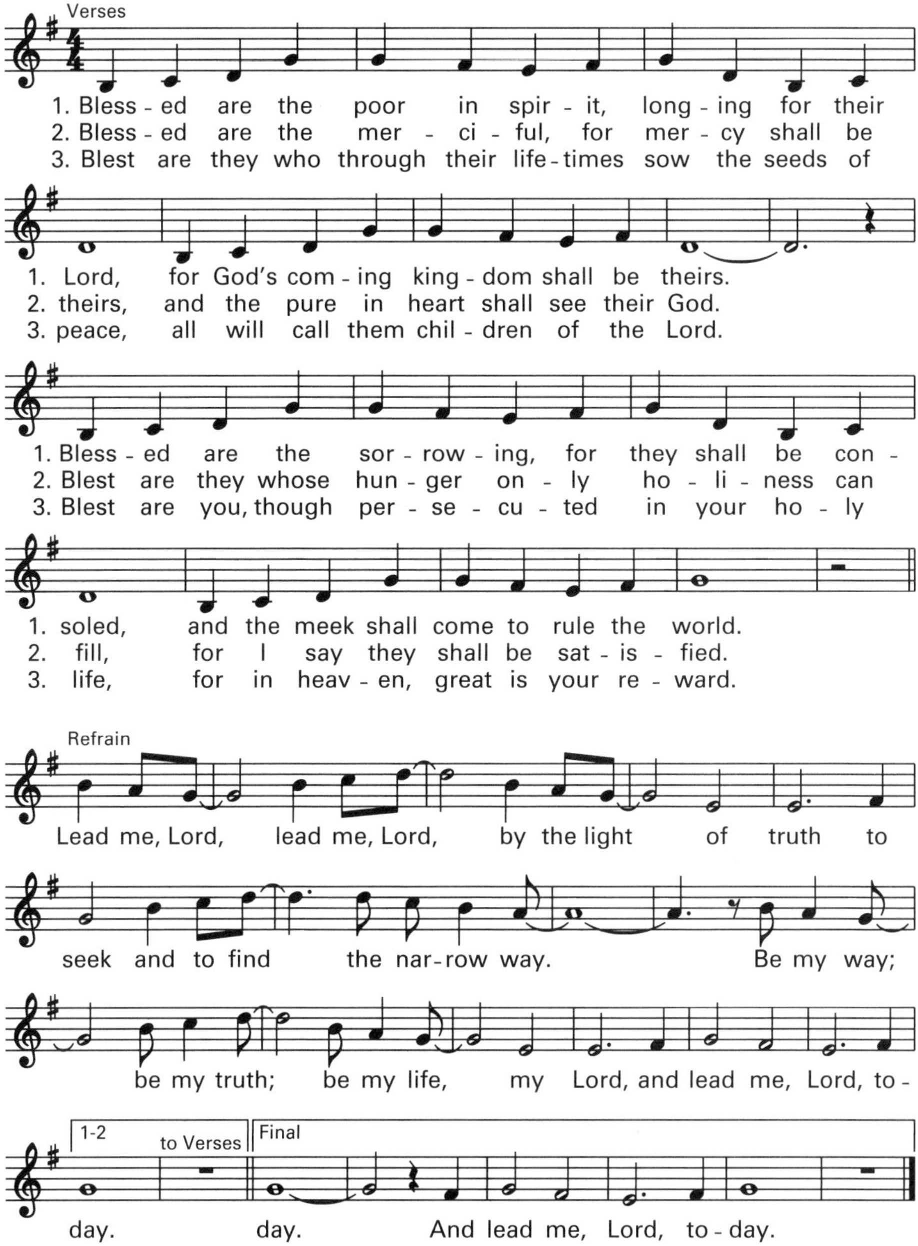

Text: Based on Matthew 5:3–12; 7:7, 13; John 14:6; John D. Becker, b. 1953.
Music: John D. Becker.

761 FIND US READY

Refrain
Find us read-y, Lord, not stand-ing still.
Find us work-ing and lov-ing and do-ing your will. Find us read-y, Lord, faith-ful in love, build-ing the king-dom that's here and a-bove, build-ing the king-dom of mer-cy and love.
Verses
1. We must wait for the Lord for we know not the time. So here and to-day we gath-er and pray, dis-cov-er-ing love in our midst.
2. We must make straight the path, God's love re-vealed. With sin cast a-side, God's mer-cy a-live, fear not for here is your God.
3. Lift-ing up those bowed down, we pre-pare for our God. Re-joice in the Lord, for hope has been born in hearts where our God finds a home.
to Refrain

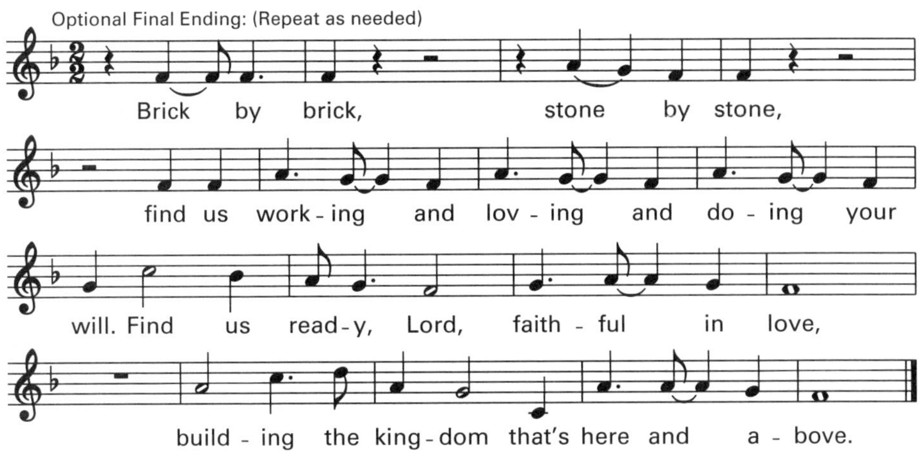
Optional Final Ending: (Repeat as needed)
Brick by brick, stone by stone,
find us work - ing and lov - ing and do - ing your
will. Find us read - y, Lord, faith - ful in love,
build - ing the king - dom that's here and a - bove.

There Is a River 762

Refrain

There is a riv - er, a great flow - ing riv - er, and it makes glad the cit - y of God. Broad are its wa - ters, and deep are its voic - es. Its songs are of peace in the house of the Lord.

Verses

1. What shall we fear, though na - tions may trem - ble, and _ dark - ness may rise _ to trou - ble the sun? The king - dom is near, the rem - nants as - sem - ble, and _ lift up their eyes _ to a day just be - gun.

2. What shall we fear? The bow shall be bro - ken, the spear shall be shat - tered, _ and war - ring shall cease. The king - dom is near, the word has been spo - ken, and though we lie bat - tered, _ we are called to the feast.

to Refrain

763 THY KINGDOM COME

Verses
Cantor
All
1. O you who taught the mud to dream,
2. Like seed and rain your word goes out,
3. From hearts of stone, O Lord, you drew,
4. And ev - ery heart that's sick with sin,
5. And when the skies you break at last,
O
1-5. Lord, thy king - dom come.
Cantor
1. And make the
2. In gar - dens
3. The sword of
4. The Heal - er
5. Your king - dom
All
1. world with life to teem,
2. of the heart to sprout.
3. sin that ran them through.
4. King has come to win.
5. come to take at last.
O Lord, thy king - dom
Cantor
All
1-5. come.
1. Did spin like tops the stars in space,
2. The blooms that grow there shall re - main,
3. And won your King - ship with that sword,
4. The wound - ed spir - it he shall dress,
5. Then shall there be a joy - ful noise:
O
1-5. Lord, thy king - dom come;
Cantor
1. Did guide their paths with
2. Their scent the sign of your
3. That cut you down, O
4. With balms of love and
5. Your king - dom praise you
All
1. age - less grace.
2. ho - ly reign.
3. pre - cious Lord.
4. ten - der - ness.
5. with one voice.
O Lord, thy king - dom come.

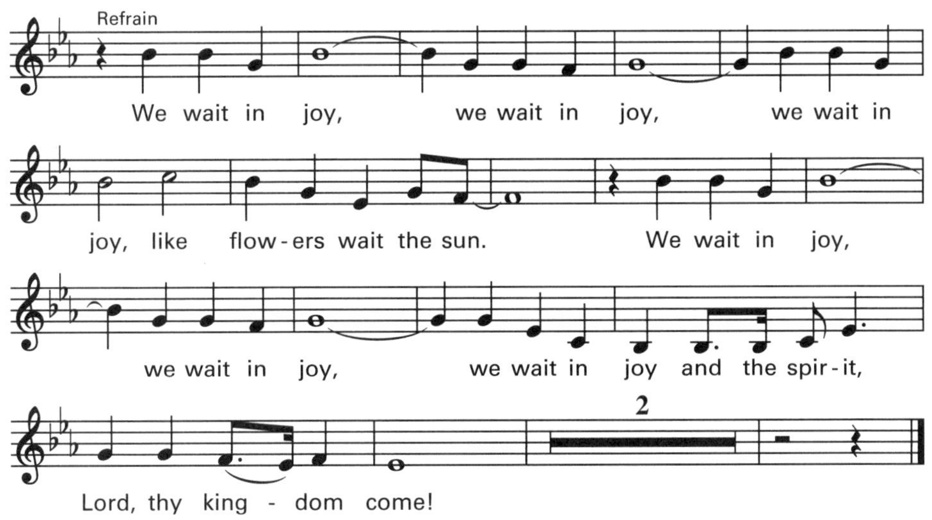
Refrain
We wait in joy, we wait in joy, we wait in
joy, like flow-ers wait the sun. We wait in joy,
we wait in joy, we wait in joy and the spir-it,
2
Lord, thy king - dom come!

Text and music: Rory Cooney, b. 1952,

If God Is for Us 764

1. If God is for us, who can be a-gainst us?
2. If God is for us, who then can con-demn us?
3. If God is for us, who can stand a-gainst us?

1. If God is on our side, what can we be de-
2. Sure-ly not Christ our Lord, who a-rose from the
3. If Christ did set us free, who can make us a

1. nied? In all these things we are more than
2. dead. There's noth-ing in this world that can
3. slave? Can pain or suf - fer-ing keep us

1. con-quer-ors in Je - sus.
2. sep-a-rate us from his love.
3. from the love of Je - sus?

If God is

1-3. on our side, what can we be de-nied?

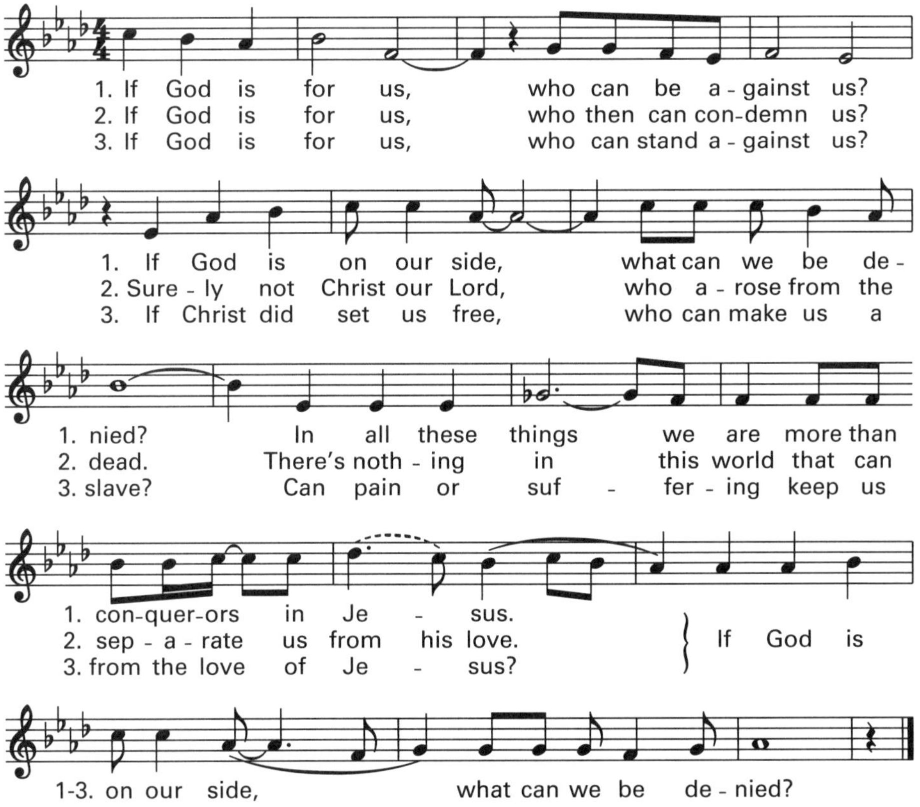

Text: Based on Romans 8:31–39; Grayson Warren Brown, b. 1948.
Music: Grayson Warren Brown.
Text and music

765 LIKE A SHEPHERD

Refrain
Like a shep-herd he feeds his flock and gath-ers the lambs in his arms, hold-ing them care-ful-ly close to his heart,
1-3 to Verses
Final
lead-ing them home. home, lead-ing them home.
Verses 1, 2
1. Say to the cit-ies of Ju - dah: Pre-pare the way of the Lord. Go to the moun-tain-top, lift your voice: Je - ru - sa - lem, here is your God.
2. I my - self will shep-herd them, for oth-ers have led them a - stray. The lost I will res - cue and heal their wounds and pas-ture them, giv-ing them rest.
to Refrain
Verse 3
3. Come un-to me if you are heav-i-ly bur-dened, and take my yoke up-on your shoul-ders. I will give you rest.
to Refrain

Text: Based on Isaiah 40:9ff; Ezekiel 34:11ff; Matthew 11:28ff; Bob Dufford, SJ, b. 1943.
Music: Bob Dufford, SJ.

Your Grace Is Enough

766

Verses
1. Great is your faith - ful-ness, O God;
2. Great is your love and jus-tice, God of Ja-cob;
1. you wres-tle with the sin-ner's rest - less heart.
2. you use the weak to lead the strong.
1. You lead us by still wa-ters in - to mer-cy,
2. You lead us in the song of your sal-va-tion,
1. and noth - ing can keep us a - part.
2. and all your peo - ple sing a - long.
1, 2. So re-mem-ber your peo-ple, re-mem-ber your chil-dren,
1, 2. re - mem - ber your prom - ise, O God.
Refrain
Your grace is e-nough, your grace is e-nough, your
grace is e-nough for me.

Text and music: Matt Maher, b. 1974, © 2003, 2008, Thankyou Music (PRS) (administered worldwide at CapitolCMGPublishing.com excluding Europe which is administered by Kingswaysongs) and Matt Maher. Published by Spirit & Song®, a division of OCP.

767 Isaiah 49

Verse 1

1. I will nev - er for - get you, my peo-ple; I have carved you on the palm of my hand. I will nev - er for - get you; I will not leave you or-phaned. I will nev - er for - get my own.

Verse 2

2. Does a moth-er for - get her ba-by? Or a wom-an the child with-in her womb? Yet e - ven if these for-get, yes, e - ven if these for-get, I will nev - er for - get my own.

(Repeat Vs 1)

Text: Based on Isaiah 49:15; Carey Landry, b. 1944.
Music: Carey Landry.

768 If God Is for Us

Refrain
If God is for us, who can be a-gainst, if the Spir - it of God has set us free?
If God is for us, who can be a-gainst, if the Spir - it of God has set us free?

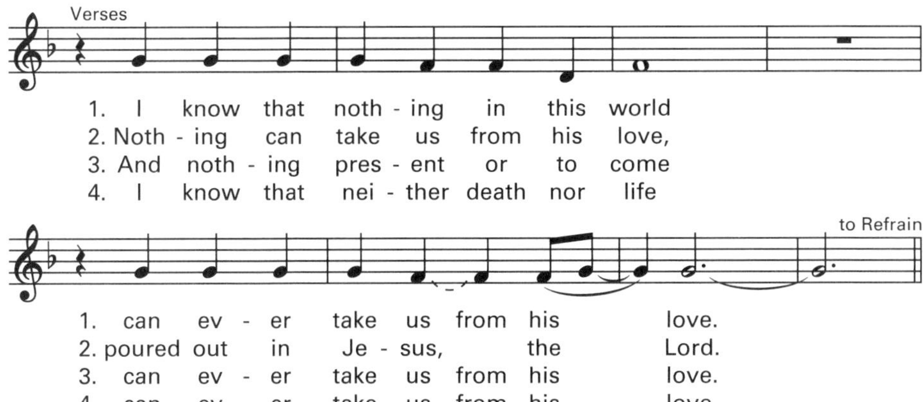
Verses
1. I know that noth - ing in this world
2. Noth - ing can take us from his love,
3. And noth - ing pres - ent or to come
4. I know that nei - ther death nor life
to Refrain
1. can ev - er take us from his love.
2. poured out in Je - sus, the Lord.
3. can ev - er take us from his love.
4. can ev - er take us from his love.

Text: Based on Romans 8; John Foley, SJ, b. 1939.
Music: John Foley, SJ.

Lord of Glory 769

Refrain

Leap-ing the moun-tains, bound-ing the hills, see how our God has come to meet us. His voice is lift-ed; his face is joy. Now is the sea-son to sing our song on high.

Verses 1, 2

1. Come, then, O Lord of glo - ry, show us your face. ___
2. He pas - tures his flock a - mong the wild ___ flow'rs ___ and

to Refrain

1. Speak, ___ for we know your words are life.
2. leads them to the moun-tain of his love.

Verse 3

3. All through the day, all through the night,

to Refrain

3. seek for the Lord and sing his love.

Text: Based on Song of Songs 2; Tim Manion, b. 1951.
Music: Tim Manion.

770 Come to the Water

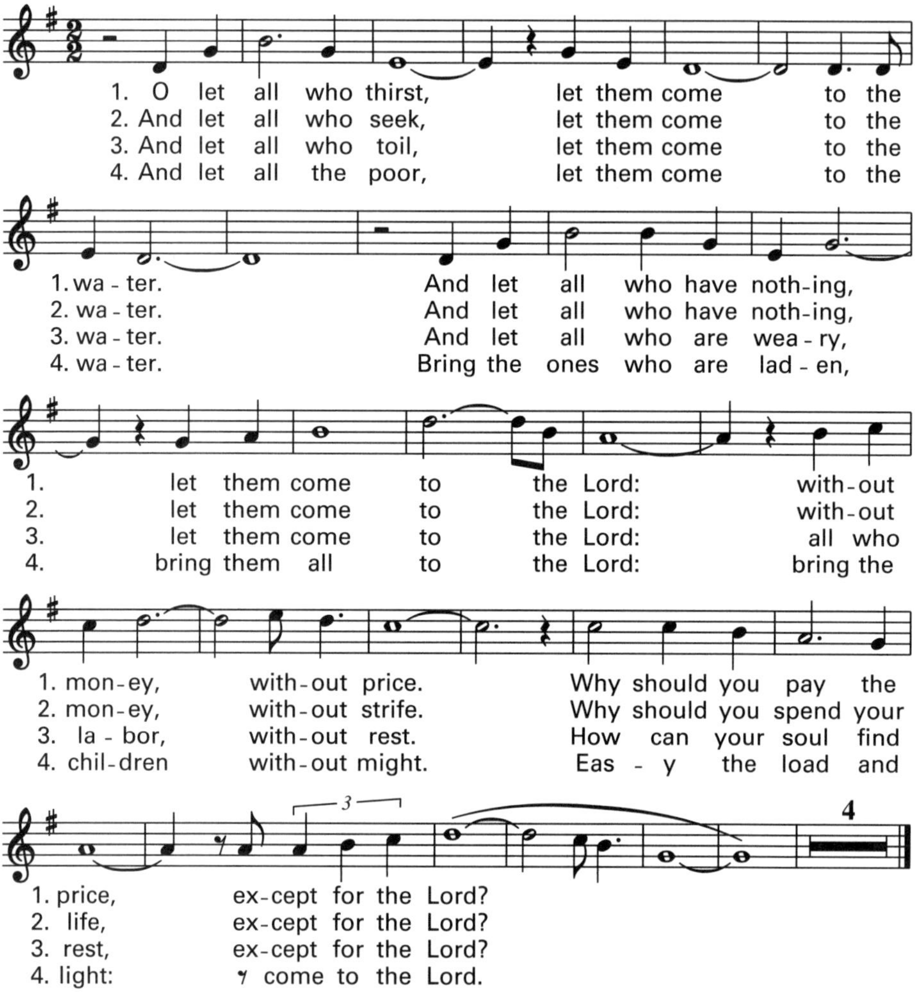

1. O let all who thirst, let them come to the water.
And let all who have nothing, let them come to the Lord:
without money, without price.
Why should you pay the price, except for the Lord?

2. And let all who seek, let them come to the water.
And let all who have nothing, let them come to the Lord:
without money, without strife.
Why should you spend your life, except for the Lord?

3. And let all who toil, let them come to the water.
And let all who are weary, let them come to the Lord:
all who labor, without rest.
How can your soul find rest, except for the Lord?

4. And let all the poor, let them come to the water.
Bring the ones who are laden, bring them all to the Lord:
bring the children without might.
Easy the load and light: come to the Lord.

Text: Based on Isaiah 55:1–2; Matthew 11:28–30; John Foley, S.J., b. 1939.
Music: John Foley, S.J.

771 Rain Down

Refrain
Rain down, rain down, rain down your
1
love on your peo - ple.
2
love, God of life.

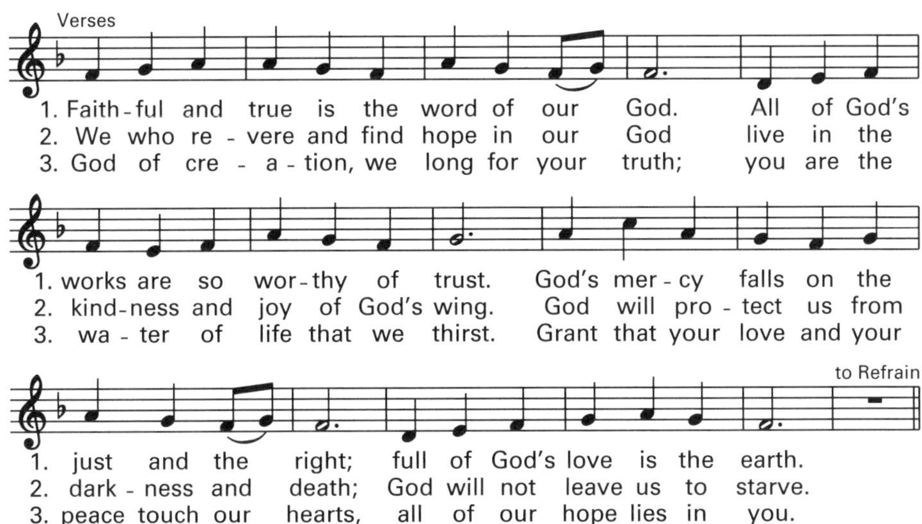
Verses
1. Faith-ful and true is the word of our God. All of God's
2. We who re-vere and find hope in our God live in the
3. God of cre-a-tion, we long for your truth; you are the
1. works are so wor-thy of trust. God's mer-cy falls on the
2. kind-ness and joy of God's wing. God will pro-tect us from
3. wa-ter of life that we thirst. Grant that your love and your
to Refrain
1. just and the right; full of God's love is the earth.
2. dark-ness and death; God will not leave us to starve.
3. peace touch our hearts, all of our hope lies in you.

Text: Based on Psalm 33; Jaime Cortez, b. 1963.
Music: Jaime Cortez.

I Have Loved You 772

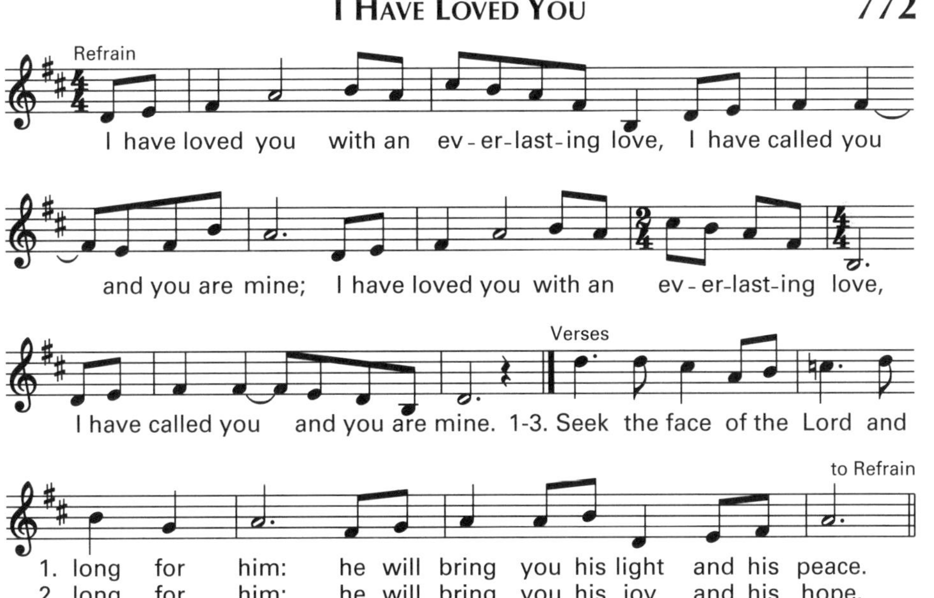
Refrain
I have loved you with an ev-er-last-ing love, I have called you
and you are mine; I have loved you with an ev-er-last-ing love,
I have called you and you are mine.
Verses
1-3. Seek the face of the Lord and
to Refrain
1. long for him: he will bring you his light and his peace.
2. long for him: he will bring you his joy and his hope.
3. long for him: he will bring you his care and his love.

Text: Based on Jeremiah 31:3; Psalm 24:3; Michael Joncas, b. 1951.
Music: Michael Joncas.

773 SHALL WE GATHER AT THE RIVER

Verses

1. Shall we gath - er at the riv - er, Where bright an - gel feet have
2. On the mar - gin of the riv - er, Wash - ing up its sil - ver
3. Ere we reach the shin - ing riv - er, Lay we ev - 'ry bur - den
4. Soon we'll reach the shin - ing riv - er, Soon our pil - grim - age will

1. trod, With its crys - tal tide for - ev - er, Flow - ing
2. spray, We will walk and wor - ship ev - er, All the
3. down; Grace our spir - its will de - liv - er, And pro -
4. cease; Soon our hap - py hearts will quiv - er With the

1. by the throne of God?
2. hap - py gold - en day.
3. vide a robe and crown.
4. mel - o - dy of peace.

Refrain

Yes, we'll gath - er at the riv - er, The beau - ti - ful, the beau - ti - ful riv - er, Gath - er with the saints at the riv - er That flows by the throne of God.

Text: 87 87 with refrain; Revelation 22:1–5; Robert Lowry, 1826–1899.
Music: HANSON PLACE; Robert Lowry.

774 SING WITH ALL THE SAINTS IN GLORY

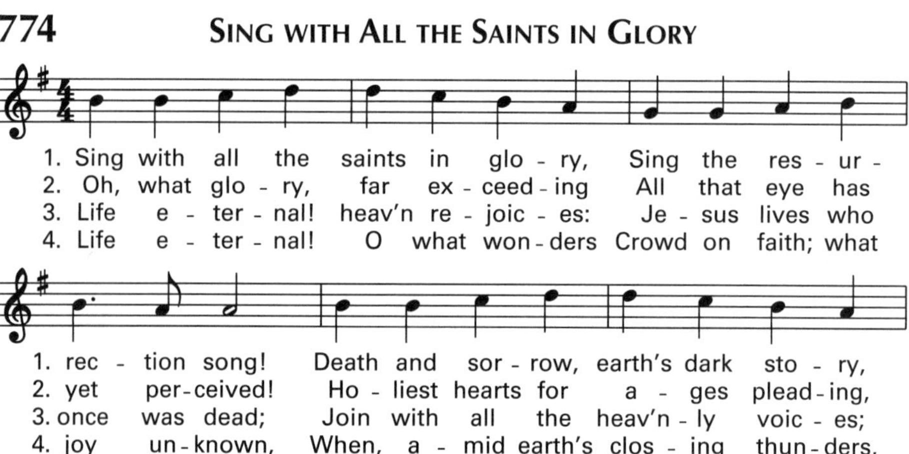
1. Sing with all the saints in glo - ry, Sing the res - ur -
2. Oh, what glo - ry, far ex - ceed - ing All that eye has
3. Life e - ter - nal! heav'n re - joic - es: Je - sus lives who
4. Life e - ter - nal! O what won - ders Crowd on faith; what
1. rec - tion song! Death and sor - row, earth's dark sto - ry,
2. yet per - ceived! Ho - liest hearts for a - ges plead - ing,
3. once was dead; Join with all the heav'n - ly voic - es;
4. joy un - known, When, a - mid earth's clos - ing thun - ders,

1. To the form - er days be - long. All a - round the
2. Nev - er that full joy con - ceived. God has prom - ised,
3. Child of God, lift up your head! Pa - tri - archs from
4. Saints shall stand be - fore the throne! Oh, to en - ter
1. clouds are break - ing, Soon the storms of time shall cease; In God's
2. Christ pre - pares it, There on high our wel - come waits; Ev - 'ry
3. dis - tant a - ges, Saints all long - ing for their heav'n, Proph - ets,
4. that bright por - tal, See that glow - ing fir - ma - ment, Know, with
1. like - ness, peo - ple wak - ing, Know the ev - er - last - ing peace.
2. hum - ble spir - it shares it, Christ has passed th'e - ter - nal gates.
3. psalm - ists, seers, and sa - ges, All a - wait the glo - ry giv'n.
4. you, O God im - mor - tal, Je - sus Christ whom you have sent!

Text: 87 87 D; 1 Corinthians 15:20; William J. Irons, 1812–1893; fr. *Psalms and Hymns*, 1873, alt.
Music: HYMN TO JOY; Ludwig van Beethoven, 1770–1827; adapt. by Edward Hodges, 1796–1867.

JERUSALEM, MY HAPPY HOME 775

1. Je - ru - sa - lem, my hap - py home, When shall I
2. O hap - py har - bor of the saints, O sweet and
3. Your gar - dens and your gal - lant walks Con - tin - ual -
4. There trees for - ev - er - more bear fruit And ev - er -
5. Je - ru - sa - lem, Je - ru - sa - lem, God grant that

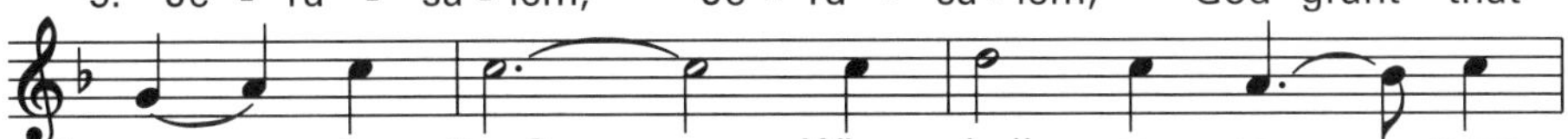

1. come to thee? When shall my sor - rows
2. pleas - ant soil! In you no sor - row
3. ly are green; There grow such sweet and
4. more do spring; There ev - er - more the
5. I may see Your end - less joy, and

1. have an end? Your joys when shall I see?
2. may be found, No grief, no care, no toil.
3. pleas - ant flow'rs As no - where else are seen.
4. an - gels sit And ev - er - more do sing!
5. of the same Par - tak - er ev - er be!

Text: CM; F. B. P., London, ca. 16th cent., alt.
Music: LAND OF REST; trad. American melody.

776 In God Alone

Verses

1. Then I saw a new earth, a new heav - en,
2. No more pain, no more death, no more weep - ing,
3. Then let all who are thirst - y find wa - ter,
4. For the world of the past is be - hind us,

1. and the first heav - en and earth dis - ap -
2. earth and heav - en are one on that
3. let it flow from the well of new
4. and the whole of cre - a - tion is

1. pear. No more war, no more hate,
2. day. For I saw all our tears
3. life. And let all who are wait -
4. new. And a feast is pre - pared

1. no more hun - ger, no more thirst,
2. form a riv - er, and I saw
3. - ing in dark - ness know that God
4. for all peo - ples, for God's prom -

1. no more loss, no more fear.
2. ev - ery tear wiped a - way.
3. will be - come their new light.
4. - ise is faith - ful and true.

Refrain

In God a - lone my hope. In God a - lone my strength. In God a - lone
my shel - ter be, my home, my heart, my lib - er - ty.

Text: Based on Revelation 7:16–17; 21:1–6; Bernadette Farrell, b. 1957.
Music: Bernadette Farrell.

Where My Father Lives 777

Refrain

Where my Fa - ther lives there is room for all; there is room for all where my Fa-ther lives, and a place for you will be wait-ing there. Come to me: I will bring you home.

Verses

1. I am the Way, the Truth and the Life. No one comes to the Fa - ther ex - cept through me.
2. Have faith in God; have faith ___ in me. Know wher - ev - er I am, you will al - so be.
3. If you love me and keep my com-mands, I will not leave you or - phan'd: I will re - turn.
4. Peace ___ I leave, my peace ___ I give. God's own Spir - it will guide you through - out your life.

to Refrain

Text and music: M.D. Ridge, © 2003, M.D. Ridge. Published by OCP.

Morning Has Broken 778

1. Morn - ing has bro - ken Like the first morn - ing, Black-bird has
2. Sweet the rain's new fall, Sun - lit from heav - en, Like the first
3. Mine is the sun - light! Mine is the morn - ing Born of the
1. spo - ken Like the first bird. Praise for the sing - ing! Praise for the
2. dew - fall On the first grass. Praise for the sweet - ness Of the wet
3. one light E - den saw play! Praise with e - la - tion, Praise ev - 'ry
1. morn - ing! Praise for them, spring - ing Fresh from the Word!
2. gar - den, Sprung in com - plete - ness Where his feet pass.
3. morn - ing, God's re - cre - a - tion Of the new day!

Text: 55 54 D; Eleanor Farjeon, 1881–1965, © 1957, Eleanor Farjeon.
Reprinted by permission of Harold Ober Assoc., Inc.
Music: BUNESSAN; trad. Gaelic melody.

779 THIS DAY GOD GIVES ME

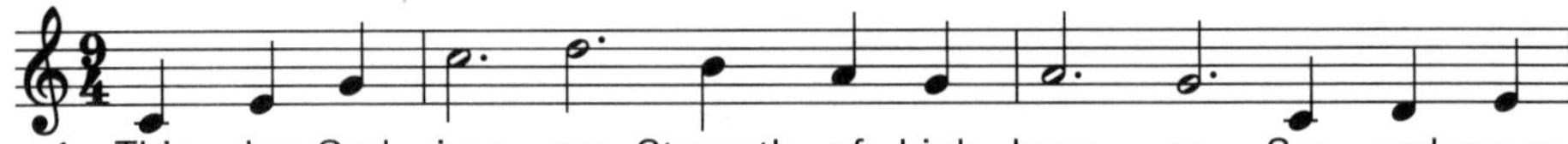

1. This day God gives me Strength of high heav - en, Sun and moon
2. This day God sends me Strength as my guard - ian, Might to up -
3. God's way is my way, God's shield is 'round me, God's host de -
4. Ris - ing I thank you, Might - y and Strong One, King of cre -

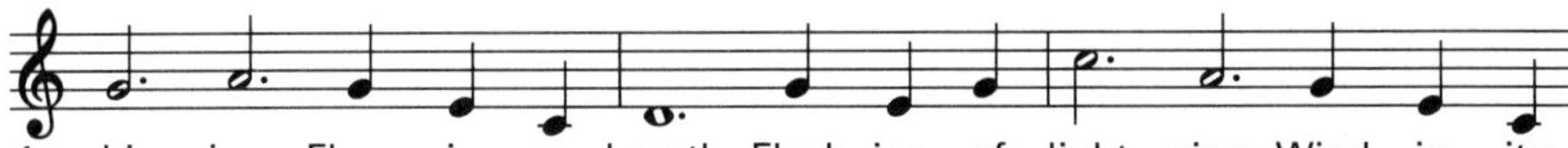

1. shin - ing, Flame in my hearth, Flash - ing of light - ning, Wind in its
2. hold me, Wis - dom as guide. Your eyes are watch - ful, Your ears are
3. fends me, Sav - ing from ill. An - gels of heav - en, Drive from me
4. a - tion, Giv - er of rest, Firm - ly con - fess - ing Three-ness of

1. swift - ness, Deeps of the o - cean, Firm - ness of earth.
2. lis - t'ning, Your lips are speak - ing, Friend at my side.
3. al - ways All that would harm me, Stand by me still.
4. Per - sons, One - ness of God - head, Trin - i - ty blest.

Text: 55 54 D; ascr. to St. Patrick, 372–466; adapt. by James Quinn, SJ, 1919–2010,
Music: BUNESSAN; trad. Gaelic melody.

780 ABIDE WITH ME

1. A - bide with me! fast falls the e - ven - tide;
2. I need your pres - ence ev - 'ry pass - ing hour:
3. I fear no foe with you at hand to bless;
4. Hold then your cross be - fore my clos - ing eyes;

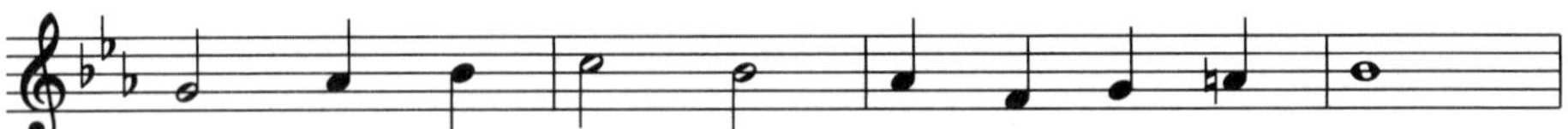

1. The dark - ness deep - ens; Lord, with me a - bide;
2. What but your grace can foil the tempt - er's pow'r?
3. Ills have no weight, and tears no bit - ter - ness.
4. Shine through the gloom and point me to the skies!

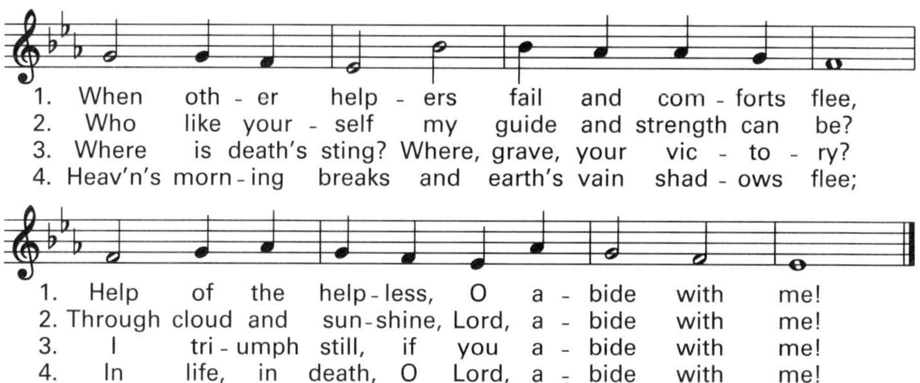
1. When oth - er help - ers fail and com - forts flee,
2. Who like your - self my guide and strength can be?
3. Where is death's sting? Where, grave, your vic - to - ry?
4. Heav'n's morn - ing breaks and earth's vain shad - ows flee;
1. Help of the help - less, O a - bide with me!
2. Through cloud and sun - shine, Lord, a - bide with me!
3. I tri - umph still, if you a - bide with me!
4. In life, in death, O Lord, a - bide with me!

Text: 10 10 10 10; Henry F. Lyte, 1793–1847, alt.; *Remains*, 1850, alt.
Music: EVENTIDE; William Henry Monk, 1823–1889; *Hymns Ancient and Modern*, 1861.

DAY IS DONE 781

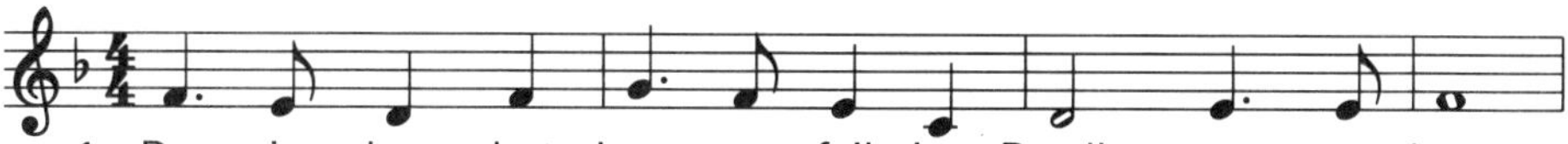

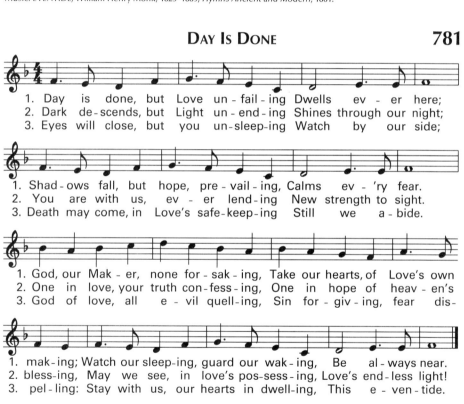

1. Day is done, but Love un - fail - ing Dwells ev - er here;
2. Dark de - scends, but Light un - end - ing Shines through our night;
3. Eyes will close, but you un - sleep - ing Watch by our side;

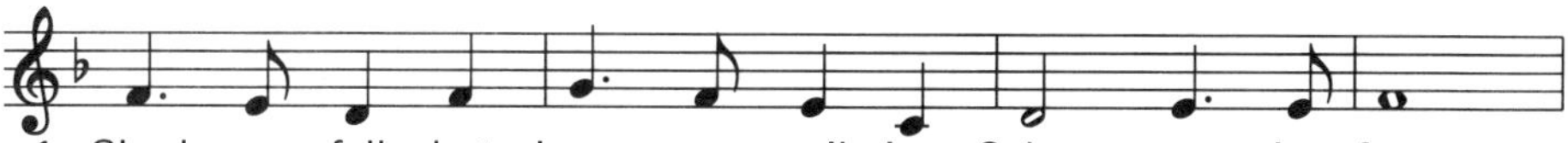

1. Shad - ows fall, but hope, pre - vail - ing, Calms ev - 'ry fear.
2. You are with us, ev - er lend - ing New strength to sight.
3. Death may come, in Love's safe - keep - ing Still we a - bide.

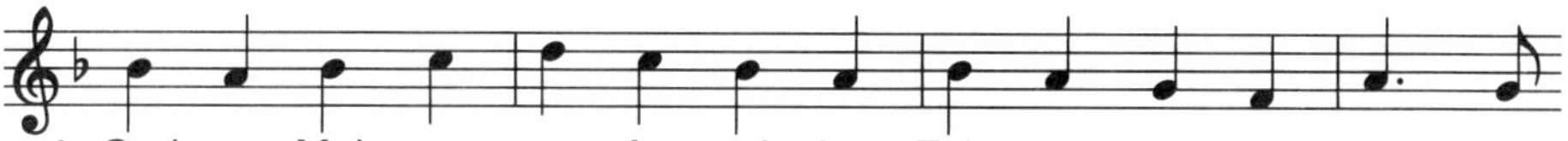

1. God, our Mak - er, none for - sak - ing, Take our hearts, of Love's own
2. One in love, your truth con - fess - ing, One in hope of heav - en's
3. God of love, all e - vil quell - ing, Sin for - giv - ing, fear dis-

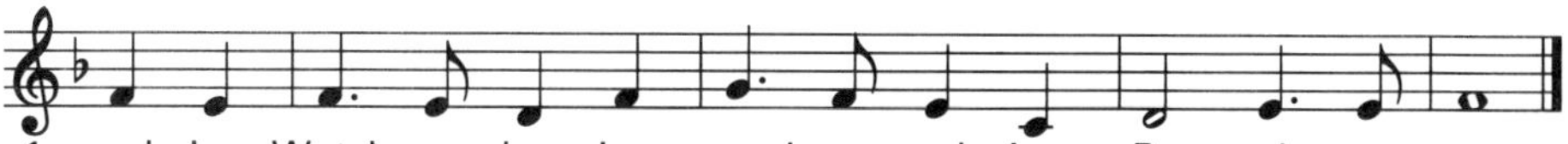

1. mak - ing; Watch our sleep - ing, guard our wak - ing, Be al - ways near.
2. bless - ing, May we see, in love's pos - sess - ing, Love's end - less light!
3. pel - ling: Stay with us, our hearts in dwell - ing, This e - ven - tide.

Text: 84 84 88 84; James Quinn, SJ, 1919–2010,
Music: AR HYD Y NOS; trad. Welsh melody.

782 DAYLIGHT'S ENDING

1. Now at the day - light's end - ing We turn, O
2. The gift you gave at day - light This night you
3. With watch - ful eyes, O Shep - herd, Look down up -
4. We praise you, heav'n - ly Fa - ther: From you all
1. God, to you: Send forth your Ho - ly
2. take a - way, To leave with - in our
3. on your sheep; Stretch forth your hands in
4. light de - scends; You give us heav - en's
1. Spir - it, Our Spir - it now re - new.
2. keep - ing The bless - ings of this day.
3. heal - ing And close our eyes in sleep.
4. glo - ry When life's brief day - light ends.
1. To you in ad - o - ra - tion, In thank - ful -
2. Take all its joy and sor - row, Take all that
3. Come down, O Ho - ly Spir - it, To be our
4. We praise you, Je - sus, Sav - ior, The light of
1. ness and praise, In faith and hope and
2. love can give, But all that needs for -
3. lov - ing Guest; Be near us, ho - ly
4. heav'n a - bove; We praise you, Ho - ly
1. glad - ness, Our lov - ing hearts we raise.
2. give - ness, Dear Fa - ther, now for - give.
3. an - gels, And guard us as we rest.
4. Spir - it, The liv - ing flame of love.

Text: James Quinn, SJ, 1919–2010,
Music: Steve Angrisano, b. 1965,

The publisher sincerely thanks the authors, composers and owners or holders of copyright who have so kindly granted permission to use their material. Every effort has been made to determine and acknowledge owners and administrators of each copyright. The publisher regrets any oversight that may have occurred and will gladly make proper acknowledgment in future printings after written notice has been received.

A.P. WATT, LTD.
A.P. Watt at United Agents
12-26 Lexington St.
London, W1F 0LE
United Kingdom
44 (0)20-3214-0973
Fax 44 (0)20-3214-0801
www.unitedagents.co.uk

ALFRED PUBLISHING CO., INC.
PO Box 10003
Van Nuys, CA 91410-0003
(818) 891-5999
Fax (818) 891-2369
www.alfred.com

AUGSBURG FORTRESS
510 Marquette Ave., Suite 800
PO Box 1209
Minneapolis, MN 55440-1209
(800) 328-4648
Fax (800) 722-7766

THE BENEDICTINE FOUNDATION OF THE STATE OF VERMONT, INC.
58 Priory Hill Rd.
Weston, VT 05161-6400

CAPITOL CMG PUBLISHING
  Birdwing Music
  Blue Raft Music
  Bud John Songs, Inc.
  CCCM Music
  Crouch Music
  Meaux Jeaux Music
  Meaux Mercy
  River Oaks Music Company
  Thankyou Music
  The Stuart Hine Trust
  Tunes From The Basement
  Universal Music Group-
    Brentwood Benson Music
    Publishing, Inc.
101 Winners Circle North
Brentwood, TN 37027-5352
(615) 371-4300
www.capitolchristianmusicgroup.com

CELEBRATION
c/o The Community of
Celebration Licensing
PO Box 309
Aliquippa, PA 15001-0309
(724) 375-1510
Fax (724) 375-1138

CHAPPELL & CO., INC.
c/o Alfred Publishing Co., Inc.

CHURCH PUBLISHING, INC.
  The Church Pension Fund
19 East 34th St.
New York, NY 10016-4304
(800) 223-6629
www.churchpublishing.org

COMISIÓN EPISCOPAL ESPAÑOLA DE LITURGIA
Añastro, 1
28033 Madrid,
Spain

CONFRATERNITY OF CHRISTIAN DOCTRINE, INC. (CCD)
3211 4th St. NE
Washington, DC 20017-1104

CONTINUUM INTERNATIONAL PUBLISHING GROUP, A BLOOMSBURY COMPANY
  Burn & Oates, Ltd.
Bloomsbury Publishing PLC
50 Bedford Square
London, WC1B 3DP
United Kingdom
011-44-(0)207-631-5657
Fax 011-44-(0)207-631-5651
www.bloomsbury.com

DAMEAN MUSIC
5329 Dijon Dr., Ste. 103
Baton Rouge, LA 70808-4378

E. C. SCHIRMER MUSIC CO.
c/o ECS Publishing
1727 Larkin Williams Rd.
Fenton, MO 63026-2024
(636) 305-0100
Fax (636) 305-0121
www.ecspublishing.com

G. SCHIRMER, INC.
  J. Curwen & Sons, Ltd.
c/o Music Sales Corporation
Kevin McGee, Mechanical/
Print Licensing
1247 6th St.
Santa Monica, CA 90401-1601
(310) 393-9900
Fax (310) 393-9925
www.musicsalesfilmtv.us

GIA PUBLICATIONS, INC. (USA)
  Ateliers et Presses de Taizé
    (France)
  Conception Abbey
  The Iona Community
7404 S. Mason Ave.
Chicago, IL 60638-6230
(800) 442-1358
Fax (708) 496-3828
www.giamusic.com

HAL LEONARD CORPORATION
  Centergetic Music
  The Willis Music Company
7777 W. Bluemound Rd.
Milwaukee, WI 53213
(414) 774-3630
Fax (414) 774-3259

HAROLD OBER ASSOC., INC.
425 Madison Ave.
New York, NY 10017
(212) 759-8600
Fax (212) 759-9428

HOPE PUBLISHING CO.
Stainer & Bell, Ltd.
The Hymn Society
The Jubilate Group
380 S. Main Place
Carol Stream, IL 60188-2448
(800) 323-1049
Fax (630) 665-2552

INTERNATIONAL COMMISSION ON ENGLISH IN THE LITURGY CORPORATION (ICEL)
1100 Connecticut Ave. NW, Ste. 710
Washington, DC 20036-4101
(202) 347-0800 Ext. 2
Fax (202) 347-1839
www.icelweb.org

INTERNATIONAL LITURGY PUBLICATIONS
PO Box 50476
Nashville, TN 37205-0476
(888) 898-SONG
www.ILPmusic.org

JAN-LEE MUSIC
PO Box 1210
Penn Valley, CA 95946-1210
(800) 211-8454

THE LITURGICAL PRESS
St. John's Abbey
PO Box 7500
Collegeville, MN 56321-7500
(800) 858-5450

LORENZ CORPORATION
F.E.L. Church Publications, Ltd.
PO Box 802
501 E. 3rd St.
Dayton, OH 45401-0802
(800) 444-1144
Fax (513) 223-2042

MRS. IRENE C. MUELLER
Melissa Craig
5044 Blue Meadow
Cincinnati, OH 45251-2707

MUSIC SERVICES, INC.
Vineyard Songs
5409 Maryland Way, Ste. 200
Brentwood, TN 37027-5042
(615) 371-1320
Fax (615) 371-1351

OXFORD UNIVERSITY PRESS
Attn: Simon Wright
Great Clarendon St.
Oxford, OX2 6DP
United Kingdom
011-44-1865-556-767
Fax 011-44-1865-556-646

ROLAND F. PALMER SSJE
c/o Msgr. Peter D. Wilkinson
25 Government Unit 209
Victoria, BC V8V 2K4
Canada

THE PILGRIM PRESS
700 Prospect Ave.
Cleveland, OH 44115-1100
(216) 736-3764
Fax (216) 736-2207
www.pilgrimpress.com

RAVEN MUSIC
c/o Ron Ellis
7866 Greenlake Dr. N #1
Seattle, WA 98103
(206) 367-0736

ROSALIND RUSBRIDGE
9 Springfield House
Cotham Rd.
Bristol, BS6 6DQ
United Kingdom

SHAWNEE PRESS, INC.
c/o Hal Leonard Corporation

DENNIS C. SMOLARSKI, SJ
Jesuit Community
Santa Clara University
Santa Clara, CA 95053

SOCIETY OF THE SACRED HEART
Estate of Anne Carter
4120 Forest Park Ave.
Saint Louis, MO 63108-2809
(314) 652-1500
Fax (314) 534-6800

WILLIAM G. STOREY
c/o Philip Schatz, Erasmus Books
1027 E. Wayne St.
South Bend, IN 46617-3025

UNITED STATES CONFERENCE OF CATHOLIC BISHOPS
The National Catholic Welfare Conference
Permissions Department,
USCCB Publishing
3211 4th St. NE
Washington, DC 20017-1994
(202) 541-3098
Fax (202) 541-3089

VERNACULAR HYMNS PUBLISHING CO.
PO Box 2304
Bakersfield, CA 93303-2304

WARNER-TAMERLANE PUBLISHING CORP.
c/o Alfred Publishing Co., Inc.

WORD MUSIC GROUP, LLC
c/o Opryland Music Group
PO Box 128469
Nashville, TN 37212-8469
(215) 587-3696
Fax (215) 587-3561

WORLD LIBRARY PUBLICATIONS
3708 River Rd., Ste. 400
Franklin Park, IL 60131-2158
(800) 566-6150
Fax (888) 957-3291
www.wlpmusic.com

A
ABBOT'S LEIGH (87 87 D) . . . 339
ADESTE FIDELES (Irregular with refrain) . . . 235
ALLELUIA NO. 1 (88 with refrain) . . . 313
AMERICA (66 4 666 4) . . . 745
ANTIOCH (CM with repeats) . . . 240
AR HYD Y NOS (84 84 88 84) . . . 697, 781
ASH GROVE (66 11 66 11 D) . . . 706
ASH GROVE (12 11 12 11 D) . . . 532
AURELIA (76 76 D) . . . 571
AUS DER TIEFE RUFE ICH (See HEINLEIN)
AVE DE LOURDES (11 11 with refrain) . . . 371

B
BALM IN GILEAD (76 76 with refrain) . . . 654
BATTLE HYMN OF THE REPUBLIC (15 15 15 6 with refrain) . . . 755
BEACH SPRING (87 87 D) . . . 422, 523
BESANÇON (87 98 87) . . . 223
BICENTENNIAL (CM with refrain) . . . 487
BUNESSAN (55 54 D) . . . 778, 779
BUNESSAN (55 8 D) . . . 391

C
CAROL (CMD) . . . 250
CHEREPONI (779 with refrain) . . . 287
CHRISTIAN LOVE (CM) . . . 288
CONDITOR ALME SIDERUM (LM) . . . 217
CORONATION (86 86 86) . . . 364
CRUCIFER (10 10 with refrain) . . . 384

D
DIADEMATA (SMD) . . . 362
DIX (77 77 77) . . . 258, 705
DRAKES BROUGHTON (87 87) . . . 477
DUGUET (LM) . . . 427
DUKE STREET (LM) . . . 318

E
EASTER HYMN (77 77 with alleluias) . . . 330
EIN' FESTE BURG (87 87 66 66 7) . . . 616
ELLACOMBE (CMD) . . . 699
ENDLESS SONG (87 87 with refrain) . . . 607
ERHALT UNS, HERR (LM) . . . 266, 273, 552
ES IST EIN' ROS' ENTSPRUNGEN (76 76 6 76) . . . 246
EVENTIDE (10 10 10 10) . . . 780

F
FINLANDIA (10 10 10 10 10 10) . . . 419
FINLANDIA (11 10 11 10 11 10) . . . 747
FOREST GREEN (CMD) . . . 105
FULDA (76 76 with refrain) . . . 499

G
GABRIEL'S MESSAGE (10 10 12 10) . . . 378
GILU HAGALIM (See KING OF GLORY)
GLORIA (77 77 with refrain) . . . 236
GO TELL IT (76 76 with refrain) . . . 242
GOD REST YOU MERRY (86 86 86 with refrain) . . . 243
GOTT VATER SEI GEPRIESEN (76 76 77 67) . . . 355, 357
GREENSLEEVES (87 87 with refrain) . . . 256
GREIF (10 6 10 6 with refrain) . . . 687
GROSSER GOTT (78 78 77 with repeat) . . . 721

H
HAMBURG (LM) . . . 302
HANSON PLACE (87 87 with refrain) . . . 773
HEINLEIN (77 77) . . . 263
HEISLMAN (76 76 D with refrain) . . . 703
HOLY ANTHEM (87 87 D) . . . 317
HOUSTON (Irregular) . . . 682
HYFRYDOL (87 87 D) . . . 361, 448, 662
HYMN TO JOY (87 87 D) . . . 321, 726, 731, 774

I
ICH GLAUB AN GOTT (87 87 55 8) . . . 360
IHR KINDERLEIN, KOMMET (11 11 11 11) . . . 248
IN BABILONE (87 87 D) . . . 386, 670
IN DULCI JUBILO (66 77 78 55) . . . 239
ITALIAN HYMN (66 4 666 4) . . . 359

J
JESU DULCIS MEMORIA (LM) . . . 110

K
KELVINGROVE (76 76 77 76) . . . 529
KENMARE (13 13 13 13) . . . 332
KING OF GLORY (12 12 with refrain) . . . 368
KINGS OF ORIENT (88 44 6 with refrain) . . . 255
KINGSFOLD (CMD) . . . 272, 646
KOMT NU MET ZANG (98 98 9 66) . . . 462
KREMSER (12 11 12 11) . . . 734

L
LAMBILLOTTE (LM with repeat) . . . 352
LAND OF REST (CM) . . . 385, 775
LASST UNS ERFREUEN (LM with additions) . . . 714
LASST UNS ERFREUEN (LM with alleluias) . . . 390
LAUDA ANIMA (87 87 87) . . . 735
LET US BREAK BREAD (10 10 with refrain) . . . 488
LIBERATOR (10 10 10 10) . . . 327
LLANFAIR (77 77 with alleluias) . . . 320, 337
LOBE DEN HERREN (14 14 47 8) . . . 732
LONDONDERRY AIR (12 10 12 10 with refrain) . . . 439
LOURDES HYMN (11 11 with refrain) . . . 370

M
MADRID (66 66 D) . . . 711
MATERNA (CMD) . . . 749
McKEE (CM) . . . 548
MELITA (88 88 88) . . . 746
MENDELSSOHN (77 77 D with refrain) . . . 245
MORNING SONG (CM) . . . 226
MUELLER (11 11 11 11) . . . 238

N
NATIONAL HYMN (10 10 10 10) . . . 748
NETTLETON (87 87 D) . . . 473, 569, 719
NEW BRITAIN (CM) . . . 112, 614
NICAEA (11 12 12 10) . . . 358
NOËL NOUVELET (11 10 10 11) . . . 328
NUN DANKET (67 67 66 66) . . . 704

O
O FILII ET FILIAE (888 with alleluias) . . . 311, 312
O WALY WALY (LM) . . . 447
O WALY WALY, alt. (Irregular) . . . 590
OLD HUNDREDTH (LM) . . . 354, 438, 456, 718

P

PASSION CHORALE (76 76 D) 297
PERFECT CHARITY (Irregular) 660
PICARDY (87 87 87) 730
PICARDY (98 98 98) 657
PLEADING SAVIOR (87 87 with refrain) 389
PLEADING SAVIOR (87 87 D) 380
PRECIOUS LORD (Irregular) 424

R

REGENT SQUARE (87 87 87) 253
RISE UP, SHEPHERD (10 7 11 7 with refrain) 249

S

SALVE REGINA COELITUM (84 84 with refrain) 376
SALZBURG (77 77 D) 254, 319
SEED, SCATTERED AND SOWN (66 66 with refrain) 502
SERVANT SONG (87 87) 537
SHANTI (CM) 594
SIMPLE GIFTS (Irregular with refrain) 583
SINE NOMINE (10 10 10 with alleluias) 388
SLANE (10 10 10 10) 633
SLANE (10 11 11 12) 623
SONG OF MARY (98 98 77 88) 374
SOON AND VERY SOON (57 57 57 86) 750
ST. AGNES (CM) 475
ST. ANNE (CM) 612
ST. BRENDAN'S (13 13 14 with refrain) 544
ST. CATHERINE (88 88 88) 593
ST. COLUMBA (CM) 399
ST. COLUMBA (87 87) 648
ST. ELIZABETH (55 7 55 8) 696
ST. ELIZABETH (Irregular) 717
ST. FLAVIAN (CM) 277
ST. GEORGE'S WINDSOR (77 77 with refrain) 365
ST. GEORGE'S WINDSOR (77 77 D) 702
ST. LOUIS (86 86 76 86) 244
ST. ROSE (55 54 D) 625
ST. THEODULPH (76 76 D) 284
ST. THOMAS (TANTUM ERGO) (87 87 87) 291, 517
STABAT MATER (88 7) 262
STILLE NACHT (Irregular) 252
STUTTGART (87 87) 212
SUO GÂN (87 87 D) 586

T

THAXTED (76 76 76 D) 733
THE FIRST NOWELL (Irregular with refrain) 259
THOMPSON (11 7 11 7 with refrain) 414
TWO OAKS (96 86 87 10 with refrain) 570

U

UNDE ET MEMORES (10 10 10 10 10 10) 476

V

VENI, VENI, EMMANUEL (LM with refrain) 228
VICTIMAE PASCHALI (77 77 D) 334
VICTIMAE PASCHALI LAUDES (Irregular) 310
VICTORY (888 with alleluias) 336
VILLE DU HAVRE (11 8 11 9 with refrain) 643

W

W ZLOBIE LEZY (87 87 88 77) 251
WERDE MUNTER (87 87 88 77) 567
WERE YOU THERE (10 10 14 10) 300
WINCHESTER NEW (LM) 218
WINTER'S SNOW (77 77 D) 247
WONDROUS LOVE (12 9 12 12 9) 668

SMD (Short Meter Double: 66 86 66 86)
DIADEMATA . . . 362

CM (Common Meter: 86 86)
CHRISTIAN LOVE . . . 288
LAND OF REST . . . 385, 775
McKEE . . . 548
MORNING SONG . . . 226
NEW BRITAIN . . . 112, 614
SHANTI . . . 594
ST. AGNES . . . 475
ST. ANNE . . . 612
ST. COLUMBA . . . 399
ST. FLAVIAN . . . 277

CM with refrain
BICENTENNIAL . . . 487

CM with repeats
ANTIOCH . . . 240

CMD (Common Meter Double: 86 86 86 86)
CAROL . . . 250
ELLACOMBE . . . 699
FOREST GREEN . . . 105
KINGSFOLD . . . 272, 646
MATERNA . . . 749

LM (Long Meter: 88 88)
CONDITOR ALME SIDERUM . . . 217
DUGUET . . . 427
DUKE STREET . . . 318
ERHALT UNS, HERR . . . 266, 273, 552
HAMBURG . . . 302
JESU DULCIS MEMORIA . . . 110
O WALY WALY . . . 447
OLD HUNDREDTH . . . 354, 438, 456, 718
WINCHESTER NEW . . . 218

LM with additions
LASST UNS ERFREUEN . . . 714

LM with alleluias
LASST UNS ERFREUEN . . . 390

LM with refrain
VENI, VENI, EMMANUEL . . . 228

LM with repeat
LAMBILLOTTE . . . 352

55 54 D
BUNESSAN . . . 778, 779
ST. ROSE . . . 625

55 7 55 8
ST. ELIZABETH . . . 696

55 8 D
BUNESSAN . . . 391

57 57 57 86
SOON AND VERY SOON . . . 750

66 4 666 4
AMERICA . . . 745
ITALIAN HYMN . . . 359

66 66 D
MADRID . . . 711

66 66 with refrain
SEED, SCATTERED AND SOWN . . . 502

66 77 78 55
IN DULCI JUBILO . . . 239

66 86 D (See SMD)

66 86 66 86 (See SMD)

66 11 66 11 D
ASH GROVE . . . 706

67 67 66 66
NUN DANKET . . . 704

76 76 with refrain
BALM IN GILEAD . . . 654
FULDA . . . 499
GO TELL IT . . . 242

76 76 6 76
ES IST EIN' ROS' ENTSPRUNGEN . . . 246

76 76 D
AURELIA . . . 571
PASSION CHORALE . . . 297
ST. THEODULPH . . . 284

76 76 D with refrain
HEISLMAN . . . 703

76 76 76 D
THAXTED . . . 733

76 76 77 67
GOTT VATER SEI GEPRIESEN . . . 355, 357

76 76 77 76
KELVINGROVE . . . 529

77 77
HEINLEIN . . . 263

77 77 with alleluias
EASTER HYMN . . . 330
LLANFAIR . . . 320, 337

77 77 with refrain
GLORIA . . . 236
ST. GEORGE'S WINDSOR . . . 365

77 77 77
DIX . . . 258, 705

77 77 D
SALZBURG . . . 254, 319
ST. GEORGE'S WINDSOR . . . 702
VICTIMAE PASCHALI . . . 334
WINTER'S SNOW . . . 247

77 77 D with refrain
MENDELSSOHN . . . 245

779 with refrain
CHEREPONI . . . 287

78 78 77 with repeat
GROSSER GOTT . . . 721

84 84 with refrain
SALVE REGINA COELITUM . . . 376

84 84 88 84
AR HYD Y NOS . . . 697, 781

86 86 (See CM)

86 86 with refrain (See CM with refrain)

86 86 with repeats (See CM with repeats)

86 86 76 86
ST. LOUIS. 244

86 86 86
CORONATION. 364

86 86 86 with refrain
GOD REST YOU MERRY. 243

86 86 D (See CMD)

86 86 86 86 (See CMD)

87 87
DRAKES BROUGHTON. 477
SERVANT SONG. 537
ST. COLUMBA 648
STUTTGART. 212

87 87 with refrain
ENDLESS SONG 607
GREENSLEEVES 256
HANSON PLACE. 773
PLEADING SAVIOR 389

87 87 55 8
ICH GLAUB AN GOTT. 360

87 87 66 66 7
EIN' FESTE BURG 616

87 87 87
LAUDA ANIMA. 735
PICARDY 730
REGENT SQUARE 253
ST. THOMAS (TANTUM ERGO) 291, 517

87 87 D
ABBOT'S LEIGH 339
BEACH SPRING. 422, 523
HOLY ANTHEM 317
HYFRYDOL 361, 448, 662
HYMN TO JOY 321, 726, 731, 774
IN BABILONE 386, 670
NETTLETON. 473, 569, 719
PLEADING SAVIOR 380
SUO GÂN 586

87 87 88 77
W ZLOBIE LEZY. 251
WERDE MUNTER 567

87 98 87
BESANÇON. 223

88 with refrain
ALLELUIA NO. 1 313

88 44 6 with refrain
KINGS OF ORIENT. 255

88 7
STABAT MATER. 262

888 with alleluias
O FILII ET FILIAE. 311, 312
VICTORY 336

88 88 (See LM)

88 88 with additions (See LM with additions)

88 88 with alleluias (See LM with alleluias)

88 88 with refrain (See LM with refrain)

88 88 with repeat (See LM with repeat)

88 88 88
MELITA. 746
ST. CATHERINE. 593

96 86 87 10 with refrain
TWO OAKS 570

98 98 77 88
SONG OF MARY 374

98 98 9 66
KOMT NU MET ZANG. 462

98 98 98
PICARDY 657

10 6 10 6 with refrain
GREIF 687

10 7 11 7 with refrain
RISE UP, SHEPHERD. 249

10 10 with refrain
CRUCIFER 384
LET US BREAK BREAD 488

10 10 10 with alleluias
SINE NOMINE. 388

10 10 10 10
EVENTIDE. 780
LIBERATOR 327
NATIONAL HYMN. 748
SLANE. 633

10 10 10 10 10 10
FINLANDIA 419
UNDE ET MEMORES 476

10 10 12 10
GABRIEL'S MESSAGE. 378

10 10 14 10
WERE YOU THERE 300

10 11 11 12
SLANE. 623

11 7 11 7 with refrain
THOMPSON 414

11 8 11 9 with refrain
VILLE DU HAVRE 643

11 10 10 11
NOËL NOUVELET. 328

11 10 11 10 11 10
FINLANDIA 747

11 11 with refrain
AVE DE LOURDES. 371
LOURDES HYMN 370

11 11 11 11
IHR KINDERLEIN, KOMMET. 248
MUELLER 238

11 12 12 10
NICAEA. 358

12 9 12 12 9
WONDROUS LOVE 668

12 10 12 10 with refrain
LONDONDERRY AIR 439

12 11 12 11
KREMSER 734

12 11 12 11 D
ASH GROVE 532

12 12 with refrain
KING OF GLORY 368

13 13 13 13
KENMARE 332

13 13 14 with refrain
ST. BRENDAN'S 544

14 14 47 8
LOBE DEN HERREN 732

15 15 15 6 with refrain
BATTLE HYMN OF THE REPUBLIC 755

Irregular
HOUSTON 682
O WALY WALY, alt. 590
PERFECT CHARITY 660
PRECIOUS LORD 424
ST. ELIZABETH 717
STILLE NACHT 252
VICTIMAE PASCHALI LAUDES 310

Irregular with refrain
ADESTE FIDELES 235
SIMPLE GIFTS 583
THE FIRST NOWELL 259

GENESIS
1 569
1:2. . . . 706
1:3–5. . . . 778
1:8–25. . . . 699
1:8–25. . . . 779
1:11–18. . . . 703
1:11–18. . . . 705
1:26. . . . 517
1:26–27. . . . 698
1:29. . . . 697
2:4–5 703
2:4–9 778
2:7 399
3:17–18 240
8:22 703
11:1. . . . 250
18:27. . . . 261

EXODUS
3:7–12 539
3:13–14 668
6:6 228
12:1–14. . . . 480
12:21–23. . . . 319
13:21–22. . . . 706
14:21–29. . . . 319
15:1–21. . . . 319
15:11. . . . 358
15:18. . . . 359
15:19–21. . . . 202
16:4–15. . . . 475
16:13–15. . . . 264
17:1–7. . . . 657
17:1–7. . . . 475
17:5–7. . . . 264
19:4. . . . 606
19:16. . . . 228
19:20. . . . 273
33:18–23 358
34. . . . 758

LEVITICUS
19:18. . . . 726

NUMBERS
6:22–27 638
6:24–26 450

DEUTERONOMY
3:23 694
7:6 364
8:3 613
8:3 475
9:8–21 273
31:8 734

JOSHUA
1:6. . . . 532

RUTH
1:16, 17. . . . 452

1 SAMUEL
2:8 261
3:1–10 539

2 SAMUEL
13:19. . . . 261

1 KINGS
8:66 532

2 KINGS
2:11 273

1 CHRONICLES
16:8. . . . 702
16:8, 34–36. . . . 704
16:23–36. . . . 732
16:31. . . . 731
17:16–17. . . . 614
20:7 732
29:10–13 694
29:10–13 735
29:11–12 359
29:11–13 699
29:13 704

EZRA
3:11 732

NEHEMIAH
9:6 731
9:6 732

JUDITH
4:11 261

ESTHER
4:1 261

1 MACCABEES
3:47 261

JOB
2:12 261
10:9. . . . 261
13:12. . . . 261
14:1–2. . . . 218
19 431
19:25. . . . 318
19:25. . . . 739
19:25ff 428
19:25–27. . . . 438
22:26 732
38:7 253
38:7 726
38:7 322
38:7 244

PSALMS
2:11 456
3:5 623
4:8 623
5:7 730
5:11 734
8. . . . 707
8. . . . 699
8. . . . 693
8:1–4 694
8:3 284
8:3–4 705
10:14. . . . 780
13 269
16 601
16 116
16 649
16:1–2, 5, 7–8, 9–10, 11. . . . 118
16:1–2, 7–11. . . . 591
16:11, 1–2, 7–10. . . . 117
17:6–9. . . . 649
18:1–3. . . . 388
18:2–3, 3–4, 47, 51. . . . 119
19:1. . . . 358
19:1. . . . 694
19:1–6. . . . 705
19:8, 9, 10, 11. . . . 121
19:8, 9, 10, 11, 15. . . . 120
19:8–11. . . . 692
21:13 731
22. . . . 269
22. . . . 296
22:2, 8–9, 17–20, 23–24 122
22:4–5 593
22:8–9, 17–18, 19–20, 23–24 123
22:8–9, 17–18a, 19–20, 23–24 124
22:27–28 253
23. . . . 641
23. . . . 644
23. . . . 652
23. . . . 642
23. . . . 648
23:1 690
23:1–3, 3–4, 5, 6 128
23:1–3a, 3b–4, 5, 6 126
23:1–3a, 3b–4, 5, 6 127
23:1–3a, 3b–4, 5, 6 125
23:5 475
24. . . . 225
24:1–2, 3–4, 5–6 129
24:3 772
24:7–10 284
24:7–10 388
24:7–10 337
24:9–10 368
25. . . . 595
25:1, 4–5, 8–9, 6–7 130
25:1, 4–5, 8–9, 10, 14 630
25:1, 4–5, 8–10, 14 131
25:1, 4–5, 8–10, 14 132
25:6–7 417
27. . . . 417
27. . . . 276
27. . . . 442
27. . . . 443
27. . . . 608
27. . . . 631
27. . . . 444
27:1, 4, 13–14 133
27:1, 4, 13–14 134
27:4 431
27:11 621
29:1–2 284
29:1–2, 3–4, 3, 9–10 135
30:2, 4–6, 11–13 136
30:4 711
30:4 721
30:5 607
31:2, 6, 12–13, 15–16, 17, 25 137
31:2, 6, 12–13, 15–16, 17, 25 138
31:2, 6, 12–13, 15–16, 17, 25 139
31:4 621
32:8 734
33. . . . 141
33. . . . 771
33:1–2, 4, 6–7, 18–19 140
33:4–5 670
33:4–5, 6–7, 12–13, 20, 22 142
33:6–8 699
33:20 612
34:2–3, 4–5, 6–7 146
34:2–3, 4–5, 6–7, 8–9 145
34:2–3, 4–5, 6–7, 8–9, 10–11, 12–13, 14–15 143

34:2–3, 18–19a,19b–20, 4. 526
34:2–4, 6, 9, 16 504
34:2–9 144
34:9 188
34:9a, 2–3, 4–5, 10 511
34:9, 2–4 507
36:7 732
37:2–3 260
37:4–5 732
38:15 612
40:8a, 9a 690
40:8, 14, 2, 4, 7–10 147
41:2–3 576
42. 590
42. 470
42. 436
42:2 775
42:2, 3, 8, 4 149
42:2–7, 9 148
43. 444
45:3 696
45:3–4 359
45:10 380
45:10, 11, 12, 16 150
46. 616
46:1 612
46:1–7 607
46:10 651
46:14 612
47:6, 2–3, 6–9 151
47:6–7 735
47:7–8 359
48:1 694
50:14, 23 705
50:23b 690
51:3–4, 12–13, 14–15 155
51:3–4, 12–13, 17 153
51:3–6, 12–14, 17 154
51:12, 3–4, 8–9, 14 152
51:12–13 359
51:12–14a .636
51:15 102
57:8–9 778
59:16 699
61. 649
62. 618
62:1, 2, 8, 11, 12 611
62:2–3, 6–9 643
62:11–12 358
63. 758
63. 436
63:2–3, 4–6, 7–9 104
63:2, 5–9 156
63:2–9 157
63:3 755
63:5 643
63:7 732
65. 723
65:5–13 749
65:5–13 699
65:7–13 697
65:9–11 703
66. 723
66. 725
66:1 364
66:1 755
66:1 690
66:1–2 718
66:1–3, 4–5, 6–7, 16, 20 159
66:1–3a, 4–5, 6–7a, 16–17 158
67:2–3, 5, 6, 8 160
67:3 711
67:3 718
67:4 690
67:6–7 702
67:6–7 697
67:6–7 704
68:4 732
68:19 702
68:29 255
69:16 670
71:6 704
71:10 255
72. 364
72. 365
72. 360
72:1–2, 7–8, 10–11, 12–13, 17 161
72:1–17 226
72:5–17 718
72:8 678
72:10 255
72:12–13 576
75:1 704
78:29 487
79:13 648
80. 229
80:1–4, 9–15 220
80:2–3, 9, 12, 13–14,
15–16, 18–19, 19–20 162
80:9–12 736
81:16 487
81:17 539
83:18 359
84. 430
84:2–7, 9, 11–12 163
84:4 648
85:8, 9–10, 11–12, 13–14 165
85:8–14 164
85:9 678
85:9–10, 11–12, 13–14 166
85:9a, 12a .690
85:10–12 220
89:2–5, 16–18, 21–22, 27 167
89:5–7 730
90:1–2, 4–6, 12, 14 441
90:1–4, 12 .653
90:1–5 612
90:2 417
90:3–4, 5–6, 12–13, 14–17 168
90:14 690
90:17 732
91. 605
91. 606
91. 418
91:1–2 612
91:1–2, 10–11, 12–13, 14–15 169
91:1–2, 10–11, 12–13, 14–16 170
91:2 260
91:4 732
92. 709
92:cf. 2a. 690
92:1 704
93. 732
94:12 734
95. 102
95:1 711
95:1–2, 6–7, 8–9 171
95:1–2, 6–7, 8–9 172
95:1–6 103
95:1–7 472
95:3–6 699
95:7 648
95:8 690
96. 226
96:1–2, 2–3, 7–8, 9–10 173
96:1–2, 2–3, 11–12 174
96:1–3, 11–12, 13 175
96:1–6 714
96:11–13 751
97:1 456
97:1 732
97:1–2, 6–7, 9 176
97:6 714
98. 712
98. 226
98:cf. 9. 690
98:1, 2–3, 3–4, 5–6 179
98:1, 2–3, 5–6 178
98:1, 3–6 177
98:1, 4–6 739
98:3–4 456
98:4–9 240
100 456
100 695
100 455
100 732
100 740
100:1. 727
100:3. 517
100:3b, 1–2, 4, 5 180
103 738
103 735
103 670
103:1–2, 3–4, 6–7, 8, 11. 182
103:1–4, 20. 732
103:1a, 8, 2a–3, 11a, 12b 181
103:2. 703
103:8, 1–2, 3–4, 8–10, 11–12. 413
103:11. 260
103:19. 359
103:20–22. 718
104 342
104 353
104 732
104 345
104 779
104:1–2, 5–6, 10, 12, 13–14,
24, 29–30, 31, 34, 35 183
104:1, 10–13. 694
104:1, 24, 29–30, 31, 34. 184
104:1, 24, 29–30, 31, 34. 185
104:24. 705
104:24. 358
104:29–30. 399
104:30. 352
104:30. 347
105 714
105 705
105:40–41. 475
106:1. 702
106:48. 732
107 675
107:2–3. 548
107:16. 321
107:21–22. 705
110:1. 364
113:1–2. 718
116:1, 3, 5. 500
116:1–9. 189
116:10, 15–18. 189
116:12–13. 188
116:12–13, 10, 15, 16–17, 18–19. . .187
116:12–13, 15–16, 17–18. 500

Psalms, cont.

116:12–13, 15–16bc, 17–18 186
117 714
117 718
117 740
117:1–2. 536
118 331
118 326
118:1. 727
118:1–2, 16–17, 22–23. 192
118:1–2, 16–17, 22–23. 191
118:1–2, 16–17, 22–23. 335
118:2–4, 13–15, 22–24. 190
118:14. 732
118:22. 571
118:24. 722
118:26–27. 284
119:89. 318
119:134. 734
122:1–2, 3–4, 4–5, 6–7, 8–9. 193
123 595
126:1–2, 2–3, 4–5. 194
127 675
128:1, 2, 3, 4–5. 195
128:1, 3, 5–6. 736
130 417
130 275
130:1–2, 3–4, 5–6, 7–8. 196
130:1–2, 3–4, 5–6, 7–8. 197
130:1, 6. 428
130:3–6. 410
131 640
133:1. 548
135:15–18. 736
136 700
136:1–9. 714
136:5–6. 507
136:5–9. 699
136:5–9. 736
137:7. 261
138:1–2, 2–3, 6–7, 7–8. 198
139 620
139 610
139:1–4, 7–8, 11–12, 17–18. 658
139:1–4, 7–12, 23–24. 647
139:11–12. 780
140:13. 704
141:1–5, 8–9. 111
142:5. 614
145 743
145 360
145:1–2. 614
145:1–2, 8–9, 10–11, 13–14. 199
145:1, 16, 8–9, 15–16,
10–13, 17–18 200
145:2. 711
145:8–21. 358
145:10. 726
145:10–12, 21. 731
145:10–13. 714
145:13. 735
145:13. 734
145:15–16. 487
145:21. 364
145:21. 718
145:21. 721
146:6–7, 8–9, 9–10. 201
148 714
148 729
148 731
148:1–2, 5. 718
148:2. 364
148:2. 735
149 742
150 470
150 740
150:1–6. 737
150:6. 714
150:6. 456
150:6. 320
150:6. 711
150:6. 718
150:6. 706
150:6. 732

Proverbs

1:20. 228
8:22–31 699
8:27–29 706
9:1–6 487

Ecclesiastes

3:1–9 440
43:1–2 424
55:1–3 487
58:5–9 523
63:1–6 755

Song of Songs

2. 769
2:1 696
2:4, 17 706
2:17 780
3:11 364
4:6 780
4:6 706
8:6 449
8:6–7 454

Wisdom

8:1 228
18:14–15. 217

Sirach

24:3 228
39:35 704
50:22–24 704

Isaiah

2. 752
2:2–3 358
2:3–4 465
6. 539
6. 522
6:1–3 719
6:1–3 721
6:1–5 730
6:1–8 358
6:3 722
7:14 253
7:14 245
7:14 228
7:14 244
7:14 378
7:14 368
9. 538
9:1–2 217
9:2, 6 241
9:6 364
9:6 231
9:6 245
9:6–7 212
9:7 245
11:1. 364
11:1. 246
11:1–10. 223
11:1–10. 634
11:1–12. 228
11:2. 352
11:2. 344
11:9. 465
12:3, 2, 4–6. 203
18:3. 242
22:2, 22 228
25 431
25 752
25:1–12 463
25:7–8 320
25:7–9 336
25:8 431
26:4 612
30:28 755
35:1 246
35:1–4 220
35:1–6 398
35:1–6 230
35:4 164
40:1, 3, 4, 9 221
40:1–5, 9–11 230
40:1–9 538
40:1–11 213
40:3 761
40:3, 4a 216
40:3–5 227
40:3–8 218
40:4 223
40:6–8 290
40:9 242
40:9ff 765
40:11, 26, 29–30 609
40:21 732
40:31 598
40:31–32 619
41 752
41:2 223
41:8–9 364
41:10 609
42:6 682
43:2–3 600
44:20 261
44:23 320
45:2 321
45:22–23 280
49:13 726
49:15 767
49:15 619
49:16 651
51:12, 4, 6 280
52:7 212
52:7 242
52:13–15 297
53:1–12 297
53:4 298
53:4–5 295
53:4–6 668
53:5 336
53:6 648
54:6–10 619
55:1–2 770
55:1–3 461
55:1–3 463
55:6 231
55:6–9 279
55:10 703
55:10 763
58:5 261

58:6–7 .260
58:6–9 .523
60:1–3 .218
60:3 .255
61 .595
61:1 .421
61:1–2 .212
61:1–3 .534
61:1–4 .542
61:3 .261
61:11 .364
62 .580
62:3 .364
62:6 .242
63:3 .755
63:9 .297
66:1 .755
66:12 .527

JEREMIAH
1:4–10 .565
5:23 .539
8:22 .654
18:6 .716
18:6 .220
31:3 .772
32:17–29 .714
33:11 .456
33:11 .735
46:11 .654

LAMENTATIONS
3:22–23 .778
5:19 .612
5:19 .735

EZEKIEL
11:19, 20 .398
11:19–20 .539
11:19–20 .230
13:6, 10 .324
21:9–10, 14–15 .755
22:1 .773
34:11ff .765
36:26–27 .539
47:1–2, 9 .304
47:1–12 .773

DANIEL
1 .273
3:51–90 .701
3:52, 53, 54, 55 .204
3:57 .714
3:77 .406
3:77 .400
4:13, 17 .390
6:16ff .273
7:9, 13, 22 .359
7:13–14 .212
9:3 .261

HOSEA
2:16, 21 .411
3:3 .411
6:1 .411
6:3 .755
10:12 .412
11:1–2, 4 .267
11:8 .412
14:2ff .412

JOEL
2:1 .260
2:12 .412
2:12–13 .272
2:12–18 .266
2:13 .260
2:28 .569
3:18 .773

AMOS
4:13 .731
5:8 .217

OBADIAH
15 .231

JONAH
3:6 .261

MICAH
4:3 .678
5:2 .245
5:2 .228
5:2 .244
6:6–8 .677
6:8 .520
6:8 .545
6:8 .524

HABAKKUK
2:20 .730
3:18–19 .726

ZEPHANIAH
1:14, 16 .231
3:14–15, 15–17, 19–20 .325

HAGGAI
2:7 .253
2:7 .212

ZECHARIAH
2:13 .730

MALACHI
3:1 .253
3:1 .662
3:1 .218
4:2 .309
4:2 .245

MATTHEW
1:15 .690
1:16–24 .389
1:21–23 .212
1:22–23 .245
1:23 .253
1:23 .228
1:23 .244
1:23 .241
2:1–2, 5–6 .244
2:1–11 .259
2:1–11 .255
2:1–11 .256
2:1–12 .253
2:1–12 .258
2:1–12 .254
2:9–10 .252
2:10–11 .235
2:13–19 .389
3:1–6, 11–12 .218
3:4 .273
3:6, 39 .231
3:11 .399
3:13–17 .254
3:13–17 .396
4:1–4 .272
4:1–11 .263
4:1–11 .277
4:4 .613
4:4 .475
4:16 .217
4:18–22 .322
4:18–22 .555
4:24 .368
5 .685
5:3 .399
5:3 .690
5:3–4, 10 .600
5:3–12 .757
5:3–12 .759
5:3–12 .760
5:3–12 .519
5:3–12, 14–16 .687
5:13 .471
5:13–16 .554
5:14 .684
5:41 .537
6:1–18 .266
6:9–10 .763
6:12–15 .680
6:12–15 .679
6:25–34 .623
6:28 .598
6:33 .613
7:7 .545
7:7–8 .613
7:7, 13 .760
8:8 .506
8:10–11 .548
8:20 .521
9:37–38 .702
10 .685
10:8 .339
11:2–6 .595
11:8–30 .212
11:16 .322
11:19 .654
11:25–28 .461
11:25–30 .646
11:28ff .765
11:28–30 .598
11:28–30 .644
11:28–30 .770
11:28–30 .580
11:28–30 .623
11:30 .521
12:9–14 .322
12:12–13 .273
12:40 .328
12:46 .548
13:1–9, 18–23, 45–46 .532
13:4–8 .440
13:4–30 .556
13:24–30, 36–43 .702
13:43 .606
13:55 .385
13:55 .389
13:55 .623
14:14 .662
15:21–22 .488
16:15–18 .571
16:24–27 .552
17:1–9 .274
18 .648
18:10–14 .267
19:19 .726
20:28 .212
20:28 .245
20:30–34 .488

Matthew, cont.

21:6–11 284
21:9 285
21:9 358
21:9 283
21:14–16 711
22:34–40 657
22:39 726
22:39–40 697
23:13 322
24:14 593
24:30–31 702
25:31 226
25:31–46 483
25:31–46 458
25:34–40 523
25:35–40 518
25:45 519
26:26–28 319
26:26–29 339
26:26–30 488
26:28 730
26:28 302
27:26–50 297
27:27–45 322
27:35, 60 300
27:46 523
27:57–66 328
27:63 336
27:66 320
28:1–7 328
28:1–9 320
28:1–9 312
28:1–9, 19 330
28:5–8 321
28:6–9 334
28:16–20 337
28:18–20 361
28:18–20 339

Mark

1:1 696
1:1–8 218
1:9–11 396
1:12–15 272
1:12–15 277
1:14–20 556
1:14–20 322
1:15 690
1:16–20 555
1:32–34 254
2:1–12 322
2:1–12 254
2:10 696
2:18–22 273
2:21 651
3:1–6 322
3:31 548
4:3–6 502
4:26–27 697
6:3 623
6:30–34 646
6:30–34 670
8:22–25 636
8:34 552
9:2–10 274
10:34 336
10:35 287
10:43–45 680
10:43–45 679
10:45 654
10:45 668
10:46–52 488
11:1–11 284
11:9–10 317
12:28–34 657
13:33 761
14:24 668
15:1–37 262
15:16–37 322
15:17–18 297
15:25–33 300
15:34 523
16:1–7 312
16:3 300
16:5–6 328
16:15 313
16:15 690
16:19 337

Luke

1:26–32 370
1:26–38 378
1:26–45 380
1:28 369
1:28, 42 372
1:31 217
1:32–35 212
1:33–35, 77–79 245
1:45–55 207
1:46–47 690
1:46–55 112
1:46–55 379
1:46–55 240
1:46–55 209
1:46–55 210
1:46–55 208
1:46–55 220
1:46–55 375
1:46–55 373
1:52 507
1:68–79 105
1:68–79 227
1:68–79 206
1:68–79 205
1:77–79 239
1:77–79 730
1:77–79 252
1:78–79 228
2:1–7, 25 212
2:1–10 259
2:4 389
2:5 217
2:6–14 252
2:6–18 239
2:6–18 256
2:6–20 236
2:6–20 253
2:6–20 251
2:7 238
2:7 246
2:7, 39–40, 51–52 380
2:8–12 237
2:8–15 249
2:8–18 245
2:8–20 242
2:8–20 247
2:9–10 243
2:10–11 240
2:10–11, 15 250
2:10–15 235
2:11 175
2:14 220
2:19 376
2:29–32 211
2:34–35 262
2:39–40, 52 623
3:2–6, 15–18 218
3:21–22 254
3:23 380
4:1–13 263
4:1–13 277
4:18 245
4:18–19 542
4:18–19 534
5:1–11 322
5:1–11 555
6:6–11 322
6:20ff 600
6:20–23 757
6:20–26 759
6:27–38 657
7 595
7:6 506
7:31 322
7:34 654
7:47 302
8:19 548
8:39 532
9:1–6 339
9:26 702
9:28b–36 274
9:58 521
10:1–12 339
10:25–28 287
10:30–37 657
11:2–4 763
11:9–10 613
11:27 376
11:27–28 380
12:2–3 553
12:22–40 576
12:31 613
13:29 548
13:34 649
14:12–24 539
14:23 569
14:25–33 552
15:3–7 648
15:11–24 410
15:20–32 623
15:24, 32 614
16:15–16 339
18:9–14 471
19:29–38 284
19:37–40 711
21:27–28 702
21:28 226
21:33 318
22:14–20 657
22:14–20 291
22:26 517
23:13–46 262
23:33–44, 50–53 300
23:33–46 322
23:34 295
23:34 339
23:46 137
23:46 138
23:50–56 328
24:1–7, 34 320
24:1–12 328
24:5 317
24:5–6 328
24:6 336

24:6 .312
24:6, 48 .330
24:13–35 .458
24:13–35 .489
24:13–35 .332
24:13–43 .594
24:26 .297
24:28–35 .475
24:29 .780
24:30 .488
24:31, 50–53 .361
24:32 .625
24:46–53 .337
24:47–53 .532
24:51–53 .662

JOHN

1:1–3 .247
1:1–5 .235
1:1–9 .688
1:4–5, 14 .730
1:6–8, 15–28 .218
1:9 .253
1:9 .110
1:9, 16 .646
1:14 .359
1:14 .245
1:14 .235
1:16–17 .614
1:29 .492
1:29 .295
1:29 .506
1:29–34 .384
1:29–34 .254
1:35–42 .555
1:41–42 .529
1:45 .385
1:45 .389
2:1–11 .254
3:1–15 .358
3:3–8 .399
3:3–17 .245
3:5 .571
3:14 .384
3:16 .292
3:16, 19 .688
3:16–21 .587
4 .513
4:4–42 .624
4:5–42 .272
4:7–15 .398
4:13–14 .646
5:1–15 .396
5:1–18 .322
5:23 .696
6 .482
6 .478
6 .458
6 .505
6 .495
6 .513
6:25ff .494
6:31, 33, 35, 44, 51, 54–59 .508
6:31–51 .361
6:32–58 .657
6:32–58 .477
6:33–35 .487
6:35 .505
6:35 .646
6:35, 44, 51, 53–54 .493
6:35, 51 .730
6:35–58 .433
6:35–63 .514
6:42 .389
6:44–58 .291
6:48 .483
6:48 .490
6:51 .515
6:53–58 .488
6:63c .690
6:63c .120
6:68 .689
6:68 .681
6:68 .121
7:37 .646
7:37–38 .657
7:38 .675
8:1–11 .624
8:12 .696
8:12 .245
8:12 .684
8:12 .646
8:12 .228
8:31–32 .527
8:31–36 .593
8:58 .668
9:14–15 .564
9:25 .614
10 .648
10:1–5, 14–15 .487
10:10 .517
10:10 .245
10:10 .726
10:10 .523
10:10 .339
10:10 .681
10:11 .297
11:1–44 .624
11:1–45 .324
11:11–18 .320
11:25–26 .329
11:25–26 .433
11:25–27 .505
11:25–27 .493
11:43–44 .327
12 .458
12:12–13 .284
12:20–33 .328
12:20–36 .384
12:24 .602
12:24 .603
12:24 .516
12:24–26 .563
12:24, 32 .298
12:26 .517
12:32 .384
12:35–36 .696
12:35–36 .717
12:35–36 .110
12:35–36 .567
12:44–45 .607
12:46 .682
12:46 .726
13 .286
13 .666
13:1–7, 34–35 .288
13:1–15 .501
13:1–20 .273
13:3–5 .287
13:3–17 .293
13:3–20 .523
13:4–5, 14–15, 34 .290
13:12–17 .680
13:12–17 .679
13:14–15 .514
13:14–17, 34–35 .487
13:34–35 .657
13:34–35 .659
13:35 .681
13:35 .544
14 .286
14 .665
14:1 .607
14:1–4 .290
14:1–12, 19–20 .318
14:1–21 .777
14:2–3, 16 .337
14:3 .482
14:3 .694
14:6 .760
14:15–16, 21, 23, 27 .681
14:16–17 .359
14:16–17, 21 .662
14:18 .361
14:23 .515
14:23, 27 .563
14:24–26 .352
14:24–26 .347
14:24–26 .341
14:24–26 .350
14:25–27 .340
14:27 .671
14:27 .678
14:27 .672
14:27ff .681
14:27 .680
14:27 .679
14:27 .651
15 .286
15 .665
15:1–8 .657
15:1–10 .540
15:1–13 .514
15:1–13 .564
15:4 .328
15:4–5, 7–8 .563
15:9–12 .288
15:9–17 .659
15:11 .681
15:12 .287
15:12–13 .292
15:13 .298
15:13 .290
15:13 .668
15:13–15 .711
15:14–15 .273
16 .286
16 .665
16:12–15 .359
16:16–24 .361
16:22 .482
16:33 .734
17:9–11, 21–23 .476
17:21 .716
17:21 .482
19:2 .297
19:2, 17–18, 34 .302
19:16–18, 36–37 .300
19:17–30 .322
19:25 .370
19:25–27 .262
19:33–36 .319
19:36–42 .322
20:11–18 .320

John, cont.

20:11–18 334
20:19–23 288
20:19–29 312
20:19–31 594
20:22 662
20:22 399
20:24–29 594
20:25–27 300
21:1–19 332

Acts

1:6–11. 337
1:7–12. 361
1:8. 352
2:1–13 352
2:5, 42, 47 571
2:23–24 336
2:24–28 320
2:41 395
2:42 489
4:24 694
4:32 352
7:55–59 755
10:34–43. 654
10:37. 218
10:38. 359
12:12. 734
14:17. 703
14:22. 734
17:25. 399
17:28. 363
20:7 488
20:28 571
20:32 388

Romans

1:4. 336
1:20. 694
3:22–24 614
4:1–25 607
4:25 217
5:1–5 607
5:1–5 567
5:2–17, 20–21 614
5:4, 13 217
5:6–8 297
5:6, 9–11 694
5:6–11 384
5:6–11 302
5:8 668
5:20 240
5:21 321
6:1–4 395
6:3–8 384
6:3–11 318
6:3–11 680
6:3–11 679
6:4–11 321
6:6 313
6:9 309
6:9–10 320
6:9–10 330
6:9–10 336
8. 353
8:14–17 548
8:15, 29 716
8:17 386
8:17 337
8:18–39 670
8:19 683
8:19–20 217
8:21 339
8:29 320
8:29–30 364
8:31 734
8:31–39 764
8:31–39 768
8:32 694
9:20–21 220
11:33–35. 670
11:33–36. 315
11:33–36. 241
11:36. 714
12:1–2. 523
12:4–8. 354
12:4–8. 477
12:5. 548
12:9–10. 705
12:9–18. 537
12:9–21. 657
12:15. 537
12:21. 527
13 220
13:9. 697
14:7–8. 290
14:8. 603
14:11. 359
14:17–19. 680
14:17–19. 679
15:11–12. 228
15:12. 634
15:13. 359

1 Corinthians

1:10. 659
1:10. 664
1:10–13. 288
1:17–18, 31. 302
1:18. 384
1:27. 589
1:27–29. 559
1:30. 228
1:31. 696
2:2 302
2:6–16 567
2:9–10 645
3:9 702
3:11 571
3:13–15 702
3:15–16 399
5:7 321
5:7–8 319
5:7–8 308
6:17 571
8:6 714
10 446
10:3–4. 508
10:14–17. 476
10:16. 500
10:16. 291
10:16–17. 657
10:16–17. 465
10:16–17. 487
10:16–17. 488
10:16–17. 498
10:16–17. 502
10:16–17. 532
10:17. 571
11:23–24. 290
11:23–25. 339
11:23–26. 657
11:23–26. 291
11:23–29. 488
11:26. 188
12 683
12 465
12 569
12 550
12 447
12:4–6, 12–13. 466
12:4–11. 352
12:4, 12–13, 20. 498
12:12–13. 544
12:12–27. 354
12:12–27. 477
12:13. 548
13 657
13 659
13 660
13 666
13 669
13 665
13 667
13 664
13 550
13 288
13:1–2, 4–8b, 11 451
13:1–7, 13. 453
13:4–7, 10, 13. 446
13:12. 662
15:3–4. 330
15:4, 20–23, 54–57. 320
15:10. 614
15:20. 774
15:20–22. 321
15:20–28, 52. 317
15:31–52. 428
15:37. 328
15:51–52. 662
15:52. 739
15:53–57. 336
15:54–57. 323
15:55. 780
15:55. 334
15:57. 726
15:57. 297
16:22. 220
16:22. 297

2 Corinthians

2:14 726
3:18 662
3:18 254
4:6 273
4:6–7 559
4:18 607
4:18 339
5:1–10 755
5:7 594
5:14 297
5:15 575
5:17 607
5:17 384
5:17 662
5:17–20 288
5:18 548
5:19 245
5:21 260
6:16 244
6:18 312
9:6–12, 15 697
9:10–14 702

9:14 614
9:15 694
12:7–10....575
12:9....614
13:11....527
13:13....354
13:13....355
13:13–14....359
13:14....448
13:14....358

Galatians

2:20 313
2:20 698
3:13 668
3:26–29 569
3:28 548
3:28 498
3:28–29 501
4:4–6 245
4:28–31 569
5:1 569
5:1, 13 517
5:13–14 287
5:13–14 537
5:14, 22 697
5:22 359
6:2, 8 697
6:2, 10 523
6:7–10 657
6:14 302

Ephesians

1:2....596
1:3–4....258
1:3–12....239
1:4–6....364
1:6–7....614
1:6–8....302
1:15–23....361
1:19–23....719
1:19–23....365
1:19–23....721
1:22–23....571
2:4–5 670
2:7–10 663
2:8 614
2:13 302
2:13–22 571
2:14, 20 228
2:14–22 548
2:19–22 569
3:14–17 596
3:14–19 523
3:17–19 668
4:1–6 548
4:1–6 401
4:2–3, 5 300
4:4–5 508
4:4–6 498
4:4–6 571
4:7–10 730
4:7–16 339
4:11–16 569
4:29–32 288
5:8–9 560
5:8–10 682
5:8–14 538
5:14 684
5:18 287
5:19–20 663
5:20 705
5:25–30 571
5:27 662
6:13–17 779
6:17 359

Philippians

2....366
2:5–7 359
2:5–8 523
2:5–11 363
2:6–11 367
2:6–11 668
2:8 245
2:8 297
2:9–11 364
2:9–11 696
2:9–11 457
2:10 313
2:10 253
2:10–11 217
2:15, 18 562
3:3–11 302
3:7–11 571
3:7–14 589
3:7–16 562
3:8 435
3:20–21 318
4:1 696
4:8 705
4:19 703

Colossians

1:12....704
1:13–23....302
1:15–18....313
1:15–19....364
1:15–20....732
1:15–20....336
1:16....217
1:16....390
1:18....571
1:20....548
1:24–29....537
2:2 726
2:13–15 336
3:1–4 320
3:11 548
3:12–17 537
3:13 288
3:14 705
3:16 711

1 Thessalonians

1:6....359
1:10....318
2:19–20 696
3:12 657
4:13–17 388
4:16 253
4:16–17 694
4:17 336
5:2 750
5:8 779
5:18 704

1 Timothy

1:15–16....614
1:17....735
2:11 313
6:12 593
6:12 388
6:13–15 730
6:15 361
6:15 359
6:16 696

2 Timothy

1:10....309
2:8–12 434
2:11–12 563
4:5–7 593
4:6–8 388
4:7 435

Titus

2:11 614

Hebrews

1:2....217
1:3....228
1:3, 9....696
1:6....364
1:6....253
1:6....245
1:6....250
1:6–9....384
1:8....719
1:8....721
2:5–9, 12 364
2:9 297
2:10 388
2:14–15 648
2:18 263
3:1–6 571
4:9 388
4:12 359
4:14 361
5:1–10 361
5:8 297
7:25 337
9:11–28 361
9:12–26 302
9:13–14, 26 321
9:28 318
10:12....321
10:20....361
11:13–16....388
11:32–40....593
12:1....682
12:1....387
12:1–2....388
12:1–3....719
12:1–3....721
12:2....320
12:2....330
12:2....273
12:5–7....734
13:8....696
13:8....318
13:15....711
13:15....702
13:15....705
13:15....704

James

1:5....567
1:17....780
1:17....703
1:17....749
1:17....702
1:17....705
1:17....718
1:17....699

JAMES, CONT.
1:17 726
1:18 337
3:13–18 567
3:17 228
5 220
5:7–9, 11 224

1 PETER
1:3 330
1:3 312
1:3–5 388
1:3–6 318
1:8–9 527
1:18–19 571
1:21 302
2:1–10 569
2:9 711
2:9 718
2:9 719
2:9 721
2:9–10 560
2:17 548
2:17 726
2:21–25 336
2:24 297
2:24 302
2:25 648
3:8 726
3:18 297
3:18–19 320
4:10–14 654
5:4 648

2 PETER
1:16 318
1:19 327
3:8 612
3:14–18 662

1 JOHN
1 538
1:5 696
1:5 717
1:5 110
1:5 682
1:5–10 726
2:9–14 726
2:10 684
2:15–16 302
2:17 399
2:25 318
2:27 352
3:1 614
3:1, 16 668
3:2 318
3:3 696
3:16–24 544
3:18 593
4:7–10, 19 668
4:7–12 659
4:7–12 664
4:7–12 527
4:7–15 726
4:7–21 355
4:7–21 696
4:7–21 717
4:7–21 657
4:7–21 487
4:7–21 567
4:7–21 288
4:16 292
4:16b 655
4:16 446
4:19 297
5:7 719
5:7 721

JUDE
1:3 593
1:24–25 662

REVELATION
1:7 750
2:7 571
2:10 388
3:7 228
3:20 646
3:20 218
4:1–11 390
4:6, 8–11 358
4:8–11 719
4:8–11 721
4:8–11 730
4:11 714
4:11 699
4:11 731
5:6–14 668
5:6–14 390
5:8, 12–14 358
5:9 571
5:9, 11–13ff 364
5:9–14 361
5:9–14 365
5:9–14 360
5:9–14 754
5:11–13 711
5:12 295
5:12–13 284
6:9–11 364
6:9–11 387
6:9–11 571
6:11 388
7:2–4, 9–14 388
7:4, 9–12 710
7:9–10 668
7:9–12 284
7:9–12, 14 364
7:9–17 384
7:9, 17 387
7:9–17 390
7:12 358
7:15 662
7:16–17 776
8:3–4 358
11:15 364
11:15 361
11:15 295
11:17 704
11:19 380
12:1–6 376
12:1–6 370
12:1–6 380
12:10 361
14:1–8 668
14:4 337
14:7 714
14:7 705
14:13 388
14:13 571
14:15 702
14:17–20 755
15:2, 4 358
15:3 228
15:3–4 696
15:4 718
15:4 719
15:4 721
19:1 313
19:1–2 336
19:1–8 390
19:6–7 732
19:6–9 319
19:11–13 364
19:11–16 359
19:11–16 365
19:11–16 730
19:11–16 226
19:11–16 360
19:12 362
19:16 361
21 571
21:1–4 317
21:1–6 776
21:1–27 517
21:2–4 775
21:3 662
21:4 750
21:21 388
21:23 682
22:1–5 317
22:1–5 517
22:1–5 775
22:1–5 384
22:1–5 773
22:5 258
22:16 696
22:17 648
22:20 212
22:20 702
22:20 750

Absolution
See Liturgical Index: Rites of the Church, Penance (Reconciliation)

Adoration
See Praise; Liturgical Index: Devotions, The Way of the Cross; Rites of the Church, Exposition of the Holy Eucharist (Including Benediction)

Agricultural Worker
See Labor

Alienation
See Lament, Social Concern

Angels
717 Blessed by Your Sacrifice
484 Bread of Angels
782 Daylight's Ending
429 Go Forth
365 Hail, Redeemer, King Divine
721 Holy God, We Praise Thy Name
358 Holy, Holy, Holy
730 Let All Mortal Flesh Keep Silence
669 Love Has Come
701 Meadows and Mountains
650 Pastures of the Lord
735 Praise, My Soul, the King of Heaven
731 Praise the Lord, Ye Heavens
198 Psalm 138: On the Day I Called
635 Sacred Silence
428 Songs of the Angels
608 The Lord Is Near/ May the Angels
535 With One Voice
390 Ye Watchers and Ye Holy Ones

Anointing
See Liturgical Index: Rites of the Church, Rite of Anointing (Care of the Sick)

Apostles
See Discipleship, Saints; Liturgical Index: Solemnities and Feasts, All Saints

Banquet
See Liturgical Index: Service Music for Mass, Communion Song, Eucharistic Hymn

Baptism
See Liturgical Index: Rites of the Church, Baptism; Rite of Christian Initiation of Adults, Rites of Initiation, Baptism

Beatitudes
See Scriptural Index: Matthew 5

Beauty
See Creation

Benediction
See Liturgical Index: Rites of the Church, Exposition of the Holy Eucharist (Including Benediction)

Blessing
See also Liturgical Index: Rites of the Church, Marriage
409 Dismissal of the Catechumens and the Elect
746 Eternal Father, Strong to Save
637 Irish Blessing
638 May God Bless and Keep You (C. Walker)
450 May God Bless You (Van Grieken)
639 May the Road Rise Up
704 Now Thank We All Our God
195 Psalm 128: O Blessed Are Those

Blood of Christ
See Liturgical Index: Service Music for Mass, Communion Song, Eucharistic Hymn; The Liturgical Year, Solemnities of the Lord during Ordinary Time, The Most Holy Body and Blood of Christ (Corpus Christi)

Body of Christ
See Liturgical Index: Service Music for Mass, Communion Song, Eucharistic Hymn; The Liturgical Year, Solemnities of the Lord during Ordinary Time, The Most Holy Body and Blood of Christ (Corpus Christi)

Call to Worship
See Gathering

Canticles
See Scriptural Index: Exodus 15, Isaiah 12, Daniel 3, Luke 1, Luke 2

Care of the Sick
See also Healing; Liturgical Index: Rites of the Church, Rite of Anointing (Care of the Sick)
598 Age to Age
643 All Is Well with My Soul
590 As the Deer Longs
600 Be Not Afraid
419 Be Still, My Soul
641 Because the Lord Is My Shepherd
407 Come to the River
770 Come to the Water
645 Eye Has Not Seen
422 Healing River of the Spirit
420 Holy Darkness
772 I Have Loved You
421 Lay Your Hands
640 Like a Child Rests
436 My Soul Is Thirsting
423 O Jesus, Healer of Wounded Souls
611 Only in God
424 Precious Lord, Take My Hand
116 Psalm 16: Path of Life/ Keep Me Safe
117 Psalm 16: The Path of Life
652 Psalm 23 (Conry)
127 Psalm 23: The Lord Is My Shepherd/ I Shall Live in the House of the Lord (Crandal)
125 Psalm 23: The Lord Is My Shepherd/I Shall Live in the House/The Lord Prepares a Banquet (Cooney)
131 Psalm 25: To You, O Lord (Joncas)
132 Psalm 25: To You, O Lord (Soper)
133 Psalm 27: The Goodness of the Lord
134 Psalm 27: The Lord Is My Light
136 Psalm 30: I Will Praise You, Lord
145 Psalm 34: Taste and See/ Gusten y Vean
148 Psalm 42: O God, for You I Long
149 Psalm 42/43: As the Deer Longs
156 Psalm 63: My Soul Is Thirsting/ As Morning Breaks (Angrisano)
157 Psalm 63: My Soul Thirsts (Schutte)
168 Psalm 90: In Every Age
170 Psalm 91: Be with Me, Lord
189 Psalm 116: In the Presence of God
198 Psalm 138: On the Day I Called
111 Psalmody: Psalm 141
642 Shepherd Me, O God
418 Show Us Your Mercy
443 The Lord Is My Light
634 There Is a Longing
631 This Alone
630 To You, O God, I Lift Up My Soul
609 We Will Rise Again

Celebrations
See Liturgical Index: Rites of the Church, Holy Orders, Rite of Religious Profession

Charity
See also Love for Others
292 Donde Hay Amor y Caridad/ Where Charity and Love Abound
518 God of the Hungry
660 In Perfect Charity
287 Jesu, Jesu
664 Ubi Caritas
519 Whatsoever You Do
288 Where Charity and Love Prevail
453 Where Love Is Found
446 Where There Is Love

Christian Initiation
See Liturgical Index: Rites of the Church, Rite of Christian Initiation of Adults

Christian Life
See also Discipleship, Love for Others
756 A Rightful Place
520 Act Justly
473 As We Gather at Your Table
480 As We Remember
757 Beatitudes
759 Blest Are They

625 Christ Be beside Me
683 Christ, Be Our Light
586 Christ before Us
566 Christ Has No Body Now but Yours
573 Christ in Me Arise
558 Come, Follow Me
676 Dona Nobis Pacem
559 Earthen Vessels
392 Enter the Journey
353 Everyone Moved by the Spirit
593 Faith of Our Fathers
659 Faithful Family
572 Father of Peace
761 Find Us Ready
517 For the Healing of the Nations
397 Give Me Ears to Listen
655 God Is Love
518 God of the Hungry
265 Gracious God
768 If God Is for Us
660 In Perfect Charity
581 Jesus in the Morning
451 Love Never Fails
399 O Breathe on Me, O Breath of God
562 Only This I Want
195 Psalm 128: O Blessed Are Those
613 Seek Ye First
532 Sent Forth by God's Blessing
547 Somos el Cuerpo de Cristo/ We Are the Body of Christ
561 Take, Lord, Receive
503 That There May Be Bread
474 The God of All Grace
537 The Servant Song
529 The Summons
544 They'll Know We Are Christians
583 'Tis the Gift to Be Simple
576 Voice of Christ
550 We Are Many Parts
687 We Are the Light of the World
405 We Belong to You
564 We Have Been Told
519 Whatsoever You Do
453 Where Love Is Found
624 You Are the Healing
557 Your Song of Love

Christian Unity

See Ecumenism, Unity

Church

See also Global Family, People of God

570 All Are Welcome
509 As Grains of Wheat
683 Christ, Be Our Light
657 Christians, Let Us Love One Another
461 Come to Us
593 Faith of Our Fathers
659 Faithful Family
388 For All the Saints
705 For the Beauty of the Earth
455 Gather Us Together
465 Gather Your People
719 God, We Praise You
476 Lord, Who at Thy First Eucharist
339 Lord, You Give the Great Commission
551 Many and One
469 Now as We Gather
466 O Love of God/Amor de Dios
401 One Lord
568 One Spirit, One Church
141 Psalm 33: Happy the People You Have Chosen
569 Sing a New Church
571 The Church's One Foundation
544 They'll Know We Are Christians
360 To Jesus Christ, Our Sovereign King
332 Two Were Bound for Emmaus
664 Ubi Caritas
550 We Are Many Parts
734 We Gather Together
462 What Is This Place
535 With One Voice

Comfort

598 Age to Age
643 All Is Well with My Soul
549 As We Celebrate
600 Be Not Afraid
641 Because the Lord Is My Shepherd
565 Before the Sun Burned Bright
759 Blest Are They
591 Center of My Life
579 Come, Lord Jesus
644 Come to Me
461 Come to Us
580 Come Unto Me
676 Dona Nobis Pacem
645 Eye Has Not Seen
647 Fly like a Bird
397 Give Me Ears to Listen
674 Give Us Your Peace
429 Go Forth
627 God, Our Source and Life, Unite Us
772 I Have Loved You
646 I Heard the Voice of Jesus
431 I Know That My Redeemer Lives
433 I, the Lord
775 Jerusalem, My Happy Home
421 Lay Your Hands
640 Like a Child Rests
765 Like a Shepherd
521 Make Your Home in Me
620 O God, You Search Me
606 On Eagle's Wings
611 Only in God
650 Pastures of the Lord
681 Peace
340 Peace, My Friends
680 Peace Prayer
679 Prayer of St. Francis/ Oración de San Francisco
424 Precious Lord, Take My Hand
116 Psalm 16: Path of Life/ Keep Me Safe
652 Psalm 23 (Conry)
128 Psalm 23: My Shepherd Is the Lord (Gelineau)
126 Psalm 23: The Lord Is My Shepherd/ El Señor Es Mi Pastor (Reza)
127 Psalm 23: The Lord Is My Shepherd/I Shall Live in the House of the Lord (Crandal)
125 Psalm 23: The Lord Is My Shepherd/I Shall Live in the House/The Lord Prepares a Banquet (Cooney)
133 Psalm 27: The Goodness of the Lord
136 Psalm 30: I Will Praise You, Lord
156 Psalm 63: My Soul Is Thirsting/ As Morning Breaks
189 Psalm 116: In the Presence of God
187 Psalm 116: Our Blessing-Cup/ El Cáliz que Bendecimos
649 Shelter Me, O God
642 Shepherd Me, O God
629 Stand by Me
526 The Cry of the Poor
648 The King of Love My Shepherd Is
654 There Is a Balm in Gilead
280 Turn to Me
777 Where My Father Lives
693 You Are Child
651 You Are Mine
610 You Are Near

Commandments

121 Psalm 19: Lord, You Have the Words
280 Turn to Me
692 Your Words Are Spirit and Life

Commissioning

See also Discipleship, Ministry/Mission

553 All That Is Hidden
473 As We Gather at Your Table
757 Beatitudes
625 Christ Be beside Me
683 Christ, Be Our Light
586 Christ before Us
538 City of God
580 Come Unto Me
409 Dismissal of the Catechumens and the Elect
554 Go Make a Difference
542 God Has Chosen Me
604 Here I Am (Booth)
539 Here I Am, Lord (Schutte)
684 I Am the Light of the World
287 Jesu, Jesu
528 Light of Christ
523 Lord, Whose Love in Humble Service
339 Lord, You Give the Great Commission
555 Pescador de Hombres/ Lord, You Have Come
679 Prayer of St. Francis/ Oración de San Francisco
147 Psalm 40: Here I Am/God, My God, Come to My Aid

173 Psalm 96: Proclaim His Marvelous Deeds
532 Sent Forth by God's Blessing
541 Servant Song
537 The Servant Song
351 The Spirit Is A-Movin'
529 The Summons
632 These Alone Are Enough
687 We Are the Light of the World
534 You Have Anointed Me
402 You Have Called Us

COMMITMENT
See Discipleship

COMMUNION
See Liturgical Index: Service Music for Mass, Communion Song, Eucharistic Hymn

COMMUNION OF SAINTS
See Liturgical Index: Solemnities and Feasts, All Saints

COMMUNITY
See Church, Global Family, Love for Others, People of God

COMPASSION
See Love for Others, Love of God for Us, Mercy

CONFESSION
See Liturgical Index: Rites of the Church, Penance (Reconciliation)

CONFIDENCE
See also Hope
616 A Mighty Fortress
600 Be Not Afraid
605 Blest Be the Lord
591 Center of My Life
625 Christ Be beside Me
601 For You Are My God
607 How Can I Keep from Singing
611 Only in God (Foley)
618 Only in God (Talbot)
116 Psalm 16: Path of Life/Keep Me Safe (Balhoff/Daigle/Ducote)
117 Psalm 16: The Path of Life (Soper)
121 Psalm 19: Lord, You Have the Words
652 Psalm 23 (Conry)
128 Psalm 23: My Shepherd Is the Lord (Gelineau)
127 Psalm 23: The Lord Is My Shepherd/ I Shall Live in the House of the Lord (Crandal)
125 Psalm 23: The Lord Is My Shepherd/ I Shall Live in the House/ The Lord Prepares a Banquet (Cooney)
133 Psalm 27: The Goodness of the Lord
144 Psalm 34: Taste and See
642 Shepherd Me, O God
511 Taste and See
443 The Lord Is My Light
779 This Day God Gives Me
619 Though the Mountains May Fall
527 We Shall Overcome
610 You Are Near

CONFIRMATION
See Liturgical Index: Rites of the Church, Confirmation; Rite of Christian Initiation of Adults, Rites of Initiation, Confirmation; The Liturgical Year, Pentecost Sunday

CONTEMPLATION
See Liturgical Index: Devotions

CONTRITION
See Liturgical Index: Rites of the Church, Penance (Reconciliation)

CONVERSION
See also Liturgical Index: Rites of the Church, Penance (Reconciliation)
614 Amazing Grace
261 Ashes
478 Bread of Life
264 Change Our Hearts
573 Christ in Me Arise
410 Come Home
394 Down to the River to Pray
353 Everyone Moved by the Spirit
398 Flow River Flow
465 Gather Your People
627 God, Our Source and Life, Unite Us
343 Holy Spirit, Come to Me
411 Hosea
603 Into Your Hands
728 May We Praise You
582 O Beauty, Ever Ancient
399 O Breathe on Me, O Breath of God
416 Pardon Your People
153 Psalm 51: Be Merciful, O Lord
152 Psalm 51: Create in Me (Hurd)
154 Psalm 51: Create in Me (Kendzia)
155 Psalm 51: Create in Me/ Oh Dios, Crea en Mí (Cortés)
171 Psalm 95: If Today You Hear God's Voice (B. Farrell)
172 Psalm 95: If Today You Hear His Voice (Soper)
185 Psalm 104: Lord, Send Out Your Spirit
197 Psalm 130: With Our God There Is Mercy
417 Remember Your Love
267 Return to Me
412 Return to the Lord Your God
404 River of Glory
276 Save Your People
279 Seek the Lord
414 Softly and Tenderly Jesus Is Calling
278 Somebody's Knockin' at Your Door
346 Spirit, Come
561 Take, Lord, Receive
351 The Spirit Is A-Movin'
529 The Summons
632 These Alone Are Enough
382 Transfiguration
274 Transfigure Us, O Lord
524 We Are Called
617 You Are All that I Need
557 Your Song of Love

COURAGE
See also Trust
780 Abide with Me
600 Be Not Afraid
641 Because the Lord Is My Shepherd
565 Before the Sun Burned Bright
605 Blest Be the Lord
591 Center of My Life
461 Come to Us
593 Faith of Our Fathers
601 For You Are My God
471 Gather Us In
604 Here I Am (Booth)
539 Here I Am, Lord (Schutte)
607 How Can I Keep from Singing
684 I Am the Light of the World
764 If God Is for Us
752 In the Day of the Lord
606 On Eagle's Wings
618 Only in God
123 Psalm 22: My God, My God
125 Psalm 23: The Lord Is My Shepherd/ I Shall Live in the House/ The Lord Prepares a Banquet
133 Psalm 27: The Goodness of the Lord
134 Psalm 27: The Lord Is My Light
143 Psalm 34: Taste and See (Dean)
145 Psalm 34: Taste and See/ Gusten y Vean (Reza)
156 Psalm 63: My Soul Is Thirsting/ As Morning Breaks
190 Psalm 118: Give Thanks to the Lord
613 Seek Ye First
629 Stand by Me
608 The Lord Is Near/ May the Angels
654 There Is a Balm in Gilead
762 There Is a River
280 Turn to Me
524 We Are Called
609 We Will Rise Again
685 What You Hear in the Dark
651 You Are Mine

COVENANT
105 Gospel Canticle (Benedictus)
379 Holy Is His Name
269 How Long, O Lord
449 Like a Seal on Your Heart
669 Love Has Come
206 Luke 1: Benedictus (Angrisano/Stephan)
205 Luke 1: Benedictus (B. Farrell)
209 Luke 1: Magnificat (Angrisano/Stephan)
210 Luke 1: Magnificat (B. Farrell)
208 Luke 1: Magnificat (Rubalcava)
131 Psalm 25: To You, O Lord
167 Psalm 89: For Ever I Will Sing
632 These Alone Are Enough

630 To You, O God,
I Lift Up My Soul
452 Wherever You Go
766 Your Grace Is Enough

CREATION

714 All Creatures of Our God and King
703 All Good Gifts
695 All the Earth
696 Beautiful Savior
342 Come, O Spirit of the Lord
702 Come, Ye Thankful People, Come
658 Endless Is Your Love
705 For the Beauty of the Earth
697 For the Fruits of This Creation
700 Give Thanks to the Lord
698 God, Beyond All Names
694 How Great Thou Art
592 I Believe in the Sun
699 I Sing the Mighty Power of God
726 Joyful, Joyful, We Adore Thee
706 Let All Things Now Living
751 Let the Heavens Be Glad
663 Lover of Us All
701 Meadows and Mountains
778 Morning Has Broken
582 O Beauty, Ever Ancient
729 O Bless the Lord
357 O God, Almighty Father
738 Praise the Lord, My Soul
731 Praise the Lord, Ye Heavens
129 Psalm 24: Lord, This Is the People/Let the Lord Enter
183 Psalm 104: Send Forth Your Spirit, O Lord
345 Send Out Your Spirit
744 Sing, O Sing
474 The God of All Grace
779 This Day God Gives Me
763 Thy Kingdom Come
395 We Have Been Baptized in Christ
693 You Are Child

CRISIS

See Social Concern, Suffering

CROSS

780 Abide with Me
262 At the Cross Her Station Keeping/ Stabat Mater Dolorosa
295 Behold the Lamb of God
298 Behold the Wood
589 Do Not Fear to Hope
281 Faithful Cross
289 Glory in the Cross
753 Jesus Died upon the Cross
384 Lift High the Cross
294 O Sacred Head (Hurd)
297 O Sacred Head, Surrounded (PASSION CHORALE)
562 Only This I Want
122 Psalm 22: My God, My God (Manion)
123 Psalm 22: My God, My God (T.R. Smith)
124 Psalm 22: My God, My God/ Dios Mío, Dios Mío (Schiavone)
383 Take Up Our Cross (Stephan/Hart/Byrd)
552 Take Up Your Cross (ERHALT UNS, HERR)
327 Up from the Earth
299 We Venerate Your Cross/ Tu Cruz Adoramos
300 Were You There
302 When I Survey the Wondrous Cross
296 Wood of the Cross

DANCE

315 Join in the Dance
325 Let Us Sing and Be Glad/ And the Father Will Dance
322 Lord of the Dance
663 Lover of Us All
737 Praise God in This Holy Dwelling
198 Psalm 138: On the Day I Called

DARKNESS

See also Liturgical Index: The Liturgical Year, The Sacred Paschal Triduum

780 Abide with Me
553 All That Is Hidden
683 Christ, Be Our Light
782 Daylight's Ending
627 God, Our Source and Life, Unite Us
420 Holy Darkness
682 I Want to Walk as a Child of the Light
776 In God Alone
468 Lead Us to the Water
728 May We Praise You
306 Out of Darkness (Kendzia)
560 Out of Darkness (C. Walker)
680 Peace Prayer
404 River of Glory
688 The Light of Christ
634 There Is a Longing
597 Those Who See Light
274 Transfigure Us, O Lord
685 What You Hear in the Dark

DEATH/DYING

See also Eternal Life/Heaven; Liturgical Index: Rites of the Church, Order of Christian Funerals, Rite of Anointing (Care of the Sick)

780 Abide with Me
602 Entre Tus Manos
601 For You Are My God
435 Give Me Jesus
433 I, the Lord
653 In Every Age
424 Precious Lord, Take My Hand
773 Shall We Gather at the River
443 The Lord Is My Light

DEDICATION OF A CHURCH

See Liturgical Index: Rites of the Church, Dedication of a Church

DEVOTIONAL

696 Beautiful Savior
567 Jesu, Joy of Our Desiring
622 Jesus, Come to Us
587 Jesus, Lord
499 O Sacrament Most Holy
636 Open My Eyes/Abre Mis Ojos
477 See Us, Lord, About Your Altar
632 These Alone Are Enough
302 When I Survey the Wondrous Cross

DISCIPLESHIP

756 A Rightful Place
520 Act Justly
553 All That Is Hidden
39 Alleluia! Give the Glory
556 Anthem
286 As I Have Done for You
757 Beatitudes
565 Before the Sun Burned Bright
759 Blest Are They
530 Celtic Alleluia: Sending Forth
591 Center of My Life
625 Christ Be beside Me
683 Christ, Be Our Light
586 Christ before Us
566 Christ Has No Body Now but Yours
573 Christ in Me Arise
538 City of God
558 Come, Follow Me
407 Come to the River
580 Come Unto Me
394 Down to the River to Pray
593 Faith of Our Fathers
572 Father of Peace
397 Give Me Ears to Listen
542 God Has Chosen Me
539 Here I Am, Lord
684 I Am the Light of the World
592 I Believe in the Sun
531 I Send You Out
682 I Want to Walk as a Child of the Light
574 I Will Choose Christ
548 In Christ There Is No East or West
603 Into Your Hands
581 Jesus in the Morning
621 Lead Me, Guide Me
760 Lead Me, Lord
384 Lift High the Cross
528 Light of Christ
339 Lord, You Give the Great Commission
665 Love One Another
546 Many and Great
562 Only This I Want
560 Out of Darkness
501 Pan de Vida
340 Peace, My Friends
680 Peace Prayer
522 People of Peace
555 Pescador de Hombres/ Lord, You Have Come
691 Praise to You, O Christ, Our Savior

679 Prayer of St. Francis/ Oración de San Francisco
187 Psalm 116: Our Blessing-Cup/ El Cáliz que Bendecimos
195 Psalm 128: O Blessed Are Those
532 Sent Forth by God's Blessing
541 Servant Song
569 Sing a New Church
561 Take, Lord, Receive
543 Take the Word of God with You
383 Take Up Our Cross (Stephan/Hart/Byrd)
552 Take Up Your Cross (ERHALT UNS, HERR)
585 The Eyes and Hands of Christ
293 The Lord Jesus
351 The Spirit Is A-Movin'
529 The Summons
544 They'll Know We Are Christians
630 To You, O God, I Lift Up My Soul
563 Unless a Grain of Wheat
576 Voice of Christ
524 We Are Called
687 We Are the Light of the World
405 We Belong to You
564 We Have Been Told
685 What You Hear in the Dark
519 Whatsoever You Do
533 Without You
577 Women of the Church
534 You Have Anointed Me
402 You Have Called Us
557 Your Song of Love

ECOLOGY/ENVIRONMENT
See Creation

ECUMENISM
See also Church, Unity
659 Faithful Family
548 In Christ There Is No East or West
672 Let There Be Peace on Earth
568 One Spirit, One Church
569 Sing a New Church

ENCOURAGEMENT
See Courage, Hope

ENTRANCE SONG
See Gathering

ETERNAL LIFE/HEAVEN
See also Liturgical Index: Rites of the Church, Order of Christian Funerals
780 Abide with Me
714 All Creatures of Our God and King
614 Amazing Grace
480 As We Remember
641 Because the Lord Is My Shepherd
759 Blest Are They
410 Come Home
580 Come Unto Me
505 Eat This Bread
602 Entre Tus Manos
645 Eye Has Not Seen
659 Faithful Family
388 For All the Saints
601 For You Are My God
435 Give Me Jesus
429 Go Forth
661 God of Love
694 How Great Thou Art
430 How Lovely Is Your Dwelling Place
493 I Am the Bread of Life
318 I Know That My Redeemer Lives (DUKE STREET)
431 I Know That My Redeemer Lives (Soper)
433 I, the Lord
752 In the Day of the Lord
603 Into Your Hands
775 Jerusalem, My Happy Home
515 Jesus, the Bread of Life
434 Keep in Mind
760 Lead Me, Lord
640 Like a Child Rests
662 Love Divine, All Loves Excelling
357 O God, Almighty Father
612 O God, Our Help in Ages Past
606 On Eagle's Wings
508 One Love Released
440 Parable
650 Pastures of the Lord
680 Peace Prayer
679 Prayer of St. Francis/ Oración de San Francisco
424 Precious Lord, Take My Hand
121 Psalm 19: Lord, You Have the Words
133 Psalm 27: The Goodness of the Lord
134 Psalm 27: The Lord Is My Light
163 Psalm 84: How Lovely Is Your Dwelling Place
189 Psalm 116: In the Presence of God
193 Psalm 122: Let Us Go Rejoicing
441 Restless Is the Heart
773 Shall We Gather at the River
642 Shepherd Me, O God
774 Sing with All the Saints in Glory
750 Soon and Very Soon
571 The Church's One Foundation
688 The Light of Christ
443 The Lord Is My Light
608 The Lord Is Near/ May the Angels
336 The Strife Is O'er
563 Unless a Grain of Wheat
327 Up from the Earth
609 We Will Rise Again
668 What Wondrous Love Is This
777 Where My Father Lives
390 Ye Watchers and Ye Holy Ones
444 Yes, I Shall Arise

EUCHARIST
See also First Communion; Liturgical Index: Service Music for Mass, Communion Song, Eucharistic Hymn
481 Ang Katawan ni Kristo/ Behold, the Body of Christ
480 As We Remember
426 Blessed Be (Divine Praises)
484 Bread of Angels
485 Bread of Heaven
486 Draw Near
505 Eat This Bread
487 Gift of Finest Wheat
493 I Am the Bread of Life
497 Miracle of Grace
498 One Bread, One Body
463 Table of Plenty
513 The Supper of the Lord

EVANGELIZATION
See also Discipleship, Ministry/Mission
756 A Rightful Place
556 Anthem
473 As We Gather at Your Table
530 Celtic Alleluia: Sending Forth
539 Here I Am, Lord
411 Hosea
546 Many and Great
160 Psalm 67: O God, Let All the Nations
173 Psalm 96: Proclaim His Marvelous Deeds
178 Psalm 98: All the Ends of the Earth
569 Sing a New Church
535 With One Voice

EVENING
See also Liturgical Index: The Liturgy of the Hours, Evening Prayer
780 Abide with Me
781 Day Is Done
782 Daylight's Ending
110 Evening Hymn: O Radiant Light
699 I Sing the Mighty Power of God
653 In Every Age
623 Lord of All Hopefulness
111 Psalmody: Psalm 141

EXILE/EXODUS
See also Freedom, Global Family
590 As the Deer Longs
589 Do Not Fear to Hope
767 Isaiah 49
775 Jerusalem, My Happy Home
675 Peace Is Flowing like a River
148 Psalm 42: O God, for You I Long
194 Psalm 126: The Lord Has Done Great Things
229 Save Us, O Lord
750 Soon and Very Soon
527 We Shall Overcome

FAITH
See also Hope, Trust
553 All That Is Hidden
614 Amazing Grace
419 Be Still, My Soul
759 Blest Are They
591 Center of My Life
558 Come, Follow Me
589 Do Not Fear to Hope
676 Dona Nobis Pacem
596 Dwelling Place

392 Enter the Journey
645 Eye Has Not Seen
593 Faith of Our Fathers
471 Gather Us In
435 Give Me Jesus
595 Hold Me in Life
607 How Can I Keep from Singing
430 How Lovely Is Your Dwelling Place
493 I Am the Bread of Life
592 I Believe in the Sun
431 I Know That My Redeemer Lives
758 I Will Not Die
764 If God Is for Us (Brown)
768 If God Is for Us (Foley)
753 Jesus Died upon the Cross
587 Jesus, Lord
434 Keep in Mind
640 Like a Child Rests
667 May Love Be Ours
612 O God, Our Help in Ages Past
620 O God, You Search Me
606 On Eagle's Wings
615 Only a Shadow
611 Only in God (Foley)
618 Only in God (Talbot)
562 Only This I Want
306 Out of Darkness
224 Patience, People
522 People of Peace
117 Psalm 16: The Path of Life
128 Psalm 23: My Shepherd Is the Lord (Gelineau)
127 Psalm 23: The Lord Is My Shepherd/I Shall Live in the House of the Lord (Crandal)
125 Psalm 23: The Lord Is My Shepherd/I Shall Live in the House/The Lord Prepares a Banquet (Cooney)
133 Psalm 27: The Goodness of the Lord
137 Psalm 31: Father, I Put My Life in Your Hands
144 Psalm 34: Taste and See
156 Psalm 63: My Soul Is Thirsting/ As Morning Breaks
167 Psalm 89: For Ever I Will Sing
170 Psalm 91: Be with Me, Lord
189 Psalm 116: In the Presence of God
324 Roll Away the Stone
279 Seek the Lord
613 Seek Ye First
773 Shall We Gather at the River
418 Show Us Your Mercy
774 Sing with All the Saints in Glory
629 Stand by Me
571 The Church's One Foundation
474 The God of All Grace
608 The Lord Is Near/ May the Angels
632 These Alone Are Enough
597 Those Who See Light
630 To You, O God, I Lift Up My Soul
563 Unless a Grain of Wheat
588 We Remember
594 We Walk by Faith
609 We Will Rise Again
777 Where My Father Lives
651 You Are Mine

Fear
See Courage, Faith, Hope

First Communion
549 As We Celebrate
484 Bread of Angels
392 Enter the Journey
592 I Believe in the Sun
501 Pan de Vida

Forgiveness
See also Liturgical Index: Rites of the Church, Penance (Reconciliation)
480 As We Remember
659 Faithful Family
421 Lay Your Hands
413 Loving and Forgiving
677 Make Our Lives a Prayer of Peace
416 Pardon Your People
680 Peace Prayer
181 Psalm 103: The Lord Is Kind and Merciful

Freedom
See also Social Concern
264 Change Our Hearts
461 Come to Us
202 Exodus 15: To God Be Praise and Glory
518 God of the Hungry
768 If God Is for Us
675 Peace Is Flowing like a River
522 People of Peace
691 Praise to You, O Christ, Our Savior
194 Psalm 126: The Lord Has Done Great Things
524 We Are Called
527 We Shall Overcome
624 You Are the Healing

Funerals
See Liturgical Index: Rites of the Church, Order of Christian Funerals

Gathering
See also Liturgical Index: Service Music for Mass, The Introductory Rites
616 A Mighty Fortress
710 Alabaré/O Come and Sing
570 All Are Welcome
456 All People That on Earth Do Dwell
39 Alleluia! Give the Glory
509 As Grains of Wheat
473 As We Gather at Your Table
348 By the Waking of Our Hearts
711 Come, Christians, Join to Sing
457 Come, Now Is the Time to Worship
458 Come to the Feast/ Ven al Banquete
407 Come to the River
461 Come to Us
472 Come, Worship the Lord
460 Gather the People
471 Gather Us In
455 Gather Us Together
465 Gather Your People
724 I Will Rejoice
467 In This Place
103 Invitatory Psalm: Psalm 95
468 Lead Us to the Water
470 Let Us Go to the Altar
663 Lover of Us All
546 Many and Great
469 Now as We Gather
466 O Love of God/Amor de Dios
738 Praise the Lord, My Soul
732 Praise to the Lord
569 Sing a New Church
463 Table of Plenty
474 The God of All Grace
664 Ubi Caritas
734 We Gather Together
462 What Is This Place
446 Where There Is Love

Global Family
See also Church, Love for Others, People of God, Unity
520 Act Justly
456 All People That on Earth Do Dwell
712 All the Ends of the Earth
482 Bread of Life
683 Christ, Be Our Light
461 Come to Us
659 Faithful Family
718 From All That Dwell Below the Skies/Praise God from Whom All Blessings Flow
471 Gather Us In
465 Gather Your People
518 God of the Hungry
678 Grant Us Peace
694 How Great Thou Art
548 In Christ There Is No East or West
752 In the Day of the Lord
287 Jesu, Jesu
672 Let There Be Peace on Earth
528 Light of Christ
677 Make Our Lives a Prayer of Peace
546 Many and Great
551 Many and One
469 Now as We Gather
498 One Bread, One Body
501 Pan de Vida
159 Psalm 66: Let All the Earth (Soper)
158 Psalm 66: Let All the Earth Cry Out (Cooney)
160 Psalm 67: O God, Let All the Nations
161 Psalm 72: JusticeShall Flourish/ Lord, Every Nation
173 Psalm 96: Proclaim His Marvelous Deeds
178 Psalm 98: All the Ends of the Earth (Canedo)
177 Psalm 98: All the Ends of the Earth (Hurd)

569 Sing a New Church
740 Sing of the Lord's Goodness
547 Somos el Cuerpo de Cristo/ We Are the Body of Christ
747 This Is My Song
405 We Belong to You
288 Where Charity and Love Prevail

GOOD SHEPHERD
39 Alleluia! Give the Glory
641 Because the Lord Is My Shepherd
487 Gift of Finest Wheat
765 Like a Shepherd
652 Psalm 23 (Conry)
128 Psalm 23: My Shepherd Is the Lord (Gelineau)
126 Psalm 23: The Lord Is My Shepherd/ El Señor Es Mi Pastor (Reza)
127 Psalm 23: The Lord Is My Shepherd/I Shall Live in the House of the Lord (Crandal)
125 Psalm 23: The Lord Is My Shepherd/I Shall Live in the House/The Lord Prepares a Banquet (Cooney)
180 Psalm 100: We Are God's People
267 Return to Me
642 Shepherd Me, O God
475 Shepherd of Souls
648 The King of Love My Shepherd Is
332 Two Were Bound for Emmaus
609 We Will Rise Again

GOSPEL
See Ministry/Mission, Word

GRACE
See Salvation

GRADUATION
See also Holy Spirit
647 Fly like a Bird
672 Let There Be Peace on Earth
523 Lord, Whose Love in Humble Service
191 Psalm 118: This Is the Day
632 These Alone Are Enough
779 This Day God Gives Me
734 We Gather Together

GRIEF
See also Comfort, Lament
419 Be Still, My Soul
644 Come to Me
627 God, Our Source and Life, Unite Us
420 Holy Darkness
328 Now the Green Blade Rises
189 Psalm 116: In the Presence of God
634 There Is a Longing
275 With the Lord

HARVEST
703 All Good Gifts
509 As Grains of Wheat
702 Come, Ye Thankful People, Come
705 For the Beauty of the Earth
697 For the Fruits of This Creation
440 Parable
166 Psalm 85: Lord, Let Us See Your Kindness
463 Table of Plenty

HEALING
See also Liturgical Index: Rites of the Church, Rite of Anointing (Care of the Sick)
598 Age to Age
509 As Grains of Wheat
641 Because the Lord Is My Shepherd
483 Bread for the World
482 Bread of Life
538 City of God
644 Come to Me
407 Come to the River
770 Come to the Water
673 Day of Peace
589 Do Not Fear to Hope
676 Dona Nobis Pacem
398 Flow River Flow
517 For the Healing of the Nations
627 God, Our Source and Life, Unite Us
422 Healing River of the Spirit
425 Healing Waters
604 Here I Am
420 Holy Darkness
646 I Heard the Voice of Jesus
421 Lay Your Hands
468 Lead Us to the Water
765 Like a Shepherd
423 O Jesus, Healer of Wounded Souls
606 On Eagle's Wings
675 Peace Is Flowing like a River
522 People of Peace
652 Psalm 23 (Conry)
127 Psalm 23: The Lord Is My Shepherd/I Shall Live in the House of the Lord (Crandal)
125 Psalm 23: The Lord Is My Shepherd/ I Shall Live in the House/ The Lord Prepares a Banquet (Cooney)
170 Psalm 91: Be with Me, Lord
182 Psalm 103: The Lord Is Kind and Merciful
267 Return to Me
649 Shelter Me, O God
443 The Lord Is My Light
654 There Is a Balm in Gilead
634 There Is a Longing
670 There's a Wideness in God's Mercy
275 With the Lord
651 You Are Mine
624 You Are the Healing
557 Your Song of Love

HEAVEN
See Eternal Life/Heaven

HOLY NAME
364 All Hail the Power of Jesus' Name
313 Alleluia No. 1
366 At the Name of Jesus
379 Holy Is His Name
384 Lift High the Cross
725 Lift Up Your Hearts
413 Loving and Forgiving
209 Luke 1: Magnificat
160 Psalm 67: O God, Let All the Nations
199 Psalm 145: I Will Praise Your Name/ The Hand of the Lord Feeds Us

HOLY ORDERS
See Liturgical Index: Rites of the Church, Holy Orders

HOLY SPIRIT
39 Alleluia! Give the Glory
391 Baptized in Water
348 By the Waking of Our Hearts
352 Come, Holy Ghost
342 Come, O Spirit of the Lord
347 Envía Tu Espíritu
353 Everyone Moved by the Spirit
422 Healing River of the Spirit
344 Holy Spirit
408 Holy Spirit, Come Now/ Santo Espíritu, Ven
343 Holy Spirit, Come to Me
768 If God Is for Us
578 Now Is the Time
399 O Breathe on Me, O Breath of God
357 O God, Almighty Father
568 One Spirit, One Church
349 Pentecost Sequence
184 Psalm 104: Lord, Send Out Your Spirit (Canedo)
185 Psalm 104: Lord, Send Out Your Spirit (Zsigray)
183 Psalm 104: Send Forth Your Spirit, O Lord (C. Walker)
635 Sacred Silence
345 Send Out Your Spirit (Schoenbachler)
341 Send Us Your Spirit (Schutte)
346 Spirit, Come
351 The Spirit Is A-Movin'
544 They'll Know We Are Christians
350 Veni Sancte Spiritus
534 You Have Anointed Me

HOLY TRINITY
See Liturgical Index: Solemnities of the Lord during Ordinary Time, The Most Holy Trinity

HOMELESSNESS
See Global Family, Justice, Social Concern

HOPE
See also Faith, Trust
780 Abide with Me
553 All That Is Hidden

614 Amazing Grace
590 As the Deer Longs
549 As We Celebrate
600 Be Not Afraid
419 Be Still, My Soul
482 Bread of Life
264 Change Our Hearts
683 Christ, Be Our Light
538 City of God
770 Come to the Water
545 Companions on the Journey
673 Day of Peace
589 Do Not Fear to Hope
676 Dona Nobis Pacem
559 Earthen Vessels
392 Enter the Journey
221 Every Valley
645 Eye Has Not Seen
601 For You Are My God
471 Gather Us In
661 God of Love
105 Gospel Canticle (Benedictus)
720 Hallelujah Is Our Song
595 Hold Me in Life
420 Holy Darkness
607 How Can I Keep from Singing
430 How Lovely Is Your Dwelling Place
431 I Know That My Redeemer Lives
433 I, the Lord
758 I Will Not Die
764 If God Is for Us
584 In Christ Alone
653 In Every Age
776 In God Alone
270 In Your Love Remember Me
775 Jerusalem, My Happy Home
567 Jesu, Joy of Our Desiring
434 Keep in Mind
325 Let Us Sing and Be Glad/ And the Father Will Dance
640 Like a Child Rests
769 Lord of Glory
689 Lord, to Whom Shall We Go
206 Luke 1: Benedictus (Angrisano/Stephan)
205 Luke 1: Benedictus (B. Farrell)
667 May Love Be Ours
728 May We Praise You
612 O God, Our Help in Ages Past
606 On Eagle's Wings
611 Only in God
440 Parable
681 Peace
522 People of Peace
117 Psalm 16: The Path of Life
127 Psalm 23: The Lord Is My Shepherd/I Shall Live in the House of the Lord (Crandal)
125 Psalm 23: The Lord Is My Shepherd/I Shall Live in the House/The Lord Prepares a Banquet (Cooney)
130 Psalm 25: I Lift Up My Soul
131 Psalm 25: To You, O Lord (Joncas)
132 Psalm 25: To You, O Lord (Soper)
137 Psalm 31: Father, I Put My Life in Your Hands
141 Psalm 33: Happy the People You Have Chosen
142 Psalm 33: The Lord Fills the Earth with His Love
143 Psalm 34: Taste and See (Dean)
144 Psalm 34: Taste and See (Talbot)
148 Psalm 42: O God, for You I Long
156 Psalm 63: My Soul Is Thirsting/ As Morning Breaks
167 Psalm 89: For Ever I Will Sing
170 Psalm 91: Be with Me, Lord
111 Psalmody: Psalm 141
771 Rain Down
279 Seek the Lord
613 Seek Ye First
649 Shelter Me, O God
642 Shepherd Me, O God
346 Spirit, Come
561 Take, Lord, Receive
511 Taste and See
526 The Cry of the Poor
474 The God of All Grace
443 The Lord Is My Light
608 The Lord Is Near/ May the Angels
631 This Alone
763 Thy Kingdom Come
630 To You, O God, I Lift Up My Soul
563 Unless a Grain of Wheat
222 Waiting in Silence
588 We Remember
527 We Shall Overcome
609 We Will Rise Again
275 With the Lord
651 You Are Mine

Hospitality

See Welcome

House of God

See Liturgical Index: Rites of the Church, Dedication of a Church

Humility

379 Holy Is His Name
660 In Perfect Charity
270 In Your Love Remember Me
363 Jesus, the Lord
640 Like a Child Rests
207 Luke 1: Mary's Song (Joncas)
677 Make Our Lives a Prayer of Peace
375 Mary's Song (Rieth)
373 My Soul Magnifies the Lord
416 Pardon Your People
130 Psalm 25: I Lift Up My Soul
561 Take, Lord, Receive
526 The Cry of the Poor
583 'Tis the Gift to Be Simple
524 We Are Called
687 We Are the Light of the World

Hunger

509 As Grains of Wheat
483 Bread for the World
657 Christians, Let Us Love One Another
458 Come to the Feast/ Ven al Banquete
487 Gift of Finest Wheat
518 God of the Hungry
464 Here at This Table
489 In the Breaking of the Bread
467 In This Place
140 Psalm 33: Lord, Let Your Mercy
143 Psalm 34: Taste and See
463 Table of Plenty

Illness

See Healing; Liturgical Index: Rites of the Church, Rite of Anointing (Care of the Sick)

Incarnation

669 Love Has Come
357 O God, Almighty Father
688 The Light of Christ

Jesus Christ

See Good Shepherd, Holy Name; Liturgical Index: Solemnities of the Lord during Ordinary Time

John the Baptist

See Liturgical Index: The Liturgical Year, Season of Advent; Solemnities and Feasts, The Nativity of St. John the Baptist

Journey

656 All I Ask of You
614 Amazing Grace
556 Anthem
600 Be Not Afraid
538 City of God
461 Come to Us
580 Come Unto Me
545 Companions on the Journey
589 Do Not Fear to Hope
392 Enter the Journey
593 Faith of Our Fathers
572 Father of Peace
647 Fly like a Bird
435 Give Me Jesus
422 Healing River of the Spirit
646 I Heard the Voice of Jesus
574 I Will Choose Christ
489 In the Breaking of the Bread
621 Lead Me, Guide Me
760 Lead Me, Lord
706 Let All Things Now Living
765 Like a Shepherd
677 Make Our Lives a Prayer of Peace
440 Parable
555 Pescador de Hombres/ Lord, You Have Come
691 Praise to You, O Christ, Our Savior
424 Precious Lord, Take My Hand
117 Psalm 16: The Path of Life
131 Psalm 25: To You, O Lord
773 Shall We Gather at the River
750 Soon and Very Soon
571 The Church's One Foundation
537 The Servant Song
779 This Day God Gives Me
597 Those Who See Light

583 'Tis the Gift to Be Simple
274 Transfigure Us, O Lord
332 Two Were Bound for Emmaus
405 We Belong to You
527 We Shall Overcome
594 We Walk by Faith
452 Wherever You Go
402 You Have Called Us
557 Your Song of Love

JOY

714 All Creatures of Our God and King
695 All the Earth
712 All the Ends of the Earth
549 As We Celebrate
538 City of God
711 Come, Christians, Join to Sing
676 Dona Nobis Pacem
705 For the Beauty of the Earth
718 From All That Dwell Below the Skies/ Praise God from Whom All Blessings Flow
708 Grateful
720 Hallelujah Is Our Song
727 He Is the Lord
724 I Will Rejoice
768 If God Is for Us
752 In the Day of the Lord
270 In Your Love Remember Me
103 Invitatory Psalm: Psalm 95
203 Isaiah 12: We Shall Draw Water
567 Jesu, Joy of Our Desiring
315 Join in the Dance
726 Joyful, Joyful, We Adore Thee
333 Let Heaven Rejoice
470 Let Us Go to the Altar
325 Let Us Sing and Be Glad/ And the Father Will Dance
725 Lift Up Your Hearts
769 Lord of Glory
209 Luke 1: Magnificat (Angrisano/Stephan)
210 Luke 1: Magnificat (B. Farrell)
208 Luke 1: Magnificat (Rubalcava)
207 Luke 1: Mary's Song (Joncas)
373 My Soul Magnifies the Lord
338 One Sacrifice of Christ
735 Praise, My Soul, the King of Heaven
159 Psalm 66: Let All the Earth (Soper)
158 Psalm 66: Let All the Earth Cry Out (Cooney)
167 Psalm 89: For Ever I Will Sing
177 Psalm 98: All the Ends of the Earth
180 Psalm 100: We Are God's People
192 Psalm 118: This Is the Day (Joncas)
191 Psalm 118: This Is the Day (Soper)
193 Psalm 122: Let Us Go Rejoicing
194 Psalm 126: The Lord Has Done Great Things
323 Resucitó/He Is Risen
743 Sing a Joyful Song
742 Sing a New Song (Brown)
739 Sing a New Song (Schutte)
722 Sing to the Mountains
474 The God of All Grace
331 This Day Was Made by the Lord
335 This Is the Day (Fisher)
326 This Is the Day (Kendzia)
763 Thy Kingdom Come
327 Up from the Earth

JUBILATION

See Joy, Praise

JUBILEE/HOLY YEAR/MILLENNIUM

See Liturgical Index: Rites of the Church, Holy Orders, Rite of Religious Profession

JUDGMENT

See also Second Coming

755 Mine Eyes Have Seen the Glory
519 Whatsoever You Do

JUSTICE

520 Act Justly
525 Alleluia! Raise the Gospel
556 Anthem
538 City of God
458 Come to the Feast/ Ven al Banquete
589 Do Not Fear to Hope
347 Envía Tu Espíritu
659 Faithful Family
697 For the Fruits of This Creation
517 For the Healing of the Nations
542 God Has Chosen Me
758 I Will Not Die
752 In the Day of the Lord
339 Lord, You Give the Great Commission
665 Love One Another
209 Luke 1: Magnificat (Angrisano/Stephan)
210 Luke 1: Magnificat (B. Farrell)
207 Luke 1: Mary's Song (Joncas)
677 Make Our Lives a Prayer of Peace
375 Mary's Song (Rieth)
373 My Soul Magnifies the Lord
522 People of Peace
161 Psalm 72: Justice Shall Flourish/Lord, Every Nation
164 Psalm 85: Come, O Lord/ Lord, Let Us See Your Kindness (Balhoff/Daigle/Ducote)
165 Psalm 85: Let Us See Your Kindness (MacAller)
166 Psalm 85: Lord, Let Us See Your Kindness (Soper)
176 Psalm 97: The Lord Is King
547 Somos el Cuerpo de Cristo/ We Are the Body of Christ
507 Taste and See
526 The Cry of the Poor
524 We Are Called
687 We Are the Light of the World
527 We Shall Overcome
519 Whatsoever You Do
535 With One Voice
533 Without You
692 Your Words Are Spirit and Life

KINGDOM/REIGN OF GOD

See also Liturgical Index: Solemnities of the Lord during Ordinary Time, Our Lord Jesus Christ, King of the Universe

756 A Rightful Place
364 All Hail the Power of Jesus' Name
366 At the Name of Jesus
757 Beatitudes
295 Behold the Lamb of God
717 Blessed by Your Sacrifice
759 Blest Are They
538 City of God
362 Crown Him with Many Crowns
471 Gather Us In
719 God, We Praise You
105 Gospel Canticle (Benedictus)
365 Hail, Redeemer, King Divine
721 Holy God, We Praise Thy Name
758 I Will Not Die
775 Jerusalem, My Happy Home
760 Lead Me, Lord
730 Let All Mortal Flesh Keep Silence
751 Let the Heavens Be Glad
528 Light of Christ
206 Luke 1: Benedictus (Angrisano/Stephan)
205 Luke 1: Benedictus (B. Farrell)
459 Our God Is Here
735 Praise, My Soul, the King of Heaven
151 Psalm 47: God Mounts His Throne
176 Psalm 97: The Lord Is King
193 Psalm 122: Let Us Go Rejoicing
613 Seek Ye First
750 Soon and Very Soon
463 Table of Plenty
368 The King of Glory
226 The King Shall Come When Morning Dawns
762 There Is a River
631 This Alone
763 Thy Kingdom Come
360 To Jesus Christ, Our Sovereign King
524 We Are Called

LABOR

770 Come to the Water
697 For the Fruits of This Creation
623 Lord of All Hopefulness
555 Pescador de Hombres/ Lord, You Have Come
195 Psalm 128: O Blessed Are Those

LAMENT

122 Psalm 22: My God, My God (Manion)
123 Psalm 22: My God, My God (T.R. Smith)

124 Psalm 22: My God, My God/ Dios Mío, Dios Mío (Schiavone)
196 Psalm 130: Out of the Depths
634 There Is a Longing
275 With the Lord

LAW
See Commandments, Covenant, Word

LIBERATION
See Freedom

LIGHT
39 Alleluia! Give the Glory
549 As We Celebrate
683 Christ, Be Our Light
538 City of God
559 Earthen Vessels
353 Everyone Moved by the Spirit
659 Faithful Family
471 Gather Us In
723 Glory and Praise to Our God
627 God, Our Source and Life, Unite Us
684 I Am the Light of the World
592 I Believe in the Sun
646 I Heard the Voice of Jesus
682 I Want to Walk as a Child of the Light
776 In God Alone
325 Let Us Sing and Be Glad/ And the Father Will Dance
528 Light of Christ
689 Lord, to Whom Shall We Go
728 May We Praise You
306 Out of Darkness (Kendzia)
560 Out of Darkness (C. Walker)
134 Psalm 27: The Lord Is My Light
404 River of Glory
688 The Light of Christ
443 The Lord Is My Light
608 The Lord Is Near/ May the Angels
597 Those Who See Light
382 Transfiguration
274 Transfigure Us, O Lord
524 We Are Called
687 We Are the Light of the World
395 We Have Been Baptized in Christ
685 What You Hear in the Dark
535 With One Voice
533 Without You
693 You Are Child
557 Your Song of Love

LONELINESS
See also Longing for God
647 Fly like a Bird
604 Here I Am
420 Holy Darkness
269 How Long, O Lord
122 Psalm 22: My God, My God (Manion)
123 Psalm 22: My God, My God (T.R. Smith)
124 Psalm 22: My God, My God/ Dios Mío, Dios Mío (Schiavone)
418 Show Us Your Mercy
222 Waiting in Silence

LONGING FOR GOD
590 As the Deer Longs
633 Be Thou My Vision
348 By the Waking of Our Hearts
579 Come, Lord Jesus
461 Come to Us
435 Give Me Jesus
628 God Be in My Head
422 Healing River of the Spirit
595 Hold Me in Life
269 How Long, O Lord
430 How Lovely Is Your Dwelling Place
772 I Have Loved You
682 I Want to Walk as a Child of the Light
467 In This Place
567 Jesu, Joy of Our Desiring
622 Jesus, Come to Us
436 My Soul Is Thirsting
582 O Beauty, Ever Ancient
636 Open My Eyes/Abre Mis Ojos
424 Precious Lord, Take My Hand
117 Psalm 16: The Path of Life
130 Psalm 25: I Lift Up My Soul
132 Psalm 25: To You, O Lord
133 Psalm 27: The Goodness of the Lord
134 Psalm 27: The Lord Is My Light
147 Psalm 40: Here I Am/God, My God, Come to My Aid
148 Psalm 42: O God, for You I Long
149 Psalm 42/43: As the Deer Longs
156 Psalm 63: My Soul Is Thirsting/ As Morning Breaks
157 Psalm 63: My Soul Thirsts
163 Psalm 84: How Lovely Is Your Dwelling Place
166 Psalm 85: Lord, Let Us See Your Kindness
168 Psalm 90: In Every Age
196 Psalm 130: Out of the Depths
197 Psalm 130: With Our God There Is Mercy
441 Restless Is the Heart
229 Save Us, O Lord
279 Seek the Lord
629 Stand by Me
634 There Is a Longing
631 This Alone
222 Waiting in Silence
405 We Belong to You
594 We Walk by Faith
275 With the Lord
533 Without You
444 Yes, I Shall Arise
617 You Are All that I Need
693 You Are Child

LOVE FOR GOD
598 Age to Age
696 Beautiful Savior
602 Entre Tus Manos
659 Faithful Family
581 Jesus in the Morning
119 Psalm 18: I Love You, Lord, My Strength
561 Take, Lord, Receive
632 These Alone Are Enough
533 Without You

LOVE FOR OTHERS
520 Act Justly
656 All I Ask of You
286 As I Have Done for You
478 Bread of Life
657 Christians, Let Us Love One Another
579 Come, Lord Jesus
292 Donde Hay Amor y Caridad/ Where Charity and Love Abound
659 Faithful Family
517 For the Healing of the Nations
518 God of the Hungry
548 In Christ There Is No East or West
660 In Perfect Charity
287 Jesu, Jesu
449 Like a Seal on Your Heart
523 Lord, Whose Love in Humble Service
666 Love Goes On
451 Love Never Fails
665 Love One Another
677 Make Our Lives a Prayer of Peace
466 O Love of God/Amor de Dios
501 Pan de Vida
680 Peace Prayer
522 People of Peace
679 Prayer of St. Francis/ Oración de San Francisco
547 Somos el Cuerpo de Cristo/ We Are the Body of Christ
544 They'll Know We Are Christians
583 'Tis the Gift to Be Simple
510 Ubi Caritas (Hurd)
664 Ubi Caritas (Rosania)
514 Vine and Branches
524 We Are Called
550 We Are Many Parts
687 We Are the Light of the World
564 We Have Been Told
519 Whatsoever You Do
288 Where Charity and Love Prevail
453 Where Love Is Found
446 Where There Is Love
533 Without You

LOVE OF GOD FOR US
616 A Mighty Fortress
598 Age to Age
707 All My Days
549 As We Celebrate
366 At the Name of Jesus
565 Before the Sun Burned Bright
295 Behold the Lamb of God
298 Behold the Wood
410 Come Home
545 Companions on the Journey
589 Do Not Fear to Hope
292 Donde Hay Amor y Caridad/ Where Charity and Love Abound
596 Dwelling Place
658 Endless Is Your Love

353 Everyone Moved by the Spirit
659 Faithful Family
647 Fly like a Bird
697 For the Fruits of This Creation
575 For the Sake of Christ
455 Gather Us Together
700 Give Thanks to the Lord
655 God Is Love (Joncas)
661 God of Love (Schutte)
627 God, Our Source and Life, Unite Us
105 Gospel Canticle (Benedictus)
678 Grant Us Peace
708 Grateful
539 Here I Am, Lord
329 I Am the Resurrection
540 I Am the Vine
772 I Have Loved You
764 If God Is for Us (Brown)
768 If God Is for Us (Foley)
584 In Christ Alone
270 In Your Love Remember Me
767 Isaiah 49
587 Jesus, Lord
325 Let Us Sing and Be Glad/ And the Father Will Dance
725 Lift Up Your Hearts
709 Like Cedars
662 Love Divine, All Loves Excelling
666 Love Goes On
663 Lover of Us All
413 Loving and Forgiving
206 Luke 1: Benedictus
209 Luke 1: Magnificat
521 Make Your Home in Me
375 Mary's Song
667 May Love Be Ours
728 May We Praise You
704 Now Thank We All Our God
582 O Beauty, Ever Ancient
620 O God, You Search Me
466 O Love of God/Amor de Dios
338 One Sacrifice of Christ
615 Only a Shadow
611 Only in God
340 Peace, My Friends
116 Psalm 16: Path of Life/ Keep Me Safe
652 Psalm 23
132 Psalm 25: To You, O Lord
140 Psalm 33: Lord, Let Your Mercy
142 Psalm 33: The Lord Fills the Earth with His Love
146 Psalm 34: I Will Always Thank the Lord
144 Psalm 34: Taste and See
156 Psalm 63: My Soul Is Thirsting/ As Morning Breaks
166 Psalm 85: Lord, Let Us See Your Kindness
167 Psalm 89: For Ever I Will Sing
181 Psalm 103: The Lord Is Kind and Merciful (Dufford)
182 Psalm 103: The Lord Is Kind and Merciful (Manalo)
189 Psalm 116: In the Presence of God
197 Psalm 130: With Our God There Is Mercy
198 Psalm 138: On the Day I Called
200 Psalm 145: I Will Praise Your Name/The Hand of the Lord (T.R. Smith)
199 Psalm 145: I Will Praise Your Name/The Hand of the Lord Feeds Us (Soper)
201 Psalm 146: Praise the Lord, My Soul/Lord, Come and Save Us
393 Put On Christ
771 Rain Down
417 Remember Your Love
267 Return to Me
404 River of Glory
414 Softly and Tenderly Jesus Is Calling
463 Table of Plenty
561 Take, Lord, Receive
507 Taste and See (Hurd)
511 Taste and See (Moore)
526 The Cry of the Poor
474 The God of All Grace
648 The King of Love My Shepherd Is
688 The Light of Christ
608 The Lord Is Near/ May the Angels
670 There's a Wideness in God's Mercy
619 Though the Mountains May Fall
514 Vine and Branches
564 We Have Been Told
588 We Remember
668 What Wondrous Love Is This
415 You Alone
651 You Are Mine
610 You Are Near
402 You Have Called Us
766 Your Grace Is Enough
557 Your Song of Love

Marriage

See Liturgical Index: Rites of the Church, Marriage

Mary

See also Liturgical Index: The Liturgical Year, Season of Christmas, Mary, the Holy Mother of God; Solemnities and Feasts, The Assumption of the Blessed Virgin Mary, The Immaculate Conception of the Blessed Virgin Mary, Our Lady of Guadalupe

262 At the Cross Her Station Keeping/ Stabat Mater Dolorosa
369 Ave Maria
371 Del Cielo Ha Bajado
112 Gospel Canticle (Magnificat)
376 Hail, Holy Queen
372 Hail Mary: Gentle Woman
379 Holy Is His Name
370 Immaculate Mary
209 Luke 1: Magnificat (Angrisano/Stephan)
210 Luke 1: Magnificat (B. Farrell)
208 Luke 1: Magnificat (Rubalcava)
207 Luke 1: Mary's Song (Joncas)
375 Mary's Song (Rieth)
373 My Soul Magnifies the Lord
150 Psalm 45: The Queen Stands
635 Sacred Silence
380 Sing of Mary
374 Song of Mary
378 The Angel Gabriel from Heaven Came
377 There Is Nothing Told
241 Who Has Known

Meditation

716 Abba! Father
590 As the Deer Longs
600 Be Not Afraid
295 Behold the Lamb of God
478 Bread of Life
348 By the Waking of Our Hearts
591 Center of My Life
644 Come to Me
770 Come to the Water
580 Come Unto Me
472 Come, Worship the Lord
658 Endless Is Your Love
761 Find Us Ready
647 Fly like a Bird
628 God Be in My Head
698 God, Beyond All Names
343 Holy Spirit, Come to Me
269 How Long, O Lord
660 In Perfect Charity
640 Like a Child Rests
620 O God, You Search Me
690 O Word of God
606 On Eagle's Wings
618 Only in God
636 Open My Eyes/Abre Mis Ojos
440 Parable
224 Patience, People
301 Pietà
679 Prayer of St. Francis/ Oración de San Francisco
417 Remember Your Love
441 Restless Is the Heart
267 Return to Me
635 Sacred Silence
613 Seek Ye First
634 There Is a Longing
632 These Alone Are Enough
631 This Alone
280 Turn to Me
610 You Are Near

Mercy

480 As We Remember
723 Glory and Praise to Our God
265 Gracious God
425 Healing Waters
604 Here I Am
269 How Long, O Lord
270 In Your Love Remember Me
421 Lay Your Hands
765 Like a Shepherd
413 Loving and Forgiving
210 Luke 1: Magnificat
551 Many and One
373 My Soul Magnifies the Lord
416 Pardon Your People
301 Pietà
735 Praise, My Soul, the King of Heaven
738 Praise the Lord, My Soul
136 Psalm 30: I Will Praise You, Lord

140 Psalm 33: Lord, Let Your Mercy
143 Psalm 34: Taste and See (Dean)
145 Psalm 34: Taste and See/ Gusten y Vean (Reza)
153 Psalm 51: Be Merciful, O Lord
152 Psalm 51: Create in Me (Hurd)
154 Psalm 51: Create in Me (Kendzia)
155 Psalm 51: Create in Me/ Oh Dios, Crea en Mí (Cortés)
164 Psalm 85: Come, O Lord/ Lord, Let Us See Your Kindness
181 Psalm 103: The Lord Is Kind and Merciful (Dufford)
182 Psalm 103: The Lord Is Kind and Merciful (Manalo)
190 Psalm 118: Give Thanks to the Lord
196 Psalm 130: Out of the Depths
197 Psalm 130: With Our God There Is Mercy
417 Remember Your Love
276 Save Your People
279 Seek the Lord
418 Show Us Your Mercy
414 Softly and Tenderly Jesus Is Calling
599 The Jesus Song
608 The Lord Is Near/ May the Angels
634 There Is a Longing
670 There's a Wideness in God's Mercy
619 Though the Mountains May Fall
763 Thy Kingdom Come
687 We Are the Light of the World
275 With the Lord
415 You Alone

Ministry/Mission

See also Church, Discipleship

570 All Are Welcome
553 All That Is Hidden
525 Alleluia! Raise the Gospel
556 Anthem
286 As I Have Done for You
473 As We Gather at Your Table
600 Be Not Afraid
530 Celtic Alleluia: Sending Forth
683 Christ, Be Our Light
538 City of God
579 Come, Lord Jesus
580 Come Unto Me
392 Enter the Journey
593 Faith of Our Fathers
761 Find Us Ready
517 For the Healing of the Nations
554 Go Make a Difference
536 Go Out, Go Out
542 God Has Chosen Me
518 God of the Hungry
531 I Send You Out
287 Jesu, Jesu
528 Light of Christ
523 Lord, Whose Love in Humble Service
339 Lord, You Give the Great Commission
665 Love One Another
546 Many and Great
560 Out of Darkness
501 Pan de Vida
680 Peace Prayer
555 Pescador de Hombres/ Lord, You Have Come
679 Prayer of St. Francis/ Oración de San Francisco
532 Sent Forth by God's Blessing
541 Servant Song
569 Sing a New Church
547 Somos el Cuerpo de Cristo/ We Are the Body of Christ
561 Take, Lord, Receive
543 Take the Word of God with You
383 Take Up Our Cross
585 The Eyes and Hands of Christ
293 The Lord Jesus
537 The Servant Song
529 The Summons
544 They'll Know We Are Christians
563 Unless a Grain of Wheat
576 Voice of Christ
524 We Are Called
687 We Are the Light of the World
405 We Belong to You
519 Whatsoever You Do
535 With One Voice
534 You Have Anointed Me
402 You Have Called Us

Morning

See also Liturgical Index: The Liturgy of the Hours, Morning Prayer

714 All Creatures of Our God and King
435 Give Me Jesus
358 Holy, Holy, Holy
699 I Sing the Mighty Power of God
709 Like Cedars
623 Lord of All Hopefulness
778 Morning Has Broken
104 Psalmody: Psalm 63
345 Send Out Your Spirit
226 The King Shall Come When Morning Dawns
779 This Day God Gives Me

Multilingual

See Language Index

Music Ministry

714 All Creatures of Our God and King
718 From All That Dwell Below the Skies/ Praise God from Whom All Blessings Flow
607 How Can I Keep from Singing
699 I Sing the Mighty Power of God
103 Invitatory Psalm: Psalm 95
726 Joyful, Joyful, We Adore Thee
470 Let Us Go to the Altar
709 Like Cedars
737 Praise God in This Holy Dwelling
178 Psalm 98: All the Ends of the Earth
541 Servant Song
743 Sing a Joyful Song
742 Sing a New Song (Brown)
739 Sing a New Song (Schutte)
741 Sing Alleluia, Sing
740 Sing of the Lord's Goodness

Nation

See Patriotic

Nature

See Creation

Night

See Liturgical Index: The Liturgy of the Hours, Night Prayer

Obedience

574 I Will Choose Christ
555 Pescador de Hombres/ Lord, You Have Come
121 Psalm 19: Lord, You Have the Words
147 Psalm 40: Here I Am/God, My God, Come to My Aid
171 Psalm 95: If Today You Hear God's Voice (B. Farrell)
172 Psalm 95: If Today You Hear His Voice (Soper)
195 Psalm 128: O Blessed Are Those
541 Servant Song
529 The Summons
632 These Alone Are Enough
280 Turn to Me
564 We Have Been Told
777 Where My Father Lives

Ordination

See Liturgical Index: Rites of the Church, Holy Orders

Our Lady of Guadalupe

See Liturgical Index: Solemnities and Feasts, Our Lady of Guadalupe

Pardon

See Mercy; Liturgical Index: Rites of the Church, Penance (Reconciliation)

Paschal Mystery

See also Liturgical Index: The Liturgical Year, The Sacred Paschal Triduum

480 As We Remember
319 At the Lamb's High Feast
295 Behold the Lamb of God
298 Behold the Wood
460 Gather the People
318 I Know That My Redeemer Lives
753 Jesus Died upon the Cross
363 Jesus, the Lord
384 Lift High the Cross
322 Lord of the Dance
328 Now the Green Blade Rises
297 O Sacred Head, Surrounded
336 The Strife Is O'er

563 Unless a Grain of Wheat (B. Farrell)
516 Unless a Grain of Wheat (Hurd)
327 Up from the Earth
588 We Remember
668 What Wondrous Love Is This
754 Worthy Is the Lamb

Patriotic

703 All Good Gifts
745 America
749 America the Beautiful
746 Eternal Father, Strong to Save
748 God of Our Fathers
672 Let There Be Peace on Earth
755 Mine Eyes Have Seen the Glory
747 This Is My Song
734 We Gather Together

Peace

461 Come to Us
673 Day of Peace
589 Do Not Fear to Hope
676 Dona Nobis Pacem (Norbet)
671 Dona Nobis Pacem (Traditional)
596 Dwelling Place
517 For the Healing of the Nations
674 Give Us Your Peace
748 God of Our Fathers
678 Grant Us Peace
720 Hallelujah Is Our Song
422 Healing River of the Spirit
270 In Your Love Remember Me
672 Let There Be Peace on Earth
640 Like a Child Rests
677 Make Our Lives a Prayer of Peace
551 Many and One
416 Pardon Your People
681 Peace
675 Peace Is Flowing like a River
340 Peace, My Friends
680 Peace Prayer
522 People of Peace
679 Prayer of St. Francis/ Oración de San Francisco
161 Psalm 72: Justice Shall Flourish/Lord, Every Nation
164 Psalm 85: Come, O Lord/ Lord, Let Us See Your Kindness
165 Psalm 85: Let Us See Your Kindness
166 Psalm 85: Lord, Let Us See Your Kindness
762 There Is a River
747 This Is My Song
527 We Shall Overcome
533 Without You
651 You Are Mine

Penance

See Conversion; Liturgical Index: Rites of the Church, Penance (Reconciliation)

People of God

See also Church

456 All People That on Earth Do Dwell
509 As Grains of Wheat
683 Christ, Be Our Light
566 Christ Has No Body Now but Yours
471 Gather Us In
465 Gather Your People
528 Light of Christ
469 Now as We Gather
498 One Bread, One Body
401 One Lord
560 Out of Darkness
501 Pan de Vida
141 Psalm 33: Happy the People You Have Chosen
180 Psalm 100: We Are God's People
547 Somos el Cuerpo de Cristo/ We Are the Body of Christ
588 We Remember
577 Women of the Church

Petition/Prayer

See also Liturgical Index: Service Music for Mass, Prayer of the Faithful

780 Abide with Me
633 Be Thou My Vision
625 Christ Be beside Me
579 Come, Lord Jesus
673 Day of Peace
676 Dona Nobis Pacem (Norbet)
671 Dona Nobis Pacem (Traditional)
394 Down to the River to Pray
596 Dwelling Place
746 Eternal Father, Strong to Save
572 Father of Peace
575 For the Sake of Christ
435 Give Me Jesus
674 Give Us Your Peace
628 God Be in My Head
425 Healing Waters
344 Holy Spirit (Canedo)
343 Holy Spirit, Come to Me (Hoy)
269 How Long, O Lord
653 In Every Age
660 In Perfect Charity
622 Jesus, Come to Us
581 Jesus in the Morning
587 Jesus, Lord
621 Lead Me, Guide Me
305 Litany of the Saints (Becker)
307 Litany of the Saints (Chant)
623 Lord of All Hopefulness
677 Make Our Lives a Prayer of Peace
728 May We Praise You
399 O Breathe on Me, O Breath of God
357 O God, Almighty Father
626 O God, Hear Us
690 O Word of God
636 Open My Eyes/Abre Mis Ojos
680 Peace Prayer
301 Pietà
679 Prayer of St. Francis/ Oración de San Francisco
147 Psalm 40: Here I Am/God, My God, Come to My Aid
152 Psalm 51: Create in Me (Hurd)
155 Psalm 51: Create in Me/Oh Dios, Crea en Mí (Cortés)
196 Psalm 130: Out of the Depths
197 Psalm 130: With Our God There Is Mercy
111 Psalmody: Psalm 141
635 Sacred Silence
229 Save Us, O Lord
276 Save Your People
613 Seek Ye First
341 Send Us Your Spirit
649 Shelter Me, O God
346 Spirit, Come
599 The Jesus Song
648 The King of Love My Shepherd Is
634 There Is a Longing
630 To You, O God, I Lift Up My Soul
274 Transfigure Us, O Lord
275 With the Lord
624 You Are the Healing

Pilgrim Church

See also Journey

593 Faith of Our Fathers
466 O Love of God/ Amor de Dios
571 The Church's One Foundation

Pilgrimage

See Journey

Power of God

616 A Mighty Fortress
39 Alleluia! Give the Glory
342 Come, O Spirit of the Lord
589 Do Not Fear to Hope
202 Exodus 15: To God Be Praise and Glory
700 Give Thanks to the Lord
723 Glory and Praise to Our God
694 How Great Thou Art
699 I Sing the Mighty Power of God
584 In Christ Alone
752 In the Day of the Lord
103 Invitatory Psalm: Psalm 95
203 Isaiah 12: We Shall Draw Water
726 Joyful, Joyful, We Adore Thee
413 Loving and Forgiving
209 Luke 1: Magnificat (Angrisano/Stephan)
210 Luke 1: Magnificat (B. Farrell)
755 Mine Eyes Have Seen the Glory
729 O Bless the Lord
611 Only in God
738 Praise the Lord, My Soul
159 Psalm 66: Let All the Earth (Soper)
158 Psalm 66: Let All the Earth Cry Out (Cooney)
176 Psalm 97: The Lord Is King
178 Psalm 98: All the Ends of the Earth (Canedo)
177 Psalm 98: All the Ends of the Earth (Hurd)
179 Psalm 98: The Lord Has Revealed
185 Psalm 104: Lord, Send Out Your Spirit (Zsigray)

183 Psalm 104: Send Forth Your Spirit, O Lord (C. Walker)
192 Psalm 118: This Is the Day
194 Psalm 126: The Lord Has Done Great Things
744 Sing, O Sing
507 Taste and See
474 The God of All Grace
335 This Is the Day
382 Transfiguration
754 Worthy Is the Lamb
624 You Are the Healing

PRAISE

616 A Mighty Fortress
716 Abba! Father
710 Alabaré/O Come and Sing
714 All Creatures of Our God and King
354 All Hail, Adored Trinity
364 All Hail the Power of Jesus' Name
707 All My Days
456 All People That on Earth Do Dwell
355 All Praise and Glad Thanksgiving
695 All the Earth (Deiss)
712 All the Ends of the Earth (Dufford)
713 Alle, Alle, Alleluia
39 Alleluia! Give the Glory
313 Alleluia No. 1
361 Alleluia! Sing to Jesus
549 As We Celebrate
366 At the Name of Jesus
696 Beautiful Savior
715 Been So Busy
717 Blessed by Your Sacrifice
605 Blest Be the Lord
711 Come, Christians, Join to Sing
359 Come Now, Almighty King
457 Come, Now Is the Time to Worship
342 Come, O Spirit of the Lord
472 Come, Worship the Lord
362 Crown Him with Many Crowns
204 Daniel 3: Glory and Praise for Ever
202 Exodus 15: To God Be Praise and Glory
705 For the Beauty of the Earth
718 From All That Dwell Below the Skies/ Praise God from Whom All Blessings Flow
455 Gather Us Together
700 Give Thanks to the Lord
723 Glory and Praise to Our God
536 Go Out, Go Out
719 God, We Praise You
112 Gospel Canticle (Magnificat)
708 Grateful
365 Hail, Redeemer, King Divine
727 He Is the Lord
721 Holy God, We Praise Thy Name
358 Holy, Holy, Holy
379 Holy Is His Name
694 How Great Thou Art
356 Hymn of Praise
699 I Sing the Mighty Power of God
724 I Will Rejoice
103 Invitatory Psalm: Psalm 95
581 Jesus in the Morning
363 Jesus, the Lord
726 Joyful, Joyful, We Adore Thee
730 Let All Mortal Flesh Keep Silence
706 Let All Things Now Living
333 Let Heaven Rejoice
470 Let Us Go to the Altar
725 Lift Up Your Hearts
662 Love Divine, All Loves Excelling
669 Love Has Come
663 Lover of Us All
209 Luke 1: Magnificat (Angrisano/Stephan)
210 Luke 1: Magnificat (B. Farrell)
208 Luke 1: Magnificat (Rubalcava)
207 Luke 1: Mary's Song (Joncas)
375 Mary's Song (Rieth)
728 May We Praise You
701 Meadows and Mountains
778 Morning Has Broken
373 My Soul Magnifies the Lord
704 Now Thank We All Our God
729 O Bless the Lord
357 O God, Almighty Father
733 O God beyond All Praising
611 Only in God
459 Our God Is Here
675 Peace Is Flowing like a River
737 Praise God in This Holy Dwelling
735 Praise, My Soul, the King of Heaven
738 Praise the Lord, My Soul
731 Praise the Lord, Ye Heavens
732 Praise to the Lord
691 Praise to You, O Christ, Our Savior
135 Psalm 29: The Lord Will Bless His People with Peace
136 Psalm 30: I Will Praise You, Lord
141 Psalm 33: Happy the People You Have Chosen
146 Psalm 34: I Will Always Thank the Lord
143 Psalm 34: Taste and See (Dean)
144 Psalm 34: Taste and See (Talbot)
151 Psalm 47: God Mounts His Throne
159 Psalm 66: Let All the Earth (Soper)
158 Psalm 66: Let All the Earth Cry Out (Cooney)
167 Psalm 89: For Ever I Will Sing
171 Psalm 95: If Today You Hear God's Voice (B. Farrell)
172 Psalm 95: If Today You Hear His Voice (Soper)
173 Psalm 96: Proclaim His Marvelous Deeds
176 Psalm 97: The Lord Is King
178 Psalm 98: All the Ends of the Earth (Canedo)
177 Psalm 98: All the Ends of the Earth (Hurd)
179 Psalm 98: The Lord Has Revealed
180 Psalm 100: We Are God's People
185 Psalm 104: Lord, Send Out Your Spirit
192 Psalm 118: This Is the Day
194 Psalm 126: The Lord Has Done Great Things
200 Psalm 145: I Will Praise Your Name/The Hand of the Lord (T.R. Smith)
199 Psalm 145: I Will Praise Your Name/The Hand of the Lord Feeds Us (Soper)
201 Psalm 146: Praise the Lord, My Soul/Lord, Come and Save Us
532 Sent Forth by God's Blessing
743 Sing a Joyful Song
742 Sing a New Song (Brown)
739 Sing a New Song (Schutte)
741 Sing Alleluia, Sing
744 Sing, O Sing
740 Sing of the Lord's Goodness
722 Sing to the Mountains
774 Sing with All the Saints in Glory
383 Take Up Our Cross
507 Taste and See (Hurd)
511 Taste and See (Moore)
474 The God of All Grace
763 Thy Kingdom Come
327 Up from the Earth
734 We Gather Together
754 Worthy Is the Lamb
390 Ye Watchers and Ye Holy Ones
693 You Are Child

PRAYER

See Petition/Prayer; Musical Style Index: Ostinato Prayer Songs

PROVIDENCE

703 All Good Gifts
419 Be Still, My Soul
641 Because the Lord Is My Shepherd
702 Come, Ye Thankful People, Come
746 Eternal Father, Strong to Save
430 How Lovely Is Your Dwelling Place
772 I Have Loved You
699 I Sing the Mighty Power of God
764 If God Is for Us (Brown)
768 If God Is for Us (Foley)
767 Isaiah 49
765 Like a Shepherd
769 Lord of Glory
210 Luke 1: Magnificat (B. Farrell)
208 Luke 1: Magnificat (Rubalcava)
207 Luke 1: Mary's Song (Joncas)
677 Make Our Lives a Prayer of Peace
375 Mary's Song (Rieth)
704 Now Thank We All Our God
733 O God beyond All Praising
440 Parable

652 Psalm 23
141 Psalm 33: Happy the People You Have Chosen
143 Psalm 34: Taste and See
167 Psalm 89: For Ever I Will Sing
168 Psalm 90: In Every Age
170 Psalm 91: Be with Me, Lord
194 Psalm 126: The Lord Has Done Great Things
200 Psalm 145: I Will Praise Your Name/The Hand of the Lord
771 Rain Down
613 Seek Ye First
475 Shepherd of Souls
463 Table of Plenty
576 Voice of Christ
610 You Are Near

PSALMS
See Scriptural Index; Index of Suggested Psalms for the Liturgical Year

QUINCE AÑOS
See Liturgical Index: Rites of the Church, Order for the Blessing on the Fifteenth Birthday

QUODLIBET (COUNTER-MELODY)
See Musical Style Index

REAL PRESENCE
479 Amén. El Cuerpo de Cristo
549 As We Celebrate
486 Draw Near

RECONCILIATION
See Conversion, Mercy; Liturgical Index: Rites of the Church, Penance (Reconciliation)

REDEMPTION
See also Salvation
295 Behold the Lamb of God
289 Glory in the Cross
434 Keep in Mind

REFUGE
See also Comfort
616 A Mighty Fortress
605 Blest Be the Lord
644 Come to Me
422 Healing River of the Spirit
607 How Can I Keep from Singing
430 How Lovely Is Your Dwelling Place
646 I Heard the Voice of Jesus
653 In Every Age
612 O God, Our Help in Ages Past
606 On Eagle's Wings
618 Only in God
133 Psalm 27: The Goodness of the Lord
137 Psalm 31: Father, I Put My Life in Your Hands (Talbot)
138 Psalm 31: Father, into Your Hands I Commend My Spirit (DeBruyn)
145 Psalm 34: Taste and See/ Gusten y Vean
149 Psalm 42/43: As the Deer Longs
156 Psalm 63: My Soul Is Thirsting/ As Morning Breaks (Angrisano)
157 Psalm 63: My Soul Thirsts (Schutte)
163 Psalm 84: How Lovely Is Your Dwelling Place
168 Psalm 90: In Every Age
170 Psalm 91: Be with Me, Lord
111 Psalmody: Psalm 141
771 Rain Down
441 Restless Is the Heart
642 Shepherd Me, O God
418 Show Us Your Mercy
526 The Cry of the Poor
608 The Lord Is Near/ May the Angels
610 You Are Near

RELIGIOUS PROFESSION
See Christian Life, Discipleship; Liturgical Index: Rites of the Church, Rite of Religious Profession

REPENTENCE
See Conversion; Liturgical Index: Rites of the Church, Penance (Reconciliation)

RESPECT FOR LIFE
See Creation, Global Family, Love for Others, Love of God for Us, Social Concern

RESURRECTION
780 Abide with Me
311 Aleluya, Aleluya
309 All Shall Be Well
321 Alleluia! Alleluia! (HYMN TO JOY)
317 Alleluia! Alleluia! Let the Holy Anthem Rise (HOLY ANTHEM)
313 Alleluia No. 1
319 At the Lamb's High Feast
316 Behold the Glory of God
485 Bread of Heaven
505 Eat This Bread
602 Entre Tus Manos
720 Hallelujah Is Our Song
493 I Am the Bread of Life
329 I Am the Resurrection
318 I Know That My Redeemer Lives (DUKE STREET)
431 I Know That My Redeemer Lives (Soper)
433 I, the Lord
584 In Christ Alone
315 Join in the Dance
434 Keep in Mind
333 Let Heaven Rejoice
325 Let Us Sing and Be Glad/ And the Father Will Dance
528 Light of Christ
322 Lord of the Dance
328 Now the Green Blade Rises
606 On Eagle's Wings
508 One Love Released
306 Out of Darkness
323 Resucitó/He Is Risen
324 Roll Away the Stone
739 Sing a New Song
774 Sing with All the Saints in Glory
443 The Lord Is My Light
336 The Strife Is O'er
331 This Day Was Made by the Lord
335 This Is the Day (Fisher)
326 This Is the Day (Kendzia)
360 To Jesus Christ, Our Sovereign King
563 Unless a Grain of Wheat
327 Up from the Earth
609 We Will Rise Again
754 Worthy Is the Lamb
444 Yes, I Shall Arise
624 You Are the Healing

RETREATS
See also Petition/Prayer
780 Abide with Me
598 Age to Age
600 Be Not Afraid
757 Beatitudes
641 Because the Lord Is My Shepherd
478 Bread of Life
348 By the Waking of Our Hearts
625 Christ Be beside Me
644 Come to Me
770 Come to the Water
580 Come Unto Me
472 Come, Worship the Lord
658 Endless Is Your Love
647 Fly like a Bird
628 God Be in My Head
698 God, Beyond All Names
604 Here I Am (Booth)
539 Here I Am, Lord (Schutte)
344 Holy Spirit (Canedo)
343 Holy Spirit, Come to Me (Hoy)
411 Hosea
607 How Can I Keep from Singing
772 I Have Loved You
646 I Heard the Voice of Jesus
574 I Will Choose Christ
660 In Perfect Charity
760 Lead Me, Lord
468 Lead Us to the Water
272 Led by the Spirit
640 Like a Child Rests
450 May God Bless You
582 O Beauty, Ever Ancient
620 O God, You Search Me
690 O Word of God
618 Only in God
562 Only This I Want
636 Open My Eyes/Abre Mis Ojos
440 Parable
224 Patience, People
679 Prayer of St. Francis/ Oración de San Francisco
117 Psalm 16: The Path of Life
128 Psalm 23: My Shepherd Is the Lord (Gelineau)
127 Psalm 23: The Lord Is My Shepherd/I Shall Live in the House of the Lord (Crandal)
131 Psalm 25: To You, O Lord
111 Psalmody: Psalm 141
441 Restless Is the Heart

635 Sacred Silence
279 Seek the Lord
613 Seek Ye First
541 Servant Song
414 Softly and Tenderly Jesus Is Calling
346 Spirit, Come
543 Take the Word of God with You
585 The Eyes and Hands of Christ
648 The King of Love My Shepherd Is
654 There Is a Balm in Gilead
632 These Alone Are Enough
779 This Day God Gives Me
583 'Tis the Gift to Be Simple
274 Transfigure Us, O Lord
446 Where There Is Love
415 You Alone
610 You Are Near
692 Your Words Are Spirit and Life

Round/Canon
See Musical Style Index

Sacred Heart of Jesus
See Liturgical Index: Solemnities of the Lord during Ordinary Time, The Most Sacred Heart of Jesus

Sacrifice
See also Cross, Love of God for Us, Paschal Mystery, Salvation, Suffering
298 Behold the Wood
338 One Sacrifice of Christ
516 Unless a Grain of Wheat

Saints
See also Liturgical Index: Solemnities and Feasts, All Saints
757 Beatitudes
386 Blessed Feasts of Blessed Martyrs
759 Blest Are They
593 Faith of Our Fathers
388 For All the Saints
719 God, We Praise You
365 Hail, Redeemer, King Divine
721 Holy God, We Praise Thy Name
358 Holy, Holy, Holy
775 Jerusalem, My Happy Home
305 Litany of the Saints (Becker)
307 Litany of the Saints (Chant)
476 Lord, Who at Thy First Eucharist
731 Praise the Lord, Ye Heavens
129 Psalm 24: Lord, This Is the People/Let the Lord Enter
141 Psalm 33: Happy the People You Have Chosen
635 Sacred Silence
387 Saints of God
773 Shall We Gather at the River
774 Sing with All the Saints in Glory
571 The Church's One Foundation
577 Women of the Church
390 Ye Watchers and Ye Holy Ones

Salvation
712 All the Ends of the Earth
317 Alleluia! Alleluia! Let the Holy Anthem Rise
361 Alleluia! Sing to Jesus
614 Amazing Grace
316 Behold the Glory of God
295 Behold the Lamb of God
298 Behold the Wood
485 Bread of Heaven
686 Christ the Lord
217 Creator of the Stars of Night
202 Exodus 15: To God Be Praise and Glory
723 Glory and Praise to Our God
661 God of Love
105 Gospel Canticle (Benedictus)
379 Holy Is His Name
694 How Great Thou Art
318 I Know That My Redeemer Lives
758 I Will Not Die
776 In God Alone
203 Isaiah 12: We Shall Draw Water
587 Jesus, Lord
315 Join in the Dance
434 Keep in Mind
384 Lift High the Cross
689 Lord, to Whom Shall We Go
662 Love Divine, All Loves Excelling
669 Love Has Come
206 Luke 1: Benedictus
210 Luke 1: Magnificat
611 Only in God (Foley)
618 Only in God (Talbot)
119 Psalm 18: I Love You, Lord, My Strength
136 Psalm 30: I Will Praise You, Lord
137 Psalm 31: Father, I Put My Life in Your Hands
144 Psalm 34: Taste and See
164 Psalm 85: Come, O Lord/Lord, Let Us See Your Kindness (Balhoff/Daigle/Ducote)
165 Psalm 85: Let Us See Your Kindness (MacAller)
166 Psalm 85: Lord, Let Us See Your Kindness
177 Psalm 98: All the Ends of the Earth
179 Psalm 98: The Lord Has Revealed
181 Psalm 103: The Lord Is Kind and Merciful
188 Psalm 116: Our Blessing-Cup (Joncas)
187 Psalm 116: Our Blessing-Cup/El Cáliz que Bendecimos (Cortez)
404 River of Glory
229 Save Us, O Lord
722 Sing to the Mountains
368 The King of Glory
688 The Light of Christ
670 There's a Wideness in God's Mercy
331 This Day Was Made by the Lord
335 This Is the Day
360 To Jesus Christ, Our Sovereign King
280 Turn to Me
327 Up from the Earth
668 What Wondrous Love Is This
302 When I Survey the Wondrous Cross
275 With the Lord
754 Worthy Is the Lamb

Searching/Seeking
See Longing for God

Second Coming
See also Kingdom/Reign of God; Liturgical Index: The Liturgical Year, Season of Advent
231 Alleluia! Hurry, the Lord Is Near
286 As I Have Done for You
366 At the Name of Jesus
212 Come, Thou Long-Expected Jesus
702 Come, Ye Thankful People, Come
217 Creator of the Stars of Night
761 Find Us Ready
694 How Great Thou Art
682 I Want to Walk as a Child of the Light
752 In the Day of the Lord
753 Jesus Died upon the Cross
751 Let the Heavens Be Glad
662 Love Divine, All Loves Excelling
755 Mine Eyes Have Seen the Glory
224 Patience, People
229 Save Us, O Lord
750 Soon and Very Soon
226 The King Shall Come When Morning Dawns
762 There Is a River
763 Thy Kingdom Come
588 We Remember
777 Where My Father Lives
754 Worthy Is the Lamb

Self-Esteem
See Love of God for Us

Sending Forth
See also Discipleship, Ministry/Mission
756 A Rightful Place
710 Alabaré/O Come and Sing
473 As We Gather at Your Table
600 Be Not Afraid
530 Celtic Alleluia: Sending Forth
538 City of God
392 Enter the Journey
761 Find Us Ready
554 Go Make a Difference
536 Go Out, Go Out
542 God Has Chosen Me
518 God of the Hungry
539 Here I Am, Lord
531 I Send You Out
724 I Will Rejoice
768 If God Is for Us
706 Let All Things Now Living
528 Light of Christ
523 Lord, Whose Love in Humble Service
339 Lord, You Give the Great Commission
663 Lover of Us All

677 Make Our Lives a Prayer of Peace
728 May We Praise You
560 Out of Darkness
532 Sent Forth by God's Blessing
569 Sing a New Church
496 Spirit and Grace
543 Take the Word of God with You
585 The Eyes and Hands of Christ
529 The Summons
779 This Day God Gives Me
763 Thy Kingdom Come
687 We Are the Light of the World
685 What You Hear in the Dark
535 With One Voice
534 You Have Anointed Me

Serenity
See Confidence, Faith, Love of God for Us, Trust

Service
See Commissioning, Discipleship, Ministry/Mission, Social Concern

Shepherd
See Good Shepherd

Sickness
See Healing; Liturgical Index: Rites of the Church, Rite of Anointing (Care of the Sick)

Sin
589 Do Not Fear to Hope
723 Glory and Praise to Our God
269 How Long, O Lord
621 Lead Me, Guide Me
413 Loving and Forgiving
416 Pardon Your People
153 Psalm 51: Be Merciful, O Lord
152 Psalm 51: Create in Me (Hurd)
154 Psalm 51: Create in Me (Kendzia)
155 Psalm 51: Create in Me/Oh Dios, Crea en Mí (Cortés)
181 Psalm 103: The Lord Is Kind and Merciful
196 Psalm 130: Out of the Depths
197 Psalm 130: With Our God There Is Mercy
412 Return to the Lord Your God
276 Save Your People
278 Somebody's Knockin' at Your Door
654 There Is a Balm in Gilead
670 There's a Wideness in God's Mercy
516 Unless a Grain of Wheat
275 With the Lord
415 You Alone

Social Concern
525 Alleluia! Raise the Gospel
556 Anthem
483 Bread for the World
482 Bread of Life
683 Christ, Be Our Light
566 Christ Has No Body Now but Yours
538 City of God
458 Come to the Feast/ Ven al Banquete
770 Come to the Water
545 Companions on the Journey
589 Do Not Fear to Hope
347 Envía Tu Espíritu
517 For the Healing of the Nations
471 Gather Us In
465 Gather Your People
542 God Has Chosen Me
518 God of the Hungry
265 Gracious God
720 Hallelujah Is Our Song
422 Healing River of the Spirit
758 I Will Not Die
548 In Christ There Is No East or West
776 In God Alone
287 Jesu, Jesu
621 Lead Me, Guide Me
672 Let There Be Peace on Earth
523 Lord, Whose Love in Humble Service
339 Lord, You Give the Great Commission
665 Love One Another
521 Make Your Home in Me
546 Many and Great
501 Pan de Vida
522 People of Peace
201 Psalm 146: Praise the Lord, My Soul/Lord, Come and Save Us
569 Sing a New Church
547 Somos el Cuerpo de Cristo/ We Are the Body of Christ
526 The Cry of the Poor
664 Ubi Caritas
576 Voice of Christ
524 We Are Called
687 We Are the Light of the World
527 We Shall Overcome
519 Whatsoever You Do
535 With One Voice

Solidarity
See Justice, Social Concern, Unity

Sorrow
See Comfort, Lament

Spanish Language
See Language Index

Spiritual
See Musical Style Index

Spiritual Gifts
See Holy Spirit; Liturgical Index: Rites of the Church, Confirmation

Stewardship
757 Beatitudes
683 Christ, Be Our Light
347 Envía Tu Espíritu
705 For the Beauty of the Earth
697 For the Fruits of This Creation
698 God, Beyond All Names
518 God of the Hungry
287 Jesu, Jesu
581 Jesus in the Morning
523 Lord, Whose Love in Humble Service
569 Sing a New Church
561 Take, Lord, Receive
526 The Cry of the Poor
576 Voice of Christ
687 We Are the Light of the World
519 Whatsoever You Do

Suffering
See also Global Family, Justice, Social Concern
759 Blest Are They
770 Come to the Water
627 God, Our Source and Life, Unite Us
269 How Long, O Lord
764 If God Is for Us
423 O Jesus, Healer of Wounded Souls
122 Psalm 22: My God, My God (Manion)
123 Psalm 22: My God, My God (T.R. Smith)
124 Psalm 22: My God, My God/ Dios Mío, Dios Mío (Schiavone)
137 Psalm 31: Father, I Put My Life in Your Hands
187 Psalm 116: Our Blessing-Cup/ El Cáliz que Bendecimos
552 Take Up Your Cross
527 We Shall Overcome
651 You Are Mine

Suffering of Christ
298 Behold the Wood
584 In Christ Alone
363 Jesus, the Lord
297 O Sacred Head, Surrounded
383 Take Up Our Cross
302 When I Survey the Wondrous Cross

Sunday, the Lord's Day
480 As We Remember
470 Let Us Go to the Altar
384 Lift High the Cross
192 Psalm 118: This Is the Day (Joncas)
191 Psalm 118: This Is the Day (Soper)
722 Sing to the Mountains
779 This Day God Gives Me
331 This Day Was Made by the Lord
335 This Is the Day

Thanksgiving
703 All Good Gifts
707 All My Days
717 Blessed by Your Sacrifice
702 Come, Ye Thankful People, Come
705 For the Beauty of the Earth
697 For the Fruits of This Creation
700 Give Thanks to the Lord
708 Grateful
581 Jesus in the Morning
706 Let All Things Now Living
709 Like Cedars
663 Lover of Us All
701 Meadows and Mountains

704 Now Thank We All Our God
146 Psalm 34: I Will Always Thank the Lord
190 Psalm 118: Give Thanks to the Lord
198 Psalm 138: On the Day I Called
200 Psalm 145: I Will Praise Your Name/The Hand of the Lord
532 Sent Forth by God's Blessing
474 The God of All Grace
734 We Gather Together

THIRST
See also Longing for God
590 As the Deer Longs
483 Bread for the World
657 Christians, Let Us Love One Another
458 Come to the Feast/ Ven al Banquete
770 Come to the Water
518 God of the Hungry
464 Here at This Table
646 I Heard the Voice of Jesus
436 My Soul Is Thirsting
522 People of Peace
148 Psalm 42: O God, for You I Long
149 Psalm 42/43: As the Deer Longs
156 Psalm 63: My Soul Is Thirsting/ As Morning Breaks
157 Psalm 63: My Soul Thirsts
400 Water of Life

TRANSFIGURATION
See Liturgical Index: Solemnities and Feasts, The Transfiguration of the Lord

TRIDUUM
See Liturgical Index: The Liturgical Year, The Sacred Paschal Triduum

TRINITY
See Liturgical Index: Solemnities of the Lord during Ordinary Time, The Most Holy Trinity

TRUST
See also Faith, Hope
616 A Mighty Fortress
643 All Is Well with My Soul
590 As the Deer Longs
600 Be Not Afraid
591 Center of My Life
625 Christ Be beside Me
580 Come Unto Me
602 Entre Tus Manos
645 Eye Has Not Seen
517 For the Healing of the Nations
723 Glory and Praise to Our God
604 Here I Am
595 Hold Me in Life
411 Hosea
607 How Can I Keep from Singing
431 I Know That My Redeemer Lives
724 I Will Rejoice
603 Into Your Hands
622 Jesus, Come to Us
621 Lead Me, Guide Me
640 Like a Child Rests
623 Lord of All Hopefulness
769 Lord of Glory
582 O Beauty, Ever Ancient
612 O God, Our Help in Ages Past
620 O God, You Search Me
606 On Eagle's Wings
615 Only a Shadow
611 Only in God
681 Peace
116 Psalm 16: Path of Life/Keep Me Safe (Balhoff/Daigle/Ducote)
117 Psalm 16: The Path of Life (Soper)
128 Psalm 23: My Shepherd Is the Lord (Gelineau)
127 Psalm 23: The Lord Is My Shepherd/I Shall Live in the House of the Lord (Crandal)
125 Psalm 23: The Lord Is My Shepherd/I Shall Live in the House/The Lord Prepares a Banquet (Cooney)
130 Psalm 25: I Lift Up My Soul
132 Psalm 25: To You, O Lord
138 Psalm 31: Father, into Your Hands I Commend My Spirit
140 Psalm 33: Lord, Let Your Mercy
143 Psalm 34: Taste and See (Dean)
145 Psalm 34: Taste and See/ Gusten y Vean (Reza)
157 Psalm 63: My Soul Thirsts
170 Psalm 91: Be with Me, Lord
196 Psalm 130: Out of the Depths
111 Psalmody: Psalm 141
771 Rain Down
417 Remember Your Love
613 Seek Ye First
649 Shelter Me, O God
642 Shepherd Me, O God
418 Show Us Your Mercy
511 Taste and See
599 The Jesus Song
648 The King of Love My Shepherd Is
608 The Lord Is Near/ May the Angels
654 There Is a Balm in Gilead
619 Though the Mountains May Fall
327 Up from the Earth
222 Waiting in Silence
685 What You Hear in the Dark
275 With the Lord
617 You Are All that I Need
610 You Are Near
766 Your Grace Is Enough

TRUTH
756 A Rightful Place
645 Eye Has Not Seen
653 In Every Age
567 Jesu, Joy of Our Desiring
522 People of Peace
121 Psalm 19: Lord, You Have the Words
583 'Tis the Gift to Be Simple
533 Without You
692 Your Words Are Spirit and Life

UNITY
See also Global Family, Love for Others, People of God
716 Abba! Father
570 All Are Welcome
509 As Grains of Wheat
549 As We Celebrate
480 As We Remember
492 Behold the Lamb
490 Bread of Life (Cooney)
482 Bread of Life (B. Farrell)
478 Bread of Life (Fisher)
348 By the Waking of Our Hearts
657 Christians, Let Us Love One Another
545 Companions on the Journey
659 Faithful Family
460 Gather the People
471 Gather Us In
455 Gather Us Together
465 Gather Your People
487 Gift of Finest Wheat
627 God, Our Source and Life, Unite Us
548 In Christ There Is No East or West
672 Let There Be Peace on Earth
476 Lord, Who at Thy First Eucharist
665 Love One Another
546 Many and Great
551 Many and One
469 Now as We Gather
357 O God, Almighty Father
466 O Love of God/Amor de Dios
498 One Bread, One Body
401 One Lord
508 One Love Released
568 One Spirit, One Church
501 Pan de Vida
502 Seed, Scattered and Sown
569 Sing a New Church
547 Somos el Cuerpo de Cristo/ We Are the Body of Christ
571 The Church's One Foundation
544 They'll Know We Are Christians
510 Ubi Caritas (Hurd)
664 Ubi Caritas (Rosania)
550 We Are Many Parts
734 We Gather Together
527 We Shall Overcome
288 Where Charity and Love Prevail
453 Where Love Is Found
446 Where There Is Love
535 With One Voice

UNIVERSE
See Creation

VINE
39 Alleluia! Give the Glory
286 As I Have Done for You
540 I Am the Vine
665 Love One Another

162 Psalm 80: The Vineyard of the Lord/Lord, Make Us Turn to You
514 Vine and Branches
564 We Have Been Told

VOCATIONS
See Christian Life, Commissioning, Discipleship, Ministry/Mission; Liturgical Index: Rites of the Church, Holy Orders, Marriage, Rite of Religious Profession

WATER
See also Liturgical Index: Service Music for Mass, Rite for the Blessing and Sprinkling of Water; Rites of the Church, Baptism
590 As the Deer Longs
391 Baptized in Water
407 Come to the River
770 Come to the Water
394 Down to the River to Pray
398 Flow River Flow
425 Healing Waters
646 I Heard the Voice of Jesus
203 Isaiah 12: We Shall Draw Water
468 Lead Us to the Water
148 Psalm 42: O God, for You I Long
149 Psalm 42/43: As the Deer Longs
393 Put On Christ
771 Rain Down
404 River of Glory
635 Sacred Silence
396 Wade in the Water
400 Water of Life
405 We Belong to You
395 We Have Been Baptized in Christ

WELCOME
570 All Are Welcome
656 All I Ask of You
458 Come to the Feast/ Ven al Banquete
770 Come to the Water
545 Companions on the Journey
659 Faithful Family
460 Gather the People
518 God of the Hungry
469 Now as We Gather
463 Table of Plenty

WISDOM
633 Be Thou My Vision
645 Eye Has Not Seen
667 May Love Be Ours
121 Psalm 19: Lord, You Have the Words
441 Restless Is the Heart
692 Your Words Are Spirit and Life

WITNESS
See Discipleship, Ministry/Mission

WORD
39 Alleluia! Give the Glory
572 Father of Peace
684 I Am the Light of the World
689 Lord, to Whom Shall We Go
669 Love Has Come
677 Make Our Lives a Prayer of Peace
546 Many and Great
690 O Word of God
440 Parable
691 Praise to You, O Christ, Our Savior
121 Psalm 19: Lord, You Have the Words
771 Rain Down
763 Thy Kingdom Come
405 We Belong to You
535 With One Voice
692 Your Words Are Spirit and Life

WORK
See Labor

WORLD
See Creation, Global Family

WORSHIP
See Praise

792 Index of Suggested Psalms for the Liturgical Year

Suggested psalms for the church's three-year Lectionary cycle are listed below. Whenever possible, the psalm of the day or a seasonal (common) psalm has been indicated. If a suitable setting of the psalm is not available, a substitute has been recommended. These alternate settings are marked with an asterisk (*).

Proper of Seasons

Advent Season

Common Psalm

130 Psalm 25: I Lift Up My Soul (Manion)
630 *(Psalm 25)* To You, O God, I Lift Up My Soul (Hurd)
131 Psalm 25: To You, O Lord (Joncas)
132 Psalm 25: To You, O Lord (Soper)
165 Psalm 85: Let Us See Your Kindness (MacAller)
166 Psalm 85: Lord, Let Us See Your Kindness (Soper)
164 Psalm 85: Lord, Let Us See Your Kindness/ Come, O Lord (Balhoff/Daigle/Ducote)

Advent I

A 193 Psalm 122: Let Us Go Rejoicing (Hurd)
B 162 Psalm 80: Lord, Make Us Turn to You/ The Vineyard of the Lord (Keil)
C 130 Psalm 25: I Lift Up My Soul (Manion)
630 *(Psalm 25)* To You, O God, I Lift Up My Soul (Hurd)
131 Psalm 25: To You, O Lord (Joncas)
132 Psalm 25: To You, O Lord (Soper)

Advent II

A 161 Psalm 72: Justice Shall Flourish/ Lord Every Nation (Cooney)
B 165 Psalm 85: Let Us See Your Kindness (MacAller)
166 Psalm 85: Lord, Let Us See Your Kindness (Soper)
164 Psalm 85: Lord, Let Us See Your Kindness/ Come, O Lord (Balhoff/Daigle/Ducote)
C 194 Psalm 126: The Lord Has Done Great Things (Cortez)

Advent III

A 201 Psalm 146: Lord, Come and Save Us/ Praise the Lord, My Soul (Hurd)
B 209 Luke 1: Magnificat (Angrisano/Stephan)
208 Luke 1: Magnificat (Rubalcava)
C 165 Psalm 85: Let Us See Your Kindness (MacAller)
166 Psalm 85: Lord, Let Us See Your Kindness (Soper)
164 Psalm 85: Lord, Let Us See Your Kindness/ Come, O Lord (Balhoff/Daigle/Ducote)

Advent IV

A 129 Psalm 24: Let the Lord Enter/ Lord, This Is the People (T.R. Smith)
B 167 Psalm 89: For Ever I Will Sing (Schoenbachler)
C 162 Psalm 80: Lord, Make Us Turn to You/ The Vineyard of the Lord (Keil)

Christmas Season

Common Psalm

178 Psalm 98: All the Ends of the Earth (Canedo)
177 Psalm 98: All the Ends of the Earth (Hurd)

The Nativity of the Lord (Christmas): At the Vigil Mass

167 Psalm 89: For Ever I Will Sing (Schoenbachler)

The Nativity of the Lord (Christmas): At the Mass during the Night

174 Psalm 96: Today a Savior Is Born (B. Farrell)
175 Psalm 96: Today Our Savior Is Born (Cortez)

The Nativity of the Lord (Christmas): At the Mass at Dawn

178 Psalm 98: All the Ends of the Earth (Canedo)
177 Psalm 98: All the Ends of the Earth (Hurd)

The Nativity of the Lord (Christmas): At the Mass during the Day

178 Psalm 98: All the Ends of the Earth (Canedo)
177 Psalm 98: All the Ends of the Earth (Hurd)

The Holy Family of Jesus, Mary, and Joseph

A 195 Psalm 128: O Blessed Are Those (Inwood)
B 195 Psalm 128: O Blessed Are Those (Inwood)
C 430 **(Psalm 84)* How Lovely Is Your Dwelling Place (DeBruyn)
163 *Psalm 84: How Lovely Is Your Dwelling Place (Joncas)
195 Psalm 128: O Blessed Are Those (Inwood)

Mary, the Holy Mother of God

160 *Psalm 67: O God, Let All the Nations (T.R. Smith)
178 Psalm 98: All the Ends of the Earth (Canedo)
177 Psalm 98: All the Ends of the Earth (Hurd)

Second Sunday after the Nativity (Christmas) (ABC)

178 Psalm 98: All the Ends of the Earth (Canedo)
177 Psalm 98: All the Ends of the Earth (Hurd)

The Epiphany of the Lord

161 Psalm 72: Lord Every Nation/ Justice Shall Flourish (Cooney)

The Baptism of the Lord

A 135 Psalm 29: The Lord Will Bless His People with Peace (Canter)
B 203 Isaiah 12: We Shall Draw Water (Inwood)
135 Psalm 29: The Lord Will Bless His People with Peace (Canter)
C 135 Psalm 29: The Lord Will Bless His People with Peace (Canter)

Lenten Season

Common Psalm

153 Psalm 51: Be Merciful, O Lord (Angrisano)
169 Psalm 91: Be with Me, Lord (Canedo)
170 Psalm 91: Be with Me, Lord (Joncas)
275 *(Psalm 130)* With the Lord (Joncas)
197 Psalm 130: With Our God There Is Mercy (Manion)

Ash Wednesday

153 Psalm 51: Be Merciful, O Lord (Angrisano)

Lent I

A 153 Psalm 51: Be Merciful, O Lord (Angrisano)
B 169 Psalm 91: Be with Me, Lord (Canedo)
170 Psalm 91: Be with Me, Lord (Joncas)

C 169 Psalm 91: Be with Me, Lord (Canedo)
170 Psalm 91: Be with Me, Lord (Joncas)

Lent II
A 140 Psalm 33: Lord, Let Your Mercy (Dufford)
B 186 Psalm 116: I Will Walk with the Lord/ Our Blessing-Cup/The Cup of Salvation (Soper)
189 Psalm 116: In the Presence of God (Kendzia)
C 134 Psalm 27: The Lord Is My Light (DeBruyn)
443 *(Psalm 27)* The Lord Is My Light (C. Walker)

Lent III
A 171 Psalm 95: If Today You Hear God's Voice (B. Farrell)
172 Psalm 95: If Today You Hear His Voice (Soper)
B 121 Psalm 19: Lord, You Have the Words (Joncas)
C 181 Psalm 103: The Lord Is Kind and Merciful (Dufford)
182 Psalm 103: The Lord Is Kind and Merciful (Manalo)

Lent IV
A 128 Psalm 23: My Shepherd Is the Lord (Gelineau)
126 Psalm 23: The Lord Is My Shepherd/ El Señor Es Mi Pastor (Reza)
127 Psalm 23: The Lord Is My Shepherd/ I Shall Live in the House of the Lord (Crandal)
125 Psalm 23: The Lord Is My Shepherd/ I Shall Live in the House of the Lord/ The Lord Prepares a Banquet (Cooney)
B 169 Psalm 91: Be with Me, Lord (Canedo)
170 Psalm 91: Be with Me, Lord (Joncas)
C 143 Psalm 34: Taste and See (Dean)
507 *(Psalm 34)* Taste and See (Hurd)
504 *(Psalm 34)* Taste and See (Kendzia)
511 *(Psalm 34)* Taste and See (Moore)
144 Psalm 34: Taste and See (Talbot)
145 Psalm 34: Taste and See/ Gusten y Vean (Reza)

Lent V
A 275 *(Psalm 130)* With the Lord (Joncas)
197 Psalm 130: With Our God There Is Mercy (Manion)
B 152 Psalm 51: Create in Me (Hurd)
154 Psalm 51: Create in Me (Kendzia)
155 Psalm 51: Create in Me/ Oh Dios, Crea en Mí (Cortés)
C 194 Psalm 126: The Lord Has Done Great Things (Cortez)

Holy Week

Common Psalm
122 Psalm 22: My God, My God (Manion)
123 Psalm 22: My God, My God (T.R. Smith)
124 Psalm 22: My God, My God/ Dios Mío, Dios Mío (Schiavone)

Palm Sunday of the Passion of the Lord
122 Psalm 22: My God, My God (Manion)
123 Psalm 22: My God, My God (T.R. Smith)
124 Psalm 22: My God, My God/ Dios Mío, Dios Mío (Schiavone)

Chrism Mass
167 Psalm 89: For Ever I Will Sing (Schoenbachler)

Easter Triduum

Thursday of the Lord's Supper at the Evening Mass
500 *(Psalm 116)* Our Blessing Cup (Hurd)
188 Psalm 116: Our Blessing-Cup (Joncas)
187 Psalm 116: Our Blessing-Cup/ El Cáliz que Bendecimos (Cortez)
186 Psalm 116: Our Blessing-Cup/I Will Walk with the Lord/The Cup of Salvation (Soper)

Friday of the Passion of the Lord (Good Friday)
137 Psalm 31: Father, I Put My Life in Your Hands (Talbot)
139 Psalm 31: Father, into Your Hands/ Padre, en Tus Manos (Hurd)
138 Psalm 31: Father, into Your Hands I Commend My Spirit (DeBruyn)

The Easter Vigil in the Holy Night
Reading 1
183 Psalm 104: Send Forth Your Spirit, O Lord (C. Walker)
or
142 Psalm 33: The Lord Fills the Earth with His Love (Inwood)

Reading 2
118 Psalm 16: You Are My Inheritance (Bridge)

Reading 3
202 *Exodus 15: To God Be Praise and Glory (Whitaker)

Reading 4
136 Psalm 30: I Will Praise You, Lord (Inwood)

Reading 5
203 Isaiah 12: We Shall Draw Water (Inwood)

Reading 6
121 Psalm 19: Lord, You Have the Words (Joncas)

Reading 7
148 Psalm 42: O God, for You I Long (B. Farrell)
149 Psalm 42/43: As the Deer Longs (Hurd)
or
203 Isaiah 12: We Shall Draw Water (Inwood)
or
152 Psalm 51: Create in Me (Hurd)
154 Psalm 51: Create in Me (Kendzia)
155 Psalm 51: Create in Me/ Oh Dios, Crea en Mí (Cortés)

Reading 8 (Epistle)
39 *(Psalm 118)* Alleluia! Give the Glory (Canedo/Hurd) (NOTE: Verses 9–11)
335 **(Psalm 118)* This Is the Day (Fisher)
192 *Psalm 118: This Is the Day (Joncas)
191 *Psalm 118: This Is the Day (Soper)

Easter Season

Common Psalm
159 Psalm 66: Let All the Earth (Soper)
158 Psalm 66: Let All the Earth Cry Out (Cooney)
335 *(Psalm 118)* This Is the Day (Fisher)
192 Psalm 118: This Is the Day (Joncas)
191 Psalm 118: This Is the Day (Soper)

Easter Sunday
335 *(Psalm 118)* This Is the Day (Fisher)
192 Psalm 118: This Is the Day (Joncas)
191 Psalm 118: This Is the Day (Soper)

EASTER II
A 190 Psalm 118: Give Thanks to the Lord (T.R. Smith)
B 190 Psalm 118: Give Thanks to the Lord (T.R. Smith)
C 190 Psalm 118: Give Thanks to the Lord (T.R. Smith)

EASTER III
A 117 Psalm 16: The Path of Life (Soper)
116 Psalm 16: The Path of Life/Keep Me Safe (Balhoff/Daigle/Ducote)
B 159 Psalm 66: Let All the Earth (Soper)
158 Psalm 66: Let All the Earth Cry Out (Cooney)
C 136 Psalm 30: I Will Praise You, Lord (Inwood)

EASTER IV
A 128 Psalm 23: My Shepherd Is the Lord (Gelineau)
126 Psalm 23: The Lord Is My Shepherd/ El Señor Es Mi Pastor (Reza)
127 Psalm 23: The Lord Is My Shepherd/ I Shall Live in the House of the Lord (Crandal)
125 Psalm 23: The Lord Is My Shepherd/ I Shall Live in the House of the Lord/ The Lord Prepares a Banquet (Cooney)
B 335 *(Psalm 118)* This Is the Day (Fisher)
192 Psalm 118: This Is the Day (Joncas)
191 Psalm 118: This Is the Day (Soper)
C 180 Psalm 100: We Are God's People (T.R. Smith)

EASTER V
A 140 Psalm 33: Lord, Let Your Mercy (Dufford)
B 159 Psalm 66: Let All the Earth (Soper)
158 Psalm 66: Let All the Earth Cry Out (Cooney)
C 200 Psalm 145: I Will Praise Your Name/ The Hand of the Lord (T.R. Smith)
199 Psalm 145: I Will Praise Your Name/ The Hand of the Lord Feeds Us (Soper)

EASTER VI
A 159 Psalm 66: Let All the Earth (Soper)
158 Psalm 66: Let All the Earth Cry Out (Cooney)
B 179 Psalm 98: The Lord Has Revealed (T.R. Smith)
C 160 Psalm 67: O God, Let All the Nations (T.R. Smith)

THE ASCENSION OF THE LORD
151 Psalm 47: God Mounts His Throne (Inwood)

EASTER VII
A 133 *Psalm 27: The Goodness of the Lord (Soper)
B 335 *(Psalm 118)* This Is the Day (Fisher)
192 Psalm 118: This Is the Day (Joncas)
191 Psalm 118: This Is the Day (Soper)
C 176 Psalm 97: The Lord Is King (Cooney)

PENTECOST: VIGIL
184 Psalm 104: Lord, Send Out Your Spirit (Canedo)
185 Psalm 104: Lord, Send Out Your Spirit (Zsigray)
183 Psalm 104: Send Forth Your Spirit, O Lord (C. Walker)

PENTECOST SUNDAY: DAY
184 Psalm 104: Lord, Send Out Your Spirit (Canedo)
185 Psalm 104: Lord, Send Out Your Spirit (Zsigray)
183 Psalm 104: Send Forth Your Spirit, O Lord (C. Walker)

ORDINARY TIME

COMMON PSALM
121 Psalm 19: Lord, You Have the Words (Joncas)
692 *(Psalm 19)* Your Words Are Spirit and Life (B. Farrell)
120 Psalm 19: Your Words, Lord, Are Spirit and Life (Hurd)
134 Psalm 27: The Lord Is My Light (DeBruyn)
443 *(Psalm 27)* The Lord Is My Light (C. Walker)
146 Psalm 34: I Will Always Thank the Lord (Soper)
143 Psalm 34: Taste and See (Dean)
507 *(Psalm 34)* Taste and See (Hurd)
504 *(Psalm 34)* Taste and See (Kendzia)
511 *(Psalm 34)* Taste and See (Moore)
144 Psalm 34: Taste and See (Talbot)
145 Psalm 34: Taste and See/Gusten y Vean (Reza)
156 Psalm 63: My Soul Is Thirsting/ As Morning Breaks (Angrisano)
157 Psalm 63: My Soul Thirsts (Schutte)
171 Psalm 95: If Today You Hear God's Voice (B. Farrell)
172 Psalm 95: If Today You Hear His Voice (Soper)
180 Psalm 100: We Are God's People (T.R. Smith)
181 Psalm 103: The Lord Is Kind and Merciful (Dufford)
182 Psalm 103: The Lord Is Kind and Merciful (Manalo)
200 Psalm 145: I Will Praise Your Name/ The Hand of the Lord (T.R. Smith)
199 Psalm 145: I Will Praise Your Name/ The Hand of the Lord Feeds Us (Soper)

COMMON PSALM FOR LAST WEEKS IN ORDINARY TIME
193 Psalm 122: Let Us Go Rejoicing (Hurd)

SECOND ORDINARY
A 147 Psalm 40: Here I Am/ God, My God, Come to My Aid (Cooney)
B 147 Psalm 40: Here I Am/ God, My God, Come to My Aid (Cooney)
C 173 Psalm 96: Proclaim His Marvelous Deeds (T.R. Smith)

THIRD ORDINARY
A 134 Psalm 27: The Lord Is My Light (DeBruyn)
443 *(Psalm 27)* The Lord Is My Light (C. Walker)
B 156 Psalm 63: My Soul Is Thirsting/ As Morning Breaks (Angrisano)
157 Psalm 63: My Soul Thirsts (Schutte)
C 692 *(Psalm 19)* Your Words Are Spirit and Life (B. Farrell)
120 Psalm 19: Your Words, Lord, Are Spirit and Life (Hurd)

FOURTH ORDINARY
A 201 *Psalm 146: Praise the Lord, My Soul/ Lord, Come and Save Us (Hurd)
B 171 Psalm 95: If Today You Hear God's Voice (B. Farrell)
172 Psalm 95: If Today You Hear His Voice (Soper)
C 134 Psalm 27: The Lord Is My Light (DeBruyn)
443 *(Psalm 27)* The Lord Is My Light (C. Walker)

FIFTH ORDINARY
A 121 Psalm 19: Lord, You Have the Words (Joncas)
692 *(Psalm 19)* Your Words Are Spirit and Life (B. Farrell)
120 Psalm 19: Your Words, Lord, Are Spirit and Life (Hurd)
B 156 Psalm 63: My Soul Is Thirsting/ As Morning Breaks (Angrisano)
157 Psalm 63: My Soul Thirsts (Schutte)
C 171 Psalm 95: If Today You Hear God's Voice (B. Farrell)
172 Psalm 95: If Today You Hear His Voice (Soper)

SIXTH ORDINARY
A 121 Psalm 19: Lord, You Have the Words (Joncas)
692 *(Psalm 19)* Your Words Are Spirit and Life (B. Farrell)
120 Psalm 19: Your Words, Lord, Are Spirit and Life (Hurd)
B 181 Psalm 103: The Lord Is Kind and Merciful (Dufford)
182 Psalm 103: The Lord Is Kind and Merciful (Manalo)
C 171 Psalm 95: If Today You Hear God's Voice (B. Farrell)
172 Psalm 95: If Today You Hear His Voice (Soper)

SEVENTH ORDINARY
A 181 Psalm 103: The Lord Is Kind and Merciful (Dufford)
182 Psalm 103: The Lord Is Kind and Merciful (Manalo)
B 181 Psalm 103: The Lord Is Kind and Merciful (Dufford)
182 Psalm 103: The Lord Is Kind and Merciful (Manalo)
C 181 Psalm 103: The Lord Is Kind and Merciful (Dufford)
182 Psalm 103: The Lord Is Kind and Merciful (Manalo)

EIGHTH ORDINARY
A 134 Psalm 27: The Lord Is My Light (DeBruyn)
443 *(Psalm 27)* The Lord Is My Light (C. Walker)
B 181 Psalm 103: The Lord Is Kind and Merciful (Dufford)
182 Psalm 103: The Lord Is Kind and Merciful (Manalo)
C 200 Psalm 145: I Will Praise Your Name/ The Hand of the Lord (T.R. Smith)
199 Psalm 145: I Will Praise Your Name/ The Hand of the Lord Feeds Us (Soper)

NINTH ORDINARY
A 134 Psalm 27: The Lord Is My Light (DeBruyn)
443 *(Psalm 27)* The Lord Is My Light (C. Walker)
B 200 Psalm 145: I Will Praise Your Name/ The Hand of the Lord (T.R. Smith)
199 Psalm 145: I Will Praise Your Name/ The Hand of the Lord Feeds Us (Soper)
C 200 Psalm 145: I Will Praise Your Name/ The Hand of the Lord (T.R. Smith)
199 Psalm 145: I Will Praise Your Name/ The Hand of the Lord Feeds Us (Soper)

TENTH ORDINARY
A 171 Psalm 95: If Today You Hear God's Voice (B. Farrell)
172 Psalm 95: If Today You Hear His Voice (Soper)
B 275 *(Psalm 130)* With the Lord (Joncas)
197 Psalm 130: With Our God There Is Mercy (Manion)
C 136 Psalm 30: I Will Praise You, Lord (Inwood)

ELEVENTH ORDINARY
A 180 Psalm 100: We Are God's People (T.R. Smith)
B 200 Psalm 145: I Will Praise Your Name/ The Hand of the Lord (T.R. Smith)
199 Psalm 145: I Will Praise Your Name/ The Hand of the Lord Feeds Us (Soper)
C 181 Psalm 103: The Lord Is Kind and Merciful (Dufford)
182 Psalm 103: The Lord Is Kind and Merciful (Manalo)

TWELFTH ORDINARY
A 146 Psalm 34: I Will Always Thank the Lord (Soper)
143 Psalm 34: Taste and See (Dean)
507 *(Psalm 34)* Taste and See (Hurd)
504 *(Psalm 34)* Taste and See (Kendzia)
511 *(Psalm 34)* Taste and See (Moore)
144 Psalm 34: Taste and See (Talbot)
145 Psalm 34: Taste and See/Gusten y Vean (Reza)
B 200 Psalm 145: I Will Praise Your Name/ The Hand of the Lord (T.R. Smith)
199 Psalm 145: I Will Praise Your Name/ The Hand of the Lord Feeds Us (Soper)
C 156 Psalm 63: My Soul Is Thirsting/ As Morning Breaks (Angrisano)
157 Psalm 63: My Soul Thirsts (Schutte)

THIRTEENTH ORDINARY
A 167 Psalm 89: For Ever I Will Sing (Schoenbachler)
B 136 Psalm 30: I Will Praise You, Lord (Inwood)
C 118 Psalm 16: You Are My Inheritance (Bridge)

FOURTEENTH ORDINARY
A 200 Psalm 145: I Will Praise Your Name/ The Hand of the Lord (T.R. Smith)
199 Psalm 145: I Will Praise Your Name/ The Hand of the Lord Feeds Us (Soper)
B 171 Psalm 95: If Today You Hear God's Voice (B. Farrell)
172 Psalm 95: If Today You Hear His Voice (Soper)
C 159 Psalm 66: Let All the Earth (Soper)
158 Psalm 66: Let All the Earth Cry Out (Cooney)

FIFTEENTH ORDINARY
A 121 Psalm 19: Lord, You Have the Words (Joncas)
692 *(Psalm 19)* Your Words Are Spirit and Life (B. Farrell)
120 Psalm 19: Your Words, Lord, Are Spirit and Life (Hurd)
B 165 Psalm 85: Let Us See Your Kindness (MacAller)
166 Psalm 85: Lord, Let Us See Your Kindness (Soper)
164 Psalm 85: Lord, Let Us See Your Kindness/ Come, O Lord (Balhoff/Daigle/Ducote)

C 692 *(Psalm 19)* Your Words Are Spirit and Life (B. Farrell)
120 Psalm 19: Your Words, Lord, Are Spirit and Life (Hurd)

SIXTEENTH ORDINARY

A 181 Psalm 103: The Lord Is Kind and Merciful (Dufford)
182 Psalm 103: The Lord Is Kind and Merciful (Manalo)

B 128 Psalm 23: My Shepherd Is the Lord (Gelineau)
126 Psalm 23: The Lord Is My Shepherd/ El Señor Es Mi Pastor (Reza)
127 Psalm 23: The Lord Is My Shepherd/ I Shall Live in the House of the Lord (Crandal)
125 Psalm 23: The Lord Is My Shepherd/ I Shall Live in the House of the Lord/ The Lord Prepares a Banquet (Cooney)

C 171 Psalm 95: If Today You Hear God's Voice (B. Farrell)
172 Psalm 95: If Today You Hear His Voice (Soper)

SEVENTEENTH ORDINARY

A 121 Psalm 19: Lord, You Have the Words (Joncas)
692 *(Psalm 19)* Your Words Are Spirit and Life (B. Farrell)
120 Psalm 19: Your Words, Lord, Are Spirit and Life (Hurd)

B 200 Psalm 145: The Hand of the Lord/ I Will Praise Your Name (T.R. Smith)
199 Psalm 145: The Hand of the Lord Feeds Us/ I Will Praise Your Name (Soper)

C 198 Psalm 138: On the Day I Called (Cooney)

EIGHTEENTH ORDINARY

A 200 Psalm 145: The Hand of the Lord/ I Will Praise Your Name (T.R. Smith)
199 Psalm 145: The Hand of the Lord Feeds Us/ I Will Praise Your Name (Soper)

B 143 Psalm 34: Taste and See (Dean)
507 *(Psalm 34)* Taste and See (Hurd)
504 *(Psalm 34)* Taste and See (Kendzia)
511 *(Psalm 34)* Taste and See (Moore)
144 Psalm 34: Taste and See (Talbot)
145 Psalm 34: Taste and See/Gusten y Vean (Reza)

C 168 *Psalm 90: In Every Age (T.R. Smith) (NOTE: See Psalm 95 for Response)
171 Psalm 95: If Today You Hear God's Voice (B. Farrell)
172 Psalm 95: If Today You Hear His Voice (Soper)

NINETEENTH ORDINARY

A 165 Psalm 85: Let Us See Your Kindness (MacAller)
166 Psalm 85: Lord, Let Us See Your Kindness (Soper)
164 Psalm 85: Lord, Let Us See Your Kindness/ Come, O Lord (Balhoff/Daigle/Ducote)

B 143 Psalm 34: Taste and See (Dean)
507 *(Psalm 34)* Taste and See (Hurd)
504 *(Psalm 34)* Taste and See (Kendzia)
511 *(Psalm 34)* Taste and See (Moore)
144 Psalm 34: Taste and See (Talbot)
145 Psalm 34: Taste and See/Gusten y Vean (Reza)

C 141 Psalm 33: Happy the People You Have Chosen (Cooney)

TWENTIETH ORDINARY

A 160 Psalm 67: O God, Let All the Nations (T.R. Smith)

B 143 Psalm 34: Taste and See (Dean)
507 *(Psalm 34)* Taste and See (Hurd)
504 *(Psalm 34)* Taste and See (Kendzia)
511 *(Psalm 34)* Taste and See (Moore)
144 Psalm 34: Taste and See (Talbot)
145 Psalm 34: Taste and See/Gusten y Vean (Reza)

C 147 Psalm 40: God, My God, Come to My Aid/ Here I Am (Cooney)

TWENTY-FIRST ORDINARY

A 198 *Psalm 138: On the Day I Called (Cooney)

B 143 Psalm 34: Taste and See (Dean)
507 *(Psalm 34)* Taste and See (Hurd)
504 *(Psalm 34)* Taste and See (Kendzia)
511 *(Psalm 34)* Taste and See (Moore)
144 Psalm 34: Taste and See (Talbot)
145 Psalm 34: Taste and See/Gusten y Vean (Reza)

C 200 Psalm 145: I Will Praise Your Name/ The Hand of the Lord (T.R. Smith)
199 Psalm 145: I Will Praise Your Name/ The Hand of the Lord Feeds Us (Soper)

TWENTY-SECOND ORDINARY

A 156 Psalm 63: My Soul Is Thirsting/ As Morning Breaks (Angrisano)
157 Psalm 63: My Soul Thirsts (Schutte)

B 121 Psalm 19: Lord, You Have the Words (Joncas)
692 *(Psalm 19)* Your Words Are Spirit and Life (B. Farrell)
120 Psalm 19: Your Words, Lord, Are Spirit and Life (Hurd)

C 146 Psalm 34: I Will Always Thank the Lord (Soper)
143 Psalm 34: Taste and See (Dean)
507 *(Psalm 34)* Taste and See (Hurd)
504 *(Psalm 34)* Taste and See (Kendzia)
511 *(Psalm 34)* Taste and See (Moore)
144 Psalm 34: Taste and See (Talbot)
145 Psalm 34: Taste and See/ Gusten y Vean (Reza)

TWENTY-THIRD ORDINARY

A 171 Psalm 95: If Today You Hear God's Voice (B. Farrell)
172 Psalm 95: If Today You Hear His Voice (Soper)

B 201 Psalm 146: Praise the Lord, My Soul/ Lord, Come and Save Us (Hurd)

C 168 Psalm 90: In Every Age (T.R. Smith)

TWENTY-FOURTH ORDINARY

A 181 Psalm 103: The Lord Is Kind and Merciful (Dufford)
182 Psalm 103: The Lord Is Kind and Merciful (Manalo)

B 186 Psalm 116: I Will Walk with the Lord/ Our Blessing-Cup/ The Cup of Salvation (Soper)
189 Psalm 116: In the Presence of God (Kendzia)

C 153 *Psalm 51: Be Merciful, O Lord (Angrisano)
152 *Psalm 51: Create in Me (Hurd)
154 *Psalm 51: Create in Me (Kendzia)
155 *Psalm 51: Create in Me/ Oh Dios, Crea en Mí (Cortés)

TWENTY-FIFTH ORDINARY

A 200 Psalm 145: I Will Praise Your Name/ The Hand of the Lord (T.R. Smith)
199 Psalm 145: I Will Praise Your Name/ The Hand of the Lord Feeds Us (Soper)

B 134 Psalm 27: The Lord Is My Light (DeBruyn)
443 *(Psalm 27)* The Lord Is My Light (C. Walker)

C 200 Psalm 145: I Will Praise Your Name/ The Hand of the Lord (T.R. Smith)
199 Psalm 145: I Will Praise Your Name/ The Hand of the Lord (Soper)

Twenty-Sixth Ordinary

A 130 *Psalm 25: I Lift Up My Soul (Manion)
630 **(Psalm 25)* To You, O God, I Lift Up My Soul (Hurd)
131 *Psalm 25: To You, O Lord (Joncas)
132 *Psalm 25: To You, O Lord (Soper)

B 121 Psalm 19: Lord, You Have the Words (Joncas)
692 *(Psalm 19)* Your Words Are Spirit and Life (B. Farrell)
120 Psalm 19: Your Words, Lord, Are Spirit and Life (Hurd)

C 201 Psalm 146: Praise the Lord, My Soul/ Lord, Come and Save Us (Hurd)

Twenty-Seventh Ordinary

A 162 Psalm 80: The Vineyard of the Lord/ Lord Make Us Turn to You (Keil)

B 195 *Psalm 128: O Blessed Are Those (Inwood)
200 Psalm 145: I Will Praise Your Name/ The Hand of the Lord (T.R. Smith)
199 Psalm 145: I Will Praise Your Name/ The Hand of the Lord Feeds Us (Soper)

C 171 Psalm 95: If Today You Hear God's Voice (B. Farrell)
172 Psalm 95: If Today You Hear His Voice (Soper)

Twenty-Eighth Ordinary

A 127 Psalm 23: I Shall Live in the House of the Lord/ The Lord Is My Shepherd (Crandal)
125 Psalm 23: I Shall Live in the House of the Lord/ The Lord Is My Shepherd/ The Lord Prepares a Banquet (Cooney)

B 168 *Psalm 90: In Every Age (T.R. Smith)

C 179 Psalm 98: The Lord Has Revealed (T.R. Smith)

Twenty-Ninth Ordinary

A 173 *Psalm 96: Proclaim His Marvelous Deeds (T.R. Smith)

B 140 Psalm 33: Lord, Let Your Mercy (Dufford)

C 134 Psalm 27: The Lord Is My Light (DeBruyn)
443 *(Psalm 27)* The Lord Is My Light (C. Walker)

Thirtieth Ordinary

A 119 Psalm 18: I Love You, Lord, My Strength (Honoré)

B 194 Psalm 126: The Lord Has Done Great Things (Cortez)

C 526 *(Psalm 34)* The Cry of the Poor (Foley)

Thirty-First Ordinary

A 171 Psalm 95: If Today You Hear God's Voice (B. Farrell)
172 Psalm 95: If Today You Hear His Voice (Soper)

B 119 Psalm 18: I Love You, Lord, My Strength (Honoré)

C 200 Psalm 145: I Will Praise Your Name/ The Hand of the Lord (T.R. Smith)
199 Psalm 145: I Will Praise Your Name/ The Hand of the Lord Feeds Us (Soper)

Thirty-Second Ordinary

A 156 Psalm 63: My Soul Is Thirsting/ As Morning Breaks (Angrisano)
157 Psalm 63: My Soul Thirsts (Schutte)

B 201 Psalm 146: Praise the Lord, My Soul/ Lord, Come and Save Us (Hurd)

C 134 Psalm 27: The Lord Is My Light (DeBruyn)
443 *(Psalm 27)* The Lord Is My Light (C. Walker)

Thirty-Third Ordinary

A 195 Psalm 128: O Blessed Are Those (Inwood)

B 118 Psalm 16: You Are My Inheritance (Bridge)

C 178 *Psalm 98: All the Ends of the Earth (Canedo)
177 *Psalm 98: All the Ends of the Earth (Hurd)
179 *Psalm 98: The Lord Has Revealed (T.R. Smith)

Solemnities of the Lord

The Most Holy Trinity (Trinity Sunday)

A 204 Daniel 3: Glory and Praise For Ever (T.R. Smith)

B 141 Psalm 33: Happy the People You Have Chosen (Cooney)

C 200 Psalm 145: I Will Praise Your Name/ The Hand of the Lord (T.R. Smith)
199 Psalm 145: I Will Praise Your Name/ The Hand of the Lord Feeds Us (Soper)

The Most Holy Body and Blood of Christ (Corpus Christi)

A 200 Psalm 145: I Will Praise Your Name/ The Hand of the Lord (T.R. Smith)
199 Psalm 145: I Will Praise Your Name/ The Hand of the Lord Feeds Us (Soper)

B 186 Psalm 116: The Cup of Salvation/ Our Blessing Cup/ I Will Walk with the Lord (Soper)
500 **(Psalm 116)* Our Blessing Cup (Hurd)
188 *Psalm 116: Our Blessing-Cup (Joncas)
187 *Psalm 116: Our Blessing-Cup/ El Cáliz que Bendecimos (Cortez)

C 146 Psalm 34: I Will Always Thank the Lord (Soper)
143 Psalm 34: Taste and See (Dean)
507 *(Psalm 34)* Taste and See (Hurd)
504 *(Psalm 34)* Taste and See (Kendzia)
511 *(Psalm 34)* Taste and See (Moore)
144 Psalm 34: Taste and See (Talbot)
145 Psalm 34: Taste and See/Gusten y Vean (Reza)

The Most Sacred Heart of Jesus

A 181 Psalm 103: The Lord Is Kind and Merciful (Dufford)
182 Psalm 103: The Lord Is Kind and Merciful (Manalo)

B 203 Isaiah 12: We Shall Draw Water (Inwood)

C 128 Psalm 23: My Shepherd Is the Lord (Gelineau)
126 Psalm 23: The Lord Is My Shepherd/ El Señor Es Mi Pastor (Reza)
127 Psalm 23: The Lord Is My Shepherd/ I Shall Live in the House of the Lord (Crandal)
125 Psalm 23: The Lord Is My Shepherd/ I Shall Live in the House of the Lord/ The Lord Prepares a Banquet (Cooney)

Our Lord Jesus Christ, King of the Universe
A 128 Psalm 23: My Shepherd Is the Lord (Gelineau)
126 Psalm 23: The Lord Is My Shepherd/ El Señor Es Mi Pastor (Reza)
127 Psalm 23: The Lord Is My Shepherd/ I Shall Live in the House of the Lord (Crandal)
125 Psalm 23: The Lord Is My Shepherd/ I Shall Live in the House of the Lord/ The Lord Prepares a Banquet (Cooney)
B 176 *Psalm 97: The Lord Is King (Cooney)
C 193 Psalm 122: Let Us Go Rejoicing (Hurd)

Solemnities and Feasts

The Presentation of the Lord (February 2)
129 *Psalm 24: Let the Lord Enter/ Lord, This Is the People (T.R. Smith)

St. Joseph, Spouse of the Blessed Virgin Mary (March 19)
167 *Psalm 89: For Ever I Will Sing (Schoenbachler)

The Annunciation of the Lord (March 25)
147 Psalm 40: Here I Am/ God, My God, Come to My Aid (Cooney)

The Nativity of John the Baptist: Vigil (June 24)
147 *Psalm 40: Here I Am/ God, My God, Come to My Aid (Cooney)

The Nativity of John the Baptist: Day (June 24)
147 *Psalm 40: Here I Am/ God, My God, Come to My Aid (Cooney)
610 **(Psalm 139)* You Are Near (Schutte)
200 Psalm 145: I Will Praise Your Name/ The Hand of the Lord (T.R. Smith)
199 Psalm 145: I Will Praise Your Name/ The Hand of the Lord Feeds Us (Soper)

Ss. Peter and Paul, Apostles: Vigil (June 29)
200 Psalm 145: I Will Praise Your Name/ The Hand of the Lord (T.R. Smith)
199 Psalm 145: I Will Praise Your Name/ The Hand of the Lord Feeds Us (Soper)

Ss. Peter and Paul, Apostles: Day (June 29)
146 *Psalm 34: I Will Always Thank the Lord (Soper)
143 *Psalm 34: Taste and See (Dean)
507 **(Psalm 34)* Taste and See (Hurd)
504 **(Psalm 34)* Taste and See (Kendzia)
511 **(Psalm 34)* Taste and See (Moore)
144 *Psalm 34: Taste and See (Talbot)
145 *Psalm 34: Taste and See/Gusten y Vean (Reza)

The Transfiguration of the Lord (August 6)
176 Psalm 97: The Lord Is King (Cooney)

The Assumption of the Blessed Virgin Mary: Vigil (August 15)
193 *Psalm 122: Let Us Go Rejoicing (Hurd)

The Assumption of the Blessed Virgin Mary: Day (August 15)
150 Psalm 45: The Queen Stands (Keil)

The Exaltation of the Holy Cross (September 14)
171 Psalm 95: If Today You Hear God's Voice (B. Farrell)
172 Psalm 95: If Today You Hear His Voice (Soper)

All Saints (November 1)
129 Psalm 24: Lord, This Is the People/ Let the Lord Enter (T.R. Smith)

The Commemoration of All the Faithful Departed (All Souls' Day) (November 2)
128 Psalm 23: My Shepherd Is the Lord (Gelineau)
126 Psalm 23: The Lord Is My Shepherd/ El Señor Es Mi Pastor (Reza)
127 Psalm 23: The Lord Is My Shepherd/ I Shall Live in the House of the Lord (Crandal)
125 Psalm 23: The Lord Is My Shepherd/ I Shall Live in the House of the Lord/ The Lord Prepares a Banquet (Cooney)
630 *(Psalm 25)* To You, O God, I Lift Up My Soul (Hurd)
131 Psalm 25: To You, O Lord (Joncas)
132 Psalm 25: To You, O Lord (Soper)
133 Psalm 27: The Goodness of the Lord (Soper)
134 Psalm 27: The Lord Is My Light (DeBruyn)
443 *(Psalm 27)* The Lord Is My Light (C. Walker)

The Dedication of the Lateran Basilica (November 9)
430 **(Psalm 84)* How Lovely Is Your Dwelling Place (DeBruyn)
163 *Psalm 84: How Lovely Is Your Dwelling Place (Joncas)
193 Psalm 122: Let Us Go Rejoicing (Hurd)

Thanksgiving Day
200 Psalm 145: I Will Praise Your Name/ The Hand of the Lord (T.R. Smith)
199 Psalm 145: I Will Praise Your Name/ The Hand of the Lord Feeds Us (Soper)

The Immaculate Conception of the Blessed Virgin Mary (December 8)
178 *Psalm 98: All the Ends of the Earth (Canedo)
177 *Psalm 98: All the Ends of the Earth (Hurd)
179 *Psalm 98: The Lord Has Revealed (T.R. Smith)

Our Lady of Guadalupe (December 12)
209 *Luke 1: Magnificat (Angrisano/Stephan)
208 *Luke 1: Magnificat (Rubalcava)

SERVICE MUSIC FOR MASS

THE INTRODUCTORY RITES

Entrance Antiphon

299 We Venerate Your Cross/ Tu Cruz Adoramos

Entrance Song (Gathering or Processional)

616 A Mighty Fortress
756 A Rightful Place
598 Age to Age
710 Alabaré/O Come and Sing
570 All Are Welcome
714 All Creatures of Our God and King
703 All Good Gifts
456 All People That on Earth Do Dwell
355 All Praise and Glad Thanksgiving
695 All the Earth (Deiss)
712 All the Ends of the Earth (Dufford)
39 Alleluia! Give the Glory *(Mass of Glory)*
525 Alleluia! Raise the Gospel
361 Alleluia! Sing to Jesus
509 As Grains of Wheat
549 As We Celebrate
600 Be Not Afraid
715 Been So Busy
605 Blest Be the Lord
348 By the Waking of Our Hearts
538 City of God
711 Come, Christians, Join to Sing
458 Come to the Feast/ Ven al Banquete
407 Come to the River *(Mass of Glory)*
461 Come to Us
472 Come, Worship the Lord
545 Companions on the Journey
392 Enter the Journey
353 Everyone Moved by the Spirit
202 Exodus 15: To God Be Praise and Glory
705 For the Beauty of the Earth
601 For You Are My God
718 From All That Dwell Below the Skies/Praise God from Whom All Blessings Flow
460 Gather the People
471 Gather Us In
455 Gather Us Together
465 Gather Your People
700 Give Thanks to the Lord
723 Glory and Praise to Our God
661 God of Love
105 Gospel Canticle (Benedictus)
727 He Is the Lord
464 Here at This Table
721 Holy God, We Praise Thy Name
358 Holy, Holy, Holy
684 I Am the Light of the World
699 I Sing the Mighty Power of God
764 If God Is for Us
103 Invitatory Psalm: Psalm 95
726 Joyful, Joyful, We Adore Thee
760 Lead Me, Lord
468 Lead Us to the Water
333 Let Heaven Rejoice
470 Let Us Go to the Altar
725 Lift Up Your Hearts
769 Lord of Glory
662 Love Divine, All Loves Excelling
663 Lover of Us All
546 Many and Great
778 Morning Has Broken
469 Now as We Gather
578 Now Is the Time
729 O Bless the Lord
733 O God beyond All Praising
612 O God, Our Help in Ages Past
466 O Love of God/ Amor de Dios
690 O Word of God
401 One Lord
735 Praise, My Soul, the King of Heaven
731 Praise the Lord, Ye Heavens
732 Praise to the Lord
771 Rain Down
279 Seek the Lord
743 Sing a Joyful Song
569 Sing a New Church
742 Sing a New Song (Brown)
739 Sing a New Song (Schutte)
744 Sing, O Sing
740 Sing of the Lord's Goodness
722 Sing to the Mountains
547 Somos el Cuerpo de Cristo/ We Are the Body of Christ
463 Table of Plenty
571 The Church's One Foundation
474 The God of All Grace
368 The King of Glory
648 The King of Love My Shepherd Is
670 There's a Wideness in God's Mercy
779 This Day God Gives Me
331 This Day Was Made by the Lord
335 This Is the Day (Fisher)
326 This Is the Day (Kendzia)
619 Though the Mountains May Fall
664 Ubi Caritas
550 We Are Many Parts
734 We Gather Together
736 We Praise You
588 We Remember
462 What Is This Place
402 You Have Called Us

Rite for the Blessing and Sprinkling of Water

406 Agua de Vida/Water of Life
391 Baptized in Water
407 Come to the River *(Mass of Glory)*
398 Flow River Flow
425 Healing Waters
304 I Saw Water Flowing
203 Isaiah 12: We Shall Draw Water
47 Living Streams *(Mass of Christ the Savior)*
404 River of Glory
474 The God of All Grace
396 Wade in the Water
400 Water of Life

Penitential Act: Confiteor

2 Penitential Act (Confiteor) *(Roman Missal Chants)*

Penitential Act: Dialogue

3 Penitential Act: Dialogue *(Roman Missal Chants)*

Penitential Act with Invocations

76 Acto Penitencial, Formulario 3/ Penitential Act with Invocations *(Misa Santa Fe)*
37 Penitential Act with Invocations *(Mass of Glory)*
4 Penitential Act with Invocations *(Roman Missal Chants)*

Lord, Have Mercy

68 Lord, Have Mercy *(Heritage Mass)*
27 Lord, Have Mercy *(Mass of the Sacred Heart)*
5 Lord, Have Mercy *(Roman Missal Chants)*

Kyrie, Eleison

6 Kyrie, Eleison *(Roman Missal Chants)*

Lord, Have Mercy/Kyrie, Eleison

92 Kyrie, Eleison/Lord, Have Mercy *(Mass of Renewal)*
58 Lord, Have Mercy/Kyrie, Eleison *(Mass of a Joyful Heart)*
48 Lord, Have Mercy/Kyrie, Eleison *(Mass of Christ the Savior)*

Gloria

7 Gloria *(Roman Missal Chants)*
77 Gloria/Glory to God *(Misa Santa Fe)*
83 Glory to God *(Celtic Mass)*
69 Glory to God *(Heritage Mass)*
59 Glory to God *(Mass of a Joyful Heart)*
49 Glory to God *(Mass of Christ the Savior)*
38 Glory to God *(Mass of Glory)*
93 Glory to God *(Mass of Renewal)*
28 Glory to God *(Mass of the Sacred Heart)*

THE LITURGY OF THE WORD

Responsorial Psalm

203 Isaiah 12: We Shall Draw Water
118 Psalm 16: You Are My Inheritance

119 Psalm 18: I Love You, Lord, My Strength
121 Psalm 19: Lord, You Have the Words
692 *(Psalm 19)* Your Words Are Spirit and Life (B. Farrell)
120 Psalm 19: Your Words, Lord, Are Spirit and Life (Hurd)
122 Psalm 22: My God, My God (Manion)
123 Psalm 22: My God, My God (T.R. Smith)
124 Psalm 22: My God, My God/ Dios Mío, Dios Mío (Schiavone)
128 Psalm 23: My Shepherd Is the Lord (Gelineau)
126 Psalm 23: The Lord Is My Shepherd/ El Señor Es Mi Pastor (Reza)
127 Psalm 23: The Lord Is My Shepherd/I Shall Live in the House of the Lord (Crandal)
125 Psalm 23: The Lord Is My Shepherd/I Shall Live in the House/The Lord Prepares a Banquet (Cooney)
129 Psalm 24: Lord, This Is the People/Let the Lord Enter
130 Psalm 25: I Lift Up My Soul
131 Psalm 25: To You, O Lord (Joncas)
132 Psalm 25: To You, O Lord (Soper)
133 Psalm 27: The Goodness of the Lord
134 Psalm 27: The Lord Is My Light
135 Psalm 29: The Lord Will Bless His People with Peace
136 Psalm 30: I Will Praise You, Lord
137 Psalm 31: Father, I Put My Life in Your Hands (Talbot)
138 Psalm 31: Father, into Your Hands I Commend My Spirit (DeBruyn)
139 Psalm 31: Father, into Your Hands/ Padre, en Tus Manos (Hurd)
141 Psalm 33: Happy the People You Have Chosen
140 Psalm 33: Lord, Let Your Mercy
142 Psalm 33: The Lord Fills the Earth with His Love
146 Psalm 34: I Will Always Thank the Lord
143 Psalm 34: Taste and See (Dean)
144 Psalm 34: Taste and See (Talbot)
145 Psalm 34: Taste and See/ Gusten y Vean (Reza)
147 Psalm 40: Here I Am/God, My God, Come to My Aid
148 Psalm 42: O God, for You I Long
149 Psalm 42/43: As the Deer Longs
150 Psalm 45: The Queen Stands
151 Psalm 47: God Mounts His Throne
153 Psalm 51: Be Merciful, O Lord
152 Psalm 51: Create in Me (Hurd)
154 Psalm 51: Create in Me (Kendzia)
155 Psalm 51: Create in Me/Oh Dios, Crea en Mí (Cortés)
156 Psalm 63: My Soul Is Thirsting/ As Morning Breaks (Angrisano)
157 Psalm 63: My Soul Thirsts (Schutte)
159 Psalm 66: Let All the Earth (Soper)
158 Psalm 66: Let All the Earth Cry Out (Cooney)
160 Psalm 67: O God, Let All the Nations
161 Psalm 72: Justice Shall Flourish/ Lord, Every Nation
162 Psalm 80: The Vineyard of the Lord/Lord, Make Us Turn to You
163 Psalm 84: How Lovely Is Your Dwelling Place
165 Psalm 85: Let Us See Your Kindness (MacAller)
166 Psalm 85: Lord, Let Us See Your Kindness (Soper)
167 Psalm 89: For Ever I Will Sing
168 Psalm 90: In Every Age
169 Psalm 91: Be with Me, Lord (Canedo)
170 Psalm 91: Be with Me, Lord (Joncas)
171 Psalm 95: If Today You Hear God's Voice (B. Farrell)
172 Psalm 95: If Today You Hear His Voice (Soper)
173 Psalm 96: Proclaim His Marvelous Deeds
174 Psalm 96: Today a Savior Is Born (B. Farrell)
175 Psalm 96: Today Our Savior Is Born (Cortez)
176 Psalm 97: The Lord Is King
178 Psalm 98: All the Ends of the Earth (Canedo)
177 Psalm 98: All the Ends of the Earth (Hurd)
179 Psalm 98: The Lord Has Revealed
180 Psalm 100: We Are God's People
181 Psalm 103: The Lord Is Kind and Merciful (Dufford)
182 Psalm 103: The Lord Is Kind and Merciful (Manalo)
184 Psalm 104: Lord, Send Out Your Spirit (Canedo)
183 Psalm 104: Send Forth Your Spirit, O Lord (C. Walker)
189 Psalm 116: In the Presence of God
188 Psalm 116: Our Blessing-Cup (Joncas)
500 *(Psalm 116)* Our Blessing Cup (Hurd)
187 Psalm 116: Our Blessing-Cup/ El Cáliz que Bendecimos (Cortez)
186 Psalm 116: Our Blessing-Cup/ I Will Walk with the Lord/ The Cup of Salvation (Soper)
190 Psalm 118: Give Thanks to the Lord
335 *(Psalm 118)* This Is the Day (Fisher)
192 Psalm 118: This Is the Day (Joncas)
326 *(Psalm 118)* This Is the Day (Kendzia)
191 Psalm 118: This Is the Day (Soper)
193 Psalm 122: Let Us Go Rejoicing
194 Psalm 126: The Lord Has Done Great Things
195 Psalm 128: O Blessed Are Those
196 Psalm 130: Out of the Depths
197 Psalm 130: With Our God There Is Mercy
198 Psalm 138: On the Day I Called
200 Psalm 145: I Will Praise Your Name/The Hand of the Lord (T.R. Smith)
199 Psalm 145: I Will Praise Your Name/The Hand of the Lord Feeds Us (Soper)
201 Psalm 146: Praise the Lord, My Soul/ Lord, Come and Save Us

Gospel Acclamation (Alleluia)

233 Advent/Christmas Gospel Acclamation
60 Alleluia *(Mass of a Joyful Heart)*
50 Alleluia *(Mass of Christ the Savior)*
94 Alleluia *(Mass of Renewal)*
29 Alleluia *(Mass of the Sacred Heart)*
39 Alleluia! Give the Glory *(Mass of Glory)*
84 Celtic Alleluia *(Celtic Mass)*

Lenten Gospel Acclamation

85 Lenten Gospel Acclamation *(Celtic Mass)*
61 Lenten Gospel Acclamation *(Mass of a Joyful Heart)*
51 Lenten Gospel Acclamation *(Mass of Christ the Savior)*
40 Lenten Gospel Acclamation *(Mass of Glory)*
95 Lenten Gospel Acclamation *(Mass of Renewal)*
30 Lenten Gospel Acclamation *(Mass of the Sacred Heart)*
691 Praise to You, O Christ, Our Savior

Dismissal of the Catechumens and the Elect

See Rites of the Church, Rite of Christian Initiation of Adults, Dismissal of the Catechumens and the Elect

Profession of Faith

9 Profession of Faith *(Roman Missal Chants)*

Prayer of the Faithful
113 Intercessions: Evening Prayer
106 Intercessions: Morning Prayer
626 O God, Hear Us
10 Universal Prayer

THE LITURGY OF THE EUCHARIST

Presentation and Preparation of the Gifts

The norms on the manner of singing [this song] are the same as for the Entrance chant. The purpose of this chant is to foster the unity of those who have been gathered, introduce their thoughts to the mystery of the liturgical season or festivity, and accompany the procession of the priest and ministers. Instrumental music is also appropriate. (Sing to the Lord, from #173, #142, #174)

473 As We Gather at Your Table

Preface Dialogue
13 Preface Dialogue *(Roman Missal Chants)*

Holy
86 Holy *(Celtic Mass)*
70 Holy *(Heritage Mass)*
62 Holy *(Mass of a Joyful Heart)*
52 Holy *(Mass of Christ the Savior)*
41 Holy *(Mass of Glory)*
96 Holy *(Mass of Renewal)*
31 Holy *(Mass of the Sacred Heart)*
14 Holy *(Roman Missal Chants)*
78 Santo/Holy *(Misa Santa Fe)*

We Proclaim Your Death
79 Anunciamos Tu Muerte/ We Proclaim Your Death *(Misa Santa Fe)*
71 We Proclaim Your Death *(Heritage Mass)*
63 We Proclaim Your Death *(Mass of a Joyful Heart)*
53 We Proclaim Your Death *(Mass of Christ the Savior)*
42 We Proclaim Your Death *(Mass of Glory)*
97 We Proclaim Your Death *(Mass of Renewal)*
32 We Proclaim Your Death *(Mass of the Sacred Heart)*
15 We Proclaim Your Death *(Roman Missal Chants)*

When We Eat This Bread
88 When We Eat This Bread *(Celtic Mass)*
72 When We Eat This Bread *(Heritage Mass)*
64 When We Eat This Bread *(Mass of a Joyful Heart)*
54 When We Eat This Bread *(Mass of Christ the Savior)*
43 When We Eat This Bread *(Mass of Glory)*
98 When We Eat This Bread *(Mass of Renewal)*
33 When We Eat This Bread *(Mass of the Sacred Heart)*
16 When We Eat This Bread *(Roman Missal Chants)*

Save Us, Savior
89 Save Us, Savior *(Celtic Mass)*
73 Save Us, Savior *(Heritage Mass)*
65 Save Us, Savior *(Mass of a Joyful Heart)*
55 Save Us, Savior *(Mass of Christ the Savior)*
44 Save Us, Savior *(Mass of Glory)*
99 Save Us, Savior *(Mass of Renewal)*
34 Save Us, Savior *(Mass of the Sacred Heart)*
17 Save Us, Savior *(Roman Missal Chants)*

Doxology and Amen
90 Amen *(Celtic Mass)*
56 Amen *(Mass of Christ the Savior)*
35 Amen *(Mass of the Sacred Heart)*

Amen
74 Amen *(Heritage Mass)*
66 Amen *(Mass of a Joyful Heart)*
45 Amen *(Mass of Glory)*
100 Amen *(Mass of Renewal)*
80 Amén/Amen *(Misa Santa Fe)*

The Lord's Prayer
18 The Lord's Prayer *(Roman Missal Chants)*

Lamb of God/ Breaking of the Bread
232 Advent Lamb of God
81 Cordero de Dios/Lamb of God *(Misa Santa Fe)*
91 Lamb of God *(Celtic Mass)*
75 Lamb of God *(Heritage Mass)*
67 Lamb of God *(Mass of a Joyful Heart)*
57 Lamb of God *(Mass of Christ the Savior)*
46 Lamb of God *(Mass of Glory)*
101 Lamb of God *(Mass of Renewal)*
36 Lamb of God *(Mass of the Sacred Heart)*
19 Lamb of God *(Roman Missal Chants)*

Communion Song

See also Topical Index: Good Shepherd, Love for God, Love of God for Us, Paschal Mystery, Praise, Thanksgiving, Unity

598 Age to Age
707 All My Days
695 All the Earth
479 Amén. El Cuerpo de Cristo
481 Ang Katawan ni Kristo/ Behold, the Body of Christ
509 As Grains of Wheat
480 As We Remember
641 Because the Lord Is My Shepherd
492 Behold the Lamb
512 Bread, Blessed and Broken
483 Bread for the World
484 Bread of Angels
485 Bread of Heaven
490 Bread of Life (Cooney)
482 Bread of Life (B. Farrell)
591 Center of My Life
458 Come to the Feast/ Ven al Banquete
461 Come to Us
545 Companions on the Journey
486 Draw Near
505 Eat This Bread
460 Gather the People
455 Gather Us Together
487 Gift of Finest Wheat
655 God Is Love
464 Here at This Table
493 I Am the Bread of Life
495 I Am the Living Bread
489 In the Breaking of the Bread
467 In This Place
515 Jesus, the Bread of Life
468 Lead Us to the Water
494 Look Beyond
665 Love One Another
208 Luke 1: Magnificat
677 Make Our Lives a Prayer of Peace
546 Many and Great
497 Miracle of Grace
498 One Bread, One Body
401 One Lord
508 One Love Released
615 Only a Shadow
500 Our Blessing Cup
501 Pan de Vida
652 Psalm 23
143 Psalm 34: Taste and See (Dean)
144 Psalm 34: Taste and See (Talbot)
145 Psalm 34: Taste and See/ Gusten y Vean (Reza)
156 Psalm 63: My Soul Is Thirsting/ As Morning Breaks (Angrisano)
157 Psalm 63: My Soul Thirsts (Schutte)
180 Psalm 100: We Are God's People
188 Psalm 116: Our Blessing-Cup (Joncas)
187 Psalm 116: Our Blessing-Cup/ El Cáliz que Bendecimos (Cortez)
186 Psalm 116: Our Blessing-Cup/ I Will Walk with the Lord/ The Cup of Salvation (Soper)
200 Psalm 145: I Will Praise Your Name/The Hand of the Lord (T.R. Smith)
199 Psalm 145: I Will Praise Your Name/The Hand of the Lord Feeds Us (Soper)
502 Seed, Scattered and Sown
496 Spirit and Grace
463 Table of Plenty
507 Taste and See (Hurd)
504 Taste and See (Kendzia)
511 Taste and See (Moore)
503 That There May Be Bread
513 The Supper of the Lord
491 To Be Your Bread
510 Ubi Caritas (Hurd)

664 Ubi Caritas (Rosania)
563 Unless a Grain of Wheat (B. Farrell)
516 Unless a Grain of Wheat (Hurd)
514 Vine and Branches
222 Waiting in Silence
550 We Are Many Parts
736 We Praise You
588 We Remember
506 We, the Body of Christ

Eucharistic Hymn
478 Bread of Life
657 Christians, Let Us Love One Another
488 Let Us Break Bread Together
476 Lord, Who at Thy First Eucharist
475 Shepherd of Souls

Hymn/Psalm of Praise
See Topical Index: Charity, Church, Good Shepherd, Joy, Kingdom/Reign of God, Love for God, Love for Others, Love of God for Us, Paschal Mystery, Praise, Thanksgiving, Unity

THE CONCLUDING RITES

Greeting
21 The Concluding Rites: Greeting/Final Blessing *(Roman Missal Chants)*

Blessing
21 The Concluding Rites: Greeting/Final Blessing *(Roman Missal Chants)*

Dismissal
26 Dismissal: Easter Solemn (Verse and Response) *(Roman Missal Chants)*
23 Dismissal (Verse and Response: Go and Announce) *(Roman Missal Chants)*
22 Dismissal (Verse and Response: Go Forth) *(Roman Missal Chants)*
25 Dismissal (Verse and Response: Go in Peace) *(Roman Missal Chants)*
24 Dismissal (Verse and Response: Go in Peace, Glorifying the Lord) *(Roman Missal Chants)*
468 Lead Us to the Water

Recessional
See Liturgical Index: The Liturgical Year; Topical Index: Discipleship, Evangelization, Ministry/Mission, Praise, Sending Forth, Thanksgiving

Although it is not necessary to sing a recessional hymn, when it is a custom, all may join in a hymn or song after the dismissal…At times, e.g., if there has been a song after Communion, it may be appropriate to choose an option other than congregational song for the recessional. Other options include a choral or instrumental piece or, particularly during Lent, silence. (Sing to the Lord, #199)

SUNDAY CELEBRATIONS IN THE ABSENCE OF A PRIEST

Responsorial Psalm (See Scriptural Index)
203 Isaiah 12: We Shall Draw Water
118 Psalm 16: You Are My Inheritance
119 Psalm 18: I Love You, Lord, My Strength
121 Psalm 19: Lord, You Have the Words
692 *(Psalm 19)* Your Words Are Spirit and Life (B. Farrell)
120 Psalm 19: Your Words, Lord, Are Spirit and Life (Hurd)
122 Psalm 22: My God, My God (Manion)
123 Psalm 22: My God, My God (T.R. Smith)
124 Psalm 22: My God, My God/Dios Mío, Dios Mío (Schiavone)
128 Psalm 23: My Shepherd Is the Lord (Gelineau)
126 Psalm 23: The Lord Is My Shepherd/El Señor Es Mi Pastor (Reza)
127 Psalm 23: The Lord Is My Shepherd/I Shall Live in the House of the Lord (Crandal)
125 Psalm 23: The Lord Is My Shepherd/I Shall Live in the House/The Lord Prepares a Banquet (Cooney)
129 Psalm 24: Lord, This Is the People/Let the Lord Enter
130 Psalm 25: I Lift Up My Soul
131 Psalm 25: To You, O Lord (Joncas)
132 Psalm 25: To You, O Lord (Soper)
133 Psalm 27: The Goodness of the Lord
134 Psalm 27: The Lord Is My Light
135 Psalm 29: The Lord Will Bless His People with Peace
136 Psalm 30: I Will Praise You, Lord
141 Psalm 33: Happy the People You Have Chosen
140 Psalm 33: Lord, Let Your Mercy
142 Psalm 33: The Lord Fills the Earth with His Love
146 Psalm 34: I Will Always Thank the Lord
143 Psalm 34: Taste and See (Dean)
144 Psalm 34: Taste and See (Talbot)
145 Psalm 34: Taste and See/Gusten y Vean (Reza)
147 Psalm 40: Here I Am/God, My God, Come to My Aid
148 Psalm 42: O God, for You I Long
149 Psalm 42/43: As the Deer Longs
150 Psalm 45: The Queen Stands
151 Psalm 47: God Mounts His Throne
153 Psalm 51: Be Merciful, O Lord
152 Psalm 51: Create in Me (Hurd)
154 Psalm 51: Create in Me (Kendzia)
155 Psalm 51: Create in Me/Oh Dios, Crea en Mí (Cortés)
156 Psalm 63: My Soul Is Thirsting/As Morning Breaks (Angrisano)
157 Psalm 63: My Soul Thirsts (Schutte)
159 Psalm 66: Let All the Earth (Soper)
158 Psalm 66: Let All the Earth Cry Out (Cooney)
160 Psalm 67: O God, Let All the Nations
161 Psalm 72: Justice Shall Flourish/Lord, Every Nation
162 Psalm 80: The Vineyard of the Lord/Lord, Make Us Turn to You
163 Psalm 84: How Lovely Is Your Dwelling Place
165 Psalm 85: Let Us See Your Kindness (MacAller)
166 Psalm 85: Lord, Let Us See Your Kindness (Soper)
167 Psalm 89: For Ever I Will Sing
168 Psalm 90: In Every Age
169 Psalm 91: Be with Me, Lord (Canedo)
170 Psalm 91: Be with Me, Lord (Joncas)
171 Psalm 95: If Today You Hear God's Voice (B. Farrell)
172 Psalm 95: If Today You Hear His Voice (Soper)
173 Psalm 96: Proclaim His Marvelous Deeds
174 Psalm 96: Today a Savior Is Born (B. Farrell)
175 Psalm 96: Today Our Savior Is Born (Cortez)
176 Psalm 97: The Lord Is King
178 Psalm 98: All the Ends of the Earth (Canedo)
177 Psalm 98: All the Ends of the Earth (Hurd)
179 Psalm 98: The Lord Has Revealed
180 Psalm 100: We Are God's People
181 Psalm 103: The Lord Is Kind and Merciful (Dufford)
182 Psalm 103: The Lord Is Kind and Merciful (Manalo)
184 Psalm 104: Lord, Send Out Your Spirit (Canedo)
183 Psalm 104: Send Forth Your Spirit, O Lord (C. Walker)
189 Psalm 116: In the Presence of God
190 Psalm 118: Give Thanks to the Lord
335 *(Psalm 118)* This Is the Day (Fisher)
192 Psalm 118: This Is the Day (Joncas)
326 *(Psalm 118)* This Is the Day (Kendzia)
191 Psalm 118: This Is the Day (Soper)

193 Psalm 122: Let Us Go Rejoicing
194 Psalm 126: The Lord Has Done Great Things
195 Psalm 128: O Blessed Are Those
196 Psalm 130: Out of the Depths
197 Psalm 130: With Our God There Is Mercy
198 Psalm 138: On the Day I Called
200 Psalm 145: I Will Praise Your Name/The Hand of the Lord (T.R. Smith)
199 Psalm 145: I Will Praise Your Name/The Hand of the Lord Feeds Us (Soper)
201 Psalm 146: Praise the Lord, My Soul/Lord, Come and Save Us

Gospel Acclamation (Alleluia)

233 Advent/Christmas Gospel Acclamation
60 Alleluia *(Mass of a Joyful Heart)*
50 Alleluia *(Mass of Christ the Savior)*
94 Alleluia *(Mass of Renewal)*
29 Alleluia *(Mass of the Sacred Heart)*
39 Alleluia! Give the Glory *(Mass of Glory)*
84 Celtic Alleluia *(Celtic Mass)*

Lenten Gospel Acclamation

85 Lenten Gospel Acclamation *(Celtic Mass)*
61 Lenten Gospel Acclamation *(Mass of a Joyful Heart)*
51 Lenten Gospel Acclamation *(Mass of Christ the Savior)*
40 Lenten Gospel Acclamation *(Mass of Glory)*
95 Lenten Gospel Acclamation *(Mass of Renewal)*
30 Lenten Gospel Acclamation *(Mass of the Sacred Heart)*
691 Praise to You, O Christ, Our Savior

Dismissal of the Catechumens and the Elect

See Rites of the Church, Rite of Christian Initiation of Adults, Dismissal of the Catechumens and the Elect

Profession of Faith

9 Profession of Faith *(Roman Missal Chants)*

Prayer of the Faithful

113 Intercessions: Evening Prayer
106 Intercessions: Morning Prayer
626 O God, Hear Us
10 Universal Prayer

The Lord's Prayer

18 The Lord's Prayer *(Roman Missal Chants)*

Communion Song

598 Age to Age
707 All My Days
695 All the Earth
481 Ang Katawan ni Kristo/ Behold, the Body of Christ
509 As Grains of Wheat
480 As We Remember
641 Because the Lord Is My Shepherd
591 Center of My Life
458 Come to the Feast/ Ven al Banquete
461 Come to Us
545 Companions on the Journey
486 Draw Near
460 Gather the People
455 Gather Us Together
655 God Is Love
467 In This Place
677 Make Our Lives a Prayer of Peace
497 Miracle of Grace
401 One Lord
615 Only a Shadow
652 Psalm 23
143 Psalm 34: Taste and See (Dean)
144 Psalm 34: Taste and See (Talbot)
145 Psalm 34: Taste and See/ Gusten y Vean (Reza)
156 Psalm 63: My Soul Is Thirsting/ As Morning Breaks (Angrisano)
157 Psalm 63: My Soul Thirsts (Schutte)
180 Psalm 100: We Are God's People
200 Psalm 145: I Will Praise Your Name/The Hand of the Lord (T.R. Smith)
199 Psalm 145: I Will Praise Your Name/The Hand of the Lord Feeds Us (Soper)
507 Taste and See (Hurd)
504 Taste and See (Kendzia)
511 Taste and See (Moore)
503 That There May Be Bread
510 Ubi Caritas (Hurd)
664 Ubi Caritas (Rosania)
563 Unless a Grain of Wheat (B. Farrell)
516 Unless a Grain of Wheat (Hurd)
550 We Are Many Parts
736 We Praise You
506 We, the Body of Christ

Eucharistic Hymn

476 Lord, Who at Thy First Eucharist

Act of Thanksgiving

721 Holy God, We Praise Thy Name
209 Luke 1: Magnificat (Angrisano/Stephan)
210 Luke 1: Magnificat (B. Farrell)
208 Luke 1: Magnificat (Rubalcava)
207 Luke 1: Mary's Song (Joncas)
375 Mary's Song (Rieth)
180 Psalm 100: We Are God's People
192 Psalm 118: This Is the Day

Blessing

115 Blessing: Evening Prayer

Recessional

See Liturgical Index: The Liturgical Year; Topical Index: Discipleship, Evangelization, Ministry/Mission, Praise, Sending Forth, Thanksgiving

A song, instrumental music or choral anthem of the day may conclude the celebration. (Sunday Celebrations in the Absence of a Priest, #151, #185, #216)

Liturgy of the Hours

Morning Prayer

Verse and Response

102 Opening Verse: Invitatory

Invitatory Psalm

472 Come, Worship the Lord
103 Invitatory Psalm: Psalm 95

Hymn

616 A Mighty Fortress
714 All Creatures of Our God and King
456 All People That on Earth Do Dwell
695 All the Earth
696 Beautiful Savior
711 Come, Christians, Join to Sing
593 Faith of Our Fathers
705 For the Beauty of the Earth
718 From All That Dwell Below the Skies/Praise God from Whom All Blessings Flow
455 Gather Us Together
435 Give Me Jesus
628 God Be in My Head
719 God, We Praise You
358 Holy, Holy, Holy
699 I Sing the Mighty Power of God
103 Invitatory Psalm: Psalm 95
581 Jesus in the Morning
726 Joyful, Joyful, We Adore Thee
623 Lord of All Hopefulness
662 Love Divine, All Loves Excelling
778 Morning Has Broken
733 O God beyond All Praising
612 O God, Our Help in Ages Past
731 Praise the Lord, Ye Heavens
345 Send Out Your Spirit (Schoenbachler)
341 Send Us Your Spirit (Schutte)
742 Sing a New Song
744 Sing, O Sing
740 Sing of the Lord's Goodness
474 The God of All Grace
226 The King Shall Come When Morning Dawns
779 This Day God Gives Me
734 We Gather Together
736 We Praise You
453 Where Love Is Found
390 Ye Watchers and Ye Holy Ones

Morning Psalms, Canticles

203 Isaiah 12: We Shall Draw Water
121 Psalm 19: Lord, You Have the Words
129 Psalm 24: Lord, This Is the People/Let the Lord Enter
141 Psalm 33: Happy the People You Have Chosen
142 Psalm 33: The Lord Fills the Earth with His Love

590 *(Psalm 42)* As the Deer Longs
151 Psalm 47: God Mounts His Throne
152 Psalm 51: Create in Me (Hurd)
154 Psalm 51: Create in Me (Kendzia)
155 Psalm 51: Create in Me/ Oh Dios, Crea en Mí (Cortés)
156 Psalm 63: My Soul Is Thirsting/ As Morning Breaks
158 Psalm 66: Let All the Earth Cry Out (Cooney)
160 Psalm 67: O God, Let All the Nations
430 *(Psalm 84)* How Lovely Is Your Dwelling Place (DeBruyn)
163 Psalm 84: How Lovely Is Your Dwelling Place (Joncas)
165 Psalm 85: Let Us See Your Kindness (MacAller)
166 Psalm 85: Lord, Let Us See Your Kindness (Soper)
168 Psalm 90: In Every Age
173 Psalm 96: Proclaim His Marvelous Deeds
176 Psalm 97: The Lord Is King
178 Psalm 98: All the Ends of the Earth (Canedo)
177 Psalm 98: All the Ends of the Earth (Hurd)
179 Psalm 98: The Lord Has Revealed
739 *(Psalm 98)* Sing a New Song
695 *(Psalm 100)* All the Earth
180 Psalm 100: We Are God's People
190 Psalm 118: Give Thanks to the Lord
722 *(Psalm 118)* Sing to the Mountains
331 *(Psalm 118)* This Day Was Made by the Lord (C. Walker)
335 *(Psalm 118)* This Is the Day (Fisher)
192 Psalm 118: This Is the Day (Joncas)
191 Psalm 118: This Is the Day (Soper)
743 *(Psalm 145)* Sing a Joyful Song
104 Psalmody: Psalm 63

Gospel Canticle

105 Gospel Canticle (Benedictus)
206 Luke 1: Benedictus (Angrisano/Stephan)
205 Luke 1: Benedictus (B. Farrell)

Intercessions

113 Intercessions (Inwood)
106 Intercessions (Joncas)
626 O God, Hear Us
10 Universal Prayer

Lord's Prayer

107 The Lord's Prayer

Blessing

115 Blessing (Inwood)
108 Blessing (Joncas)

Evening Prayer

Thanksgiving for the Light

109 Thanksgiving for the Light

Hymn

616 A Mighty Fortress
780 Abide with Me
217 Creator of the Stars of Night
781 Day Is Done
110 Evening Hymn: O Radiant Light
593 Faith of Our Fathers
705 For the Beauty of the Earth
628 God Be in My Head
684 I Am the Light of the World
699 I Sing the Mighty Power of God
653 In Every Age
581 Jesus in the Morning
623 Lord of All Hopefulness
769 Lord of Glory
612 O God, Our Help in Ages Past
594 We Walk by Faith
453 Where Love Is Found
651 You Are Mine
610 You Are Near

Evening Psalms, Canticles

116 Psalm 16: Path of Life/Keep Me Safe (Balhoff/Daigle/Ducote)
117 Psalm 16: The Path of Life (Soper)
133 Psalm 27: The Goodness of the Lord
134 Psalm 27: The Lord Is My Light (DeBruyn)
443 *(Psalm 27)* The Lord Is My Light (C. Walker)
136 Psalm 30: I Will Praise You, Lord
160 Psalm 67: O God, Let All the Nations
161 Psalm 72: Justice Shall Flourish/ Lord, Every Nation
189 Psalm 116: In the Presence of God
186 Psalm 116: Our Blessing-Cup/ I Will Walk with the Lord/ The Cup of Salvation (Soper)
193 Psalm 122: Let Us Go Rejoicing
194 Psalm 126: The Lord Has Done Great Things
197 Psalm 130: With Our God There Is Mercy
275 *(Psalm 130)* With the Lord
640 *(Psalm 131)* Like a Child Rests
198 Psalm 138: On the Day I Called
200 Psalm 145: I Will Praise Your Name/The Hand of the Lord
111 Psalmody: Psalm 141

Gospel Canticle

112 Gospel Canticle (Magnificat)
379 Holy Is His Name
209 Luke 1: Magnificat (Angrisano/Stephan)
210 Luke 1: Magnificat (B. Farrell)
208 Luke 1: Magnificat (Rubalcava)
207 Luke 1: Mary's Song (Joncas)
375 Mary's Song (Rieth)
373 My Soul Magnifies the Lord

Intercessions

113 Intercessions (Inwood)
106 Intercessions (Joncas)
626 O God, Hear Us
10 Universal Prayer

Lord's Prayer

114 The Lord's Prayer

Blessing

115 Blessing (Inwood)
108 Blessing (Joncas)

Night Prayer

Hymn

598 Age to Age
781 Day Is Done
782 Daylight's Ending
110 Evening Hymn: O Radiant Light
628 God Be in My Head
646 I Heard the Voice of Jesus
653 In Every Age
623 Lord of All Hopefulness
769 Lord of Glory
636 Open My Eyes/Abre Mis Ojos
650 Pastures of the Lord
610 You Are Near

Night Psalms

138 Psalm 31: Father, into Your Hands I Commend My Spirit (DeBruyn)
139 Psalm 31: Father, into Your Hands/ Padre, en Tus Manos (Hurd)
169 Psalm 91: Be with Me, Lord (Canedo)
170 Psalm 91: Be with Me, Lord (Joncas)
605 *(Psalm 91)* Blest Be the Lord
606 *(Psalm 91)* On Eagle's Wings
196 Psalm 130: Out of the Depths

Gospel Canticle

211 Luke 2: Song of Simeon

Antiphon in Honor of the Blessed Virgin Mary

371 Del Cielo Ha Bajado
376 Hail, Holy Queen
372 Hail Mary: Gentle Woman

Rites of the Church

Baptism

406 Agua de Vida/Water of Life
553 All That Is Hidden
313 Alleluia No. 1
391 Baptized in Water
625 Christ Be beside Me
407 Come to the River *(Mass of Glory)*
580 Come Unto Me
394 Down to the River to Pray
398 Flow River Flow
592 I Believe in the Sun
304 I Saw Water Flowing
531 I Send You Out
574 I Will Choose Christ
468 Lead Us to the Water
384 Lift High the Cross
305 Litany of the Saints (Becker)
307 Litany of the Saints (Chant)
399 O Breathe on Me, O Breath of God
401 One Lord
560 Out of Darkness

128 Psalm 23: My Shepherd Is the Lord (Gelineau)
126 Psalm 23: The Lord Is My Shepherd/ El Señor Es Mi Pastor (Reza)
127 Psalm 23: The Lord Is My Shepherd/I Shall Live in the House of the Lord (Crandal)
132 Psalm 25: To You, O Lord
134 Psalm 27: The Lord Is My Light
143 Psalm 34: Taste and See (Dean)
145 Psalm 34: Taste and See/ Gusten y Vean (Reza)
393 Put On Christ
771 Rain Down
404 River of Glory
341 Send Us Your Spirit
569 Sing a New Church
474 The God of All Grace
688 The Light of Christ
331 This Day Was Made by the Lord
396 Wade in the Water
400 Water of Life
395 We Have Been Baptized in Christ
693 You Are Child
402 You Have Called Us

CONFIRMATION

600 Be Not Afraid
757 Beatitudes
565 Before the Sun Burned Bright
759 Blest Are They
348 By the Waking of Our Hearts
591 Center of My Life
352 Come, Holy Ghost
342 Come, O Spirit of the Lord
580 Come Unto Me
392 Enter the Journey
347 Envía Tu Espíritu
353 Everyone Moved by the Spirit
542 God Has Chosen Me
539 Here I Am, Lord
344 Holy Spirit (Canedo)
408 Holy Spirit, Come Now/Santo Espíritu, Ven (Manibusan)
343 Holy Spirit, Come to Me (Hoy)
574 I Will Choose Christ
752 In the Day of the Lord
760 Lead Me, Lord
384 Lift High the Cross
523 Lord, Whose Love in Humble Service
578 Now Is the Time
399 O Breathe on Me, O Breath of God
568 One Spirit, One Church
611 Only in God
562 Only This I Want
560 Out of Darkness
128 Psalm 23: My Shepherd Is the Lord (Gelineau)
126 Psalm 23: The Lord Is My Shepherd/ El Señor Es Mi Pastor (Reza)
127 Psalm 23: The Lord Is My Shepherd/I Shall Live in the House of the Lord (Crandal)
173 Psalm 96: Proclaim His Marvelous Deeds
184 Psalm 104: Lord, Send Out Your Spirit (Canedo)
185 Psalm 104: Lord, Send Out Your Spirit (Zsigray)
183 Psalm 104: Send Forth Your Spirit, O Lord (C. Walker)
200 Psalm 145: I Will Praise Your Name/The Hand of the Lord (T.R. Smith)
199 Psalm 145: I Will Praise Your Name/The Hand of the Lord Feeds Us (Soper)
393 Put On Christ
771 Rain Down
345 Send Out Your Spirit (Schoenbachler)
341 Send Us Your Spirit (Schutte)
541 Servant Song
346 Spirit, Come
561 Take, Lord, Receive
585 The Eyes and Hands of Christ
351 The Spirit Is A-Movin'
529 The Summons
350 Veni Sancte Spiritus
687 We Are the Light of the World
564 We Have Been Told
685 What You Hear in the Dark

DEDICATION OF A CHURCH

570 All Are Welcome
456 All People That on Earth Do Dwell
538 City of God
455 Gather Us Together
719 God, We Praise You
721 Holy God, We Praise Thy Name
304 I Saw Water Flowing
305 Litany of the Saints (Becker)
307 Litany of the Saints (Chant)
163 Psalm 84: How Lovely Is Your Dwelling Place
171 Psalm 95: If Today You Hear God's Voice (B. Farrell)
172 Psalm 95: If Today You Hear His Voice (Soper)
193 Psalm 122: Let Us Go Rejoicing
569 Sing a New Church
571 The Church's One Foundation
332 Two Were Bound for Emmaus
462 What Is This Place

EUCHARIST

See Topical Index: Eucharist, First Communion

EXPOSITION OF THE HOLY EUCHARIST (INCLUDING BENEDICTION)

696 Beautiful Savior
426 Blessed Be (Divine Praises)
625 Christ Be beside Me
718 From All That Dwell Below the Skies/Praise God from Whom All Blessings Flow
721 Holy God, We Praise Thy Name
499 O Sacrament Most Holy
427 O Saving Victim/ O Salutaris Hostia
291 Pange, Lingua, Gloriosi/ Sing, My Tongue, the Savior's Glory
477 See Us, Lord, About Your Altar

HOLY ORDERS

565 Before the Sun Burned Bright
591 Center of My Life
586 Christ before Us
352 Come, Holy Ghost
628 God Be in My Head
542 God Has Chosen Me
539 Here I Am, Lord
356 Hymn of Praise
574 I Will Choose Christ
548 In Christ There Is No East or West
760 Lead Me, Lord
384 Lift High the Cross
305 Litany of the Saints (Becker)
307 Litany of the Saints (Chant)
523 Lord, Whose Love in Humble Service
290 No Greater Love
611 Only in God
560 Out of Darkness
680 Peace Prayer
555 Pescador de Hombres/ Lord, You Have Come
679 Prayer of St. Francis/ Oración de San Francisco
128 Psalm 23: My Shepherd Is the Lord (Gelineau)
126 Psalm 23: The Lord Is My Shepherd/ El Señor Es Mi Pastor (Reza)
127 Psalm 23: The Lord Is My Shepherd/I Shall Live in the House of the Lord (Crandal)
125 Psalm 23: The Lord Is My Shepherd/I Shall Live in the House/The Lord Prepares a Banquet (Cooney)
147 Psalm 40: Here I Am/God, My God, Come to My Aid
173 Psalm 96: Proclaim His Marvelous Deeds
188 Psalm 116: Our Blessing-Cup
541 Servant Song
561 Take, Lord, Receive
585 The Eyes and Hands of Christ
529 The Summons
632 These Alone Are Enough
350 Veni Sancte Spiritus
564 We Have Been Told

MARRIAGE

707 All My Days
549 As We Celebrate
478 Bread of Life
84 Celtic Alleluia *(Celtic Mass)*
591 Center of My Life
545 Companions on the Journey

292 Donde Hay Amor y Caridad/ Where Charity and Love Abound
448 Hear Us Now, Our God and Father
449 Like a Seal on Your Heart
623 Lord of All Hopefulness
451 Love Never Fails
665 Love One Another
450 May God Bless You
667 May Love Be Ours
639 May the Road Rise Up
142 Psalm 33: The Lord Fills the Earth with His Love
143 Psalm 34: Taste and See (Dean)
144 Psalm 34: Taste and See (Talbot)
145 Psalm 34: Taste and See/ Gusten y Vean (Reza)
195 Psalm 128: O Blessed Are Those
454 Set Me as a Seal
537 The Servant Song
331 This Day Was Made by the Lord
510 Ubi Caritas (Hurd)
664 Ubi Caritas (Rosania)
736 We Praise You
447 When Love Is Found (O WALY, WALY)
453 Where Love Is Found (Schutte)
446 Where There Is Love
452 Wherever You Go
402 You Have Called Us

Order for the Blessing on the Fifteenth Birthday

554 Go Make a Difference
112 Gospel Canticle (Magnificat)
210 Luke 1: Magnificat (B. Farrell)
208 Luke 1: Magnificat (Rubalcava)
207 Luke 1: Mary's Song (Joncas)
375 Mary's Song (Rieth)
555 Pescador de Hombres/ Lord, You Have Come

Order of Christian Funerals

Vigil for the Deceased

590 As the Deer Longs
600 Be Not Afraid
641 Because the Lord Is My Shepherd
589 Do Not Fear to Hope
645 Eye Has Not Seen
435 Give Me Jesus
445 Go in Peace
420 Holy Darkness
329 I Am the Resurrection
653 In Every Age
270 In Your Love Remember Me
432 May the Angels
620 O God, You Search Me
439 O Loving God
618 Only in God
680 Peace Prayer
679 Prayer of St. Francis/ Oración de San Francisco
126 Psalm 23: The Lord Is My Shepherd/ El Señor Es Mi Pastor (Reza)
133 Psalm 27: The Goodness of the Lord
134 Psalm 27: The Lord Is My Light
148 Psalm 42: O God, for You I Long
149 Psalm 42/43: As the Deer Longs
441 Restless Is the Heart
773 Shall We Gather at the River
428 Songs of the Angels
634 There Is a Longing
563 Unless a Grain of Wheat
651 You Are Mine
610 You Are Near

Funeral Liturgy

Those involved in planning the funeral rites for a deceased child should take into account the age of the child, the circumstances of death, the grief of the family, and the needs and customs of those taking part in the rites.
(Order of Christian Funerals, #241)

643 All Is Well with My Soul
590 As the Deer Longs
600 Be Not Afraid
641 Because the Lord Is My Shepherd
759 Blest Are They
558 Come, Follow Me
410 Come Home
644 Come to Me
589 Do Not Fear to Hope
505 Eat This Bread
645 Eye Has Not Seen
388 For All the Saints
435 Give Me Jesus
429 Go Forth
445 Go in Peace
420 Holy Darkness
430 How Lovely Is Your Dwelling Place
493 I Am the Bread of Life
329 I Am the Resurrection
646 I Heard the Voice of Jesus
318 I Know That My Redeemer Lives (DUKE STREET)
431 I Know That My Redeemer Lives (Soper)
433 I, the Lord
764 If God Is for Us
653 In Every Age
437 In Paradisum/ May Angels Guide You
270 In Your Love Remember Me
603 Into Your Hands
767 Isaiah 49
775 Jerusalem, My Happy Home
515 Jesus, the Bread of Life
434 Keep in Mind
760 Lead Me, Lord
640 Like a Child Rests
765 Like a Shepherd
211 Luke 2: Song of Simeon
432 May the Angels
639 May the Road Rise Up
436 My Soul Is Thirsting
328 Now the Green Blade Rises
620 O God, You Search Me
439 O Loving God
606 On Eagle's Wings
611 Only in God (Foley)
618 Only in God (Talbot)
562 Only This I Want
440 Parable
650 Pastures of the Lord
680 Peace Prayer
679 Prayer of St. Francis/ Oración de San Francisco
117 Psalm 16: The Path of Life
652 Psalm 23 (Conry)
128 Psalm 23: My Shepherd Is the Lord (Gelineau)
126 Psalm 23: The Lord Is My Shepherd/ El Señor Es Mi Pastor (Reza)
127 Psalm 23: The Lord Is My Shepherd/I Shall Live in the House of the Lord (Crandal)
125 Psalm 23: The Lord Is My Shepherd/I Shall Live in the House/The Lord Prepares a Banquet (Cooney)
130 Psalm 25: I Lift Up My Soul
131 Psalm 25: To You, O Lord (Joncas)
132 Psalm 25: To You, O Lord (Soper)
133 Psalm 27: The Goodness of the Lord
149 Psalm 42/43: As the Deer Longs
148 Psalm 42: O God, for You I Long
156 Psalm 63: My Soul Is Thirsting/ As Morning Breaks (Angrisano)
157 Psalm 63: My Soul Thirsts (Schutte)
163 Psalm 84: How Lovely Is Your Dwelling Place
168 Psalm 90: In Every Age
181 Psalm 103: The Lord Is Kind and Merciful (Dufford)
182 Psalm 103: The Lord Is Kind and Merciful (Manalo)
189 Psalm 116: In the Presence of God
193 Psalm 122: Let Us Go Rejoicing
196 Psalm 130: Out of the Depths
197 Psalm 130: With Our God There Is Mercy
441 Restless Is the Heart
773 Shall We Gather at the River
649 Shelter Me, O God
642 Shepherd Me, O God
774 Sing with All the Saints in Glory
438 Song of Farewell (OLD HUNDREDTH)
442 Song of Farewell (Sands)
428 Songs of the Angels
750 Soon and Very Soon
648 The King of Love My Shepherd Is
443 The Lord Is My Light
608 The Lord Is Near/ May the Angels
336 The Strife Is O'er

634 There Is a Longing
631 This Alone
563 Unless a Grain of Wheat (B. Farrell)
516 Unless a Grain of Wheat (Hurd)
609 We Will Rise Again
777 Where My Father Lives
275 With the Lord
444 Yes, I Shall Arise
651 You Are Mine
610 You Are Near
557 Your Song of Love

Rite of Committal

589 Do Not Fear to Hope
445 Go in Peace
329 I Am the Resurrection
318 I Know That My Redeemer Lives (DUKE STREET)
431 I Know That My Redeemer Lives (Soper)
434 Keep in Mind
639 May the Road Rise Up
439 O Loving God
562 Only This I Want
126 Psalm 23: The Lord Is My Shepherd/ El Señor Es Mi Pastor (Reza)
438 Song of Farewell (OLD HUNDREDTH)
442 Song of Farewell (Sands)
777 Where My Father Lives
444 Yes, I Shall Arise

Penance (Reconciliation)

553 All That Is Hidden
614 Amazing Grace
261 Ashes
600 Be Not Afraid
605 Blest Be the Lord
478 Bread of Life
264 Change Our Hearts
410 Come Home
644 Come to Me
589 Do Not Fear to Hope
645 Eye Has Not Seen
659 Faithful Family
647 Fly like a Bird
723 Glory and Praise to Our God
628 God Be in My Head
518 God of the Hungry
604 Here I Am
411 Hosea
269 How Long, O Lord
772 I Have Loved You
646 I Heard the Voice of Jesus
752 In the Day of the Lord
270 In Your Love Remember Me
421 Lay Your Hands
621 Lead Me, Guide Me
760 Lead Me, Lord
672 Let There Be Peace on Earth
322 Lord of the Dance
413 Loving and Forgiving
677 Make Our Lives a Prayer of Peace
578 Now Is the Time
582 O Beauty, Ever Ancient
416 Pardon Your People
680 Peace Prayer
735 Praise, My Soul, the King of Heaven
738 Praise the Lord, My Soul
691 Praise to You, O Christ, Our Savior
679 Prayer of St. Francis/ Oración de San Francisco
133 Psalm 27: The Goodness of the Lord
136 Psalm 30: I Will Praise You, Lord
147 Psalm 40: Here I Am/God, My God, Come to My Aid
148 Psalm 42: O God, for You I Long
153 Psalm 51: Be Merciful, O Lord
152 Psalm 51: Create in Me (Hurd)
154 Psalm 51: Create in Me (Kendzia)
155 Psalm 51: Create in Me/ Oh Dios, Crea en Mí (Cortés)
168 Psalm 90: In Every Age
170 Psalm 91: Be with Me, Lord
181 Psalm 103: The Lord Is Kind and Merciful
196 Psalm 130: Out of the Depths
197 Psalm 130: With Our God There Is Mercy
111 Psalmody: Psalm 141
417 Remember Your Love
267 Return to Me
412 Return to the Lord Your God
635 Sacred Silence
229 Save Us, O Lord
276 Save Your People
279 Seek the Lord
418 Show Us Your Mercy
414 Softly and Tenderly Jesus Is Calling
278 Somebody's Knockin' at Your Door
346 Spirit, Come
561 Take, Lord, Receive
654 There Is a Balm in Gilead
634 There Is a Longing
670 There's a Wideness in God's Mercy
631 This Alone
619 Though the Mountains May Fall
274 Transfigure Us, O Lord
280 Turn to Me
664 Ubi Caritas
516 Unless a Grain of Wheat
668 What Wondrous Love Is This
275 With the Lord
415 You Alone
651 You Are Mine
610 You Are Near
624 You Are the Healing
402 You Have Called Us

Rite of Anointing (Care of the Sick)

598 Age to Age
590 As the Deer Longs
600 Be Not Afraid
419 Be Still, My Soul
641 Because the Lord Is My Shepherd
410 Come Home
644 Come to Me
407 Come to the River (*Mass of Glory)*
770 Come to the Water
580 Come Unto Me
645 Eye Has Not Seen
422 Healing River of the Spirit
425 Healing Waters
420 Holy Darkness
772 I Have Loved You
646 I Heard the Voice of Jesus
603 Into Your Hands
765 Like a Shepherd
709 Like Cedars
623 Lord of All Hopefulness
436 My Soul Is Thirsting
423 O Jesus, Healer of Wounded Souls
606 On Eagle's Wings
618 Only in God
650 Pastures of the Lord
424 Precious Lord, Take My Hand
117 Psalm 16: The Path of Life
119 Psalm 18: I Love You, Lord, My Strength
128 Psalm 23: My Shepherd Is the Lord (Gelineau)
127 Psalm 23: The Lord Is My Shepherd/I Shall Live in the House of the Lord (Crandal)
125 Psalm 23: The Lord Is My Shepherd/I Shall Live in the House/The Lord Prepares a Banquet (Cooney)
131 Psalm 25: To You, O Lord (Joncas)
132 Psalm 25: To You, O Lord (Soper)
136 Psalm 30: I Will Praise You, Lord
145 Psalm 34: Taste and See/ Gusten y Vean
148 Psalm 42: O God, for You I Long
149 Psalm 42/43: As the Deer Longs
156 Psalm 63: My Soul Is Thirsting/ As Morning Breaks (Angrisano)
157 Psalm 63: My Soul Thirsts (Schutte)
168 Psalm 90: In Every Age
170 Psalm 91: Be with Me, Lord
189 Psalm 116: In the Presence of God
197 Psalm 130: With Our God There Is Mercy
198 Psalm 138: On the Day I Called
649 Shelter Me, O God
642 Shepherd Me, O God
418 Show Us Your Mercy
526 The Cry of the Poor
443 The Lord Is My Light
634 There Is a Longing
670 There's a Wideness in God's Mercy
631 This Alone
630 To You, O God, I Lift Up My Soul
609 We Will Rise Again
651 You Are Mine

610 You Are Near
624 You Are the Healing
557 Your Song of Love

Rite of Christian Initiation of Adults

Rite of Entrance into the Order of Catechumens

601 For You Are My God
542 God Has Chosen Me
772 I Have Loved You
682 I Want to Walk as a Child of the Light
574 I Will Choose Christ
760 Lead Me, Lord
582 O Beauty, Ever Ancient
636 Open My Eyes/Abre Mis Ojos
141 Psalm 33: Happy the People You Have Chosen
193 Psalm 122: Let Us Go Rejoicing
529 The Summons
632 These Alone Are Enough
736 We Praise You
594 We Walk by Faith
651 You Are Mine
402 You Have Called Us
692 Your Words Are Spirit and Life

Signing of the Senses

636 Open My Eyes/Abre Mis Ojos
403 Signing of the Senses

Dismissal of the Catechumens and the Elect

409 Dismissal of the Catechumens and the Elect *(Celtic Mass)*
638 May God Bless and Keep You
450 May God Bless You
543 Take the Word of God with You
402 You Have Called Us

Celebrations of the Word of God

636 Open My Eyes/Abre Mis Ojos
121 Psalm 19: Lord, You Have the Words
149 Psalm 42/43: As the Deer Longs
610 You Are Near

Sending of the Catechumens for Election

556 Anthem
759 Blest Are They
625 Christ Be beside Me
435 Give Me Jesus
560 Out of Darkness
691 Praise to You, O Christ, Our Savior
117 Psalm 16: The Path of Life
543 Take the Word of God with You
571 The Church's One Foundation
402 You Have Called Us

Signing the Book of the Elect

772 I Have Loved You
402 You Have Called Us

Rite of Election

556 Anthem
392 Enter the Journey
435 Give Me Jesus
682 I Want to Walk as a Child of the Light
560 Out of Darkness
691 Praise to You, O Christ, Our Savior
117 Psalm 16: The Path of Life
571 The Church's One Foundation

Enrollment of Names

759 Blest Are They
625 Christ Be beside Me
761 Find Us Ready
772 I Have Loved You
682 I Want to Walk as a Child of the Light
548 In Christ There Is No East or West
562 Only This I Want
402 You Have Called Us

Scrutinies (General)

614 Amazing Grace
264 Change Our Hearts
422 Healing River of the Spirit
604 Here I Am (Booth)
539 Here I Am, Lord (Schutte)
595 Hold Me in Life
646 I Heard the Voice of Jesus
636 Open My Eyes/Abre Mis Ojos
117 Psalm 16: The Path of Life
134 Psalm 27: The Lord Is My Light
147 Psalm 40: Here I Am/God, My God, Come to My Aid
152 Psalm 51: Create in Me (Hurd)
154 Psalm 51: Create in Me (Kendzia)
441 Restless Is the Heart
418 Show Us Your Mercy
443 The Lord Is My Light
274 Transfigure Us, O Lord
610 You Are Near

Penitential Rite (Scrutiny—2nd Sunday of Lent)

604 Here I Am
689 Lord, to Whom Shall We Go
652 Psalm 23 (Conry)
127 Psalm 23: The Lord Is My Shepherd/I Shall Live in the House of the Lord (Crandal)
133 Psalm 27: The Goodness of the Lord
134 Psalm 27: The Lord Is My Light
140 Psalm 33: Lord, Let Your Mercy
147 Psalm 40: Here I Am/God, My God, Come to My Aid
153 Psalm 51: Be Merciful, O Lord
152 Psalm 51: Create in Me (Hurd)
154 Psalm 51: Create in Me (Kendzia)
155 Psalm 51: Create in Me/ Oh Dios, Crea en Mí (Cortés)
189 Psalm 116: In the Presence of God
196 Psalm 130: Out of the Depths
382 Transfiguration
651 You Are Mine

First Scrutiny (3rd Sunday of Lent)

407 Come to the River *(Mass of Glory)*
542 God Has Chosen Me
343 Holy Spirit, Come to Me
620 O God, You Search Me
117 Psalm 16: The Path of Life
171 Psalm 95: If Today You Hear God's Voice (B. Farrell)
172 Psalm 95: If Today You Hear His Voice (Soper)
404 River of Glory
773 Shall We Gather at the River

Second Scrutiny (4th Sunday of Lent)

683 Christ, Be Our Light
398 Flow River Flow
595 Hold Me in Life
343 Holy Spirit, Come to Me
399 O Breathe on Me, O Breath of God
636 Open My Eyes/Abre Mis Ojos
560 Out of Darkness
652 Psalm 23 (Conry)
128 Psalm 23: My Shepherd Is the Lord (Gelineau)
126 Psalm 23: The Lord Is My Shepherd/ El Señor Es Mi Pastor (Reza)
127 Psalm 23: The Lord Is My Shepherd/I Shall Live in the House of the Lord (Crandal)
125 Psalm 23: The Lord Is My Shepherd/I Shall Live in the House/The Lord Prepares a Banquet (Cooney)
642 Shepherd Me, O God
443 The Lord Is My Light
597 Those Who See Light
685 What You Hear in the Dark

Third Scrutiny (5th Sunday of Lent)

431 I Know That My Redeemer Lives
758 I Will Not Die
197 Psalm 130: With Our God There Is Mercy
609 We Will Rise Again

Rites of Initiation

Baptism

See also Rites of the Church: Baptism

406 Agua de Vida/Water of Life
531 I Send You Out
305 Litany of the Saints (Becker)
307 Litany of the Saints (Chant)

Confirmation

See also Rites of the Church: Confirmation

344 Holy Spirit (Canedo)
408 Holy Spirit, Come Now/Santo Espíritu, Ven (Manibusan)
341 Send Us Your Spirit
346 Spirit, Come

Rite of Reception of Baptized Christians

See also Rites of the Church: Baptism, Confirmation

134 Psalm 27: The Lord Is My Light
156 Psalm 63: My Soul Is Thirsting/ As Morning Breaks (Angrisano)
157 Psalm 63: My Soul Thirsts (Schutte)

MYSTAGOGIA

See also Topical Index: Christian Life, Church, Good Shepherd, Holy Spirit, Ministry/Mission, Paschal Mystery, People of God, Pilgrim Church, Praise, Resurrection, Social Concern, Thanksgiving, Wisdom

715 Been So Busy
539 Here I Am, Lord
493 I Am the Bread of Life
531 I Send You Out
752 In the Day of the Lord
272 Led by the Spirit
528 Light of Christ
413 Loving and Forgiving
401 One Lord
568 One Spirit, One Church
560 Out of Darkness
501 Pan de Vida
679 Prayer of St. Francis/ Oración de San Francisco
128 Psalm 23: My Shepherd Is the Lord (Gelineau)
127 Psalm 23: The Lord Is My Shepherd/I Shall Live in the House of the Lord (Crandal)
136 Psalm 30: I Will Praise You, Lord
148 Psalm 42: O God, for You I Long
154 Psalm 51: Create in Me
183 Psalm 104: Send Forth Your Spirit, O Lord
541 Servant Song
403 Signing of the Senses
585 The Eyes and Hands of Christ
608 The Lord Is Near/ May the Angels
351 The Spirit Is A-Movin'
524 We Are Called
535 With One Voice
275 With the Lord
692 Your Words Are Spirit and Life

GENERAL USE

479 Amén. El Cuerpo de Cristo
319 At the Lamb's High Feast
565 Before the Sun Burned Bright
591 Center of My Life
625 Christ Be beside Me
683 Christ, Be Our Light
407 Come to the River *(Mass of Glory)*
394 Down to the River to Pray
645 Eye Has Not Seen
761 Find Us Ready
397 Give Me Ears to Listen
554 Go Make a Difference
542 God Has Chosen Me
343 Holy Spirit, Come to Me
431 I Know That My Redeemer Lives
640 Like a Child Rests
339 Lord, You Give the Great Commission
663 Lover of Us All
450 May God Bless You
578 Now Is the Time
620 O God, You Search Me
606 On Eagle's Wings
636 Open My Eyes/Abre Mis Ojos
555 Pescador de Hombres/ Lord, You Have Come
143 Psalm 34: Taste and See (Dean)
145 Psalm 34: Taste and See/ Gusten y Vean (Reza)
149 Psalm 42/43: As the Deer Longs
154 Psalm 51: Create in Me
156 Psalm 63: My Soul Is Thirsting/ As Morning Breaks (Angrisano)
157 Psalm 63: My Soul Thirsts (Schutte)
393 Put On Christ
771 Rain Down
547 Somos el Cuerpo de Cristo/ We Are the Body of Christ
688 The Light of Christ
335 This Is the Day
274 Transfigure Us, O Lord
510 Ubi Caritas
687 We Are the Light of the World
405 We Belong to You
535 With One Voice
651 You Are Mine
624 You Are the Healing
402 You Have Called Us
692 Your Words Are Spirit and Life

RITE OF RELIGIOUS PROFESSION

757 Beatitudes
565 Before the Sun Burned Bright
591 Center of My Life
586 Christ before Us
352 Come, Holy Ghost
542 God Has Chosen Me
539 Here I Am, Lord
356 Hymn of Praise
574 I Will Choose Christ
548 In Christ There Is No East or West
660 In Perfect Charity
523 Lord, Whose Love in Humble Service
677 Make Our Lives a Prayer of Peace
582 O Beauty, Ever Ancient
680 Peace Prayer
555 Pescador de Hombres/ Lord, You Have Come
679 Prayer of St. Francis/ Oración de San Francisco
129 Psalm 24: Lord, This Is the People/Let the Lord Enter
143 Psalm 34: Taste and See (Dean)
145 Psalm 34: Taste and See/ Gusten y Vean (Reza)
156 Psalm 63: My Soul Is Thirsting/ As Morning Breaks (Angrisano)
157 Psalm 63: My Soul Thirsts (Schutte)
541 Servant Song
561 Take, Lord, Receive
585 The Eyes and Hands of Christ
529 The Summons
632 These Alone Are Enough
687 We Are the Light of the World
564 We Have Been Told
577 Women of the Church

DEVOTIONS

ADORATION OF THE BLESSED SACRAMENT

426 Blessed Be (Divine Praises)
499 O Sacrament Most Holy
427 O Saving Victim/ O Salutaris Hostia
291 Pange, Lingua, Gloriosi/ Sing, My Tongue, the Savior's Glory
477 See Us, Lord, About Your Altar

ROSARY

369 Ave Maria
376 Hail, Holy Queen
372 Hail Mary: Gentle Woman
370 Immaculate Mary
373 My Soul Magnifies the Lord
380 Sing of Mary

THE WAY OF THE CROSS

262 At the Cross Her Station Keeping/Stabat Mater Dolorosa
295 Behold the Lamb of God
298 Behold the Wood
281 Faithful Cross
297 O Sacred Head, Surrounded
562 Only This I Want
301 Pietà
552 Take Up Your Cross
300 Were You There
668 What Wondrous Love Is This
302 When I Survey the Wondrous Cross
296 Wood of the Cross

THE LITURGICAL YEAR

SEASON OF ADVENT

Advent (Sundays and Weekdays)

213 A Voice Cries Out
233 Advent/Christmas Gospel Acclamation
232 Advent Lamb of God
231 Alleluia! Hurry, the Lord Is Near
683 Christ, Be Our Light
215 Christ, Circle Round Us
686 Christ the Lord
359 Come Now, Almighty King
212 Come, Thou Long-Expected Jesus
217 Creator of the Stars of Night
219 Emmanuel
221 Every Valley
761 Find Us Ready
105 Gospel Canticle (Benedictus)
379 Holy Is His Name
269 How Long, O Lord
752 In the Day of the Lord
622 Jesus, Come to Us
730 Let All Mortal Flesh Keep Silence

225 Let the King of Glory Come
227 Let the Valleys Be Raised
528 Light of Christ
662 Love Divine, All Loves Excelling
206 Luke 1: Benedictus (Angrisano/Stephan)
205 Luke 1: Benedictus (B. Farrell)
209 Luke 1: Magnificat
220 Maranatha
728 May We Praise You
436 My Soul Is Thirsting
228 O Come, O Come, Emmanuel
218 On Jordan's Bank
224 Patience, People
223 People, Look East
130 Psalm 25: I Lift Up My Soul
131 Psalm 25: To You, O Lord (Joncas)
132 Psalm 25: To You, O Lord (Soper)
164 Psalm 85: Come, O Lord/Lord, Let Us See Your Kindness
230 Ready the Way (Hurd)
216 Ready the Way (Stephan)
229 Save Us, O Lord
374 Song of Mary
750 Soon and Very Soon
378 The Angel Gabriel from Heaven Came
226 The King Shall Come When Morning Dawns
634 There Is a Longing
763 Thy Kingdom Come
630 To You, O God, I Lift Up My Soul
222 Waiting in Silence
241 Who Has Known

Season of Christmas

Christmas (Days of)

233 Advent/Christmas Gospel Acclamation
712 All the Ends of the Earth
253 Angels, from the Realms of Glory
236 Angels We Have Heard on High
238 Away in a Manger
257 Child of the Poor
237 Children, Run Joyfully
538 City of God
242 Go, Tell It on the Mountain
243 God Rest You Merry, Gentlemen
239 Good Christian Friends, Rejoice
245 Hark! the Herald Angels Sing
251 Infant Holy, Infant Lowly
250 It Came upon the Midnight Clear
240 Joy to the World
730 Let All Mortal Flesh Keep Silence
246 Lo, How a Rose E'er Blooming
669 Love Has Come
209 Luke 1: Magnificat
235 O Come, All Ye Faithful/ Venid, Fieles Todos
248 O Come, Little Children
244 O Little Town of Bethlehem
306 Out of Darkness
691 Praise to You, O Christ, Our Savior
174 Psalm 96: Today a Savior Is Born (B. Farrell)
175 Psalm 96: Today Our Savior Is Born (Cortez)
178 Psalm 98: All the Ends of the Earth (Canedo)
177 Psalm 98: All the Ends of the Earth (Hurd)
179 Psalm 98: The Lord Has Revealed
249 Rise Up, Shepherd, and Follow
247 See Amid the Winter's Snow
252 Silent Night/Noche de Paz
259 The First Nowell
234 Wake from Your Sleep
256 What Child Is This
241 Who Has Known

The Holy Family of Jesus, Mary, and Joseph

236 Angels We Have Heard on High
257 Child of the Poor
243 God Rest You Merry, Gentlemen
248 O Come, Little Children
195 Psalm 128: O Blessed Are Those
380 Sing of Mary
234 Wake from Your Sleep
256 What Child Is This

Mary, the Holy Mother of God

236 Angels We Have Heard on High
369 Ave Maria
257 Child of the Poor
112 Gospel Canticle (Magnificat)
376 Hail, Holy Queen
372 Hail Mary: Gentle Woman
245 Hark! the Herald Angels Sing
370 Immaculate Mary
246 Lo, How a Rose E'er Blooming
207 Luke 1: Mary's Song (Joncas)
375 Mary's Song (Rieth)
373 My Soul Magnifies the Lord
248 O Come, Little Children
244 O Little Town of Bethlehem
380 Sing of Mary (PLEADING SAVIOR)
374 Song of Mary (Schutte)
377 There Is Nothing Told
256 What Child Is This
241 Who Has Known

The Epiphany of the Lord

253 Angels, from the Realms of Glory
258 As with Gladness Men of Old
214 Beyond the Moon and Stars
257 Child of the Poor
242 Go, Tell It on the Mountain
240 Joy to the World
730 Let All Mortal Flesh Keep Silence
235 O Come, All Ye Faithful/ Venid, Fieles Todos
161 Psalm 72: Justice Shall Flourish/ Lord, Every Nation
249 Rise Up, Shepherd, and Follow
254 Songs of Thankfulness and Praise
259 The First Nowell
234 Wake from Your Sleep
255 We Three Kings
256 What Child Is This

The Baptism of the Lord

203 Isaiah 12: We Shall Draw Water
218 On Jordan's Bank
135 Psalm 29: The Lord Will Bless His People with Peace
396 Wade in the Water

Season of Lent

Ash Wednesday

266 Again We Keep This Solemn Fast
261 Ashes (Conry)
260 Ashes to Ashes (Schutte)
268 Beyond the Days
264 Change Our Hearts
263 Forty Days and Forty Nights
411 Hosea
271 In These Days of Lenten Journey
272 Led by the Spirit
277 Lord, Who Throughout These Forty Days
413 Loving and Forgiving
582 O Beauty, Ever Ancient
153 Psalm 51: Be Merciful, O Lord
152 Psalm 51: Create in Me (Hurd)
154 Psalm 51: Create in Me (Kendzia)
169 Psalm 91: Be with Me, Lord
417 Remember Your Love
276 Save Your People
279 Seek the Lord
278 Somebody's Knockin' at Your Door
552 Take Up Your Cross
273 The Glory of These Forty Days
280 Turn to Me

Lent (Sundays and Weekdays)

716 Abba! Father
266 Again We Keep This Solemn Fast
553 All That Is Hidden
614 Amazing Grace
590 As the Deer Longs
480 As We Remember
261 Ashes (Conry)
260 Ashes to Ashes (Schutte)
262 At the Cross Her Station Keeping/ Stabat Mater Dolorosa
600 Be Not Afraid
268 Beyond the Days
478 Bread of Life
264 Change Our Hearts
683 Christ, Be Our Light
770 Come to the Water
580 Come Unto Me
659 Faithful Family
398 Flow River Flow
263 Forty Days and Forty Nights
265 Gracious God
411 Hosea
269 How Long, O Lord
653 In Every Age

271 In These Days of Lenten Journey
270 In Your Love Remember Me
621 Lead Me, Guide Me
272 Led by the Spirit
85 Lenten Gospel Acclamation *(Celtic Mass)*
51 Lenten Gospel Acclamation *(Mass of Christ the Savior)*
40 Lenten Gospel Acclamation *(Mass of Glory)*
689 Lord, to Whom Shall We Go
277 Lord, Who Throughout These Forty Days
413 Loving and Forgiving
728 May We Praise You
436 My Soul Is Thirsting
290 No Greater Love
582 O Beauty, Ever Ancient
294 O Sacred Head
606 On Eagle's Wings
416 Pardon Your People
680 Peace Prayer
738 Praise the Lord, My Soul
691 Praise to You, O Christ, Our Savior
679 Prayer of St. Francis/ Oración de San Francisco
149 Psalm 42/43: As the Deer Longs
153 Psalm 51: Be Merciful, O Lord
152 Psalm 51: Create in Me (Hurd)
154 Psalm 51: Create in Me (Kendzia)
155 Psalm 51: Create in Me/Oh Dios, Crea en Mí (Cortés)
169 Psalm 91: Be with Me, Lord (Canedo)
170 Psalm 91: Be with Me, Lord (Joncas)
181 Psalm 103: The Lord Is Kind and Merciful
196 Psalm 130: Out of the Depths
197 Psalm 130: With Our God There Is Mercy
417 Remember Your Love
267 Return to Me
412 Return to the Lord Your God
229 Save Us, O Lord
276 Save Your People
502 Seed, Scattered and Sown
279 Seek the Lord
649 Shelter Me, O God
418 Show Us Your Mercy
414 Softly and Tenderly Jesus Is Calling
278 Somebody's Knockin' at Your Door
629 Stand by Me
561 Take, Lord, Receive
552 Take Up Your Cross
273 The Glory of These Forty Days
648 The King of Love My Shepherd Is
529 The Summons
634 There Is a Longing
670 There's a Wideness in God's Mercy
619 Though the Mountains May Fall
382 Transfiguration
280 Turn to Me
563 Unless a Grain of Wheat
668 What Wondrous Love Is This
275 With the Lord
533 Without You
610 You Are Near

HOLY WEEK

Palm Sunday of the Passion of the Lord

284 All Glory, Laud, and Honor
262 At the Cross Her Station Keeping/ Stabat Mater Dolorosa
366 At the Name of Jesus
295 Behold the Lamb of God
285 Blessings on the King
283 Hosanna to the Son of David
363 Jesus, the Lord
384 Lift High the Cross
294 O Sacred Head (Hurd)
297 O Sacred Head, Surrounded (PASSION CHORALE)
122 Psalm 22: My God, My God (Manion)
123 Psalm 22: My God, My God (T.R. Smith)
124 Psalm 22: My God, My God/ Dios Mío, Dios Mío (Schiavone)
552 Take Up Your Cross
282 The Children of Jerusalem
368 The King of Glory
300 Were You There
668 What Wondrous Love Is This
302 When I Survey the Wondrous Cross

The Chrism Mass

539 Here I Am, Lord
523 Lord, Whose Love in Humble Service
339 Lord, You Give the Great Commission
534 You Have Anointed Me

THE SACRED PASCHAL TRIDUUM

Thursday of the Lord's Supper at the Evening Mass

479 Amén. El Cuerpo de Cristo
286 As I Have Done for You
480 As We Remember
657 Christians, Let Us Love One Another
292 Donde Hay Amor y Caridad/ Where Charity and Love Abound
505 Eat This Bread
659 Faithful Family
460 Gather the People
289 Glory in the Cross
655 God Is Love
287 Jesu, Jesu
476 Lord, Who at Thy First Eucharist
666 Love Goes On
665 Love One Another
290 No Greater Love
500 Our Blessing Cup
560 Out of Darkness
501 Pan de Vida
291 Pange, Lingua, Gloriosi/ Sing, My Tongue, the Savior's Glory
188 Psalm 116: Our Blessing-Cup (Joncas)
187 Psalm 116: Our Blessing-Cup/ El Cáliz que Bendecimos (Cortez)
186 Psalm 116: Our Blessing-Cup/ I Will Walk with the Lord/ The Cup of Salvation (Soper)
502 Seed, Scattered and Sown
475 Shepherd of Souls
293 The Lord Jesus
513 The Supper of the Lord
510 Ubi Caritas (Hurd)
664 Ubi Caritas (Rosania)
514 Vine and Branches
668 What Wondrous Love Is This
519 Whatsoever You Do
288 Where Charity and Love Prevail
453 Where Love Is Found

Friday of the Passion of the Lord (Good Friday)

262 At the Cross Her Station Keeping/ Stabat Mater Dolorosa
295 Behold the Lamb of God
298 Behold the Wood
281 Faithful Cross
289 Glory in the Cross
363 Jesus, the Lord
384 Lift High the Cross
290 No Greater Love
294 O Sacred Head (Hurd)
297 O Sacred Head, Surrounded (PASSION CHORALE)
301 Pietà
137 Psalm 31: Father, I Put My Life in Your Hands (Talbot)
138 Psalm 31: Father, into Your Hands I Commend My Spirit (DeBruyn)
139 Psalm 31: Father, into Your Hands/Padre, en Tus Manos (Hurd)
383 Take Up Our Cross (Stephan/Hart/Byrd)
552 Take Up Your Cross (ERHALT UNS, HERR)
299 We Venerate Your Cross/ Tu Cruz Adoramos
300 Were You There
668 What Wondrous Love Is This
302 When I Survey the Wondrous Cross
296 Wood of the Cross

The Easter Vigil in the Holy Night

316 Behold the Glory of God
303 Christ, Be Our Light
202 Exodus 15: To God Be Praise and Glory
289 Glory in the Cross

304 I Saw Water Flowing
203 Isaiah 12: We Shall Draw Water
305 Litany of the Saints (Becker)
307 Litany of the Saints (Chant)
308 Our Paschal Sacrifice/ El Cordero Pascual
306 Out of Darkness
118 Psalm 16: You Are My Inheritance
121 Psalm 19: Lord, You Have the Words
142 Psalm 33: The Lord Fills the Earth with His Love
149 Psalm 42/43: As the Deer Longs
155 Psalm 51: Create in Me/ Oh Dios, Crea en Mí (Cortés)
184 Psalm 104: Lord, Send Out Your Spirit (Canedo)
183 Psalm 104: Send Forth Your Spirit, O Lord (C. Walker)
327 Up from the Earth
395 We Have Been Baptized in Christ

Season of Easter

Easter Sunday

192 Psalm 118: This Is the Day (Joncas)
191 Psalm 118: This Is the Day (Soper)
335 This Is the Day (Fisher)

Easter (Sundays and Weekdays)

311 Aleluya, Aleluya
309 All Shall Be Well
713 Alle, Alle, Alleluia
321 Alleluia! Alleluia! (HYMN TO JOY)
317 Alleluia! Alleluia! Let the Holy Anthem Rise (HOLY ANTHEM)
314 Alleluia! Love Is Alive
313 Alleluia No. 1
361 Alleluia! Sing to Jesus
549 As We Celebrate
480 As We Remember
319 At the Lamb's High Feast
366 At the Name of Jesus
320 Christ, the Lord, Is Risen Today (LLANFAIR)
334 Christ, the Lord, Is Risen Today (VICTIMAE PASCHALI)
310 Christians, to the Paschal Victim
362 Crown Him with Many Crowns
589 Do Not Fear to Hope
202 Exodus 15: To God Be Praise and Glory
700 Give Thanks to the Lord
289 Glory in the Cross
720 Hallelujah Is Our Song
329 I Am the Resurrection
318 I Know That My Redeemer Lives
304 I Saw Water Flowing
433 I, the Lord
489 In the Breaking of the Bread
752 In the Day of the Lord
330 Jesus Christ Is Risen Today
315 Join in the Dance
434 Keep in Mind
333 Let Heaven Rejoice
325 Let Us Sing and Be Glad/ And the Father Will Dance
384 Lift High the Cross
528 Light of Christ
322 Lord of the Dance
328 Now the Green Blade Rises
308 Our Paschal Sacrifice/ El Cordero Pascual
560 Out of Darkness
737 Praise God in This Holy Dwelling
159 Psalm 66: Let All the Earth (Soper)
158 Psalm 66: Let All the Earth Cry Out (Cooney)
190 Psalm 118: Give Thanks to the Lord
192 Psalm 118: This Is the Day (Joncas)
191 Psalm 118: This Is the Day (Soper)
771 Rain Down
323 Resucitó/He Is Risen
404 River of Glory
324 Roll Away the Stone
739 Sing a New Song
722 Sing to the Mountains
648 The King of Love My Shepherd Is
336 The Strife Is O'er
331 This Day Was Made by the Lord
335 This Is the Day (Fisher)
326 This Is the Day (Kendzia)
360 To Jesus Christ, Our Sovereign King
332 Two Were Bound for Emmaus
563 Unless a Grain of Wheat
327 Up from the Earth
668 What Wondrous Love Is This
754 Worthy Is the Lamb
312 Ye Sons and Daughters
390 Ye Watchers and Ye Holy Ones

The Ascension of the Lord

364 All Hail the Power of Jesus' Name
361 Alleluia! Sing to Jesus
711 Come, Christians, Join to Sing
362 Crown Him with Many Crowns
365 Hail, Redeemer, King Divine
337 Hail the Day That Sees Him Rise
339 Lord, You Give the Great Commission
338 One Sacrifice of Christ
340 Peace, My Friends
151 Psalm 47: God Mounts His Throne
390 Ye Watchers and Ye Holy Ones

Pentecost Sunday

309 All Shall Be Well
600 Be Not Afraid
348 By the Waking of Our Hearts
352 Come, Holy Ghost
347 Envía Tu Espíritu
698 God, Beyond All Names
344 Holy Spirit (Canedo)
343 Holy Spirit, Come to Me (Hoy)
339 Lord, You Give the Great Commission
578 Now Is the Time
399 O Breathe on Me, O Breath of God
568 One Spirit, One Church
349 Pentecost Sequence
184 Psalm 104: Lord, Send Out Your Spirit (Canedo)
185 Psalm 104: Lord, Send Out Your Spirit (Zsigray)
183 Psalm 104: Send Forth Your Spirit, O Lord (C. Walker)
345 Send Out Your Spirit (Schoenbachler)
341 Send Us Your Spirit (Schutte)
346 Spirit, Come
351 The Spirit Is A-Movin'
544 They'll Know We Are Christians
350 Veni Sancte Spiritus
534 You Have Anointed Me

Solemnities of the Lord during Ordinary Time

The Most Holy Trinity

710 Alabaré/O Come and Sing
714 All Creatures of Our God and King
354 All Hail, Adored Trinity
355 All Praise and Glad Thanksgiving
713 Alle, Alle, Alleluia
359 Come Now, Almighty King
204 Daniel 3: Glory and Praise for Ever
596 Dwelling Place
718 From All That Dwell Below the Skies/Praise God from Whom All Blessings Flow
698 God, Beyond All Names
719 God, We Praise You
721 Holy God, We Praise Thy Name
358 Holy, Holy, Holy
356 Hymn of Praise
724 I Will Rejoice
660 In Perfect Charity
476 Lord, Who at Thy First Eucharist
728 May We Praise You
704 Now Thank We All Our God
357 O God, Almighty Father
737 Praise God in This Holy Dwelling
141 Psalm 33: Happy the People You Have Chosen
722 Sing to the Mountains
779 This Day God Gives Me

The Most Holy Body and Blood of Christ (Corpus Christi)

479 Amén. El Cuerpo de Cristo
481 Ang Katawan ni Kristo/ Behold, the Body of Christ
509 As Grains of Wheat
480 As We Remember
319 At the Lamb's High Feast

492 Behold the Lamb
426 Blessed Be (Divine Praises)
484 Bread of Angels
490 Bread of Life
657 Christians, Let Us Love One Another
505 Eat This Bread
460 Gather the People
487 Gift of Finest Wheat
464 Here at This Table
493 I Am the Bread of Life
495 I Am the Living Bread
489 In the Breaking of the Bread
515 Jesus, the Bread of Life
730 Let All Mortal Flesh Keep Silence
488 Let Us Break Bread Together
494 Look Beyond
476 Lord, Who at Thy First Eucharist
498 One Bread, One Body
501 Pan de Vida
291 Pange, Lingua, Gloriosi/ Sing, My Tongue, the Savior's Glory
186 Psalm 116: Our Blessing-Cup/ I Will Walk with the Lord/ The Cup of Salvation (Soper)
475 Shepherd of Souls
547 Somos el Cuerpo de Cristo/ We Are the Body of Christ
463 Table of Plenty
507 Taste and See
664 Ubi Caritas
506 We, the Body of Christ

The Most Sacred Heart of Jesus

696 Beautiful Savior
641 Because the Lord Is My Shepherd
625 Christ Be beside Me
657 Christians, Let Us Love One Another
644 Come to Me
461 Come to Us
580 Come Unto Me
487 Gift of Finest Wheat
646 I Heard the Voice of Jesus
548 In Christ There Is No East or West
203 Isaiah 12: We Shall Draw Water
567 Jesu, Joy of Our Desiring
765 Like a Shepherd
662 Love Divine, All Loves Excelling
413 Loving and Forgiving
636 Open My Eyes/Abre Mis Ojos
128 Psalm 23: My Shepherd Is the Lord (Gelineau)
126 Psalm 23: The Lord Is My Shepherd/ El Señor Es Mi Pastor (Reza)
127 Psalm 23: The Lord Is My Shepherd/I Shall Live in the House of the Lord (Crandal)
125 Psalm 23: The Lord Is My Shepherd/I Shall Live in the House/The Lord Prepares a Banquet (Cooney)
181 Psalm 103: The Lord Is Kind and Merciful
642 Shepherd Me, O God
648 The King of Love My Shepherd Is
670 There's a Wideness in God's Mercy
668 What Wondrous Love Is This
302 When I Survey the Wondrous Cross

Our Lord Jesus Christ, King of the Universe

364 All Hail the Power of Jesus' Name
313 Alleluia No. 1
361 Alleluia! Sing to Jesus
319 At the Lamb's High Feast
366 At the Name of Jesus
295 Behold the Lamb of God
686 Christ the Lord
711 Come, Christians, Join to Sing
362 Crown Him with Many Crowns
719 God, We Praise You
365 Hail, Redeemer, King Divine
752 In the Day of the Lord
567 Jesu, Joy of Our Desiring
367 Jesus Christ Is Lord
363 Jesus, the Lord
730 Let All Mortal Flesh Keep Silence
384 Lift High the Cross
769 Lord of Glory
669 Love Has Come
737 Praise God in This Holy Dwelling
735 Praise, My Soul, the King of Heaven
128 Psalm 23: My Shepherd Is the Lord (Gelineau)
126 Psalm 23: The Lord Is My Shepherd/ El Señor Es Mi Pastor (Reza)
193 Psalm 122: Let Us Go Rejoicing
771 Rain Down
642 Shepherd Me, O God
750 Soon and Very Soon
368 The King of Glory
648 The King of Love My Shepherd Is
226 The King Shall Come When Morning Dawns
763 Thy Kingdom Come
360 To Jesus Christ, Our Sovereign King
519 Whatsoever You Do

Solemnities and Feasts

The Presentation of the Lord (February 2)

211 Luke 2: Song of Simeon
380 Sing of Mary

St. Joseph, Spouse of the Blessed Virgin Mary (March 19)

385 Come Now, and Praise the Humble Saint
389 Holy Patron, Thee Saluting

The Annunciation of the Lord (March 25)

369 Ave Maria
371 Del Cielo Ha Bajado
372 Hail Mary: Gentle Woman
379 Holy Is His Name
370 Immaculate Mary
209 Luke 1: Magnificat (Angrisano/Stephan)
210 Luke 1: Magnificat (B. Farrell)
208 Luke 1: Magnificat (Rubalcava)
207 Luke 1: Mary's Song (Joncas)
375 Mary's Song (Rieth)
147 Psalm 40: Here I Am/God, My God, Come to My Aid
380 Sing of Mary (PLEADING SAVIOR)
374 Song of Mary (Schutte)
378 The Angel Gabriel from Heaven Came
377 There Is Nothing Told
241 Who Has Known

The Nativity of St. John the Baptist (June 24)

221 Every Valley
105 Gospel Canticle (Benedictus)
227 Let the Valleys Be Raised
206 Luke 1: Benedictus (Angrisano/Stephan)
205 Luke 1: Benedictus (B. Farrell)
218 On Jordan's Bank

Ss. Peter and Paul, Apostles (June 29)

386 Blessed Feasts of Blessed Martyrs
719 God, We Praise You
339 Lord, You Give the Great Commission
685 What You Hear in the Dark

The Transfiguration of the Lord (August 6)

366 At the Name of Jesus
567 Jesu, Joy of Our Desiring
730 Let All Mortal Flesh Keep Silence
662 Love Divine, All Loves Excelling
755 Mine Eyes Have Seen the Glory
176 Psalm 97: The Lord Is King
443 The Lord Is My Light
382 Transfiguration (Landry)
381 Transfiguration (Manalo)
274 Transfigure Us, O Lord

The Assumption of the Blessed Virgin Mary (August 15)

369 Ave Maria
376 Hail, Holy Queen
372 Hail Mary: Gentle Woman
379 Holy Is His Name
209 Luke 1: Magnificat (Angrisano/Stephan)
210 Luke 1: Magnificat (B. Farrell)
208 Luke 1: Magnificat (Rubalcava)
207 Luke 1: Mary's Song (Joncas)
375 Mary's Song (Rieth)
373 My Soul Magnifies the Lord
150 Psalm 45: The Queen Stands
380 Sing of Mary (PLEADING SAVIOR)
374 Song of Mary (Schutte)
377 There Is Nothing Told

The Exaltation of the Holy Cross (September 14)

262 At the Cross Her Station Keeping/ Stabat Mater Dolorosa
319 At the Lamb's High Feast
298 Behold the Wood
580 Come Unto Me
753 Jesus Died upon the Cross
384 Lift High the Cross
297 O Sacred Head, Surrounded
562 Only This I Want
552 Take Up Your Cross
327 Up from the Earth
299 We Venerate Your Cross/ Tu Cruz Adoramos
300 Were You There
668 What Wondrous Love Is This
302 When I Survey the Wondrous Cross
296 Wood of the Cross

All Saints (November 1)

710 Alabaré/O Come and Sing
757 Beatitudes
386 Blessed Feasts of Blessed Martyrs
759 Blest Are They
593 Faith of Our Fathers
388 For All the Saints
719 God, We Praise You
721 Holy God, We Praise Thy Name
775 Jerusalem, My Happy Home
305 Litany of the Saints (Becker)
307 Litany of the Saints (Chant)
476 Lord, Who at Thy First Eucharist
129 Psalm 24: Lord, This Is the People/Let the Lord Enter
387 Saints of God
774 Sing with All the Saints in Glory
571 The Church's One Foundation
687 We Are the Light of the World
390 Ye Watchers and Ye Holy Ones

The Commemoration of All the Faithful Departed (All Souls' Day) (November 2)

710 Alabaré/O Come and Sing
590 As the Deer Longs
600 Be Not Afraid
641 Because the Lord Is My Shepherd
644 Come to Me
388 For All the Saints
420 Holy Darkness
430 How Lovely Is Your Dwelling Place
431 I Know That My Redeemer Lives
433 I, the Lord
653 In Every Age
775 Jerusalem, My Happy Home
515 Jesus, the Bread of Life
434 Keep in Mind
760 Lead Me, Lord
328 Now the Green Blade Rises
680 Peace Prayer
679 Prayer of St. Francis/ Oración de San Francisco
652 Psalm 23 (Conry)
128 Psalm 23: My Shepherd Is the Lord (Gelineau)
126 Psalm 23: The Lord Is My Shepherd/El Señor Es Mi Pastor (Reza)
133 Psalm 27: The Goodness of the Lord
134 Psalm 27: The Lord Is My Light
149 Psalm 42/43: As the Deer Longs
163 Psalm 84: How Lovely Is Your Dwelling Place
168 Psalm 90: In Every Age
193 Psalm 122: Let Us Go Rejoicing
196 Psalm 130: Out of the Depths
441 Restless Is the Heart
773 Shall We Gather at the River
649 Shelter Me, O God
642 Shepherd Me, O God
774 Sing with All the Saints in Glory
438 Song of Farewell (OLD HUNDREDTH)
442 Song of Farewell (Sands)
648 The King of Love My Shepherd Is
443 The Lord Is My Light
336 The Strife Is O'er
631 This Alone
563 Unless a Grain of Wheat (B. Farrell)
516 Unless a Grain of Wheat (Hurd)
609 We Will Rise Again
444 Yes, I Shall Arise

The Dedication of the Lateran Basilica (November 9)

570 All Are Welcome
456 All People That on Earth Do Dwell
538 City of God
455 Gather Us Together
719 God, We Praise You
476 Lord, Who at Thy First Eucharist
339 Lord, You Give the Great Commission
569 Sing a New Church
571 The Church's One Foundation
550 We Are Many Parts
462 What Is This Place

The Immaculate Conception of the Blessed Virgin Mary (December 8)

369 Ave Maria
371 Del Cielo Ha Bajado
112 Gospel Canticle (Magnificat)
372 Hail Mary: Gentle Woman
370 Immaculate Mary
209 Luke 1: Magnificat
207 Luke 1: Mary's Song (Joncas)
375 Mary's Song (Rieth)
373 My Soul Magnifies the Lord
380 Sing of Mary (PLEADING SAVIOR)
374 Song of Mary (Schutte)
377 There Is Nothing Told

Our Lady of Guadalupe (December 12)

369 Ave Maria
371 Del Cielo Ha Bajado
112 Gospel Canticle (Magnificat)
376 Hail, Holy Queen
372 Hail Mary: Gentle Woman
370 Immaculate Mary
208 Luke 1: Magnificat
375 Mary's Song
373 My Soul Magnifies the Lord
380 Sing of Mary
377 There Is Nothing Told

Subtitles and alternate titles that differ from those used in Glory & Praise, Third Edition *are given in italics.*

HYMNS AND SONGS

A

616 A Mighty Fortress
756 A Rightful Place
213 A Voice Cries Out
716 Abba! Father
780 Abide with Me
636 *Abre Mis Ojos/Open My Eyes*
520 Act Justly
235 *Adeste Fideles*
233 Advent/Christmas Gospel Acclamation
232 Advent Lamb of God
266 Again We Keep This Solemn Fast
598 Age to Age
406 Agua de Vida/Water of Life
710 Alabaré/O Come and Sing
311 Aleluya, Aleluya
570 All Are Welcome
698 *All around us we have known you*
714 All Creatures of Our God and King
284 All Glory, Laud, and Honor
703 All Good Gifts
354 All Hail, Adored Trinity
364 All Hail the Power of Jesus' Name
656 All I Ask of You
643 All Is Well with My Soul
707 All My Days
456 All People That on Earth Do Dwell
355 All Praise and Glad Thanksgiving
309 All Shall Be Well
553 All That Is Hidden
695 All the Earth (Deiss)
178 *All the Ends of the Earth* (Canedo)
712 All the Ends of the Earth (Dufford)
177 *All the Ends of the Earth* (Hurd)
713 Alle, Alle, Alleluia (Ho Lung)
321 Alleluia! Alleluia! (HYMN TO JOY)
336 *Alleluia! Alleluia! Alleluia! The strife is o'er, the battle done* (VICTORY)
317 Alleluia! Alleluia! Let the Holy Anthem Rise
231 Alleluia! Hurry, the Lord Is Near (Sands)
314 Alleluia! Love Is Alive
313 Alleluia No. 1
525 Alleluia! Raise the Gospel
361 Alleluia! Sing to Jesus
614 Amazing Grace
479 Amén. El Cuerpo de Cristo
745 America (AMERICA)
749 America the Beautiful (MATERNA)
466 *Amor de Dios/O Love of God*
639 *An Irish Blessing*
606 *And he will raise you up on eagle's wings*
493 *And I will raise you up*
325 *And the Father Will Dance/ Let Us Sing and Be Glad*
542 *And to tell the world that God's kingdom is near*
459 *And we cry: "Holy! Holy! Holy are you!"*
481 Ang Katawan ni Kristo/ Behold, the Body of Christ
253 Angels, from the Realms of Glory
236 Angels We Have Heard on High
556 Anthem
509 As Grains of Wheat
286 As I Have Done for You
394 *As I went down to the river to pray*
104 *As morning breaks I look to you*
156 *As Morning Breaks/My Soul Is Thirsting*
590 As the Deer Longs
549 As We Celebrate
473 As We Gather at Your Table
480 As We Remember
258 As with Gladness Men of Old
261 Ashes (Conry)
260 Ashes to Ashes (Schutte)
476 *At That First Eucharist*
262 At the Cross Her Station Keeping/ Stabat Mater Dolorosa
319 At the Lamb's High Feast
366 At the Name of Jesus
370 *Ave, Ave, Ave, Maria* (LOURDES HYMN)
371 *Ave, ave, ave María* (AVE DE LOURDES)
369 Ave Maria (Norbet)
238 Away in a Manger

B

391 Baptized in Water
755 *Battle Hymn of the Republic*
659 *Be like our God, who chose to live and learn our ways*
153 *Be Merciful, O Lord*
600 Be Not Afraid
419 Be Still, My Soul
528 *Be the light of Christ in the world*
633 Be Thou My Vision
169 *Be with Me, Lord* (Canedo)
170 *Be with Me, Lord* (Joncas)
757 Beatitudes
696 Beautiful Savior
641 Because the Lord Is My Shepherd
715 Been So Busy
565 Before the Sun Burned Bright
481 *Behold, the Body of Christ/ Ang Katawan ni Kristo*
316 Behold the Glory of God
492 Behold the Lamb (Willett)
295 Behold the Lamb of God (Dufford)
298 Behold the Wood (Schutte)
296 *Behold the wood of the cross* (Alstott)
206 *Benedictus* (Angrisano/Stephan)
205 *Benedictus* (B. Farrell)
105 *Benedictus* (FOREST GREEN)
268 Beyond the Days
214 Beyond the Moon and Stars
426 Blessed Be (Divine Praises)
206 *Blessed be the Lord*
717 Blessed by Your Sacrifice
386 Blessed Feasts of Blessed Martyrs
47 *Blessed Savior, pour upon us living streams of water (Mass of Christ the Savior)*

637 *Blessing Prayer*
285 Blessings on the King
759 Blest Are They
105 *Blest be the God of Israel*
605 Blest Be the Lord (Schutte)
205 *Blest be the Lord, the God of Israel* (B. Farrell)
512 Bread, Blessed and Broken
483 Bread for the World
484 Bread of Angels
485 Bread of Heaven
490 Bread of Life (Cooney)
482 Bread of Life (B. Farrell)
478 Bread of Life (Fisher)
497 *Bread of Life* (Stephan)
348 By the Waking of Our Hearts
403 *By this sign may you receive Christ's love*

C

209 *Canticle of Mary* (Angrisano/Stephan)
210 *Canticle of Mary* (B. Farrell)
207 *Canticle of Mary* (Joncas)
375 *Canticle of Mary* (Rieth)
373 *Canticle of Mary* (Romer/Hillebrand)
208 *Canticle of Mary* (Rubalcava)
379 *Canticle of Mary* (Talbot)
211 *Canticle of Simeon*
206 *Canticle of Zechariah* (Angrisano/Stephan)
205 *Canticle of Zechariah* (B. Farrell)
84 Celtic Alleluia *(Celtic Mass)*
530 Celtic Alleluia: Sending Forth *(Celtic Mass)*
591 Center of My Life
264 Change Our Hearts
257 Child of the Poor
237 Children, Run Joyfully
625 Christ Be beside Me
683 Christ, Be Our Light
303 Christ, Be Our Light (Easter Vigil)
586 Christ before Us
215 Christ, Circle Round Us
308 *Christ has become our paschal sacrifice*
566 Christ Has No Body Now but Yours
573 Christ in Me Arise
686 Christ the Lord
320 Christ, the Lord, Is Risen Today (LLANFAIR)
334 Christ, the Lord, Is Risen Today (VICTIMAE PASCHALI)
657 Christians, Let Us Love One Another
310 Christians, to the Paschal Victim
538 City of God
464 *Come and be filled here at this table*
301 *Come and see what I have done*
711 Come, Christians, Join to Sing
219 *Come, come, Emmanuel*
558 Come, Follow Me
352 Come, Holy Ghost (LAMBILLOTTE)
568 *Come, Holy Ghost, Creator blest* (Keil)
349 *Come, Holy Spirit, come* (Kendzia)
410 Come Home (Landry)
414 *Come home, come home* (THOMPSON)
579 Come, Lord Jesus
359 Come Now, Almighty King
385 Come Now, and Praise the Humble Saint
457 Come, Now Is the Time to Worship
220 *Come, O Lord, and set us free*
164 *Come, O Lord/Lord, Let Us See Your Kindness*
342 Come, O Spirit of the Lord
740 *Come, then, all you nations*
212 Come, Thou Long-Expected Jesus
644 Come to Me
463 *Come to the feast of heaven and earth*
458 Come to the Feast/Ven al Banquete
407 Come to the River *(Mass of Glory)*
770 Come to the Water
461 Come to Us (Cooney)
578 *Come to us, you who say, "I will not forget you"* (Kendzia)
580 Come Unto Me
472 Come, Worship the Lord
702 Come, Ye Thankful People, Come
545 Companions on the Journey
152 *Create in Me* (Hurd)
154 *Create in Me* (Kendzia)
155 *Create in Me/Oh Dios, Crea en Mí* (Cortés)
217 Creator of the Stars of Night
308 *Cristo, el Cordero Pascual, es inmolado*
362 Crown Him with Many Crowns

D

322 *Dance, then, wherever you may be*
204 Daniel 3: Glory and Praise for Ever
781 Day Is Done
673 Day of Peace
782 Daylight's Ending
371 Del Cielo Ha Bajado
124 *Dios Mío, Dios Mío/My God, My God*
409 Dismissal of the Catechumens and the Elect *(Celtic Mass)*
651 *Do not be afraid, I am with you*
589 Do Not Fear to Hope
676 Dona Nobis Pacem (Norbet)
671 Dona Nobis Pacem (Round)
292 Donde Hay Amor y Caridad/ Where Charity and Love Abound
394 Down to the River to Pray
486 Draw Near
596 Dwelling Place

E

606 *Eagle's Wings*
559 Earthen Vessels
310 *Easter Sequence*
505 Eat This Bread
187 *El Cáliz que Bendecimos/Our Blessing-Cup*
308 *El Cordero Pascual/Our Paschal Sacrifice*
126 *El Señor Es Mi Pastor/The Lord Is My Shepherd*
219 Emmanuel
658 Endless Is Your Love
392 Enter the Journey
602 Entre Tus Manos
347 Envía Tu Espíritu
746 Eternal Father, Strong to Save
110 Evening Hymn: O Radiant Light
221 Every Valley
353 Everyone Moved by the Spirit
202 Exodus 15: To God Be Praise and Glory
645 Eye Has Not Seen

F

593 Faith of Our Fathers
281 Faithful Cross
659 Faithful Family

137 *Father, I Put My Life in Your Hands* (Talbot)
138 *Father, into Your Hands I Commend My Spirit* (DeBruyn)
139 *Father, into Your Hands/ Padre, en Tus Manos* (Hurd)
572 Father of Peace
761 Find Us Ready
398 Flow River Flow
647 Fly like a Bird
249 *Follow, follow; rise up, shepherd, and follow*
388 For All the Saints
509 *For many are we*
705 For the Beauty of the Earth
697 For the Fruits of This Creation
517 For the Healing of the Nations
575 For the Sake of Christ
241 *For who has known the mind of God*
601 For You Are My God
758 *For your right hand has delivered us from death*
167 *For Ever I Will Sing*
263 Forty Days and Forty Nights
718 From All That Dwell Below the Skies/ Praise God from Whom All Blessings Flow

G

460 Gather the People (Schutte)
471 Gather Us In
455 Gather Us Together
465 Gather Your People (Hurd)
372 *Gentle woman, quiet light*
487 Gift of Finest Wheat
397 Give Me Ears to Listen
435 Give Me Jesus
561 *Give me only your love and your grace*
700 Give Thanks to the Lord (Schutte)
190 *Give Thanks to the Lord* (Smith)
674 Give Us Your Peace
204 *Glory and Praise for Ever*
723 Glory and Praise to Our God
755 *Glory! Glory! Hallelujah*
289 Glory in the Cross
429 Go Forth
445 Go in Peace (Hart/Liles)
543 *Go in peace to serve the world* (C. Walker)
554 Go Make a Difference
536 Go Out, Go Out
242 Go, Tell It on the Mountain
652 *God alone may lead my spirit*
469 *God be among us as we draw near*
628 God Be in My Head
698 God, Beyond All Names
542 God Has Chosen Me
655 God Is Love (Joncas)
151 *God Mounts His Throne*
147 *God, My God, Come to My Aid/Here I Am*
661 God of Love (Schutte)
748 God of Our Fathers
518 God of the Hungry
627 God, Our Source and Life, Unite Us
243 God Rest You Merry, Gentlemen
719 God, We Praise You
239 Good Christian Friends, Rejoice
105 Gospel Canticle (Benedictus)
112 Gospel Canticle (Magnificat)
265 Gracious God
677 *Grant us, O Lord, peace in our days*
678 Grant Us Peace (Canedo)
708 Grateful
145 *Gusten y Vean/Taste and See*

H

376 Hail, Holy Queen
372 Hail Mary: Gentle Woman
365 Hail, Redeemer, King Divine
337 Hail the Day That Sees Him Rise
720 Hallelujah Is Our Song
207 *Happy are they who believe*
389 *Happy saint, in bliss adoring*
141 *Happy the People You Have Chosen*
245 Hark! the Herald Angels Sing
679 *Hazme un instrumento de tu paz*
323 *He Is Risen/Resucitó*
727 He Is the Lord
422 Healing River of the Spirit
425 Healing Waters
448 Hear Us Now, Our God and Father
464 Here at This Table
604 Here I Am (Booth)
147 *Here I Am/God, My God, Come to My Aid* (Cooney)
539 Here I Am, Lord (Schutte)
230 *Here is your God*
595 Hold Me in Life
420 Holy Darkness
721 Holy God, We Praise Thy Name
358 Holy, Holy, Holy (NICAEA)
379 Holy Is His Name
389 Holy Patron, Thee Saluting
344 Holy Spirit (Canedo)
408 Holy Spirit, Come Now/ Santo Espíritu, Ven (Manibusan)
343 Holy Spirit, Come to Me (Hoy)
282 *Hosanna! Hosanna! Hosanna in the highest*
283 Hosanna to the Son of David
285 *Hosannah! Hosannah! Blessings on the King*
411 Hosea
607 How Can I Keep from Singing
694 How Great Thou Art
269 How Long, O Lord
430 How Lovely Is Your Dwelling Place (DeBruyn)
163 *How Lovely Is Your Dwelling Place* (Joncas)
356 Hymn of Praise

I

715 *I ain't got time to die*
493 I Am the Bread of Life (Toolan)
684 I Am the Light of the World
495 I Am the Living Bread (Haas)
329 I Am the Resurrection
540 I Am the Vine (Hurd)
514 *I am the vine and you the branches* (Thomson)
592 I Believe in the Sun
772 I Have Loved You
646 I Heard the Voice of Jesus
318 I Know That My Redeemer Lives (DUKE STREET)
431 I Know That My Redeemer Lives (Soper)
673 *I know there will be a day of peace*
130 *I Lift Up My Soul*
119 *I Love You, Lord, My Strength*
490 *I myself am the bread of life*

304 I Saw Water Flowing
531 I Send You Out
127 *I Shall Live in the House of the Lord/ The Lord Is My Shepherd* (Crandal)
125 *I Shall Live in the House/The Lord Prepares a Banquet/The Lord Is My Shepherd* (Cooney)
699 I Sing the Mighty Power of God
433 I, the Lord (Kendzia)
539 *I, the Lord of sea and sky* (Schutte)
682 I Want to Walk as a Child of the Light
146 *I Will Always Thank the Lord*
574 I Will Choose Christ
767 *I will never forget you, my people*
758 I Will Not Die
709 *I will play for you on my harp*
136 *I Will Praise You, Lord* (Inwood)
200 *I Will Praise Your Name/The Hand of the Lord* (Smith)
199 *I Will Praise Your Name/The Hand of the Lord Feeds Us* (Soper)
724 I Will Rejoice
202 *I will sing to the Lord, triumphant is he*
189 *I will walk in the presence of the Lord*
186 *I Will Walk with the Lord/The Cup of Salvation/ Our Blessing-Cup*
286 *I, your Lord and Master, now become your servant*
764 If God Is for Us (Brown)
768 If God Is for Us (Foley)
171 *If Today You Hear God's Voice* (B. Farrell)
172 *If Today You Hear His Voice* (Soper)
370 Immaculate Mary
584 In Christ Alone
548 In Christ There Is No East or West
168 *In Every Age* (Smith)
653 In Every Age (Whitaker)
776 In God Alone
682 *In him there is no darkness at all*
437 In Paradisum/May Angels Guide You
660 In Perfect Charity
496 *In the bread, blessed, broken and shared*
489 In the Breaking of the Bread
752 In the Day of the Lord
189 *In the Presence of God*
271 In These Days of Lenten Journey
467 In This Place
418 *In times of trouble, God, come to our aid*
270 In Your Love Remember Me
251 Infant Holy, Infant Lowly
603 Into Your Hands
103 Invitatory Psalm: Psalm 95
637 Irish Blessing (Fabing)
203 Isaiah 12: We Shall Draw Water
767 Isaiah 49
250 It Came upon the Midnight Clear
643 *It is well with my soul*

J

775 Jerusalem, My Happy Home
287 Jesu, Jesu
567 Jesu, Joy of Our Desiring
367 Jesus Christ Is Lord
330 Jesus Christ Is Risen Today
622 Jesus, Come to Us
753 Jesus Died upon the Cross
599 *Jesus, I trust in you*
581 Jesus in the Morning
363 *Jesus. Jesus. Let all creation bend the knee*
541 *Jesus, Jesus, you are the Lord*
587 Jesus, Lord (DeBruyn)
515 Jesus, the Bread of Life
363 Jesus, the Lord (O'Connor)
624 *Jesus, you are the healing*
315 Join in the Dance
240 Joy to the World
726 Joyful, Joyful, We Adore Thee
161 *Justice Shall Flourish/Lord, Every Nation*

K

434 Keep in Mind
116 *Keep Me Safe/Path of Life*

L

421 Lay Your Hands
621 Lead Me, Guide Me
760 Lead Me, Lord
468 Lead Us to the Water
769 *Leaping the mountains, bounding the hills*
272 Led by the Spirit
730 Let All Mortal Flesh Keep Silence
159 *Let All the Earth* (Soper)
158 *Let All the Earth Cry Out* (Cooney)
706 Let All Things Now Living
333 Let Heaven Rejoice
751 Let the Heavens Be Glad
225 Let the King of Glory Come
129 *Let the Lord Enter/Lord, This Is the People*
227 Let the Valleys Be Raised
672 Let There Be Peace on Earth
488 Let Us Break Bread Together
569 *Let us bring the gifts that differ*
538 *Let us build the city of God*
193 *Let Us Go Rejoicing*
470 Let Us Go to the Altar
756 *Let us live our lives so that all might see*
165 *Let Us See Your Kindness*
325 Let Us Sing and Be Glad/ And the Father Will Dance
374 *Let us sing the praises of Mary*
757 *Let your light shine for all the world to see*
384 Lift High the Cross
225 *Lift up, you gates, lift up your arches*
725 Lift Up Your Hearts
528 Light of Christ
640 Like a Child Rests
449 Like a Seal on Your Heart
765 Like a Shepherd
709 Like Cedars
305 Litany of the Saints (Becker)
307 Litany of the Saints (Chant)
47 Living Streams *(Mass of Christ the Savior)*
246 Lo, How a Rose E'er Blooming
411 *Long have I waited for your coming home to me*
494 Look Beyond
201 *Lord, Come and Save Us/ Praise the Lord, My Soul*
161 *Lord, Every Nation/Justice Shall Flourish*
455 *Lord, Jesus Christ, gather us together*
599 *Lord Jesus Christ, Son of God*
166 *Lord, Let Us See Your Kindness* (Soper)

164 *Lord, Let Us See Your Kindness/ Come, O Lord* (Balhoff/Daigle/Ducote)
140 *Lord, Let Your Mercy*
680 *Lord, make me a means of your peace*
162 *Lord, Make Us Turn to You/ The Vineyard of the Lord*
623 Lord of All Hopefulness
769 Lord of Glory
322 Lord of the Dance
184 *Lord, Send Out Your Spirit* (Canedo)
345 *Lord, send out your Spirit* (Schoenbachler)
185 *Lord, Send Out Your Spirit* (Zsigray)
129 *Lord, This Is the People/Let the Lord Enter*
689 Lord, to Whom Shall We Go
476 Lord, Who at Thy First Eucharist
277 Lord, Who Throughout These Forty Days
523 Lord, Whose Love in Humble Service
641 *Lord, you are my shepherd*
339 Lord, You Give the Great Commission
555 *Lord, You Have Come/Pescador de Hombres*
121 *Lord, You Have the Words*
662 Love Divine, All Loves Excelling
666 Love Goes On
669 Love Has Come
451 Love Never Fails
665 Love One Another
663 Lover of Us All
413 Loving and Forgiving
206 Luke 1: Benedictus (Angrisano/Stephan)
205 Luke 1: Benedictus (B. Farrell)
209 Luke 1: Magnificat (Angrisano/Stephan)
210 Luke 1: Magnificat (B. Farrell)
208 Luke 1: Magnificat (Rubalcava)
207 Luke 1: Mary's Song
211 Luke 2: Song of Simeon

M

209 *Magnificat* (Angrisano/Stephan)
210 *Magnificat* (B. Farrell)
207 *Magnificat* (Joncas)
112 *Magnificat* (NEW BRITAIN)
375 *Magnificat* (Rieth)
373 *Magnificat* (Romer/Hillebrand)
208 *Magnificat* (Rubalcava)
379 *Magnificat* (Talbot)
679 *Make me a channel of your peace*
677 Make Our Lives a Prayer of Peace
521 Make Your Home in Me
546 Many and Great (Manalo)
551 Many and One (Angrisano/Hart/Liles)
220 Maranatha
207 Mary's Song (Joncas)
375 Mary's Song (Rieth)
437 *May Angels Guide You/In Paradisum* (Chant)
596 *May Christ find a dwelling place*
638 May God Bless and Keep You (C. Walker)
450 May God Bless You (Van Grieken)
667 May Love Be Ours
428 *May songs of the angels welcome you and guide you along your way* (Dufford)
432 May the Angels (Kendzia)
608 *May the Angels/The Lord Is Near* (Joncas)
442 *May the choirs of angels come to greet you*
639 May the Road Rise Up (Kendzia)
637 *May the road rise up to meet you* (Fabing)
409 *May the word of God strengthen you*
728 May We Praise You
701 Meadows and Mountains
755 Mine Eyes Have Seen the Glory
497 Miracle of Grace
778 Morning Has Broken
745 *My country, 'tis of thee*
122 *My God, My God* (Manion)
123 *My God, My God* (Smith)
124 *My God, My God/Dios Mío, Dios Mío* (Schiavone)
128 *My Shepherd Is the Lord*
436 My Soul Is Thirsting (Brown)
156 *My Soul Is Thirsting/As Morning Breaks* (Angrisano)
209 *My soul magnifies the Lord* (Angrisano/Stephan)
373 My Soul Magnifies the Lord (Romer/Hillebrand)
210 *My soul proclaims the greatness of the Lord*
112 *My soul proclaims the Lord my God*
157 *My Soul Thirsts*
618 *My stronghold, my Savior*

N

290 No Greater Love
607 *No storm can shake my inmost calm*
252 *Noche de Paz/Silent Night*
469 Now as We Gather
578 Now Is the Time
211 *Now, O God, let your servant go*
704 Now Thank We All Our God
328 Now the Green Blade Rises
211 *Nunc Dimittis*

O

749 *O beautiful for spacious skies*
582 O Beauty, Ever Ancient
729 O Bless the Lord
195 *O Blessed Are Those*
399 O Breathe on Me, O Breath of God
235 O Come, All Ye Faithful/Venid, Fieles Todos
710 *O Come and Sing/Alabaré*
248 O Come, Little Children
228 O Come, O Come, Emmanuel
357 O God, Almighty Father
733 O God beyond All Praising
148 *O God, for You I Long*
626 O God, Hear Us
160 *O God, Let All the Nations*
612 O God, Our Help in Ages Past
620 O God, You Search Me
430 *O how lovely is your dwelling place*
423 O Jesus, Healer of Wounded Souls
244 O Little Town of Bethlehem
610 *O Lord, I know you are near*
111 *O Lord, let my prayer rise before you like incense*
555 *O Lord, with your eyes set upon me*
591 *O Lord, you are the center of my life*
466 O Love of God/Amor de Dios
439 O Loving God
110 *O radiant Light, O Sun divine*
499 O Sacrament Most Holy
294 O Sacred Head (Hurd)
297 O Sacred Head, Surrounded (PASSION CHORALE)

427 O Saving Victim/O Salutaris Hostia
394 *O sisters, let's go down*
312 *O Sons and Daughters*
255 *O star of wonder, star of night*
690 O Word of God
155 *Oh Dios, Crea en Mí/Create in Me*
606 On Eagle's Wings
218 On Jordan's Bank
198 *On the Day I Called*
377 *On this day all earth and all paradise*
498 One Bread, One Body (Foley)
508 *One bread, one body, one cup, one call* (Frenzel/Keil)
457 *One day every tongue will confess you are God*
401 One Lord
508 One Love Released
338 One Sacrifice of Christ
568 One Spirit, One Church
631 *One thing I ask, this alone I seek*
615 Only a Shadow
611 Only in God (Foley)
618 Only in God (Talbot)
562 Only This I Want
636 Open My Eyes/Abre Mis Ojos
679 *Oración de San Francisco/ Prayer of St. Francis*
500 Our Blessing Cup (Hurd)
188 *Our Blessing-Cup* (Joncas)
187 *Our Blessing-Cup/El Cáliz que Bendecimos* (Cortez)
186 *Our Blessing-Cup/I Will Walk with the Lord/ The Cup of Salvation* (Soper)
459 Our God Is Here
615 *Our lives are in your hands*
308 Our Paschal Sacrifice/El Cordero Pascual
306 Out of Darkness (Kendzia)
560 Out of Darkness (C. Walker)
196 *Out of the Depths*

P

139 *Padre, en Tus Manos/ Father, into Your Hands* (Hurd)
282 *Palm Sunday Processional*
501 Pan de Vida
291 Pange, Lingua, Gloriosi/ Sing, My Tongue, the Savior's Glory
484 *Panis Angelicus*
440 Parable
416 Pardon Your People
650 Pastures of the Lord
116 *Path of Life/Keep Me Safe*
224 Patience, People
681 Peace (Weston Priory/Norbet)
675 Peace Is Flowing like a River (Traditional/Landry)
340 Peace, My Friends
680 Peace Prayer
349 Pentecost Sequence
223 People, Look East
522 People of Peace
555 Pescador de Hombres/Lord, You Have Come
301 Pietà
718 *Praise God from Whom All Blessings Flow/ From All That Dwell Below the Skies*
737 Praise God in This Holy Dwelling
735 Praise, My Soul, the King of Heaven (LAUDA ANIMA)
738 Praise the Lord, My Soul (Foley)
201 *Praise the Lord, My Soul/ Lord, Come and Save Us* (Hurd)
731 Praise the Lord, Ye Heavens
732 Praise to the Lord
691 Praise to You, O Christ, Our Savior
679 Prayer of St. Francis/Oración de San Francisco
513 *Precious body, precious blood*
424 Precious Lord, Take My Hand
173 *Proclaim His Marvelous Deeds*
652 Psalm 23 (Conry)
104 Psalmody: Psalm 63
111 Psalmody: Psalm 141
393 Put On Christ

R

771 Rain Down
230 Ready the Way (Hurd)
216 Ready the Way (Stephan)
438 *Receive her/his soul, O holy ones* (OLD HUNDREDTH)
439 *Receive her/his soul* (LONDONDERRY AIR)
759 *Rejoice and be glad*
417 Remember Your Love
441 Restless Is the Heart
323 Resucitó/He Is Risen
267 Return to Me
412 Return to the Lord Your God
249 Rise Up, Shepherd, and Follow
281 *Rising from the earth to heaven*
404 River of Glory
324 Roll Away the Stone

S

635 Sacred Silence
387 Saints of God
408 *Santo Espíritu, Ven/Holy Spirit, Come Now*
229 Save Us, O Lord
276 Save Your People
247 See Amid the Winter's Snow
495 *See this bread; take and eat and live in me*
477 See Us, Lord, About Your Altar
502 Seed, Scattered and Sown
279 Seek the Lord
613 Seek Ye First
183 *Send Forth Your Spirit, O Lord* (C. Walker)
345 Send Out Your Spirit (Schoenbachler)
341 Send Us Your Spirit (Schutte)
555 *Señor, me has mirado a los ojos*
532 Sent Forth by God's Blessing
541 Servant Song (McGargill)
454 Set Me as a Seal (Maher)
449 *Set me like a seal on your heart* (Landry)
773 Shall We Gather at the River
649 Shelter Me, O God
642 Shepherd Me, O God
475 Shepherd of Souls
418 Show Us Your Mercy
403 Signing of the Senses
252 Silent Night/Noche de Paz
583 *Simple Gifts*
743 Sing a Joyful Song
569 Sing a New Church

742 Sing a New Song (Brown)
739 Sing a New Song (Schutte)
741 Sing Alleluia, Sing
291 *Sing, My Tongue, the Savior's Glory/ Pange, Lingua, Gloriosi*
744 Sing, O Sing
380 Sing of Mary
740 Sing of the Lord's Goodness
727 *Sing to the Lord with shouts of joy*
722 Sing to the Mountains
774 Sing with All the Saints in Glory
414 Softly and Tenderly Jesus Is Calling
278 Somebody's Knockin' at Your Door
547 Somos el Cuerpo de Cristo/ We Are the Body of Christ
438 Song of Farewell (OLD HUNDREDTH)
442 Song of Farewell (Sands)
374 Song of Mary
211 *Song of Simeon*
254 Songs of Thankfulness and Praise
428 Songs of the Angels
750 Soon and Very Soon
496 Spirit and Grace
346 Spirit, Come
262 *Stabat Mater Dolorosa/ At the Cross Her Station Keeping*
629 Stand by Me

T

463 Table of Plenty
561 Take, Lord, Receive
543 Take the Word of God with You
383 Take Up Our Cross (Stephan/Hart/Byrd)
552 Take Up Your Cross (ERHALT UNS, HERR)
143 *Taste and See* (Dean)
507 Taste and See (Hurd)
504 Taste and See (Kendzia)
511 Taste and See (Moore)
144 *Taste and See* (Talbot)
145 *Taste and See/Gusten y Vean* (Reza)
356 *Te Deum*
343 *That I may know Jesus*
503 That There May Be Bread
378 The Angel Gabriel from Heaven Came
282 The Children of Jerusalem
571 The Church's One Foundation
526 The Cry of the Poor
186 *The Cup of Salvation/ I Will Walk with the Lord/ Our Blessing-Cup*
585 The Eyes and Hands of Christ
259 The First Nowell
273 The Glory of These Forty Days
474 The God of All Grace
133 *The Goodness of the Lord*
199 *The Hand of the Lord Feeds Us/ I Will Praise Your Name* (Soper)
200 *The Hand of the Lord/ I Will Praise Your Name* (Smith)
599 The Jesus Song
368 The King of Glory
648 The King of Love My Shepherd Is
226 The King Shall Come When Morning Dawns
688 The Light of Christ
142 *The Lord Fills the Earth with His Love*
194 *The Lord Has Done Great Things*
179 *The Lord Has Revealed*
526 *The Lord hears the cry of the poor*
181 *The Lord Is Kind and Merciful* (Dufford)
182 *The Lord Is Kind and Merciful* (Manalo)
176 *The Lord Is King*
134 *The Lord Is My Light* (DeBruyn)
443 The Lord Is My Light (C. Walker)
126 *The Lord Is My Shepherd/ El Señor Es Mi Pastor* (Reza)
127 *The Lord Is My Shepherd/ I Shall Live in the House of the Lord* (Crandal)
125 *The Lord Is My Shepherd/ I Shall Live in the House/ The Lord Prepares a Banquet* (Cooney)
608 The Lord Is Near/May the Angels
293 The Lord Jesus
125 *The Lord Prepares a Banquet/I Shall Live in the House/The Lord Is My Shepherd*
135 *The Lord Will Bless His People with Peace*
18 The Lord's Prayer *(Roman Missal Chants)*
117 *The Path of Life*
150 *The Queen Stands*
537 The Servant Song (Gillard)
351 The Spirit Is A-Movin'
336 The Strife Is O'er
529 The Summons
513 The Supper of the Lord
162 *The Vineyard of the Lord/ Lord, Make Us Turn to You*
546 *The wheat grows from springtime to fall*
694 *Then sings my soul, my Savior God, to thee*
290 *There can be no greater love*
654 There Is a Balm in Gilead
634 There Is a Longing
762 There Is a River
377 There Is Nothing Told
401 *There is one Lord, there is one faith*
670 There's a Wideness in God's Mercy
632 These Alone Are Enough
544 They'll Know We Are Christians
631 This Alone
779 This Day God Gives Me
331 This Day Was Made by the Lord
747 This Is My Song
335 This Is the Day (Fisher)
192 *This Is the Day* (Joncas)
326 This Is the Day (Kendzia)
191 *This Is the Day* (Soper)
256 *This, this is Christ the King*
597 Those Who See Light
619 Though the Mountains May Fall
763 Thy Kingdom Come
707 *Till the end of my days, O Lord*
583 'Tis the Gift to Be Simple
522 *To be people of faith in times of doubt*
491 To Be Your Bread
440 *To everything there is a season*
202 *To God Be Praise and Glory*
360 To Jesus Christ, Our Sovereign King
630 To You, O God, I Lift Up My Soul
131 *To You, O Lord* (Joncas)
132 *To You, O Lord* (Soper)

174 *Today a Savior Is Born* (B. Farrell)
175 *Today Our Savior Is Born* (Cortez)
382 Transfiguration (Landry)
381 Transfiguration (Manalo)
274 Transfigure Us, O Lord
376 *Triumph, all ye cherubim*
299 *Tu Cruz Adoramos/We Venerate Your Cross*
280 Turn to Me
332 Two Were Bound for Emmaus

U

510 Ubi Caritas (Hurd)
664 Ubi Caritas (Rosania)
292 *Ubi Caritas* (Rubalcava)
563 Unless a Grain of Wheat (B. Farrell)
516 Unless a Grain of Wheat (Hurd)
327 Up from the Earth

V

458 *Ven al Banquete/Come to the Feast*
408 *Ven, Espíritu, Santo Espíritu, ven*
350 Veni Sancte Spiritus (C. Walker)
235 *Venid, Fieles Todos/O Come, All Ye Faithful*
514 Vine and Branches
576 Voice of Christ

W

396 Wade in the Water
222 Waiting in Silence
234 Wake from Your Sleep
400 Water of Life (Dean)
406 *Water of Life/Agua de Vida* (Cortez)
568 *We are a pilgrim people*
524 We Are Called (Haas)
556 *We are called, we are chosen* (Conry)
545 *We are companions on the journey*
467 *We are gathered at table*
180 *We Are God's People*
550 We Are Many Parts
551 *We are many, yet we are one*
547 *We Are the Body of Christ/*
Somos el Cuerpo de Cristo
687 We Are the Light of the World
382 *We behold the splendor of God*
405 We Belong to You
734 We Gather Together
395 We Have Been Baptized in Christ
564 We Have Been Told
559 *We hold a treasure, not made of gold*
736 We Praise You
588 We Remember
203 *We Shall Draw Water*
527 We Shall Overcome
383 *We take up our cross and follow him*
506 We, the Body of Christ
576 *We the hands, we the eyes*
255 We Three Kings
299 We Venerate Your Cross/Tu Cruz Adoramos
763 *We wait in joy*
594 We Walk by Faith
609 We Will Rise Again
300 Were You There
256 What Child Is This
462 What Is This Place
668 What Wondrous Love Is This
685 What You Hear in the Dark
519 Whatsoever You Do
488 *When I fall on my knees*
302 When I Survey the Wondrous Cross
447 When Love Is Found (O WALY WALY)
583 *When true simplicity is gained*
292 *Where Charity and Love Abound/*
Donde Hay Amor y Caridad (Rubalcava)
453 *Where charity and love are found* (Schutte)
288 Where Charity and Love Prevail (Benoit)
453 Where Love Is Found (Schutte)
777 Where My Father Lives
446 Where There Is Love (Haas)
585 *Where two or three are gathered in my name*
452 Wherever You Go
241 Who Has Known
257 *Who is this who lives with the lowly*
663 *With all the earth we sing your praise*
535 With One Voice
197 *With Our God There Is Mercy*
275 With the Lord
533 Without You
577 Women of the Church
296 Wood of the Cross
669 *Word of God, enthroned*
754 Worthy Is the Lamb

Y

610 *Yahweh, I know you are near*
312 Ye Sons and Daughters
390 Ye Watchers and Ye Holy Ones
444 Yes, I Shall Arise
773 *Yes, we'll gather at the river*
415 You Alone
617 You Are All that I Need
693 You Are Child
651 You Are Mine
118 *You Are My Inheritance*
641 *You are my shepherd*
610 You Are Near
624 You Are the Healing
534 You Have Anointed Me
402 You Have Called Us
658 *You know my heart*
487 *You satisfy the hungry heart*
606 *You who dwell in the shelter of the Lord*
521 *Your burden's light and your yoke is easy*
766 Your Grace Is Enough
557 Your Song of Love
534 *Your Spirit, O God, is upon me*
692 Your Words Are Spirit and Life (B. Farrell)
120 *Your Words, Lord, Are Spirit and Life* (Hurd)

MORNING PRAYER (LAUDS)

102 Opening Verse: Invitatory
103 Invitatory Psalm: Psalm 95
104 Psalmody: Psalm 63
105 Gospel Canticle (Benedictus)
106 Intercessions: Morning Prayer
107 The Lord's Prayer
108 Blessing: Morning Prayer

EVENING PRAYER (VESPERS)

109 Thanksgiving for the Light
110 Evening Hymn: O Radiant Light
111 Psalmody: Psalm 141
112 Gospel Canticle (Magnificat)

113 Intercessions: Evening Prayer
114 The Lord's Prayer
115 Blessing: Evening Prayer

Psalms

116 Psalm 16: Path of Life/
Keep Me Safe
(Balhoff/Daigle/Ducote)
117 Psalm 16: The Path of Life (Soper)
118 Psalm 16: You Are My Inheritance (Bridge)
119 Psalm 18: I Love You, Lord, My Strength (Honoré)
120 Psalm 19: Your Words, Lord, Are Spirit and Life
(Hurd)
121 Psalm 19: Lord, You Have the Words (Joncas)
122 Psalm 22: My God, My God (Manion)
123 Psalm 22: My God, My God (Smith)
124 Psalm 22: My God, My God/
Dios Mío, Dios Mío (Schiavone)
125 Psalm 23: The Lord Is My Shepherd/I Shall Live
in the House/The Lord Prepares a Banquet
(Cooney)
126 Psalm 23: The Lord Is My Shepherd/
El Señor Es Mi Pastor (Reza)
127 Psalm 23: The Lord Is My Shepherd/I Shall Live
in the House of the Lord (Crandal)
128 Psalm 23: My Shepherd Is the Lord (Gelineau)
129 Psalm 24: Lord, This Is the People/
Let the Lord Enter (Smith)
130 Psalm 25: I Lift Up My Soul (Manion)
131 Psalm 25: To You, O Lord (Joncas)
132 Psalm 25: To You, O Lord (Soper)
133 Psalm 27: The Goodness of the Lord (Soper)
134 Psalm 27: The Lord Is My Light (DeBruyn)
135 Psalm 29: The Lord Will Bless His People with
Peace (Canter)
136 Psalm 30: I Will Praise You, Lord (Inwood)
137 Psalm 31: Father, I Put My Life in Your Hands
(Talbot)
138 Psalm 31: Father, into Your Hands I Commend
My Spirit (DeBruyn)
139 Psalm 31: Father, into Your Hands/
Padre, en Tus Manos (Hurd)
140 Psalm 33: Lord, Let Your Mercy (Dufford)
141 Psalm 33: Happy the People You Have Chosen
(Cooney)
142 Psalm 33: The Lord Fills the Earth with His Love
(Inwood)
143 Psalm 34: Taste and See (Dean)
144 Psalm 34: Taste and See (Talbot)
145 Psalm 34: Taste and See/Gusten y Vean (Reza)
146 Psalm 34: I Will Always Thank the Lord (Soper)
147 Psalm 40: Here I Am/
God, My God, Come to My Aid (Cooney)
148 Psalm 42: O God, for You I Long (B. Farrell)
149 Psalm 42/43: As the Deer Longs (Hurd)
150 Psalm 45: The Queen Stands (Keil)
151 Psalm 47: God Mounts His Throne (Inwood)
152 Psalm 51: Create in Me (Hurd)
153 Psalm 51: Be Merciful, O Lord (Angrisano)
154 Psalm 51: Create in Me (Kendzia)
155 Psalm 51: Create in Me/
Oh Dios, Crea en Mí (Cortés)
156 Psalm 63: My Soul Is Thirsting/
As Morning Breaks (Angrisano)
157 Psalm 63: My Soul Thirsts (Schutte)
158 Psalm 66: Let All the Earth Cry Out (Cooney)
159 Psalm 66: Let All the Earth (Soper)
160 Psalm 67: O God, Let All the Nations (Smith)
161 Psalm 72: Justice Shall Flourish/
Lord, Every Nation (Cooney)
162 Psalm 80: The Vineyard of the Lord/
Lord, Make Us Turn to You (Keil)
163 Psalm 84: How Lovely Is Your Dwelling Place
(Joncas)
164 Psalm 85: Come, O Lord/
Lord, Let Us See Your Kindness
(Balhoff/Daigle/Ducote)
165 Psalm 85: Let Us See Your Kindness (MacAller)
166 Psalm 85: Lord, Let Us See Your Kindness
(Soper)
167 Psalm 89: For Ever I Will Sing (Schoenbachler)
168 Psalm 90: In Every Age (Smith)
169 Psalm 91: Be with Me, Lord (Canedo)
170 Psalm 91: Be with Me, Lord (Joncas)
171 Psalm 95: If Today You Hear God's Voice
(B. Farrell)
172 Psalm 95: If Today You Hear His Voice (Soper)
173 Psalm 96: Proclaim His Marvelous Deeds (Smith)
174 Psalm 96: Today a Savior Is Born (B. Farrell)
175 Psalm 96: Today Our Savior Is Born (Cortez)
176 Psalm 97: The Lord Is King (Cooney)
177 Psalm 98: All the Ends of the Earth (Hurd)
178 Psalm 98: All the Ends of the Earth (Canedo)
179 Psalm 98: The Lord Has Revealed (Smith)
180 Psalm 100: We Are God's People (Smith)
181 Psalm 103: The Lord Is Kind and Merciful
(Dufford)
182 Psalm 103: The Lord Is Kind and Merciful
(Manalo)
183 Psalm 104: Send Forth Your Spirit, O Lord
(C. Walker)
184 Psalm 104: Lord, Send Out Your Spirit (Canedo)
185 Psalm 104: Lord, Send Out Your Spirit (Zsigray)
186 Psalm 116: Our Blessing-Cup/
I Will Walk with the Lord/
The Cup of Salvation (Soper)
187 Psalm 116: Our Blessing-Cup/
El Cáliz que Bendecimos (Cortez)
188 Psalm 116: Our Blessing-Cup (Joncas)
189 Psalm 116: In the Presence of God (Kendzia)
190 Psalm 118: Give Thanks to the Lord (Smith)
191 Psalm 118: This Is the Day (Soper)
192 Psalm 118: This Is the Day (Joncas)
193 Psalm 122: Let Us Go Rejoicing (Hurd)
194 Psalm 126: The Lord Has Done Great Things
(Cortez)
195 Psalm 128: O Blessed Are Those (Inwood)
196 Psalm 130: Out of the Depths (Soper)
197 Psalm 130: With Our God There Is Mercy
(Manion)
198 Psalm 138: On the Day I Called (Cooney)
199 Psalm 145: I Will Praise Your Name/
The Hand of the Lord Feeds Us (Soper)
200 Psalm 145: I Will Praise Your Name/
The Hand of the Lord (Smith)
201 Psalm 146: Praise the Lord, My Soul/
Lord, Come and Save Us (Hurd)

CANTICLES
202 Exodus 15: To God Be Praise and Glory
203 Isaiah 12: We Shall Draw Water (Inwood)
204 Daniel 3: Glory and Praise for Ever (Smith)
205 Luke 1: Benedictus (B. Farrell)
206 Luke 1: Benedictus (Angrisano/Stephan)
207 Luke 1: Mary's Song (Joncas)
208 Luke 1: Magnificat (Rubalcava)
209 Luke 1: Magnificat (Angrisano/Stephan)
210 Luke 1: Magnificat (B. Farrell)
211 Luke 2: Song of Simeon

THE ORDER OF MASS
1 The Introductory Rites: Greeting
2 Penitential Act (Confiteor)
3 Penitential Act: Dialogue
4 Penitential Act with Invocations
5 Lord, Have Mercy
6 Kyrie, Eleison
7 Gloria
9 Profession of Faith
10 Universal Prayer
12 May the Lord Accept the Sacrifice
13 Preface Dialogue
14 Holy
15 We Proclaim Your Death
16 When We Eat This Bread
17 Save Us, Savior
18 The Lord's Prayer
19 Lamb of God
20 Lord, I Am Not Worthy That You Should Enter
21 The Concluding Rites: Greeting/Final Blessing
22 Dismissal (Verse and Response: Go Forth)
23 Dismissal (Verse and Response: Go and Announce)
24 Dismissal (Verse and Response: Go in Peace, Glorifying the Lord)
25 Dismissal (Verse and Response: Go in Peace)
26 Dismissal: Easter Solemn (Verse and Response)

CELTIC MASS (C. WALKER)
82 Penitential Act with Invocations
83 Glory to God
84 Celtic Alleluia
85 Lenten Gospel Acclamation
86 Holy
87 We Proclaim Your Death
88 When We Eat This Bread
89 Save Us, Savior
90 Amen
91 Lamb of God

HERITAGE MASS (ALSTOTT)
68 Lord, Have Mercy
69 Glory to God
70 Holy
71 We Proclaim Your Death
72 When We Eat This Bread
73 Save Us, Savior
74 Amen
75 Lamb of God

MASS OF A JOYFUL HEART (ANGRISANO/TOMASZEK)
58 Lord, Have Mercy/Kyrie, Eleison
59 Glory to God
60 Alleluia
61 Lenten Gospel Acclamation
62 Holy
63 We Proclaim Your Death
64 When We Eat This Bread
65 Save Us, Savior
66 Amen
67 Lamb of God

MASS OF CHRIST THE SAVIOR (SCHUTTE)
47 Living Streams
48 Lord, Have Mercy/Kyrie, Eleison
49 Glory to God
50 Alleluia
51 Lenten Gospel Acclamation
52 Holy
53 We Proclaim Your Death
54 When We Eat This Bread
55 Save Us, Savior
56 Amen
57 Lamb of God

MASS OF GLORY (CANEDO/HURD)
37 Penitential Act with Invocations
38 Glory to God
39 Alleluia! Give the Glory
40 Lenten Gospel Acclamation
41 Holy
42 We Proclaim Your Death
43 When We Eat This Bread
44 Save Us, Savior
45 Amen
46 Lamb of God

MASS OF RENEWAL (STEPHAN)
92 Kyrie, Eleison/Lord, Have Mercy
93 Glory to God
94 Alleluia
95 Lenten Gospel Acclamation
96 Holy
97 We Proclaim Your Death
98 When We Eat This Bread
99 Save Us, Savior
100 Amen
101 Lamb of God

MASS OF THE SACRED HEART (T.R. SMITH)
27 Lord, Have Mercy
28 Glory to God
29 Alleluia
30 Lenten Gospel Acclamation
31 Holy
32 We Proclaim Your Death
33 When We Eat This Bread
34 Save Us, Savior
35 Amen
36 Lamb of God

MISA SANTA FE (REZA)
76 Acto Penitencial, Formulario 3/ Penitential Act with Invocations
77 Gloria/Glory to God
78 Santo/Holy
79 Anunciamos Tu Muerte/We Proclaim Your Death
80 Amén/Amen
81 Cordero de Dios/Lamb of God